SOME PHYSICAL CONSTANTS (see also Appendix 3)

Gravitational constant	G	6.67×10^{-11} N m²/kg²
Avogadro's number	N_0	6.02×10^{23} particles/mole
Boltzmann's constant	k	1.381×10^{-23} J/K
Gas constant	R	8.31 J/mole K
Quantum unit of charge	e	1.602×10^{-19} C
Permittivity constant (combined form)	$\dfrac{1}{4\pi\epsilon_0}$	8.99×10^9 ($\cong 9 \times 10^9$) N m²/C²
Permeability constant (combined form)	$\dfrac{\mu_0}{4\pi}$	10^{-7} N/A²
Speed of light	c	3.00×10^8 m/sec
Planck's constant	h	6.63×10^{-34} J sec
	$\hbar$	1.055×10^{-34} J sec
Mass of electron	m_e	9.11×10^{-31} kg
Mass of proton	m_p	1.673×10^{-27} kg
Bohr radius	a_0	5.29×10^{-11} m

SOME PHYSICAL DATA (see also Appendix 3)

Acceleration of gravity at earth's surface	(g)	9.8 m/sec²
Mass of earth		5.98×10^{24} kg
Radius of earth		6.37×10^6 m
Earth-moon distance (center to center)		3.84×10^8 m
Average earth-sun distance		1.50×10^{11} m
Average orbital speed of earth		2.98×10^4 m/sec
Standard conditions		1 atm = 1.013×10^5 N/m²
		0 °C = 273.15 K
Standard dry air density		1.293 kg/m³
Speed of sound in standard dry air		331 m/sec
Density of water		1.00×10^3 kg/m³

SOME CONVERSION FACTORS (see also Appendix 4)

2.54 cm/in	10^3 (kg/m³)/(gm/cm³)
0.3048 m/ft	
1.609 km/mile	10^5 dyne/N
10^{-10} m/Å	
10^{-15} m/fm	10^7 erg/J
	4.184 J/cal
3.156×10^7 sec/yr	4,184 J/kcal
	1.602×10^{-19} J/eV
0.447 (m/sec)/(mile/hr)	
57.3 deg/radian	1.80 F°/C°
0.454 kg/lb	3.00×10^9 esu/C (charge)
1.661×10^{-27} kg/amu	10^4 G/T (magnetic field)

Classical and Modern Physics

THIS BOOK IS AVAILABLE IN THREE VOLUMES
AND IN A COMBINED EDITION OF VOLUMES 1 AND 2

In Volume 1

Introduction to Physics
Mathematics
Mechanics

In Volume 2

Thermodynamics
Electromagnetism

In Volume 3

Relativity
Quantum Mechanics

Kenneth W. Ford

UNIVERSITY OF MASSACHUSETTS AT BOSTON

Volume 3

Classical and Modern Physics

A TEXTBOOK FOR STUDENTS OF SCIENCE AND ENGINEERING

XEROX

XEROX COLLEGE PUBLISHING *Lexington, Massachusetts* | *Toronto*

CONSULTING EDITOR

Brenton F. Stearns, *Hobart and William Smith Colleges*

to Joanne

Preface

This is the third of a three-volume textbook for students of science and engineering. Volumes 1 and 2, which are available in a combined edition as well as in separate volumes, cover topics of classical physics and also introduce some ideas of modern physics. Volume 3 can serve as a text for a one-semester course in modern physics. There are other ways in which the three volumes can be used. With many sections—and perhaps some whole chapters—omitted, the complete text could meet the needs of a one-year course that includes both classical and modern physics. Tackled at a more leisurely pace, the three volumes could provide a thorough introduction to physics spread over two years of study. I have tried to write the text so that it is a coherent whole yet has sufficiently independent parts to allow considerable flexibility in the way it is used. The parts of the volumes are the following:

Volume 1	1.	*Introduction to Physics*
	2.	*Mathematics*
	3.	*Mechanics*
Volume 2	4.	*Thermodynamics*
	5.	*Electromagnetism*
Volume 3	6.	*Relativity*
	7.	*Quantum Mechanics*

The appendices and the index are designed to help make the volumes useful to the student as reference works beyond the duration of a single course.

Probably every author has in mind a particular kind of student for whom he is writing. My "model student" has had high-school physics and is taking calculus concurrently with college physics. He or she is a serious but not necessarily gifted student, is interested in ideas as well as technical skills, and learns best when mathematical derivations are supplemented by verbal explanations and physical examples. In terms of the intellectual demand placed on the student, this text is comparable to the popular text by Halliday and Resnick.* It is less demanding than the Berkeley Physics Course† or the M.I.T. Introductory Physics Series.‡

As originally conceived, this book was to be a "calculus version" of my earlier text, *Basic Physics*.§ Having passed through numerous evolutionary stages of writing and rewriting, deleting and adding, however, the book as now published is distinct from the earlier one in various ways besides its mathematical level.

Some of the principal features of this text are the following: (1) I have tried to give a unified presentation of both classical and modern physics. Although theoretical developments of relativity and quantum physics are saved for the last two parts of the book, certain ideas (mass-to-energy conversion, for instance, and nature's speed limit) are introduced early, and modern examples often serve to illustrate classical laws. (2) A series of introductory chapters give time for some maturing of the student's view of physics and his command of mathematics before the intricacies of classical mechanics are approached. (3) Ideas of calculus are introduced (in Chapter 5) somewhat more fully than in most other physics texts. (4) I have tried to steer a course through the discipline of physics that keeps the student in touch with the large view of the subject—the economy and simplicity of its concepts, the elegance of its overall structure—at the same time that he is mastering practical skills and polishing his problem-solving ability. (5) As aids to study and review, the text is divided into fairly numerous sections and subsections, marginal notes highlight key ideas and important equations, and summaries of ideas and definitions appear at the end of every chapter. (6) I have tried to bring out the excitement of physics as a living, evolving discipline, powerful yet incomplete. A limited amount of historical material is included; I have taken some care with this and hope that most of it is real history and not myth.

The "Notes on the Text" that begin on page xiii are intended as a brief guide to instructors. Students, too, can be encouraged to read these notes. As an aid to selective use of the material, some sections and subsections are marked with a star (★) to indicate that they are optional. A section or subsection may be so marked either because it is of greater than average difficulty or because it is peripheral to the main development of a chapter. Any such designation of optional material is necessarily rather arbitrary. Most instructors will have their own ideas about which material to include and which to omit; the stars provide only a first set of suggestions.

At the end of each chapter appear questions, exercises, and problems. *Questions*, with few exceptions, are to be answered in words. Many of them are

---

* David Halliday and Robert Resnick, *Physics* (New York: John Wiley and Sons, Inc., 1966).
† *The Berkeley Physics Course*, a five-volume series by various authors (New York: McGraw-Hill Book Co.).
‡ *The M.I.T. Introductory Physics Series*, three volumes by A. P. French in print in 1971, with three more volumes scheduled (New York: W. W. Norton and Co.).
§ Xerox College Publishing, 1968.

intended to be thought-provoking and may have no specific right answer. Some are difficult. *Exercises* are intended to be straightforward tests of understanding of the material in the chapter without special twists or subtleties. The exercises involve numerical work as well as algebra and some calculus. Often an exercise may ask for a brief explanation as well as a quantitative result. *Problems* are, in general, more challenging. They may be in the nature of difficult exercises; they may draw together material from more than one section; or they may build on material in the text but go somewhat beyond it. The number of questions, exercises, and problems is large—much larger than the number that would ordinarily be assigned in a course. This large number is provided in order to meet the needs and tastes of different instructors, to enable the student to practice on items that are not assigned, and to enable the instructor, if he wishes, to choose examination questions from the text. Because the chapters are rather long and end-of-chapter items are numerous, marginal notes are used to classify the questions, exercises, and problems. Questions and exercises are keyed to specific sections. Problems are labeled by their subject.

I have used SI (mks) units throughout. Some special units—such as the calorie, the astronomical unit, and the electron volt—are introduced, and some exercises and problems require conversion of units. However, no effort is made to have the student develop any routine familiarity with more than one set of units. To aid the student in case he encounters Gaussian (cgs) units in another text or in a research paper, Appendix 5 contains an extensive list of equations of electromagnetism in SI and Gaussian units. My only significant deviation from "purity" in handling units occurs in Chapters 13 and 14, where calories and kilocalories are used as often as joules and where Avogadro's number is defined as the number of molecules in 1 mole rather than the number in 1 kmole.

I want students to enjoy this book and to profit from it. I think it will serve its purpose best if students are not rushed too quickly through too much of it. Careful treatment of some material and judicious omission of other material will probably provide better preparation for further work in physics, engineering, and other sciences than will a fast trip through every section.

KENNETH W. FORD

Acknowledgments

In preparing Volumes 1 and 2, I had the great benefit of collaboration with Neal D. Newby, Jr., and Brenton F. Stearns on questions, exercises, and problems. They added many useful suggestions for end-of-chapter items in Volume 3 as well. In his role of Consulting Editor, Brenton Stearns has also been of inestimable value as careful reader and thoughtful critic throughout the writing and rewriting of this text. I am indebted to Russell K. Hobbie, Donald E. Schuele, and N. S. Wall, who read one draft of the manuscript, and to David J. Cowan, who read two, for their numerous helpful suggestions. So many colleagues have contributed facts, data, photographs, and suggestions that a complete list is impossible. Among them are Olexa-Myron Bilaniuk, Alfred M. Bork, George J. Igo, Henry H. Kolm, Alexander Landé, Arthur W. Martin, Edward M. Purcell, Frederick Reines, Gerald Schubert, and Barry N. Taylor.

Yale Altman and Warren Blaisdell encouraged the initiation of this project and helped to keep it going. They deserve the credit (or blame) for turning me into an author in the first place. At Xerox College Publishing, James Piles and Arthur Evans have been agreeable and helpful mentors, and many others, including Bernice Borgeson, Barbara Johnson, Martha Johnson, and Marret McCorkle, have put their dedicated efforts into the book. I have been fortunate in having the services of two outstanding typists, Lisa Munsat and Elizabeth Higgins.

Notes on the text

Of the book's seven sections, the first two (*Introduction to Physics* and *Mathematics*) provide introductory and background material. There is great latitude in the way these two parts may be used. The remaining five parts (*Mechanics, Thermodynamics, Electromagnetism, Relativity,* and *Quantum Mechanics*) are devoted to specific major theories of physics. The fullest mathematical development is carried out for the theories of mechanics, electromagnetism, and special relativity. Thermodynamics and quantum mechanics are handled with somewhat more attention to phenomena and less to mathematical formalism. (Nevertheless, I have avoided more modest titles, such as *Heat* and *Atomic and Nuclear Phenomena*, because these parts do also emphasize the unity and power of physical theories, and they are by no means lacking in mathematics.) The division of the book into parts and the choice of rather long chapters in preference to more numerous shorter chapters are designed to serve the same end: to keep the overall structure of physics in view at a time when it is all too easy for the student to see the subject as a bewildering array of unrelated pieces.

Although this volume is part of a three-volume series, it is self-contained and there should be no difficulty in using it independently of the first two volumes. For the benefit of students who have used the first two volumes, there are occasional cross-references, but these are relatively minor and should not cause any difficulties for students who use only Volume 3. The earlier chapters most directly related to the subject matter of this volume are Chapter 3, on elementary particles, and Chapter 4, on conservation laws. Some instructors might want to direct students to these chapters in the library. A few elementary-particle processes are used for illustrative purposes in the chapters on relativity.

PART 6: Relativity requires not just new formulas or new techniques of problem solving: it requires new ways of thinking about nature. Chapter 19 is a prerelativity chapter designed to bridge the gap between classical thinking and relativistic thinking. Special relativity is developed in the next two chapters (20 and 21). The last chapter in this part (Chapter 22) is devoted to the Principle of Equivalence and selected aspects of general relativity. Although a number of spacetime diagrams appear in the text (including a Brehme diagram in a problem), the suggested methods of solving problems are usually algebraic, not graphical. To keep kinematic complexities to a minimum, almost all examples are restricted to one dimension. The Compton effect (Section 21.7) is an exception; other extensions to two dimensions appear in the problems. All of the chapters are notationally consistent; unprimed variables refer to the "stationary" frame, primed variables to the "moving" frame (as in Figure 20.6).

Chapter 19 begins (in Section 19.1) with an elucidation of the meanings of the terms *relativity* and *invariance*. The next two sections deal with Galilean relativity in classical mechanics. Section 19.4 is a largely qualitative section that attempts to make clear why classical electromagnetism seems to call for a preferred frame of reference. This leads naturally to a discussion of experimental searches for the preferred frame (or for the ether), with the Michelson-Morley experiment being selected for careful attention. (The idea of the Trouten-Noble experiment appears in a problem.) The chapter ends with a statement of Einstein's two postulates, one of which ($c = constant$) provides the entire foundation of Chapter 20 and the other of which (the invariance of physical laws) is also needed to build up the ideas of energy and momentum in Chapter 21. The instructor should probably make a special point of emphasizing that this chapter is a precursor to relativity and that with the exception of the last section, laws stated in the chapter are *not* laws of relativity. The juxtaposed comparison of ideas in the end-of-chapter summary is intended to help the student avoid confusion as he or she makes the transition from "classical thinking" to "modern thinking."

In the first part of Chapter 20 (Sections 20.1–20.5), three simple thought experiments are worked out on the basis of the invariance of the speed of light and the idea of reciprocity. Besides providing an introduction to time dilation and Lorentz contraction, these experiments provide three different special cases of the Lorentz-transformation equations, from which the full Lorentz transformation can then be developed (Section 20.6). For this development it is sufficient to consider the concepts of space and time alone and motion in only one dimension. Section 20.6 completes an *inductive* development of the general transformation from special cases. Section 20.7 turns the process around and considers various special cases as *deductive* consequences of the general transformation. As an interlude between theoretical developments, Section 20.8 touches on some experimental tests of relativistic kinematics. The Doppler shift is considered in a separate optional section (20.9), which is followed by a section introducing the important ideas of the invariant interval and the geometrical view of spacetime. The twin paradox is treated in this chapter (Section 20.11) where, in this author's opinion, it belongs, not in a chapter on general relativity. The concept of proper time makes its appearance in this section. The chapter ends with a discussion that tries to make clear the reason for the central role of the speed of light in relativity theory.

The relativistic mechanics in Chapter 21 is circumscribed, with primary emphasis on the concepts of energy and momentum. The force concept appears only in the problems. The derivations of the relativistic formulas for energy and momentum in Sections 21.1 and 21.2 are modernized versions of Einstein's original derivations (we use the decay of the neutral pion into two photons rather than the emission of two light waves by a block of matter). The derivations make use of the Doppler effect and are themselves less important than the demonstration that the definitions of E and $\mathbf{p}$ are consistent with relativistic kinematics (Section 21.4) and the exploration of the exact parallelism between momentum-energy and spacetime (Section 21.5). A separate section (21.3) deals with the important special case of massless particles. Collisions in one dimension are treated in an optional section (21.6), followed by a section on the Compton effect, a significant two-dimensional example. A final section summarizes the place of special relativity in physical theory. Except for some treatment of relativistic electric fields in two problems in Chapter 20, electromagnetism is omitted from these chapters and left to more advanced courses.

Chapter 22 is an optional chapter that is included in the text because of the general illumination of classical mechanics and gravity that is provided by the Principle of Equivalence. This principle and its consequences are discussed in Sections 22.1–22.5. Section 22.6 turns to the more difficult subject of the geodesic path as a law of motion. In a challenging subsection, motion with constant acceleration is shown (in lowest order) to be motion that maximizes elapsed proper time in a uniform gravitational field. (A special metric is chosen, but the concept of the metric is not discussed.) The chapter ends (Sections 22.7 and 22.8) with a qualitative discussion of general relativity and its implications.

PART 7: The student at this level is not ready for a formal, deductive, approach to quantum mechanics. On the other hand, he or she is ready for more than a purely descriptive, historical, introduction to atomic and nuclear physics. Mathematical developments are introduced selectively in this part of the book, where they can be applied without undue complexity—to the Paschen-Back and Zeeman effects, for example, and to the problem of a particle in a box. Other topics—lasers, nuclear shell structure, reactors, and elementary-particle phenomena, for example—are treated descriptively. As a substitute for an overall mathematical unification, which the level of treatment in this volume precludes, a set of "key ideas" are listed in Section 23.1 and are referred to in various later sections. Frequent re-emphasis of these ideas by the instructor can help to unite a wide range of atomic, nuclear, and particle phenomena. The general level of sophistication and difficulty in this part of the book peaks in the latter part of Chapter 23 (where the Schrödinger equation appears); Chapter 24 also contains some sections of above-average difficulty. In general, Chapters 25–27 are less demanding and should take less time than Chapters 23 and 24. In all of the chapters, instructors and students should be aware of a considerable unevenness of difficulty from one section to another and should apportion time (or select material) accordingly. This unevenness comes about because topics are developed in a logical order that often does not match an orderly progression of intellectual challenge.

Chapter 23 is a long and meaty chapter that divides itself naturally into two major parts. The first part contains an introduction to quantum ideas (Section 23.1), background material for Bohr's atomic theory (Sections 23.2–23.5), and the development of Bohr's theory (Sections 23.6–23.8). Instructors who are used to the standard version of the Bohr-atom theory that begins with the quantization of angular momentum in circular orbits may find this treatment, which emphasizes the correspondence principle, unfamiliar and not as simple as the standard version. It is not unduly difficult, however, and it has the advantage of being more faithful to Bohr's original work and, even more important, emphasizing those aspects of the Bohr-atom theory that remain valid in modern quantum theory. The second part of the chapter, beginning with a discussion of de Broglie waves (Section 23.9), moving through the uncertainty principle (Section 23.14), and ending with an optional section (23.15) on the Schrödinger equation, provides the principal development of quantum ideas that are applied later. The unifying theme is the wave nature of matter.

Chapter 24 picks up the thread of atomic-physics development that comprised the first part of Chapter 23 and also adds the theory of spin and angular-momentum quantization. An optional section (24.2) extends the idea of superposition introduced in Section 23.13 to the subtle topic of superposed spin states. The treatment of the hydrogen atom is completed in Section 24.4; Sections 24.5–24.8 deal with multi-electron atoms, the all-important elucidation of the periodic table appearing in Section 24.7. Sections 24.9, on fine structure, and 24.10, on magnetic effects, provide optional additional material on atomic structure. The final two sections, on interatomic bonding and lasers, are, except for the discussion of molecular rotation, entirely qualitative and rather elementary.

Chapter 25, the first of two chapters devoted to nuclei, starts immediately with a modern view of the nucleus—its composition, size, shape, and energy-level structure. Radioactivity and the early history of nuclear physics are saved for the next chapter. In Chapter 25, a special effort is made to compare and contrast nuclei and atoms as physical systems. The comparison shows up, for example, in Section 25.4, on nuclear energy levels, Section 25.5, on nuclear charts and binding energies, and Section 25.8, on nuclear shell structure. The inserted section (25.6) on pions and the nuclear force provides a chance to relate nuclear physics to particle physics and to exploit the time-energy form of the uncertainty principle. The stabilization of the neutron is included (Section 25.7) because it dramatically illustrates the importance of the mass-energy equivalence.

The principal quantitative developments in Chapter 26 occur in the first two sections, in which exponential decay is related to a law of probability acting on individual events and alpha decay is explained in terms of quantum waves penetrating a potential-energy barrier. The balance of the chapter is given to a more descriptive treatment of other nuclear decay and reaction processes. A historical discussion of radioactivity appears in Section 26.4. Because of their great practical importance, fission and fusion receive more than normal attention (Sections 26.6 and 26.7). Another practical topic, the measurement of the intensity of radiation, appears in the last part of Section 26.4.

All of Chapter 27 may be considered optional. Its discussion of elementary particles extends the introductory material on this subject that appeared in Chapter 3. This final chapter makes use of relativistic and quantum ideas, but adds no further technical developments. It affords the student the chance to confront some of the deeper ideas of contemporary physics on an unfinished frontier. A course of this kind could equally well end with a qualitative survey of solid-state physics; some instructors might wish to use material from other sources for this purpose.

Contents

* Sections and subsections marked with stars are optional.

APPENDICES

xxi

Classical and Modern Physics

PART **SIX**

Relativity

19

Frames of Reference and the Ether

The theory of relativity and the quantum theory, both born within the first five years of the twentieth century, together immensely deepened our understanding of nature. The same could, of course, be said for any important theory of nature. But there was something unique about the new theories, something symbolic of a changing relationship between science and human experience. Each of them contributed to a complete revolution in the scientists' and philosophers' ways of looking at the world. For the first time in science, concepts were introduced that violated common sense and defied visualization. Two generations later, man is no better able to picture four-dimensional spacetime or the wave-particle nature of a photon than he was when these ideas were introduced. The reason is not hard to find. We humans are classical creatures, and pre-twentieth-century science suffices quite well to describe us in the large. The quantum theory is relevant to us only at the microscopic biochemical level below the range of our perception, and relativity is likewise unimportant in normal life because we move about, even in jet travel, at speeds far less than the speed of light. You will nevertheless find, as you explore the frontiers of the very small and the very fast in this volume, that the new theories have more to offer than pure intellectual excitement and challenge. Despite their conceptual remoteness, they have engendered a wealth of practical consequences.

Concepts of modern physics are beyond direct perception

Yet the new theories have practical impact

19.1 Relativity and invariance

The theory of relativity is concerned with two seemingly opposite ideas, relativity and invariance. *Relativity* here means relativity of observation—I see a given phenomenon one way, you see it another; it refers to *disagreement*. *Invariance* refers to areas of *agreement*, those aspects of a phenomenon (and even more

Relativity = disagreement of measurement = subjectivity of observer

971

Invariance = agreement of
measurement = objectivity
of observer

More relativity and more
invariance in the theory of
relativity

important, those laws of phenomena) that are the same for different observers. In place of relativity and invariance, the words subjectivity and objectivity could serve. However, the subjectivity of relativity is a specific kind of physical subjectivity and does not refer merely to differences in human perception. And the objectivity of relativity is not the philosophers' "objective reality." It is rather objectivity by definition, an agreement among observers to accept as real the common aspects of their measurements.

The theory of relativity has, surprisingly, added both more relativity (or subjectivity) and more invariance (or objectivity) to science. Einstein showed that a number of quantities previously thought to be invariant are in fact relative, most notable of these being time. But at the same time he showed how to extract from the increased relativity of observation new invariant quantities. More important, he raised to the level of a fundamental postulate of science the principle that despite the relativity of the raw observations of phenomena, the *laws* governing these phenomena must be invariant. From the increased subjectivity of observation that relativity brought to the world came a new and deeper view of the objectivity of physical laws.

19.2 Galilean relativity

The ideas of relativity and invariance exist in ordinary Newtonian mechanics and can be illustrated with simple mechanical experiments, such as those considered in Section 7.10. Our purpose in this section and the next is to review and extend the discussion of that earlier section. Consider, for example, a child in a uniformly moving train who releases a ball and allows it to fall straight down. From his point of view, it starts from rest and falls vertically downward with uniform acceleration. Someone watching from outside the train would have a different view (Figure 19.1). The outside observer would say that the

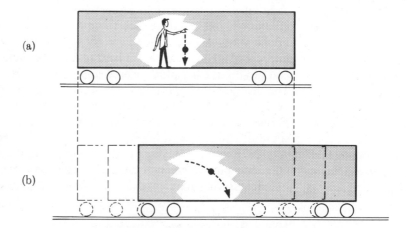

FIGURE 19.1 Relativity of observation in Newtonian mechanics. (a) In a train-fixed frame of reference, a ball falls vertically downward. (b) In a ground-based frame of reference, the same motion appears parabolic. The two observers agree about some aspects of the motion and disagree about other aspects. (See also Figures 7.20 and 7.21.)

"actual" path of the ball in space is a parabola: The ball has a forward motion when released and falls like a projectile through a parabolic arc. He would concede, however, that the child is right in assigning to the ball a uniform downward acceleration, and indeed both would agree on the magnitude of the acceleration. We may summarize the areas of agreement and disagreement between the two observers in a short table. (Bear in mind that this table refers to Newtonian mechanics and will have to be altered when we come to the new mechanics of Einstein.)

Agreement	Disagreement
Acceleration	Position
Mass	Velocity
Force	Coordinates
Time	
Laws of motion	

Agreement and disagreement in classical measurement

There is obvious disagreement about position since there is disagreement about the shape of the trajectory. There is also obvious disagreement about velocity since the outside observer considers the ball to have some horizontal component of velocity, unlike the inside observer, who considers the ball to have only vertical velocity. There is also possible disagreement about coordinates, something that is not necessarily connected with the relative motion of the observers. Any two observers are always free to choose different coordinate systems to which to refer their measurements.

Despite the disagreements, there remains a large area of agreement between the observers. Both would measure the same acceleration; this is because there is no relative acceleration between the two observers (see Sections 19.3 and 7.10). Mass and time are *assumed* in mechanics to be definite invariant quantities, and if it were not so, the theory of mechanics would be considerably upset (as indeed it *is* upset by the theory of relativity). Experimentally, train travelers do not change their weight, an indication that both observers would measure the same force.* Most important of all, if the train traveler (who now had better be a scientist and not a child) supplements the experiment of dropping a ball with many other experiments, he would arrive at Newton's laws, exactly those that the outside observer already knows to be valid at rest outside the train.

The fact that observers in different inertial frames of reference agree about the laws of motion is known as Galilean relativity (see page 246). It means that the earth is neither a better nor a worse laboratory than the train and that the traveling scientist has as much right as the earthbound scientist to claim that he is at rest and the other is moving. The invariance of the laws of motion precludes any single preferred frame of reference for mechanics, thereby precluding absolute motion.

Galilean relativity

---

* In one possible logical formulation of mechanics, force is *defined* as mass times acceleration. In that case, the invariance of mass and acceleration automatically implies the invariance of force. In a different possible logical formulation, where force is separately defined, it must be experimentally verified to be invariant.

19.3   The Galilean transformation

The idea of a transformation

It is not enough to know that the traveling observer and the observer at rest measure different positions and velocities for the same moving ball. We need to know just how they differ; i.e., we need to express the difference quantitatively. This is easy to do. In general, a set of mathematical expressions relating one observer's measurements to another observer's measurements is called a transformation. In classical mechanics, the transformation of space and time measurements from one observer to another moving uniformly relative to the first is called a *Galilean transformation*. For simplicity, we restrict our attention to a plane and suppose that our traveling observer measures horizontal distances x' forward from the rear of the train and vertical distances y' upward from the floor of the train (Figure 19.2). The observer on the ground measures horizontal distances x from some fixed pole A on the ground and vertical distances y upward from a platform at the floor level of the train. Then the measurements y and y' will agree, and the time measurements t and t' must be assumed to agree if both observers carry accurate clocks (an assumption that will soon have to be changed). Only x and x' will differ. If the rear of the train passed the pole A at $t = 0$, it will later have moved forward a distance $s = vt$, where v is the speed of the train. It is clear from Figure 19.2 that x and x' differ by this distance s. The Galilean transformation may, therefore, be written as a set of three simple equations:

$$x = x' + vt', \tag{19.1}$$

Galilean transformation

$$y = y', \tag{19.2}$$

$$t = t'. \tag{19.3}$$

On the right side of each of these three equations is a measurement (or measurements) of the observer on the train. On the left side of each equation is a measurement of the observer on the ground. Thus we have a *transformation* from x', y', t' to x, y, t. It is, of course, also equally well a transformation in the other direction. If the observers decided to have their xy axes and $x'y'$ axes in the same plane, they would then agree on coordinates perpendicular to

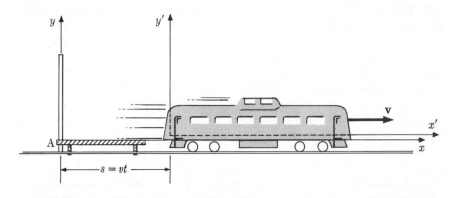

FIGURE 19.2   Definition of coordinates in two frames of reference.

this plane, and we could add a fourth equation to complete the transformation;

$$z = z'. \tag{19.4}$$

■ EXAMPLE 1: If the ball in Figure 19.1 is dropped at $t = 0$ from height h above the floor and distance x_0 from the rear of the car, what equations describe its motion for both observers? The Galilean transformation equations *relate* the two sets of observations but do not provide either one. For that, we must use the laws of motion. In this example, the ball falls vertically with acceleration g in the train-based frame of reference. Its motion in this frame is given by

$$x' = x_0,$$

$$y' = h - \tfrac{1}{2}gt'^2 = h - \tfrac{1}{2}gt^2.$$

Substituting from this pair of equations in Equations 19.1 and 19.2 then provides the description of the motion in the earth-based frame of reference,

$$x = x_0 + vt,$$

$$y = h - \tfrac{1}{2}gt^2.$$

If these two equations are then combined to eliminate the time t, the result is

$$y = h - \frac{g}{2v^2}(x - x_0)^2.$$

This is the equation of a parabola.   ■

Assuming that the coordinates x, y, z and x', y', z' are coordinates of a moving object, we may differentiate the transformation equations with respect to time to obtain the velocity transformation:

$$v_x = v'_x + v, \tag{19.5}$$

$$v_y = v'_y, \tag{19.6}$$ *Velocity transformation*

$$v_z = v'_z. \tag{19.7}$$

These equations display the Galilean relativity of velocity. Note that v is the relative speed of the two frames of reference, whereas v_x, v'_x, etc. refer to velocity components of an object observed in both frames. A further differentiation of Equations 19.5–19.7 gives

$$a_x = a'_x, \tag{19.8}$$

$$a_y = a'_y, \tag{19.9}$$ *The same acceleration for both observers*

$$a_z = a'_z, \tag{19.10}$$

confirming the invariance of acceleration for the two observers.

In the theory of relativity, the concept of an *event* is important. Anticipating the need, we introduce the idea here. An event is a point in space and in time, *Event: a spacetime point* usually (but not necessarily) an occurrence or "happening" at a particular place and a particular time. The start of the fall of the ball in Figure 19.1 is an event. Its collision with the floor is another event. The spatial and temporal separation between two events we may designate by Δx, Δy, Δz, Δt—where $\Delta x = x_2 - x_1$, $\Delta y = y_2 - y_1$, etc. For these distances and times between events there is a Galilean transformation,

$$\Delta x = \Delta x' + v \Delta t', \tag{19.11}$$

$$\Delta y = \Delta y', \tag{19.12}$$

$$\Delta z = \Delta z', \tag{19.13}$$

$$\Delta t = \Delta t'. \tag{19.14}$$

Another form of the Galilean
transformation

Although they look very much like Equations 19.1–19.4, these equations are actually somewhat more general. They require only that the x, y, and z axes be parallel to the x', y', and z' axes respectively, and that the relative motion of the frames of reference be in the x direction. The x and x' axes need not lie along the same line. Nor is it necessary that the origins of the two coordinate systems pass each other at any particular time.

■ EXAMPLE 2:   Event 1 is the dropping of the ball from height h in Figure 19.1; Event 2 is its collision with the floor. What are the spatial and temporal separations of these two events for both observers? The vertical displacement of the ball is $y_2 - y_1 = -h$; its transverse displacement (in the z direction) is zero. Therefore

$$\Delta y = \Delta y' = -h,$$

$$\Delta z = \Delta z' = 0.$$

Its time of fall is also the same in both frames:

$$\Delta t = \Delta t' = \sqrt{\frac{2h}{g}}. \tag{19.15}$$

In the train, the ball suffers no displacement in the x direction, so

$$\Delta x' = 0. \tag{19.16}$$

With the help of Equations 19.15 and 19.16, Equation 19.11 gives

$$\Delta x = v \sqrt{\frac{2h}{g}}. \tag{19.17}$$

We present this example not as a way to learn anything new about falling balls but to stimulate a way of thinking about events and observers that is useful in relativity theory.   ■

■ EXAMPLE 3:   A railroad car of length L is moving forward with speed v. A man walks from the front to the rear of the car in time T. What is his average speed in a train-based frame of reference? in a ground-based frame? What distance does he cover over the ground? In a train-based frame we may write

$$x'_1 = L, \qquad x'_2 = 0, \qquad \Delta x' = -L;$$

$$t'_1 = 0, \qquad t'_2 = T, \qquad \Delta t' = T.$$

In this frame, the man's average x component of velocity is

$$\overline{v'_x} = \frac{\Delta x'}{\Delta t'} = -\frac{L}{T}.$$

In a ground-based frame, the Galilean transformation equations yield

$$\Delta x = \Delta x' + v\,\Delta t' = -L + vT,$$

$$\Delta t = \Delta t' = T.$$

Note that Δx may be positive, negative, or zero. In this frame, the man's average x component of velocity is

$$\overline{v_x} = \frac{\Delta x}{\Delta T} = -\left(\frac{L}{T}\right) + v$$

$$= \overline{v'_x} + v.$$

His average speeds in the two frames are equal to the magnitudes of $\overline{v'_x}$ and $\overline{v_x}$. ∎

Inertial frames of reference were introduced and defined in Section 7.1. The Galilean transformation links classical measurements in different inertial frames. The entire special theory of relativity is similarly restricted to inertial frames. In considering this restriction, it is important to distinguish between the motion of the observer and the motion of the thing observed. *Observers* in the theory move with constant velocity; the *thing observed* may move in an arbitrary way.

Inertial frames of reference

19.4   The problem of electromagnetism

The fact that the laws of mechanics are the same in all inertial frames illustrates what Poincaré and Einstein called the Principle of Relativity.* The principle is true for classical mechanics if the space and time measurements of different observers are related by the Galilean transformation. Then, according to Equations 19.8–19.10, the acceleration of a given object is measured to be the same by the two observers:

The Principle of Relativity: Nature's laws are the same in all inertial frames

$$\mathbf{a} = \mathbf{a'}. \tag{19.18}$$

The force on the object is assumed to depend on the position of the object *relative* to other objects (and possibly on relative velocities as well). This means that force does not depend on the motion of the observer:

$$\mathbf{F} = \mathbf{F'}. \tag{19.19}$$

Mass, if it is an invariant scalar quantity—as it is assumed to be in classical mechanics—is also the same for both observers:

$$m = m'. \tag{19.20}$$

Newton's second law is therefore unchanged; it is said to be "invariant under the transformation." This means that, if $\mathbf{F} = m\mathbf{a}$, then also

Invariance of Newton's laws

$$\mathbf{F'} = m'\mathbf{a'}. \tag{19.21}$$

---

* Poincaré stated this as a principle of classical physics that seemed to be in trouble. Einstein stated it as a principle of nature to which classical physics, if necessary, would have to yield.

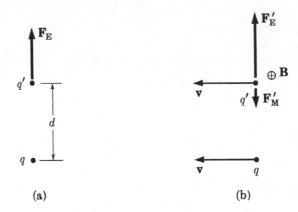

FIGURE 19.3   (a) Two charged particles are at rest in one frame of reference. Charge q' experiences an electric force $\mathbf{F}_E$. (b) In another frame of reference, moving with respect to the first, both an electric force $\mathbf{F}'_E$ and a magnetic force $\mathbf{F}'_M$ are acting on q'. The electric fields $\mathbf{E}$ and $\mathbf{E}'$ in the two frames of reference are of unequal magnitude.

Newton's first and third laws are also invariant under the Galilean transformation, and the whole structure of Newtonian mechanics can be developed with the same form in any pair of inertial frames in which space and time measurements are related by Equations 19.11–19.14.

We are naturally drawn to try out the same ideas on electromagnetism, testing the equations of this theory for invariance. The actual process of carrying out this test belongs to a more advanced treatment of physics. Here we can only state that such an effort meets at first with failure. If the space and time measurements of one observer are transformed to the space and time measurements of another observer by means of Equations 19.1–19.4 (or 19.11–19.14), the equations of electromagnetism are altered in form. Indeed, equations true in one frame of reference are transformed into equations not true in the other frame of reference. We can get a hint about the reasons for this difficulty by considering the role of velocity in the laws of electromagnetism. Suppose that a pair of positively charged particles are at rest in the laboratory, separated by distance d [Figure 19.3(a)]. According to an observer in the laboratory, each particle experiences a repulsive electric force and no magnetic force. To an observer moving to the right at speed v, the particles appear to be in motion. He finds that an attractive magnetic force acts between the particles, in addition to a repulsive electric force. If the total force on charge q' is to be the same for both observers, the electric force F'_E must be greater than the electric force F_E, since $\mathbf{F}_E = \mathbf{F}'_E + \mathbf{F}'_M$. If we assume further that charge is a scalar quantity—and therefore invariant—the electric fields seen by the two observers must also be unequal*:

Electromagnetic theory does not conform to Galilean relativity

$$E' > E.$$

It turns out, upon further reasoning of the same kind, that surface integrals of

---

* This inequality is implied by the formula for E given in a footnote on page 682.

the electric field surrounding the charge q are also unequal for the two observers *if* the Galilean transformation connects their space and time measurements:

$$\oint \mathbf{E'} \cdot d\mathbf{S} > \oint \mathbf{E} \cdot d\mathbf{S}.$$

This would mean that if Gauss's law,

$$\oint \mathbf{E} \cdot d\mathbf{S} = \frac{q}{\epsilon_0},$$

is valid in one frame of reference, it is not valid in the other.

   The role of the speed of light in electromagnetic theory gives further evidence of the apparent irreconcilability of the theory with the Principle of Relativity. Electromagnetic waves propagate at a speed c given by

$$c = \frac{1}{\sqrt{\mu_0 \epsilon_0}}. \tag{19.22}$$

However, according to the Galilean transformation (in particular, Equation 19.5), the speed of light—or of anything else—depends upon the state of motion of the observer. Therefore, if μ_0 and ϵ_0 are invariant constants, the speed c calculated with Equation 19.22 must equal the speed of light in only one inertial frame of reference. Alternatively, if Equation 19.22 is to yield the measured speed in all inertial frames, the constant ϵ_0 must vary from one frame to another (since μ_0 is chosen arbitrarily to be constant). Such a variation would make Coulomb's law of electric force depend on the state of motion of the observer.

Galilean transformation predicts variable speed of light, therefore variable ϵ_0

   In summary, the laws of mechanics are invariant under the Galilean transformation; the laws of electromagnetism are not. This difference can be viewed in several alternative ways. (1) The Principle of Relativity happens coincidentally to be satisfied by mechanics but it is not a general principle of nature and is not important. (2) The theory of electromagnetism is incorrect and must be changed to conform to the Principle of Relativity. (3) The Principle of Relativity is correct, but the Galilean transformation (and, therefore, Newtonian mechanics) must be discarded and a new transformation found that will permit the laws of electromagnetism to be invariant. Maxwell and other architects of electromagnetic theory in the latter part of the nineteenth century in effect took the first point of view (although they probably did not think in these terms). To them it was an article of faith that there exists in the cosmos a preferred frame of reference, for they imagined the existence of a physical medium—the ether—filling all of space. In an ether-filled universe, there is no reason to believe in the Principle of Relativity. Rather, one would expect the laws of nature to take on their simplest form in the frame of reference in which the ether is at rest and perhaps have a different form in other frames. Einstein, guided by a faith of his own—a faith in the universal validity of the Principle of Relativity—adopted the third bold view. On this foundation was built a new mechanics, a new view of the world, and even a deeper new insight into electromagnetism. Although the equations of electromagnetism weathered the revolution of relativity unchanged, the interpretation of these equations was somewhat altered.

Alternative views of classical theories

Einstein's faith: A philosophical outlook shapes physical theory

   Einstein's transformation law relating the space and time measurements of different observers (all in inertial frames) is called the Lorentz transformation. This new transformation and some of its remarkable consequences form the heart of the next chapter. In the remainder of this chapter we shall discuss the frustrating search for a preferred frame of reference that took place in the years before relativity, and the postulates of Einstein that gave dramatic substance to the "nothingness" of these frustrated efforts.

19.5   The Michelson-Morley experiment

In a panegyric to the ether, in 1873, Maxwell said:

> The vast interplanetary and interstellar regions will no longer be regarded as waste places in the universe, which the Creator has not seen fit to fill with the symbols of the manifold order of His kingdom. We shall find them to be already full of this wonderful medium. . . . It extends unbroken from star to star; and when a molecule of hydrogen vibrates in the dog-star, the medium receives the impulses of these vibrations; and after carrying them in its immense bosom for three years, delivers them in due course, regular order, and full tale into the spectroscope of Mr. Huggins, at Tulse Hill.*

Nineteenth-century belief in the ether unsupported by experiment

For two centuries, the ether had existed in the minds of scientists, but as yet no shred of direct experimental evidence pointed to its existence elsewhere. The time had come to find the ether. Of the various efforts to pin it down in the following decades, we shall discuss only one, the experiment of Michelson and Morley.

That a definitive experimental test for the existence of the ether should be possible was first realized by Albert Michelson, who in 1879 as a 26-year-old American naval ensign had already established a name for himself by measuring the speed of light with great precision. His first effort to discover the motion of the earth through the ether came in 1881 in Potsdam, Germany. Here he found to his surprise that he was unable to detect any relative motion of Earth and ether. But the accuracy of the measurement was not high, and no significant stir in the world of science resulted. When Michelson and Edward Morley repeated the experiment six years later in Cleveland, Ohio, with much improved apparatus, the significance of the negative finding could no longer be overlooked. No apparent motion of the earth through the ether could be detected. Many repetitions of the experiment in succeeding decades have supported the 1887 result—there is no detectable relative motion of Earth and ether.†

In order to understand the Michelson-Morley experiment, we turn temporarily from light waves to sound waves. If passengers on an airplane in flight had a way of measuring the speed of sound waves encountered in the air, they would observe quite different values for the speed of sound relative to the

---

* The complete talk from which this abstract is taken can be found in Arthur Beiser, ed., *The World of Physics* (New York: McGraw-Hill Book Company, 1960).

† A different version of an ether-wind experiment was carried out at Columbia University in 1958 by J. P. Cedarholm, G. F. Bland, B. L. Havens, and C. H. Townes and was reported in *Physical Review Letters* **1**, 342 (1958). The expected negative result was found, but to a higher precision than theretofore. Since any departure from the null result, no matter how small, would be exceedingly important, experiments will undoubtedly continue to be performed as more accurate techniques are developed.

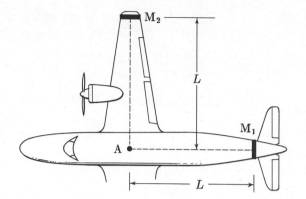

FIGURE 19.4   Unusual airspeed indicator. Sound waves start from point A and return to point A after reflecting from the equidistant plates M_1 and M_2. The time difference between the returning echoes provides a measure of the airspeed.

airplane according to the direction of motion of the sound. For example, on a plane traveling at half the speed of sound, a sound wave going the opposite direction would seem to move past the airplane at a speed 50 percent greater than the normal speed of sound. A sound wave overtaking the plane, on the other hand, would pass the plane at a relative speed of only half the normal speed of sound. According to Maxwell's view, we are all passengers on the earth which is flying through the ether. If we encounter light waves we should find them to be moving at different speeds relative to the earth, according to whether the light is encountering us head-on in our passage through the ether or overtaking us in our motion. The reason is the same for the light and for the sound. Both are supposed to move at a fixed speed relative to the medium that is responsible for their propagation.

Imagine now a rather unusual airspeed indicator mounted on the airplane. It consists of a sound generator and a sound receiver (such as a microphone) mounted on top of the plane amidships and small plates to reflect sound, one attached to the tail and one to the wingtip, equidistant from the sound generator-receiver combination (Figure 19.4). A noise is created, and after some time elapses, its echoes return from the tail and the wingtip. If the plane is in motion, the wingtip echo will arrive slightly sooner than the tail echo, and the time difference of the echoes could be displayed in the cockpit to let the captain know how fast the plane is moving. Suppose, for instance, that the speed of the plane is 170 m/sec, half the speed of sound (340 m/sec), and that the reflecting plates are 6 m from the source of the sound. Relative to the airplane, the sound wave traveling to the tail would have a speed of 510 m/sec. Its journey to the tail would therefore require 0.01176 sec (11.76 msec). On its return trip, it would be making good a speed with respect to the plane of only 170 m/sec, and would require three times as long to get back, 35.29 msec. Altogether 47.05 msec would elapse before the tail echo returned. It is useful to express this algebraically. The outbound time from the source A to the tail reflector M_1 (Figure 19.4), a distance L away, is

$$t_{\text{out}} = \frac{L}{v_{\text{s}} + v_{\text{a}}},$$

where v_{a} is the speed of the airplane and v_{s} is the speed of sound. The sum

An unusual airspeed indicator

$v_s + v_a$ is the speed of the backward-propagating sound wave relative to the airplane. The time for the echo to return is

$$t_{\text{return}} = \frac{L}{v_s - v_a}.$$

The round-trip time for the tail echo is the sum of these two expressions,

$$t_{\text{out}} + t_{\text{return}} = t(\text{tail echo}) = \frac{2L}{v_s} \cdot \frac{1}{1 - (v_a/v_s)^2}. \qquad (19.23)$$

The analysis for the wingtip echo is no more difficult. It yields

$$t(\text{wingtip echo}) = \frac{2L}{v_s} \cdot \frac{1}{\sqrt{1 - (v_a/v_s)^2}}. \qquad (19.24)$$

The important point is that this latter time is shorter, 40.75 msec in our example. Both echoes are delayed by the motion, but the tail echo is delayed more than the wingtip echo, and the difference is easily interpreted in terms of the speed of the airplane.

The Michelson-Morley apparatus

The Michelson-Morley experiment is an etherspeed indicator designed in exact analogy to our unorthodox airspeed indicator. Light is sent simultaneously in two perpendicular directions and then reflected back. The source of light and the apparatus are fixed with respect to the earth, and are therefore being carried through the ether by the earth. The time difference between the two reflected light signals is too small to measure directly, but it is inferred from the interference of the two waves. The design of the experiment is indicated in Figure 19.5. A light wave arriving from the source S [Figure 19.5(a)] is split by a lightly silvered glass plate into two waves, one running upward to mirror M_2 and the other continuing on to mirror M_1. This beam-splitting action ensures that the two waves are coherent and initially in phase. An extra glass plate G affords an equal path in glass for both beams. Some of the light returning from M_2 passes through the silvered plate and some returning from M_1 is reflected from its silvered surface to the eye of the observer (or better, to a light-sensitive device more accurate than the eye). If the mirrors M_1 and M_2 are exactly the same distance from the point R (this is not necessary, but it simplifies matters slightly) and if the apparatus is at rest with respect to the ether, the two waves arriving at the observer will be exactly in phase and will reinforce each other to give a bright spot of light. But if the apparatus is moving through the ether, for example to the left in the diagram, the light from M_1 will be slightly more delayed in its round trip than the light from M_2, and the two waves will no longer be exactly in phase. There will be partial interference of the two waves, and the light seen by the observer will be less bright.

Of course the earth cannot be stopped and started at will to look for a change of light intensity. But what is simple and just as effective is to change the orientation of the apparatus. Michelson rotated the whole apparatus through 90 deg so that the path to M_1, if initially "upwind" and "downwind," became "crosswind." A change in intensity should have been observed as the rotation proceeded. Michelson and Morley also repeated the experiment at various times of the year to catch the earth's motion in various directions through space as the earth swung around the sun.

The magnitude of the effect that Michelson hoped to observe is extremely small, because, even at its orbital speed of 3×10^4 m/sec (66,000 mile/hr), the earth moves at a crawl compared with the speed of light. To calculate the expected effect, we can use Equations 19.23 and 19.24, in which we replace v_s by c, the speed of light, and v_a by v, the speed of the earth. It is also helpful to write these equations in an approximate form that is accurate if the ratio v/c is much less than 1. From Equation 19.23,

$$t\text{(upwind-downwind)} = \frac{2L}{c} \cdot \frac{1}{1 - (v/c)^2} \cong t_0 \left[1 + \left(\frac{v}{c} \right)^2 \right]; \quad (19.25)$$

and from Equation 19.24,

$$t\text{(crosswind)} = \frac{2L}{c} \cdot \frac{1}{\sqrt{1 - (v/c)^2}} \cong t_0 \left[1 + \frac{1}{2} \left(\frac{v}{c} \right)^2 \right]. \quad (19.26)$$

*t(upwind-downwind) >
t(crosswind)*

For $2L/c$ we introduce the abbreviation t_0; it is the round-trip time in the absence of "wind." The difference in the two round-trip times is

$$\Delta t = \frac{1}{2} \left(\frac{v}{c} \right)^2 t_0. \quad (19.27)$$

If we assume, as Michelson did, that the speed of the earth through the ether is about the same as the orbital speed of the earth, we have $v/c \cong 10^{-4}$. A typical distance from the lightly silvered plate to the reflecting mirrors [Figure 19.5(b)] was 11 m. Substituted in the above equations, these numbers give

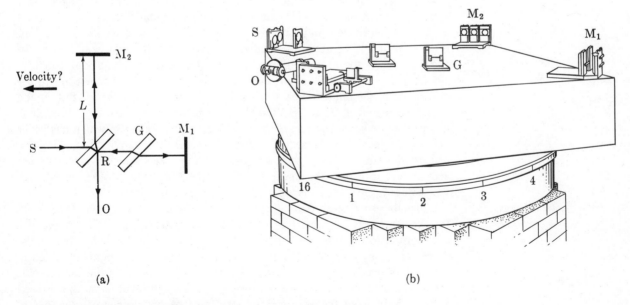

(a)   (b)

FIGURE 19.5   (a) Schematic diagram of the Michelson interferometer. The source is at S, the observer at O. (b) Apparatus of Michelson and Morley. Mirrors and glass plates are mounted on a stone about 1.5 m on a side, which floats in a trough of mercury. Multiple reflections extend the distance L to about 11 m. [Illustration adapted from W. F. Magie, ed., *A Source Book in Physics* (Cambridge, Massachusetts: Harvard University Press, 1935), p. 373.]

$t_0 = 7.3 \times 10^{-8}$ sec and $\Delta t = 3.7 \times 10^{-16}$ sec. The predicted spatial lag of one reflected beam behind the other is then $c \Delta t$, or 1.1×10^{-7} m (1,100 Å). This distance is about 5 times less than the distance spanned by a single wavelength of visible light. Therefore, as the apparatus is rotated, the expected shift of the two waves with respect to each other is somewhat less than the 3,000 Å that would be required to convert bright constructive interference into dark destructive interference. However, the resulting change of intensity would have been easy to observe. Michelson and Morley felt confident that they could have detected a change of phase 20 times smaller than the predicted value.

Predicted phase difference about $2\pi/5$

No matter what the time of day or time of year, no matter what source of light was employed, a rotation of the apparatus never produced any observable change of light intensity. The Michelson-Morley etherspeed indicator always gave a reading of zero, which indicated no motion of the earth through the ether.

19.6   Efforts to keep the ether

It proved to be far from easy to give up the ether. For nearly two decades, many efforts were made to retain the ether in spite of the Michelson-Morley result and other negative results of later ether-tracking experiments. Michelson himself gave no thought to discarding the ether. He believed that in some inexplicable way nature had tricked him, making his experimental arrangement unsuitable for detecting the ether. The simplest such trickery to imagine is that the earth drags some of the ether along with itself. According to this ether-drag hypothesis, the Michelson-Morley experiment shows no effect because just near the surface of the earth, the ether is motionless with respect to the earth. This kind of drag is well known for airplanes, which drag along a very thin shield of motionless air known as a boundary layer. An airspeed probe that penetrated only into the boundary layer would record no motion. It must protrude through the boundary layer into the airstream beyond in order to detect the motion of the airplane through the air. Today satellites would make it possible in an analogous way to put the Michelson-Morley etherspeed probe out into space beyond the ether boundary layer. But in the meantime the ether-drag hypothesis has had to be abandoned: first, because it ought to cause some bending of starlight arriving at the earth, which has never been seen; second, because the successful theory of relativity has led us to discard the ether entirely, with or without drag. Nevertheless, scientists are accustomed to expect the unexpected, and the Michelson-Morley experiment will no doubt one day be repeated far from the earth's surface.*

The ether-drag hypothesis

The "emission" hypothesis: The speed of light is fixed with respect to its source

Another suggestion that suffered the fate of the ether-drag hypothesis, and for the same reasons, was the proposal that light travels at a fixed speed not with respect to the ether but with respect to the source of the light. Before the passage of many years, this hypothesis was laid to rest by astronomical evidence. Some stars occur in pairs that rotate about each other. As one of the pair moves toward the earth, the other moves away. Yet careful observations showed that the light from the approaching star must be traveling no faster toward earth than light from the receding star.

---

*In 1926–1928 Auguste Piccard repeated the Michelson-Morley experiment in a balloon about 8,000 ft above the earth, with the expected negative result.

A more radical suggestion, made by George F. FitzGerald in 1892, also came to nought as an explanation of the Michelson-Morley results, but like so many wrong suggestions in science, it gave rise to some fruitful consequences before it died. Suppose, said FitzGerald, that the experimental apparatus shrinks in the direction of motion through the ether by just enough to compensate exactly for the slower average speed of light upwind and downwind than crosswind. Since the required shrinkage would be, on earth, only about one part in one hundred million, this subtle effect would not contradict any previous measurements. The FitzGerald contraction hypothesis was formulated mathematically in the same year by Lorentz, and his mathematical expressions eventually found their way into the theory of relativity but with a markedly different interpretation. At every point where mathematics is used to describe nature, the mathematical skeleton is meaningless without interpretation and definition of the symbols used. The formulas of Lorentz underwent a marked evolution of interpretation between the time of FitzGerald's hypothesis in 1892 and the time of Einstein's theory of relativity in 1905.

The FitzGerald contraction hypothesis

19.7   The special theory of relativity: Einstein's two postulates

By 1900 it had become clear that the ether was not easily detectable. Scientists were beginning to feel like Aesop's fox who could not reach the grapes. Henri Poincaré, perhaps the first to see clearly the potential significance of the failures to discover the ether, was led to say, "Our ether, does it really exist? I do not believe that more precise observations could ever reveal anything more than *relative* displacements." Einstein independently rejected the ether. In his first paper on relativity* in 1905 (developing what we now call the special theory of relativity), he wrote: "The introduction of a 'luminiferous ether' will prove to be superfluous inasmuch as the view to be developed here will not require an 'absolutely stationary space' provided with special properties."

The ether rejected

It is important to understand why the rejection of the ether is so important. It is because without an ether, there is no physical basis for a preferred frame of reference. All frames—at least all inertial frames—should be equivalent, and the Principle of Relativity should be a valid general principle. This is how Einstein phrased it in the paper just cited: "Examples of this sort, together with the unsuccessful attempts to detect any motion of the earth relative to the 'light medium,'† lead to the supposition that the phenomena of electrodynamics as well as of mechanics possess no properties corresponding to the idea of absolute rest; rather, ... the same laws of electrodynamics and optics are valid in all frames of reference in which the equations of mechanics are valid." This Principle of Relativity is the first of two postulates on which the special theory of relativity

* *Annalen der Physik* **17**, 891 (1905). An English translation can be found in H. A. Lorentz, A. Einstein, H. Minkowski, and H. Weyl, *The Principle of Relativity* (New York: Dover Publications, Inc., 1952); a translation of part of the paper appears also in Morris Shamos, ed., *Great Experiments in Physics* (New York: Holt, Rinehart, and Winston, 1964). The latter translation, although less reliable than the former one, is supplemented by useful notes and commentary.

† Einstein said later that he was not referring specifically to the Michelson-Morley experiment when he wrote this sentence. He was only aware at second hand, from studying papers of Lorentz, that several efforts to detect motion through the ether had failed.

rests. The second postulate, which, in Einstein's words, "is only apparently incompatible with the former one," is that the speed of light is a fixed constant, independent of the motion of the source of the light and independent of the motion of the observer. The two postulates are "incompatible" only if one thinks in terms of the Galilean transformation, which requires that all speeds, including the speed of light, are relative to the state of motion of the observer. It is the new Lorentz transformation that reconciles the two postulates.

Quite aside from its remarkable and general consequences, the special theory of relativity has a unique allure because of the simple elegance of these two postulates upon which the whole theory rests:

Einstein's two postulates

1. The laws of nature are the same in all inertial frames of reference.
2. The speed of light is the same in all inertial frames of reference.

The revolutionary import of the second postulate is the principal subject matter of Chapter 20. Locked in the innocent-looking statement, $c = constant$, is a bombshell of power. No less potent is the first postulate, the Principle of Relativity, which will be exploited in Chapter 21.

Summary of ideas and definitions

The theory of relativity deals with domains of nature remote from human perception. It has practical implications nonetheless.

Key ideas in the theory are *relativity*, referring to disagreements of measurement between observers, and *invariance*, referring to agreement of measurement for different observers.

An event is a point in space and in time, usually—but not necessarily—a point where something of physical interest occurs.

A transformation is a set of equations relating the measurements of one observer to the measurements of another observer.

The Principle of Relativity states that the laws of nature are the same in all inertial frames of reference. Its application depends on the transformation law linking different frames.

Classical Thinking about Space and Time	Modern Thinking about Space and Time
Time is an invariant concept.	Time is a relative concept.
Space and time measurements of observers in relative motion are related by the Galilean transformation (Equations 19.1–19.4 or 19.11–19.14).	A new transformation, called the Lorentz transformation, is needed to relate the space and time measurements of observers in relative motion (Chapter 20).
The Galilean transformation links inertial frames of reference.	The special theory of relativity (with its Lorentz transformation) is also limited to observers in inertial frames.
Mechanics conforms to the Principle of Relativity; electromagnetism does not.	*All* laws of nature conform to the Principle of Relativity (*Einstein's first postulate*).
The Michelson-Morley experiment (and other related experiments) should reveal the motion of the earth through the ether.	The ether concept must be abandoned. All inertial frames are equivalent. The Michelson-Morley experiment should give a null result.
The measured speed of light should depend on the motion of the observer (Equation 19.5).	The speed of light is an invariant constant, the same in all inertial frames of reference (*Einstein's second postulate*).

Q19.1   Cite an everyday observation or physical sensation that can be called *subjective*. Explain why it is *relative* (i.e., different for different observers). In what sense does it involve *disagreement*?

Q19.2   Cite an everyday observation or physical sensation that can be called *objective*. Explain why it is *invariant* (i.e., the same for different observers).

Q19.3   In the absence of friction, all falling objects near the earth have a fixed acceleration g. This is a law that is invariant only for a certain class of observers. (1) Describe the state of motion of any two observers who *agree* about this law. (2) Describe the state of motion of any observer who *disagrees* with this law.

Q19.4   If the table of agreement and disagreement in Section 19.2 is extended, into which column should each of the following concepts go: (a) momentum; (b) kinetic energy; (c) temperature; (d) charge? Explain the reason for each choice.

Q19.5   Two observers who are at rest with respect to each other refer their measurements to different coordinate systems. In what way might their descriptions of a given example of motion differ?

Q19.6   "Galilean relativity" could equally well be called "Galilean invariance." Why?

Q19.7   A man standing on the ground throws a baseball and observes its trajectory to be a parabola. (1) Is the trajectory of the ball also a parabola in the frame of reference of a person passing by in a train at constant velocity? (2) Is the trajectory a parabola in the frame of reference of someone passing in an accelerating train?

Q19.8   Illustrate by example the meaning of the statement that the class of all possible motions of a system is the same in two different inertial frames of reference.

Q19.9   Does the magnetic field created by a moving charge depend upon the state of motion of the observer? Illustrate your answer with a simple example.

Q19.10 A physicist and his equipment are shut inside a railroad car with no windows. Describe a simple experiment that would enable him to determine a *change* of velocity of the car even though he is unable by any means to measure the car's velocity when it moves with constant velocity.

Q19.11 A man in a train falls asleep while the train is stopped in a station. When he awakes, he looks out the window and sees a train on the next track moving relative to his own train. To find out which train is actually moving over the ground, he decides that it would be useful to carry out some simple experiments. He takes a marble from his pocket and drops it to the floor. Then he rolls it along the floor. By observing the motion of the marble, can he determine which train is moving relative to the ground? Explain. (Ignore effects such as vibration or unevenness of the tracks.)

Q19.12 A woman seated in a cylindrical room (see the figure) observes the wall of the room to be in rotational motion relative to the floor. By performing simple experiments with a marble (such as those described in the preceding question), can she decide which is actually rotating relative to the earth, the wall or the floor? Explain.

Section 19.3   Q19.13   An inertial guidance system translates acceleration measurements into information on velocity and position. What mathematical operations must the device perform?

Q19.14   An engineer and his equipment are abducted in the back of a closed van. The engineer makes measurements continuously from the time the van starts moving. After a while, he concludes that the van is moving at a constant speed of 50 mile/hr. Why does his ability to reach this conclusion not violate the principle of Galilean relativity?

Q19.15   Cite pairs of common events in everyday life that are (a) separated in time but not in space and (b) separated in space but not in time.

Q19.16   Cite a pair of common events in everyday life that are separated in both space and time for one observer but are separated only in time, not in space, for another observer.

Section 19.4   Q19.17   Look up the speed of sound in air, water, and iron. (1) Very roughly, how does the speed of sound in a medium correlate with the hardness, or "solidity," of the medium? (2) Based on this correlation, what would you expect to be the nature of a medium in which a wave propagates at the speed of light? How does this fit with your conception of the ether?

Q19.18   Explain in a brief paragraph why the Principle of Relativity (the principle that the laws of nature are the same in all inertial frames of reference) need not be expected to be valid in an ether-filled universe.

Section 19.5   Q19.19   ETHER ELUDES MICHELSON AND MORLEY, SCIENTISTS PERPLEXED. Write the lead paragraph of a news story to follow this headline.

Q19.20   What is typically observed in a Michelson interferometer is not a single patch of light, but a pattern of alternately dark and light fringes. Explain how a slight tilt of one of the mirrors in the interferometer produces a fringe pattern.

Q19.21   The Michelson interferometer (Figure 19.5), apart from its use in the Michelson-Morley experiment, became a valuable tool for precision measurements of wavelength. As one of its mirrors is slowly moved to lengthen one arm of the interferometer, what should happen to the observed pattern of light? Suggest a precise method of wavelength determination that makes use of such mirror motion.

Section 19.6   Q19.22   The emission hypothesis (attributed to Walther Ritz) states that light moves at a fixed speed *c relative to its source*. Explain how this hypothesis would account for the negative result of the Michelson-Morley experiment.

Section 19.7   Q19.23   Explain in your own words why sound requires a material medium for its propagation, but light requires neither matter nor even an ether.

EXERCISES

Section 19.2   E19.1   For a pair of observers whose relative motion is accelerated, how must the table of agreement and disagreement in Section 19.2 be changed?

E19.2   A particle is observed in three different inertial frames of reference. In frame S_1 the particle oscillates on the x axis, its position being given by $x =$

a sin ω*t*. In frame S_2 the particle traces out a sine curve. In frame S_3 the particle moves always in the same direction. (1) Specify the ways in which S_2 and S_3 are moving relative to S_1. (2) Is there any frame of reference in which the particle is stationary? If so, is this frame an inertial frame?

Section 19.3

E19.3   If the train in Figure 19.2 moves to the left with speed *v* instead of to the right with speed *v*, how are the Galilean transformation equations (Equations 19.1–19.4) changed, if at all?

E19.4   Re-express Equations 19.1–19.4 in such a way that all primed variables occur on the left sides of the equal signs and all unprimed variables occur on the right sides. (In so doing, you have "inverted" the Galilean transformation.) Comment on the significance of the change of sign that distinguishes Equation 19.1 from its "inverse."

E19.5   As in Figure 19.2, a frame of reference with primed coordinates *x′*, *y′* moves with speed *v* in the positive *x* direction and a frame of reference with unprimed coordinates *x*, *y* is stationary. However, the origins of the two systems do not coincide at *t* = 0. Instead the origin of the moving system is at $x = x_0$ and $y = y_0$ at *t* = *t′* = 0. (1) Generalize Equations 19.1–19.3 to cover this case. (2) Show that Equations 19.5 and 19.6 remain valid. (3) Do Equations 19.8 and 19.9 remain valid?

E19.6   In stationary frame S_1, clocks read time *t*. In a moving frame *S′*, clocks run at the same rate as in frame S (an assumption of classical physics), but are set differently so that the time *t′* shown on the moving clocks is always 1 hr later than the time *t* shown on the stationary clocks. (1) Must Equation 19.3 be altered? If so, in what way? (2) Must Equation 19.14 be altered? If so, in what way?

E19.7   In a certain building, the *x* axis is defined to point eastward, the *y* axis is defined to point northward, and the *z* axis is defined to point upward. In an elevator in the building, axes *x′*, *y′*, and *z′* are defined to be parallel, respectively, to axes *x*, *y*, and *z*. The origins of the two coordinate systems coincide at *t* = 0. (1) Write the Galilean transformation equations (analogous to Equations 19.1–19.4) if the elevator moves upward with speed *v*. (2) Write the Galilean transformation equations if the elevator moves downward with speed *v*. *Optional:* Repeat part 1 in case the origins of the two coordinate systems do *not* coincide at *t* = 0.

E19.8   Re-work Example 1 in Section 19.3 for two other sets of initial conditions : (1) In the train-based frame of reference, the ball is thrown forward from height *h* with initial speed *v* (the same as the speed of the train). (2) In the train-based frame of reference, the ball is thrown backward from height *h* with initial speed *v*. In each case, give expressions for *x(t)*, *y(t)*, *x′(t)*, and *y(′t)*.

E19.9   Children standing at opposite ends of a railroad car roll balls down the aisle toward each other. Both balls move at speed v_0 relative to the car; the car moves forward at constant speed *v* relative to the ground. (1) What is the speed of each ball relative to the ground? (2) What is the acceleration of each ball in a ground-based frame of reference? (3) If the balls start to roll at the same time, which one first reaches the midpoint between the two children?

E19.10 A railroad car moves over straight tracks at a constant speed *v* = 10 m/sec. A block on the floor of the car is pushed in such a way that it experiences a constant forward acceleration of 0.5 m/sec^2 relative to the car. (1) What is the acceleration of the block according to an observer on the ground? (2) If the block starts from rest in the car, write expressions for x' vs t' (train-based coordinates) and x vs t (ground-based coordinates), assuming the validity of the Galilean transformation. (3) Compare $x_2 - x_1$ with $x'_2 - x'_1$ and $t_2 - t_1$ with $t'_2 - t'_1$ for any chosen pair of instants t_1 and t_2.

Section 19.4   E19.11   A body acted upon by no forces drifts with constant velocity $\mathbf{v}_1$ in frame of reference S_1. Another frame of reference, S_2, moves with constant velocity $\mathbf{v}$ relative to S_1 (see the figure). (1) What is the velocity $\mathbf{v}_2$ of the body according to observers in S_2? (2) Is Newton's first law valid in frame S_1? Is it valid in S_2?

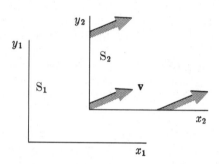

E19.12   (1) Explain why a force that depends on the displacement $\mathbf{r}_2 - \mathbf{r}_1$ between two particles is invariant under a Galilean transformation. (2) Explain why a force that depends on the relative velocity $\mathbf{v}_2 - \mathbf{v}_1$ of two particles is invariant under a Galilean transformation.

Section 19.5   E19.13   With the help of a diagram like this one, derive Equation 19.24 for the round-trip time, t(wingtip echo). The speed of the airplane relative to the air is v_a; the speed of sound relative to the air is v_s.

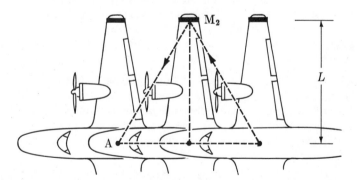

E19.14   (1) Make sketches, approximately to scale, of the successive positions of the airplane in Figure 19.4 when (a) a sound pulse leaves point A, (b) the pulse reaches mirror M_1, and (c) the pulse returns to point A, if the speed of the airplane is half the speed of sound. (2) Calculate the distance the airplane moves between sketches a and b and the distance it moves between sketches b and c if $L = 6$ m.

E19.15   For the unusual airspeed meter shown in Figure 19.4, sketch a graph of t(tail echo) vs v_a (see Equation 19.23). For what airplane speed v_a will the tail echo never return to point A?

P19.1   Design a simple device that measures acceleration. Include a sketch and a description of the operation of the device. Does it give a different reading when it is moving with constant velocity than when it is at rest?

Accelerometer

P19.2   (1) Generalize the Galilean transformation equations from the special form of Equations 19.1–19.4 to allow for an arbitrary direction of motion of the moving frame and for the possibility that the two origins need not coincide at $t = 0$. (2) Condense three of these equations into a single vector equation.

Galilean transformation

P19.3   A passenger in the front seat of a moving automobile tosses a candy bar through a parabolic arc to a passenger in the rear seat. The components of velocity of the candy bar relative to the automobile are v_x' and v_y'. The speed of the car is v. (1) (a) Write an equation that relates the kinetic energy of the candy bar in the auto-based frame of reference to its kinetic energy in a ground-based frame. (b) For what speed v, if any, are these two kinetic energies equal? (2) (a) Write an equation that relates the x component of momentum of the candy bar in the auto-based frame to its x component of momentum in a ground-based frame. (b) For what speed v, if any, are these two momentum components equal? (3) For what speed v, if any, does the flying candy bar cover the same distance in the two frames of reference?

Galilean transformation of energy and momentum

P19.4   Relaxing between speeches, a candidate plays pool in his chartered jet. He strikes a ball, which, in his frame of reference, moves forward with speed v_0 and collides head-on with a stationary ball (upper portion of figure). In an earth-fixed frame (lower portion of figure), the initial speeds of the balls are $v_0 + v$ and v. Write down and solve the equations of kinetic energy and momentum conservation in both frames of reference in order to find the final speeds of the two balls in both frames. Verify that the two sets of answers are related by the Galilean velocity transformation, Equation 19.5.

Galilean invariance of classical conservation laws

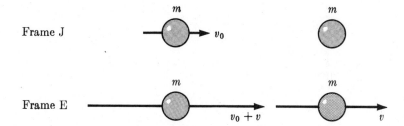

P19.5   Consider a set of observers stationed along a railroad track, all of them with synchronized clocks. Describe a procedure whereby these observers could measure the length of a train that passes at constant speed. Using Equations 19.11 and 19.14, show that the length determined by these observers is the same as the length measured by observed riding on the train.

Galilean invariance of length

Galilean invariance of Newton's second law

P19.6 Particle 1 is attracted to particle 2 by a force $\mathbf{F}_1$ which depends only on the displacement $\mathbf{r}_2 - \mathbf{r}_1$ between the particles. Newton's second law applied to particle 1 can be written

$$\mathbf{F}_1(\mathbf{r}_2 - \mathbf{r}_1) = m_1\mathbf{a}_1.$$

Show explicitly that both the left and right sides of this equation are invariant under a Galilean transformation (regard $\mathbf{F}_1$ as a vector *function* of $\mathbf{r}_2 - \mathbf{r}_1$).

Uniformly accelerated frame of reference

P19.7 A reference frame S, with Cartesian axes x, y, z, is "stationary." Another frame S′, with Cartesian axes x', y', z' is moving in the positive x direction with constant acceleration a_0. At time $t = 0$, the axes of the two frames coincide and the speed of S′ relative to S is v_0. (1) Write the transformation equations analogous to Equations 19.1–19.4 that relate the space and time measurements of observers in these two frames. (2) Write the velocity transformation equations analogous to Equations 19.5–19.7.

Hypothetical world with a preferred frame of reference

P19.8 Suppose that the Michelson-Morley experiment had yielded a positive result, showing absolute motion of the earth and revealing a preferred frame of reference. (1) How could the direction and speed of the sun in the preferred frame of reference be determined? (2) In a hypothetical world, with such a preferred frame of reference, where Newtonian mechanics remained valid, it would be possible to bring a photon to rest. Explain why.

Ether search using lunar reflector

P19.9 An experimenter decides to use laser light reflected from the moon to test for an effect of "ether wind." When his telescope is at position A and the moon is at position M_1, he accurately measures the round-trip time for a pulse of laser light (see the figure). About a week later, when the telescope is at B and the moon is at M_2, he again measures the round-trip time. Suppose that the imagined ether wind moves in the direction shown with speed $v = 10^{-4}c$. For simplicity, assume that the distances AM_1 and BM_2 are identical. (1) What is the approximate round-trip time for light reflected from the moon? (2) What is the approximate *difference* in round-trip times for the two measurements? *Optional:* If the distances AM_1 and BM_2 are known to within 0.3 m and the round-trip times can be measured to within 1 nsec, is the experiment practical?

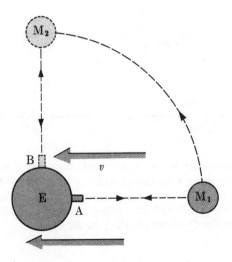

P19.10   George FitzGerald hypothesized that matter shrinks slightly in its direction of motion through the ether. (1) Show that if this hypothesis is used to account for the null result of the Michelson-Morley experiment, the factor of shrinkage of the "upwind-downwind" arm of the interferometer must be $\sqrt{1 - (v/c)^2}$, where v is the speed of the apparatus through the ether and c is the speed of light. (2) According to this hypothesis, what is the *change* in length of a meter stick produced by its motion through the ether at a speed $v = 10^{-4}c$?

FitzGerald contraction hypothesis

P19.11   The Ritz emission hypothesis is defined in Question 19.22. Consider its application to the binary star system shown in the figure: A small secondary star moves with speed v in a circular path of radius R about a massive primary star. When the secondary is at position 1, it emits some light that propagates to the earth. Later, when it is at position 2, it emits more light that propagates to the earth. How far must the binary system be from the earth in order that—according to the emission hypothesis—the secondary star would appear to be at position 2 *before* it was at position 1?

The Ritz emission hypothesis

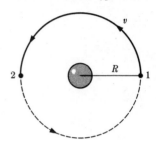

P19.12   In the figure, region I represents ether moving to the left with speed v. Region II represents a "stationary" boundary layer of ether close to the earth's surface. According to the ether-boundary-layer hypothesis, starlight should experience a deflection in passing from region I to region II. Assuming that light has the same speed c *relative to the ether* in both regions, derive a formula relating the angles θ_1 and θ_2. (Because such a deflection of starlight was never detected, the ether-boundary-layer hypothesis had to be abandoned.)

Ether boundary layer

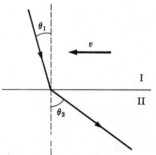

P19.13   Two pellets bearing equal and opposite charge are attached to the ends of a light rod. The rod is suspended at its midpoint by a thread and is free to turn in a horizontal plane. The figure shows a top view of this arrangement and indicates the supposed direction of motion of the charged pellets through the ether. Show that if the charges generate magnetic fields because of their motion through the ether, a torque would act on the rod and the magnitude of the torque would be

Ether search using charged particles

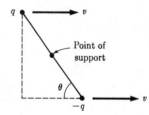

$$T = \frac{\mu_0}{8\pi} \frac{q^2 v^2}{r} \sin 2\theta = \frac{1}{2} \frac{q^2}{4\pi\epsilon_0 r} \frac{v^2}{c^2} \sin 2\theta,$$

where r is the length of the rod and the angle θ is defined in the figure. [In 1903, F. T. Trouten and H. R. Noble (*Proceedings of the Royal Society, London*, **72**, 132) looked for and did not find a torque acting on a suspended capacitor. According to relativity theory, a magnetic field results from motion of a charge relative to an observer, not relative to the ether.]

P19.14   Discuss the basic design of an inertial guidance system and the fundamental physical principles underlying its operation. Explain how its operation is related to the principle of Galilean relativity. (Outside references will be required.)

Inertial guidance

20 Spacetime

The constancy of the speed of light seems, at first thought, unremarkable, and, upon further thought, impossible. In this chapter we shall be concerned with the implications of this postulate about light for the very bedrock of nature and of science, time, and space.

20.1 The relativity of time

The direct and startling consequence of the assumption that light travels at an invariable speed with respect to all observers (in inertial frames) is that time must be relative: observers in states of relative motion must have different ideas about the measurement of time and the time interval between events.

To see just what is paradoxical about the statement $c = constant$, imagine observer A sitting beside a road and observer B traveling along the road in a supercharged rocket car (Figure 20.1). Just as B comes abreast of A, a light

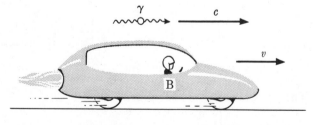

FIGURE 20.1 The "paradox" of relativity. A photon has a speed c relative to stationary observer A and the same speed c relative to an observer B in high-speed motion. The universal constancy of c is a fundamental postulate of relativity.

wave passes them both by. Later on A meets B and remarks, "Did you see that
light wave come by us this afternoon? I happened to notice that it was traveling
at exactly 300 meters per microsecond." "Nonsense," replies B. "You must
be in error. It passed me at a relative speed of 300, and I was doing 100 myself."
"No, no," retorts A, "I clocked it carefully. It's true that you were doing 100,
but the light wave passed you at a relative speed of only 200." Our common-
sense point of view is that either A or B (or both) must be in error. But according
to Einstein's postulate, both are indeed correct. Yet something has to give.
If we are prepared to admit that the light wave was moving at the same speed c
relative to both A and B, we must admit the possibility that there is some
intrinsic difference in the way they are defining speed. Since a measurement of
speed involves measurements of both distance and time, perhaps they disagree
about length measurements or about time measurements. In fact, they must
disagree about both, as we shall see presently.

An apparent paradox

   It must be remarked that the hypothetical conversation reported above is
farfetched, not merely because B is reported to have traveled at a quite phenom-
enal speed, but because in a world where such speeds are commonplace, the
constancy of the speed of light and the relativity of time would be so well known
in everyday experience that no such controversy would arise.

   Another simple thought experiment will show that the concept of time (at
least) must be different for the two observers. Suppose that B switches on the
interior light in his rocket car as he speeds past A (Figure 20.2). If the light is
located just at the center of the car, B will conclude that its illumination reaches
the front and the back of his car simultaneously, for he consistently finds that

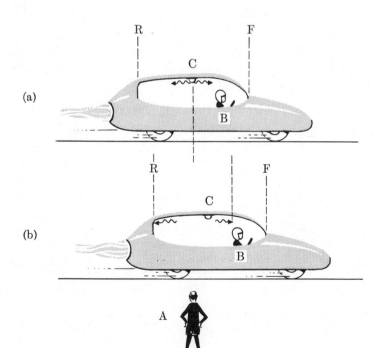

FIGURE 20.2 The relativity of time. (a) At
some instant the central light C in the rocket
car is switched on. (b) Sometime later,
according to the roadside observer A, the
light has reached the rear point R but has not
yet reached the front point F. But according
to observer B in the car, the light reaches the
equidistant points R and F simultaneously.

light travels at a fixed speed with respect to his car. But A, just as adamantly, claims to see light always traveling at the same fixed speed with respect to *him*. From A's point of view the light will spread at equal speed in each direction and reach the back of the car (which is approaching the light) before it reaches the front of the car (which is receding from the light). Two events (the arrival of light at the front and at the back of the car) are judged by B to be simultaneous and by A to occur at different times. Clearly there must be something different about time itself for the two observers.

Time must be relative, not invariant

20.2   Time dilation

An experiment with reflected light

Now A and B, with their remarkable powers of observation, undertake another experiment, this time with a view to learning by exactly how much their time scales differ. They agree that it would be useful to measure the round-trip time for a light wave starting on the floor of the car, going vertically upward with respect to the car, reflecting from a mirror on the ceiling, and returning to its starting point on the floor of the car. Using the equation for constant-speed motion, B can write

$$2D = c\,\Delta t', \tag{20.1}$$

if D is the distance from floor to ceiling and $\Delta t'$ is the round-trip time that B measures. According to A, watching from beside the road, the light beam has executed a sawtooth pattern, and traveled not a distance $2D$, but a greater distance $2H$, where H stands for the hypotenuse of the right triangle in Figure 20.3. A's equation connecting distance, speed, and time, is

$$2H = c\,\Delta t. \tag{20.2}$$

Since H is greater than D, but both observers measure the same speed c, it is already evident that Δt must be greater than $\Delta t'$ and that A will consider B's time scale to be running slow. To get the quantitative relation, we can apply the Pythagorean theorem to the right triangle in Figure 20.3:

$$H^2 = D^2 + (\tfrac{1}{2}v\,\Delta t)^2,$$

where v is the speed of the car with respect to A. Substituting for H and D

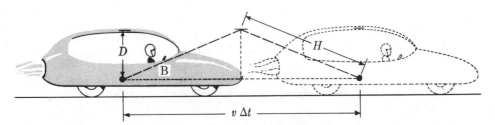

FIGURE 20.3 Experiment to determine relative time measurements. A light beam going from floor to ceiling and back travels a distance $2D$ in a time $\Delta t'$ according to driver B, and it travels a distance $2H$ in a time Δt according to the roadside observer A. In half the round-trip time, observer A sees the car move forward a distance $\tfrac{1}{2}v\,\Delta t$.

from Equations 20.1 and 20.2 makes the Pythagorean theorem read

$$\tfrac{1}{4}c^2\,(\Delta t)^2 = \tfrac{1}{4}c^2\,(\Delta t')^2 + \tfrac{1}{4}v^2\,(\Delta t)^2.$$

Some simple algebra then gives

$$\Delta t = \frac{\Delta t'}{\sqrt{1 - (v^2/c^2)}}. \qquad (20.3)$$

Measured time intervals are unequal

This is one of the most famous equations of relativity and has by now received ample experimental verification (see Section 20.8). It represents what has come to be called the *time-dilation* phenomenon. According to A, B's time is "dilated" —that is, B's clocks run slowly—and the factor giving the ratio of the rates of the clocks is $\sqrt{1 - (v^2/c^2)}$. For normal human speeds, this factor is so close to 1 that we are quite unable to detect the time-dilation effect in ordinary life.

■ EXAMPLE: A rocket car moves at 80 percent of the speed of light. As he passes a clock on the ground, the driver of the car notices that the ground-based clock reads $t = 0$. At that instant he sets his own clock to $t' = 0$. Later, when his own clock reads 6 μsec, the driver looks out at another clock on the ground. What is its reading? We must assume the ground-based clocks to be synchronized, an important matter that will be discussed in Section 20.3 and further elaborated in Section 20.7. If they are, Equation 20.3 can be applied. We have $\Delta t' = 6\,\mu$sec and $\sqrt{1 - (v^2/c^2)} = \sqrt{1 - (0.8)^2} = 0.6$. The ground-based time interval is

$$\Delta t = \frac{6\,\mu\text{sec}}{0.6} = 10\,\mu\text{sec}.$$

The second clock on the ground reads $t_2 = t_1 + \Delta t = 10\,\mu$sec.   ■

20.3   Some features of spacetime events

RECIPROCITY

Since time scales are different for different observers, we must become suddenly quite cautious, indeed suspicious, in approaching the processes of measurement. For example, dare we draw the "obvious" conclusion that since B's clocks seem to A to be slow, A's clocks must seem to B to be fast? No, B will be equally convinced that it is A's clocks that are slow. Indeed, without this reciprocity of observation, we would be able to identify absolute motion and return to a preferred frame of reference. In the experiment described above, the apparent absence of reciprocity comes about because the point to which the light returns is the same in B's frame of reference but different in A's frame. Reciprocity would re-enter if this experiment were compared with one in which it is A on the ground who shines a light vertically up and down and B who observes the sawtooth pattern.

The idea of reciprocity; time dilation works both ways

In our description of the time-dilation experiment (Section 20.2), we tacitly assumed that A and B agreed on the vertical distance D from floor to mirror. It is quite natural to be suspicious about this, but fortunately the principle of reciprocity tells us that about this measurement, at least, A and B will agree. If A judges B's car to have shrunk vertically, then B must judge A to have shrunk vertically. That these two points of view are inconsistent can be demonstrated by A if he holds out a wet paintbrush at a height equal to the

Observers agree on

height of the car when at rest. If he believes that the moving car has diminished its height, his brush will be above the car and leave no trace. But according to B, the brush should be below the roofline of the car and will leave a stripe.

*(1) distances perpendicular to
the direction of motion*

Since the car cannot emerge from the encounter both with a stripe and without one, it must be true that A and B do agree about vertical dimensions, and the brush would just graze the top of the car.

Another implication of the reciprocity principle is that the two observers

(2) relative speed

agree about their relative speed. If they disagreed, this would introduce into their observations an asymmetry inconsistent with the assumption that all inertial frames are equivalent. In terms of vector quantities, if the velocity of B as measured by A is $\mathbf{v}$, the velocity of A as measured by B is $-\mathbf{v}$. This aspect of reciprocity is displayed mathematically in Section 20.6.

There is one other essential area of agreement in the theory of relativity that needs to be stated explicitly, in the spirit of extreme caution about accepting common-sense notions. This is that all observers *do* agree about events at the

*(3) events coincident in space
and* time

same place at the same time. If at a particular place at a particular time a pion is annihilated and a muon and a neutrino are created in its place, all observers will agree that the annihilation and creation events did occur at the same place at the same time. Although different observers might have different ideas about where this pair of events occurred and at what time, there will be no disagreement about the facts that the events were simultaneous and at the same place. This much of common sense, at least, is retained in the theory of relativity. It means that two or more things that happen at the same place at the same time may be called one single event. All disagreements in the theory of relativity are concerned with measurements of differences between events.

SYNCHRONIZATION OF CLOCKS

Since clocks in relative motion keep different time, a new problem is introduced. How can one tell whether clocks at different places in the same frame of reference are running synchronously, showing the same reading at the same time? It will not do to set two clocks to the same time at the same place and then carry one of them to a different place, for the relative motion would destroy their synchronism.* The theory of relativity offers an operational definition of synchronism, using light pulses to connect clocks.

*An operational definition of
synchronism*

Consider, for example, a clock C_1 set to emit a photon at the instant it reads zero [Figure 20.4(a)]. Another clock C_2, of identical construction, is at rest with respect to C_1 and located a distance d away. As a matter of convenience, we can choose $d = 300$ m, as shown in the figure, so that the time required for the photon to move from C_1 to C_2 is 1 μsec. Let C_2 be set to read 1 (its scale is in microseconds) and triggered to start running when it receives the photon.

---

* This method would work only in the limit of zero velocity of the clock being moved. In that limit, however, an infinite time would be required to gain a finite separation of the two clocks.

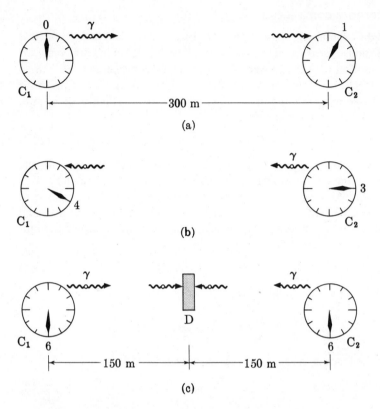

FIGURE 20.4   Synchronization of clocks. (a) Clock C_1 emits a photon at $t = 0$.
Clock C_2 is set to read $t = 1$ μsec when it receives the photon. (b) A consistency check: If Clock C_2 emits a photon at $t = 3$, Clock C_1 should read
$t = 4$ when it receives the photon. (c) Another check: A detector D receives
two photons simultaneously. The clocks are synchronous if they had the same
readings when they emitted the photons.

Then, after the photon has carried its "message" from C_1 to C_2, the two clocks
may be said to be synchronized, by definition.

The consistency of this definition could be checked in several ways. One
way, illustrated in Figure 20.4(b), would be to send back a photon from C_2 to
C_1. If, for instance, C_2 showed a reading of 3 when it emitted the photon, C_1
should show a reading of 4 when it received the photon. Another test would
make use of a detector D placed midway between C_1 and C_2 [Figure 20.4(c)].
If, by prearrangement, C_1 and C_2 emitted photons simultaneously, these should
be received simultaneously at D. It is inherent in the mathematics of the
Lorentz transformation (Section 20.6) that clocks synchronized in accordance
with the prescription of Figure 20.4(a) would indeed pass the tests illustrated in
Figures 20.4(b) and (c).

With light-pulse synchronization, we can imagine any number of clocks
keeping the same time in the same frame of reference. It is important to
remember, however, that this is synchronization by definition. Observers in one
frame of reference agree about it. As we shall discover, synchronization of
clocks is a matter of *disagreement* for observers in relative motion.

Tests of consistency

Any number of clocks can be synchronized in one frame of reference

Synchronism is a relative concept

20.4   The Lorentz contraction

A length-measuring experiment

Another thought experiment, very much like the one described in Section 20.2, shows that distance measurements, as well as time measurements, must be influenced by motion of the observer. The driver of the rocket car sets out to determine the length of a fence alongside the road by clocking his time to move past the fence. He measures the time to be $\Delta t' = t_2' - t_1'$ (Figure 20.5), and, therefore, assigns to the fence a length

$$L' = v \, \Delta t', \tag{20.4}$$

where v is both his speed relative to the fence and, conversely, the speed of the fence relative to him. To observer A on the ground, the fence has length L, and the time required for the rocket car to pass it is $\Delta t = t_2 - t_1$, related to $\Delta t'$ by Equation 20.3. The clocks of observer A must, of course, be assumed to be synchronized in accordance with the prescription of the preceding section. Since A agrees that the speed of the car is v, he can write

$$L = v \, \Delta t. \tag{20.5}$$

The ratio of L' to L is then equal to the ratio of $\Delta t'$ to Δt:

$$\frac{L'}{L} = \frac{\Delta t'}{\Delta t} = \sqrt{1 - \frac{v^2}{c^2}}.$$

The length of the fence as measured by B can therefore be written

Measured lengths are unequal

$$L' = L \sqrt{1 - \frac{v^2}{c^2}}. \tag{20.6}$$

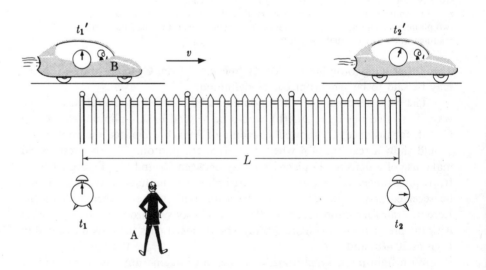

FIGURE 20.5   Lorentz-contraction experiment. The fence has length L according to the stationary observer A. A moving observer B measures its length L' by timing his passage from one end to the other. The length L' of the "moving fence" is less than the length L of the stationary fence.

He finds the fence to be shorter than the length L measured by the observer A who is at rest relative to the fence. This shortening is called the *Lorentz contraction*. Since, relative to B, the fence is in motion, we can state the result in this way: When in motion, the length of an object in its direction of motion is shortened relative to its length when at rest by a factor $\sqrt{1 - (v^2/c^2)}$.

There is more than one way to measure the length of a moving object. To find the length of a moving freight train, for example, one could measure the time required for it to pass a point (this requires knowledge of its speed and corresponds to the method just described); or one could station observers along the track and find the locations of the front and rear of the train at a particular instant of time. In Section 20.7, we show that these two methods provide the same answer in relativity theory, just as they do in classical theory.

■ EXAMPLE: A meter stick moves parallel to its longest dimension at a speed of 10^8 m/sec through a hypothetical laboratory.   What do workers in this laboratory measure the length of the meter stick to be? The length L in Equation 20.6 is the length of the stick at rest, 1 m. The measured length of the moving stick is L'. Since $v/c = 1/3$, the Lorentz-contraction factor is

$$\sqrt{1 - \tfrac{1}{9}} = 0.943,$$

and $L' = 0.943$ m.   ■

20.5   Another thought experiment

Time dilation and Lorentz contraction are inconsistent with the Galilean transformation. Equation 20.3, for instance, stands in contradiction to Equation 19.14. The Lorentz transformation that must replace the Galilean transformation can be derived on the basis of just two ideas, the constancy of the speed of light and the idea of reciprocity. These ideas have already been used in the two thought experiments described above (see Figures 20.3 and 20.5). With the help of just one more thought experiment, we shall have enough "data" to derive the full Lorentz transformation equations. What we seek are equations relating the space and time differences between a pair of events as seen by a "stationary" observer and a "moving" observer. Coordinate systems for these observers are indicated in Figure 20.6, in which the rocket car is replaced by a relativistic railroad car. In what follows we shall make use of the abbreviation

Ideas underlying the Lorentz transformation

$$\beta = \frac{v}{c}. \tag{20.7}$$

Here v means the relative speed of the two frames of reference. Occasionally, when no confusion is likely to result, v (and β) may also be used to designate the speed of a particle or object under study.

The results of the thought experiment in the last section can be concisely expressed in terms of the space and time differences—Δx, Δt, $\Delta x'$, and $\Delta t'$—between a pair of events. Event 1 is the passage of the rocket car past the left end of the fence (Figure 20.5). Event 2 is its passage past the right end of the fence. Since these events occur at the same place in the moving frame, B's space difference is $\Delta x' = 0$. For A, on the ground, the space difference of the

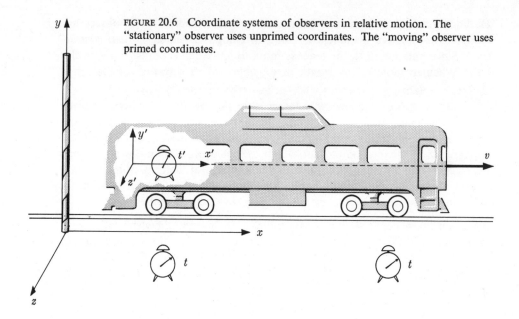

FIGURE 20.6   Coordinate systems of observers in relative motion. The "stationary" observer uses unprimed coordinates. The "moving" observer uses primed coordinates.

events is $\Delta x = L$, and their time difference is $\Delta t = \Delta x/v = L/v$. In the moving frame, the events are separated in time by $\Delta t' = \Delta t\sqrt{1 - \beta^2}$. In summary:

Summarized description of length-measuring experiment

$$\Delta x = L, \tag{20.8}$$

$$\Delta t = \frac{L}{v}, \tag{20.9}$$

$$\Delta x' = 0, \tag{20.10}$$

$$\Delta t' = \Delta t\sqrt{1 - \beta^2} = \frac{L}{v}\sqrt{1 - \beta^2}. \tag{20.11}$$

A photon-timing experiment

Now we turn attention to the additional thought experiment (Figure 20.7). In a railroad car moving in the positive x direction at speed v, a photon is emitted from the rear of the car (Event 1) and later absorbed at the front of the car (Event 2). To passengers in the car, the length of the car is l_0. To observers

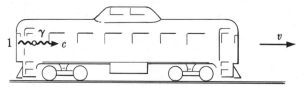

FIGURE 20.7   A photon-timing experiment. Event 1: A photon leaves the rear of the car. Event 2: The photon reaches the front of the car.

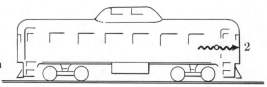

on the ground, it is Lorentz-contracted to length $l = l_0\sqrt{1 - \beta^2}$ (Equation 20.6). To both sets of observers, of course, the speed of the photon is c. What are the space and time differences assigned by the different observers to this pair of events? Within the train, the photon travels a distance l_0 at speed c, so $\Delta x' = l_0$ and $\Delta t' = l_0/c$. To observers on the ground, the photon travels the length of the car, $l_0\sqrt{1 - \beta^2}$, plus the distance the car has moved forward, $v\,\Delta t$, so Δx can be written

$$\Delta x = l_0\sqrt{1 - \beta^2} + v\,\Delta t. \qquad (20.12)$$

Since this distance is covered at the speed of light, Δx and Δt are also related by

$$\Delta x = c\,\Delta t. \qquad (20.13)$$

Equations 20.12 and 20.13 may be solved for Δx and Δt. These results, together with the two expressions already given for $\Delta x'$ and $\Delta t'$, are

$$\Delta x = \frac{l_0}{c}\,\frac{c + v}{\sqrt{1 - \beta^2}}, \qquad (20.14)$$

$$\Delta t = \frac{l_0}{c^2}\,\frac{c + v}{\sqrt{1 - \beta^2}}, \qquad (20.15)$$

Summarized description of photon experiment

$$\Delta x' = l_0, \qquad (20.16)$$

$$\Delta t' = l_0/c. \qquad (20.17)$$

20.6   The Lorentz-transformation equations

The time-dilation experiment of A and B (Figure 20.3) reveals a part of the total relationship between the space and time measurements of A and B. Numerous other experiments could be carried out to reveal other facets of the relationship. The fence-measuring experiment summarized by Equations 20.8–20.11 and the photon-timing experiment summarized by Equations 20.14–20.17 are examples. Now we seek the general relationship. It is sufficient to restrict attention to relative motion of the frames of reference along the x axis. According to the reciprocity principle, distances perpendicular to the direction of motion are unaffected by the motion, so $\Delta y = \Delta y'$ and $\Delta z = \Delta z'$. For the xt transformation equations we write

$$\Delta x = a_1\,\Delta x' + a_2\,\Delta t', \qquad (20.18)$$

$$\Delta t = a_3\,\Delta t' + a_4\,\Delta x', \qquad (20.19)$$

Assumed form of the transformation equations

where a_1, a_2, a_3, and a_4 are constants to be determined. The assumed linearity of these equations can be related to the uniformity of space and time. Suppose, for instance, that a clock fixed in the "moving" frame ticks off 2 sec while clocks in the "stationary" frame advance by 3 sec. If time is uniform—that is, if the *properties* of time are the same at all times—we expect a later 2-sec advance of the moving clock to be accompanied by another 3-sec advance of the stationary clocks. This means that for $\Delta t' = 4$ sec, $\Delta t = 6$ sec; for $\Delta t' = 6$ sec, $\Delta t = 9$ sec; and so on. This direct proportionality of Δt and $\Delta t'$ (for $\Delta x' = 0$) is

Why are the equations linear?

possible only for a linear relationship between the two quantities. A similar argument can be applied to spatial measurements. If Δx and $\Delta x'$ were not linearly related, the length of a moving meter stick would depend on its location in space, which would be inconsistent with the uniformity of space. These arguments, it must be remembered, are theoretical. The most solid eventual justification of Equations 20.18 and 20.19 is empirical: They lead to predictions that conform to experiment.

To establish the constants in these equations, we refer first to the fence-measuring experiment of Figure 20.5. Substituting from Equations 20.10 and 20.11 in Equation 20.19 gives

$$\Delta t = a_3 \, \Delta t \sqrt{1 - \beta^2},$$

from which it follows at once that

Results of thought experiments provide the coefficients

$$a_3 = \frac{1}{\sqrt{1 - \beta^2}}. \tag{20.20}$$

The same pair of equations, together with Equation 20.8, substituted in Equation 20.18, gives

$$L = a_2 \frac{L}{v} \sqrt{1 - \beta^2}.$$

This reveals the coefficient a_2 to be

$$a_2 = \frac{v}{\sqrt{1 - \beta^2}}. \tag{20.21}$$

The coefficient a_1 may be found by the following argument. A fixed point on the ground appears to observers on the train to move toward negative x at speed v. Therefore, for $\Delta x = 0$, $\Delta x' = -v \, \Delta t'$. This condition puts Equation 20.18 into the form

$$0 = -a_1 v \, \Delta t' + a_2 \, \Delta t'.$$

Therefore, $a_1 = a_2/v$, or

$$a_1 = \frac{1}{\sqrt{1 - \beta^2}}. \tag{20.22}$$

The final coefficient, a_4, may be determined by referring to the results of the photon-timing experiment of Figure 20.7. Substituting from Equations 20.15–20.17 in Equation 20.19 gives

$$\frac{l_0}{c^2} \frac{c + v}{\sqrt{1 - \beta^2}} = a_3 \frac{l_0}{c} + a_4 l_0.$$

Use of the result already obtained for a_3 (Equation 20.20) leads to the solution

$$a_4 = \frac{v/c^2}{\sqrt{1 - \beta^2}}. \tag{20.23}$$

In summary, the Lorentz transformation equations for the situation depicted in Figure 20.6 are

$$\Delta t = \frac{\Delta t' + (v \, \Delta x'/c^2)}{\sqrt{1 - (v^2/c^2)}}, \tag{20.24}$$

$$\Delta x = \frac{\Delta x' + v \, \Delta t'}{\sqrt{1 - (v^2/c^2)}}, \tag{20.25}$$

$$\Delta y = \Delta y', \tag{20.26}$$

$$\Delta z = \Delta z'. \tag{20.27}$$

The Lorentz transformation for relative velocity in the +x direction

On the right side of each equation is a measurement or measurements of the moving observer, and on the left of each equation is a measurement of the stationary observer. (We are of course using the words "moving" and "stationary" only as convenient labels for our two observers, not from any conviction about which one is "really" moving.) The Lorentz transformation ties together the subjectivity of measurement and provides a basis for extracting "objective reality" from subjective measurement.

Inspection of the Lorentz transformation equations reveals at once two interesting facts: (1) Space and time can be *mixed*. One man's space is some combination of another man's space *and* time. This mixing has led to the concept of "spacetime" as a single four-dimensional entity. (2) No two reference frames can have a relative speed greater than the speed of light. This unexpected prediction of a speed limit in nature follows from the mathematical form of the transformation equations. If v were to exceed c, the quantity $\sqrt{1 - (v^2/c^2)}$ would become an imaginary number and we would not know how to interpret the equations physically. If we accept the fact that the Lorentz transformation relates all possible physical measurements, we must accept the conclusion that no two observers can have a relative speed greater than c. There is now ample evidence that all known physical entities do obey this speed limit. Electrons have been accelerated (in the Stanford Linear Accelerator in California) to a speed of $0.9999999997c$ but cannot be pushed beyond c.*

The transformation (1) mixes space and time and (2) suggests a natural speed limit

In Equations 20.24 and 20.25 we have written out all factors of v and c explicitly. Some economy results from re-introducing the abbreviation β for v/c. In addition, there is a certain elegance that comes with using the combination $c \, \Delta t$ rather than Δt. This is made clear by writing this pair of equations in the form

$$c \, \Delta t = \frac{(c \, \Delta t') + \beta \, \Delta x'}{\sqrt{1 - \beta^2}}, \tag{20.28}$$

$$\Delta x = \frac{\Delta x' + \beta(c \, \Delta t')}{\sqrt{1 - \beta^2}}. \tag{20.29}$$

Spacetime symmetry more clearly revealed

An exact symmetry between the space and time variables is evident.

---

* A deeper study of relativity shows that there might exist another class of particles—usually called tachyons—whose speed is *always greater* than c. For these hypothetical entities, the speed of light is a lower limit, not an upper limit. Experimental searches for tachyons have so far failed to reveal any. For a discussion of tachyons, see O. M. Bilaniuk and E. C. G. Sudarshan, "Particles Beyond the Light Barrier," *Physics Today*, May, 1969, or Gerald Feinberg, "Particles That Go Faster than Light," *Scientific American*, February, 1970.

THE INVERSE TRANSFORMATION

Another aspect of the beautiful symmetry that exists in the Lorentz transformation equations is revealed by finding the inverse transformation, from the unprimed to the primed variables (from the stationary to the moving system). Equations 20.24 and 20.25 may be regarded as two equations for two unknowns, $\Delta t'$ and $\Delta x'$. It is left as an exercise to solve the equations for these unknowns, a procedure that yields

$$\Delta t' = \frac{\Delta t - (v\,\Delta x/c^2)}{\sqrt{1 - (v^2/c^2)}}, \tag{20.30}$$

The inverse transformation

$$\Delta x' = \frac{\Delta x - v\,\Delta t}{\sqrt{1 - (v^2/c^2)}}, \tag{20.31}$$

$$\Delta y' = \Delta y, \tag{20.32}$$

$$\Delta z' = \Delta z. \tag{20.33}$$

(For completeness, we have turned around Equations 20.26 and 20.27 and appended them to the list.) The transformation and its inverse are identical except for the sign of v.

Actually, the close parallelism of Equations 20.24–20.27 and 20.30–20.33 should come as no surprise. Both are Lorentz transformations. To the ground-based observers, who consider themselves stationary, the train is moving with x component of velocity equal to $+v$. To the train-based observers, who, with equal right, may consider themselves stationary, the ground is moving with x component of velocity equal to $-v$. In essence, the two sets of equations are the *same* equations. In this identity of form for the transformation and its inverse we are seeing another manifestation of the reciprocity of observations.

20.7   Consequences of the Lorentz transformation

In order to appreciate the implications of the Lorentz transformation equations, it is well to specialize to particularly simple conceptual experiments. First we re-examine the phenomena of time dilation and Lorentz contraction and then look at two other implications of the equations—the relativity of simultaneity and the addition of velocities.

TIME DILATION

Suppose that we choose $\Delta x' = 0$ in the transformation equations. From Equation 20.24 we get at once the time-dilation equation discovered earlier (Equation 20.3);

Relativity of time if
$\Delta x' = 0$

$$\Delta t = \frac{\Delta t'}{\sqrt{1 - \beta^2}}. \tag{20.34}$$

This relates the two observers' measurements of a time interval between events *at the same point in the train*, such as the time duration of a passenger's nap (Figure 20.8).

When the ratio v/c is much less than 1, a very useful approximate equation is

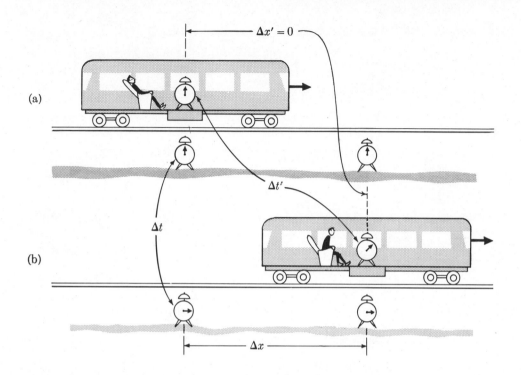

FIGURE 20.8   Time dilation. A passenger's catnap lasts a time $\Delta t'$ in his frame of reference and a longer time Δt in the ground-based frame of reference. Between the events of going to sleep and waking up, there is no spatial separation in the train ($\Delta x' = 0$), but there is a spatial separation Δx on the ground. (The difference between Δt and $\Delta t'$ is, of course, too small to observe with an actual train.)

$$\frac{1}{\sqrt{1 - \beta^2}} \cong 1 + \tfrac{1}{2}\beta^2. \qquad (20.35)$$

A useful approximation for small β

This follows from a binomial expansion (see Appendix 6C). Equations 20.34 and 20.35 together give, for the difference in the measured time intervals,

$$\Delta t - \Delta t' \cong \tfrac{1}{2}\beta^2 \, \Delta t' \cong \tfrac{1}{2}\beta^2 \, \Delta t \qquad (\beta \ll 1). \qquad (20.36)$$

■ EXAMPLE 1:   The pilot of a supersonic transport moves with respect to the earth at Mach 1.8, or $v = 600$ m/sec. How long must he fly until his watch has fallen one second behind earth-based clocks? The ratio v/c is $\beta = 2 \times 10^{-6}$; so, for the relative motion of supersonic transport and earth, the right side of Equation 20.35 is $1 + 2 \times 10^{-12}$, scarcely different from 1. If $\Delta t - \Delta t'$ is set equal to 1 sec, Equation 20.36 yields

$$\Delta t' = \frac{1 \text{ sec}}{2 \times 10^{-12}} = 5 \times 10^{11} \text{ sec.}$$

This is about 16,000 years.   ■

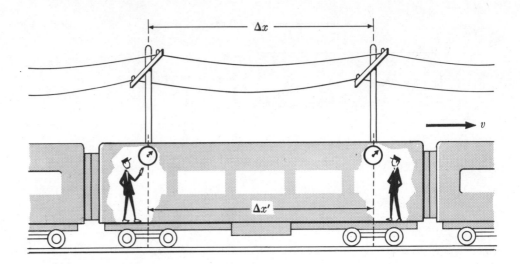

FIGURE 20.9 Another Lorentz-contraction experiment. A pair of observers on the train find themselves opposite a pair of poles on the ground at the same time according to train-based clocks ($\Delta t' = 0$). They measure a separation of poles, $\Delta x'$, less than the separation Δx measured by a ground-based observer.

■ EXAMPLE 2: An astronaut moves at 6,000 m/sec for a week ($\beta = 2 \times 10^{-5}$, $\Delta t = 6 \times 10^5$ sec). By how much does his clock lag? Equation 20.36 gives

$$\Delta t - \Delta t' = 1.2 \times 10^{-4} \text{ sec} = 120 \text{ } \mu\text{sec.}$$

It is quite feasible to send aloft a clock accurate enough to reveal this difference. Even at jet-plane speed, the effect is big enough to measure.*   ■

THE LORENTZ CONTRACTION

In Section 20.4, the rocket car driver measured the length of a stationary fence by finding out how much time he needed to pass it. An alternative way for moving observers to measure a distance on the ground is shown in Figure 20.9. Two train conductors note the position of two poles on the ground relative to their car at a fixed time in the train. The time interval between their measurements is $\Delta t' = 0$. Equation 20.25 then gives

Relativity of distance if
$\Delta t' = 0$

$$\Delta x = \frac{\Delta x'}{\sqrt{1 - \beta^2}} \cdot \qquad (20.37)$$

This agrees with Equation 20.6 if we write it as

$$\Delta x' = \Delta x \sqrt{1 - \beta^2}.$$

* See J. C. Hafele and Richard E. Keating, "Around-the-World Atomic Clocks: Predicted Relativistic Time Gains" and "Around-the-World Atomic Clocks: Observed Relativistic Time Gains," *Science*, **177**, 166, 168 (1972). [These authors confirmed the effect of gravity (Section 22.4) as well as the effect of speed.]

The distance $\Delta x'$ is *less* than the distance Δx. The relative motion causes the observers in the train to think that the outside world has become compressed (and, of course, the outside observer, noting the positions of the front and rear of the train at the same time in *his* frame of reference, concludes that it is the train that has contracted in its direction of motion).

The Lorentz contraction, described by Equation 20.37, must be carefully distinguished from the contraction hypothesized by FitzGerald and discussed by Lorentz in the early 1890s. According to FitzGerald, the contraction occurs for objects moving through the ether and is quite independent of the way an observer might be moving. And no principle of reciprocity applies to the FitzGerald contraction. Most important, the Lorentz contraction of relativity (which might better be called the Einstein contraction) arises from the properties of space and time, whereas the FitzGerald contraction was supposedly associated with the properties of matter. FitzGerald pictured a physical compression of material objects; Einstein imagined a compression and stretching of space and time itself.

The Lorentz contraction of relativity differs from the FitzGerald contraction hypothesis

■ EXAMPLE 3: By how much does the supersonic transport of Example 1 appear to be shortened by its motion? The approximation of Equation 20.35 is again useful; the fractional effect is $\frac{1}{2}\beta^2$, or 2×10^{-12}. If the length of the airplane is 50 m, the apparent contraction at Mach 1.8 (600 m/sec) is 10^{-10} m, less than the diameter of a single atom. ■

An example that illustrates the "paradoxical" character of the Lorentz contraction is shown in Figure 20.10. A train that is 300 m long at rest approaches a tunnel of length 250 m at 80 percent of the speed of light. A band of hijackers have sealed the exit of the tunnel (B), and they intend to block the entrance (A) as soon as the train gets inside the tunnel, in order to trap it there. At the rather swift pace of the train, the Lorentz contraction factor, $\sqrt{1 - (v^2/c^2)}$, is equal to 0.60. This means that the hijackers, being ground-based observers, measure the length of the moving train to be 0.60×300 m = 180 m. They believe it will fit comfortably within the 250-meter-long tunnel. To the passengers on the train, the length of the train is still 300 m, but the tunnel is shrunk to 0.60×250 m = 150 m, only half the length of the train. From their point of view, the train is far too long to fit within the tunnel.

Will the hijackers succeed in their nefarious plan? Rather than answer this question directly, let us consider what happens if the exit B is not blocked and the train continues at constant velocity. One thing all observers can agree on is that at *some* time the locomotive (L) will pass the exit point B and that at some time the observation car (O) will pass the entrance point A. What observers may differ about is when these events occur. That is the key to the apparent paradox. The relativity of distance measurement is closely related to the relativity of time measurement. Indeed, almost all the peculiarities of relativity can be traced to the fact that time, once considered absolute, has become relative. In this example, the hijackers find that the locomotive reaches the exit point B *after* the observation car has passed the entrance point A, but the passengers find, according to their clocks, that the locomotive reaches the exit point well *before* the observation car reaches the entrance. Since the two sets of observers disagree about the time sequence of events, it is not surprising that

A relativistic brain teaser

Train at rest   Tunnel at rest

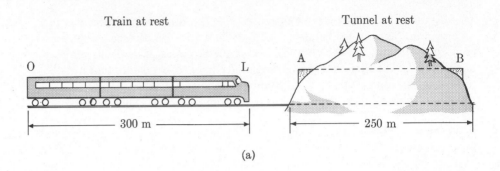

(a)

Distances according to ground-based observer

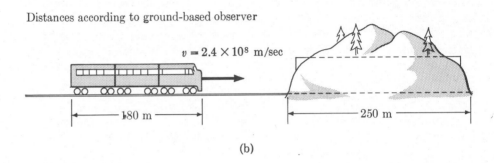

(b)

Distances according to train-based observer

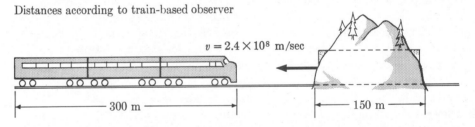

FIGURE 20.10   Will the train fit in the tunnel? (a) With both at rest, the train
is 300 m long, the tunnel 250 m long. (b) As the train approaches at $v = 0.80c$,
it appears to the ground-based observer to be 180 m long. (c) At the same
time the tunnel appears to the train-based observer to be 150 m long.

they disagree about the length of moving objects. (To make this clear, think
about what length you would measure your moving car to have if you marked
a spot in the pavement under its rear bumper at one moment, then five seconds
later marked a spot under its front bumper, and measured the distance on the
pavement between these two spots.)

Now what happens if the exit B is blocked and the train is forced to stop?
Will it first be trapped and then burst through the blockade or be crushed in
trying to do so? Or will the observation car never reach the entrance point A?
We leave these questions for the reader to think about. They are deliberately
tricky; it is possible to understand much of relativity without being able to
answer them. However, they are good exercise for those who like to wrestle
with challenging questions.

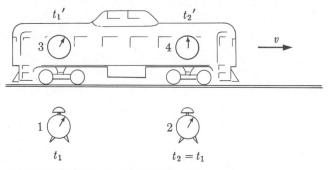

FIGURE 20.11   The passage of Clock 3 past Clock 1 and Clock 4 past Clock 2 are simultaneous events according to the ground-based observer, but not according to the train-based observer. To the observer on the ground, the clocks on the train not only run slowly but are also out of synchronism.

THE RELATIVITY OF SIMULTANEITY

The problem of the hijackers and the train shows the important connection between length measurements and time scales when motion is involved. This connection is revealed also by another simplified form of one of the Lorentz transformation equations. In Equation 20.24, set $\Delta t = 0$. This gives

$$\Delta t' = -\frac{v \, \Delta x'}{c^2}, \qquad (20.38)$$

Time difference for moving observer if $\Delta t = 0$

which defines the relativity of simultaneity. Events judged by the ground observers to be simultaneous ($\Delta t = 0$) will be judged by observers on the train to occur with a time separation $\Delta t'$ that depends on their separation in space.

The negative sign in Equation 20.38 means that of the two events judged simultaneous by the outside observer, the one farther forward in the train occurs earlier according to clocks on the train (Figure 20.11). As this figure also makes clear, the ground observers consider clocks on the train not only to run slow but also to be out of synchronism. (The fact that $t_1 = t_1'$ in the figure is arbitrary and not important to the discussion. Only time intervals matter.)

■ EXAMPLE 4:   Let us show that the equations of the inverse Lorentz transformation also give the result, $\Delta t' = -v \, \Delta x'/c^2$. The two events shown in Figure 20.11 (the passage of the rear of the car past Clock 1 and the passage of the front of the car past Clock 2) are simultaneous for ground-based observers. We may therefore set $\Delta t = 0$ in Equations 20.30 and 20.31 to obtain

$$\Delta t' = \frac{-v \, \Delta x/c^2}{\sqrt{1 - \beta^2}},$$

$$\Delta x' = \frac{\Delta x}{\sqrt{1 - \beta^2}}.$$

Elimination of Δx between these two equations leads to Equation 20.38.   ■

■ EXAMPLE 5:   The train car pictured in Figure 20.11 continues forward. At the instant when the clock at the rear of the car comes abreast of Clock 2 on the ground (Figure 20.12), what do these two adjacent clocks read? How do the stationary and the moving observers interpret the difference in the readings? According to the ground-based observer, the rear of the train moves forward a distance L (the distance between his two clocks) at speed v; so his clocks advance

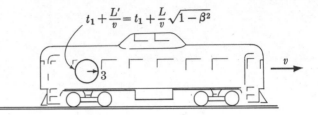

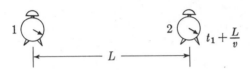

FIGURE 20.12   The later passage of Clock 3 past Clock 2. Careful analysis of this event, together with the events of Figure 20.11, supports the idea of reciprocity.

by $\Delta t = L/v$ from reading t_1 to reading $t_1 + (L/v)$. To the train-based observer, the distance between Clocks 1 and 2 is $L' = L\sqrt{1 - \beta^2}$, so his clock advances by L'/v from t_1 to $t_1 + L'/v$. In summary:

$$\text{reading of Clock 2} = t_1 + \frac{L}{v}\,;$$

$$\text{reading of clock at rear of train} = t_1 + \frac{L}{v}\sqrt{1 - \beta^2}\,;$$

$$\text{difference in readings} = \frac{L}{v}\,[1 - \sqrt{1 - \beta^2}]. \qquad (20.39)$$

An illustration of reciprocity

The ground-based observer says: "The clock at the rear of the train is running slow. It agreed with my Clock 1 when it passed it but later had lagged and read less than my Clock 2 when it passed it. The rate of the clocks on the train is less than the rate of my clocks by a factor $\sqrt{1 - \beta^2}$." The train-based observer says: "Clock 2 on the ground is running slow. When it passed the front of my car, its reading was greater than the reading of my clock (Figure 20.11). Later, when it passed the rear of my car (Figure 20.12), its reading was again greater than the reading of my clock, but the difference had diminished because of its lagging rate. I calculate that the rate of the clocks on the ground is less than the rate of my clocks by a factor $\sqrt{1 - \beta^2}$." The calculation of the train-based observer is left as a problem.   ■

Agreement on events coincident in both space and time

A final note about simultaneity: The Lorentz transformation equations confirm a statement made earlier, that events coincident in both space and time in one frame ($\Delta x' = \Delta t' = 0$) are also coincident in both space and time in the other frame ($\Delta x = \Delta t = 0$).

THE ADDITION OF VELOCITIES

Another relation of great interest concerns the addition of velocities, which puts a firm foundation under the idea of nature's speed limit. We imagine the train traveling now with speed v_1 relative to the ground, and inside the train a passenger running forward with a speed v_2 relative to the train (Figure 20.13). What is the speed of the runner with respect to the ground? We should not be surprised to learn that the answer is *not* the common-sense answer $v_1 + v_2$. The runner's speed is instead less than $v_1 + v_2$ and is given by

$$v = \frac{v_1 + v_2}{1 + (v_1 v_2/c^2)} .$$ (20.40)

This answer may be derived readily as follows. If the runner covers distance Δx in time Δt, his speed relative to the ground is $v = \Delta x/\Delta t$. From Equations 20.24 and 20.25, we may write (remembering the speed of the train to be v_1)

$$\frac{\Delta x}{\Delta t} = \frac{\Delta x' + v_1 \, \Delta t'}{\Delta t' + v_1 \, \Delta x'/c^2} .$$

Since $\Delta x'/\Delta t'$ is equal to v_2 (the runner's speed relative to the train), this equation is usefully rewritten in the form

$$\frac{\Delta x}{\Delta t} = \frac{(\Delta x'/\Delta t') + v_1}{1 + (v_1/c^2)(\Delta x'/\Delta t')} .$$

Replacement of $\Delta x/\Delta t$ by v and $\Delta x'/\Delta t'$ by v_2 then gives the velocity addition formula, Equation 20.40.

Note, in the velocity-addition law, that if the runner is replaced by a light wave ($v_2 = c$), then automatically $v = c$. *Any* speed added to c gives c again. This velocity-addition law also implies that no matter what speeds v_1 and v_2 we choose (if each is less than c), their "sum" will also be less than c.

Velocities always sum to c or less

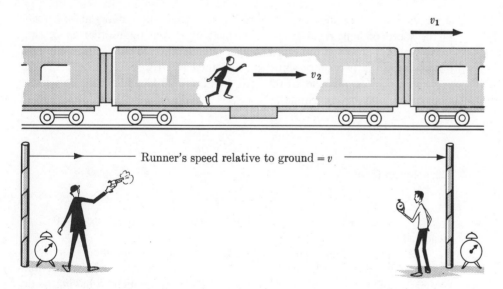

FIGURE 20.13   The addition of velocities. A passenger runs at speed v_2 relative to the train, which is moving at speed v_1 relative to the ground. The ground-based observer measures the runner's speed to be not $v_1 + v_2$ but something less (Equation 20.40).

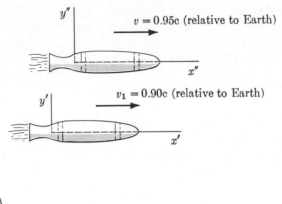

FIGURE 20.14   Two space ships move with known velocities relative to the earth. Their relative speed as measured by observers in the space ships is not $0.05c$ but nearly $0.35c$.

In Equation 20.40, the velocities are really x components of velocity. Thus if the passenger were running toward the rear of the train, his forward velocity relative to the ground would be

Velocity addition if $\mathbf{v_1}$ *in* $+x$ *direction and* $\mathbf{v_2}$ *in* $-x$ *direction*

$$v = \frac{v_1 - v_2}{1 - (v_1 v_2/c^2)}. \tag{20.41}$$

Similarly, if the train were moving toward negative x, the sign of v_1 would be reversed.

■ EXAMPLE 6:   As indicated in Figure 20.14, a space ship moving at 90 percent of the speed of light relative to the earth is overtaken by another space ship moving at 95 percent of the speed of light (also relative to the earth). What do observers on the two space ships measure their relative speed to be? Let the first space ship correspond to the train in Figure 20.13 and the second space ship correspond to the runner. Set $v_1 = 0.90c$ and $v = 0.95c$ in Equation 20.40, obtaining

$$0.95 = \frac{0.90 + \beta_2}{1 + 0.90\beta_2}.$$

The solution for β_2 is

$$\beta_2 = 0.345,$$

or $v_2 = 0.345c$, nearly seven times greater than the relative speed, $0.05c$, as measured from earth.   ■

These four results—time dilation, Lorentz contraction, the relativity of simultaneity, and the addition of velocities—constitute most of the essential kinematic consequences of special relativity, those consequences having to do with space and time. All violate common sense, and all for the same reason. Man never directly perceives motion with speed greater than a tiny fraction of the speed of light. No evidence comes directly to our senses about the remarkable properties of space and time. Through measuring instruments, though, there is no lack of evidence in support of the Lorentz transformation.

20.8   Tests of the Lorentz transformation

Human beings are clearly too slow to be significantly affected by the new effects of relativity. This will remain true for a long time to come. Speeds of space travel in the foreseeable future will remain quite small compared with the speed of light. Fortunately, however, the elementary particles are less sluggish than we, and they achieve speeds near the speed of light with great ease, making possible detailed quantitative tests of the theory of relativity. Time dilation and the velocity-addition law have each been thoroughly tested in innumerable experiments, although no direct way has ever been found to measure the Lorentz contraction or the relativity of simultaneity.

Particle decay tests time dilation

Time dilation is revealed most directly by the characteristic lifetime of unstable particles. Pions at rest, for example, have a well-defined and easily measured mean lifetime of about 10^{-8} sec. A pion emerging from an accelerator with an energy of 1 GeV is traveling at a speed 99 percent of the speed of light and has a mean life in the earth-fixed frame about seven times longer than the lifetime of its fellow pions at rest with respect to the earth. Time-dilation effects this large and even much larger are commonplace occurrences in modern experimental work with accelerators and cosmic rays. Indeed, the dilation of time has a marked effect on the intensity of cosmic radiation at the earth's surface. Protons striking nuclei near the top of the atmosphere create pions. Even with the benefit of time dilation, most of these pions decay into muons (and neutrinos) while still high above the earth's surface. At rest the mean lifetime of muons is about 2 μsec. Moving near the speed of light, a muon covers only 600 m or about a third of a mile in 2 μsec of earth time. If high-speed muons were characterized by the same lifetime as muons at rest, they too would largely disappear in the atmosphere before reaching the earth. Instead, their lifetime is so stretched by their motion (according to earth-based clocks) that many reach the earth before decaying.* A 10-GeV muon, for instance, experiences a time-dilation factor of 95 and flies, on the average, about 35 miles before it decays.

Muon flux at the earth reveals time dilation

Accelerators reveal in a direct way the law of addition of velocities. In the Stanford Linear Accelerator, electrons flying down a two-mile-long evacuated tube are repeatedly "pushed." At each push, some speed is added to what speed the electron had before. But as its speed gets closer and closer to the speed of light, the added speed gets less and less, as the electron comes tantalizingly close to, but never reaches, the speed of light. At 10 GeV, halfway to its final energy of 20 GeV, the electron is traveling at $0.999999999c$, or just 0.39 m/sec less than the speed of light. In a frame of reference moving at this speed, the addition of another 10 GeV of energy adds nearly 3×10^8 m/sec to the electron speed. In the earth-fixed frame, it adds instead only 0.29 m/sec, bringing the electron to within 0.10 m/sec (0.2 mile/hr) of the speed of light. In a frame of reference moving with the electron at its final speed, the length of

Particle acceleration tests the law of addition of velocities

---

* The flux of cosmic-ray muons at the earth's surface is about 500 m^{-2} sec^{-1} (i.e., 500 per square meter per second). Since this flux causes mutations and has thereby influenced human evolution, it is not too far-fetched to say that man's history has been affected by the time-dilation phenomenon.

the accelerator, two miles, is contracted to three inches. Under conditions of this kind, every common-sense notion about space, time, and speed becomes totally inappropriate.

★20.9   The Doppler effect*

The basic equation of a propagating electromagnetic wave,

$$\lambda v = c, \qquad (20.42)$$

refers to space (wavelength λ), time (frequency v), and the speed of light. We expect that different observers should measure different wavelength and frequency, but such that the product λv remains equal to the fixed constant c for all observers.

An experiment to reveal the relativity of frequency and wavelength

Figure 20.15 shows a thought experiment that can reveal how wavelength and frequency depend on the state of motion of the observer. An electromagnetic wave (speed c) is overtaking a moving train (speed v). Event 1 is the arrival at the rear of the train of a crest of the wave, marked A in the figure. Event 2 is the arrival at the rear of the train of the next crest of the wave, B, one wavelength behind A. Observers on the train measure wavelength λ' and frequency v'. Observers on the ground measure λ and v.

Since the events occur at the same place on the train,

$$\Delta x' = 0. \qquad (20.43)$$

Passing this point on the train has been exactly one cycle of oscillation of the wave, so the time interval on the train is the period of the wave, or the inverse of its frequency,

---

* This section is not crucial to developments in this chapter. However, its results will be used in Section 21.1.

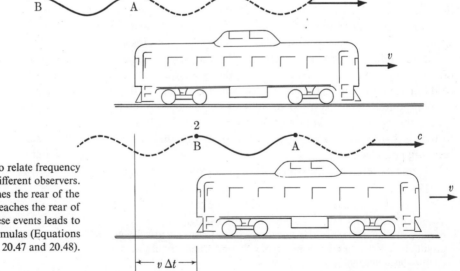

FIGURE 20.15   Experiment to relate frequency and wavelength for different observers. Event 1: Crest A reaches the rear of the train. Event 2: Crest B reaches the rear of the train. Analysis of these events leads to the Doppler-effect formulas (Equations 20.47 and 20.48).

$$\Delta t' = \frac{1}{v'}. \qquad (20.44)$$

On the ground, the separation of the events is the distance the train has moved forward,

$$\Delta x = v\,\Delta t. \qquad (20.45)$$

According to ground-based observers, the distance moved ahead by the wave is one wavelength plus Δx. Since this motion is accomplished at speed c, the elapsed time is

$$\Delta t = \frac{\lambda + \Delta x}{c}.$$

In this equation we may replace Δx by $v\,\Delta t$ and λ by c/v. The solution for Δt is

$$\Delta t = \frac{1}{v(1-\beta)}, \qquad (20.46)$$

where, as usual, $\beta = v/c$. Now the condition $\Delta x' = 0$ implies (Equation 20.24)

$$\Delta t = \frac{\Delta t'}{\sqrt{1-\beta^2}}.$$

Substituting from Equations 20.44 and 20.46 leads to

$$\frac{1}{v(1-\beta)} = \frac{1}{v'\sqrt{1-\beta^2}}.$$

The ratio of frequencies observed on the ground and in the train is, therefore,

$$\frac{v}{v'} = \sqrt{\frac{1+\beta}{1-\beta}} = \frac{1+\beta}{\sqrt{1-\beta^2}}. \qquad (20.47)$$

Light wave propagating in the direction of the moving frame

Since $v = c/\lambda$ and $v' = c/\lambda'$, the ratio of wavelengths is

$$\frac{\lambda}{\lambda'} = \sqrt{\frac{1-\beta}{1+\beta}} = \frac{1-\beta}{\sqrt{1-\beta^2}}. \qquad (20.48)$$

These equations describe the so-called Doppler effect, the change of wavelength and frequency of an electromagnetic wave produced by motion of the observer.

In a typical application, the moving frame is the source of the wave. Consider a radioactive sample being moved through the laboratory at speed v [Figure 20.16(a)]. If one of the nuclei emits a gamma ray forward, in the same direction as the motion (the only direction for which Equations 20.47 and 20.48 are valid), the frequency measured in the laboratory is

$$v = v_0\sqrt{\frac{1+\beta}{1-\beta}}. \qquad (20.49)$$

Here we have replaced v' by v_0 since the frequency in the moving frame (v') can be called the intrinsic frequency of the wave (v_0). It is the frequency that would be measured in the laboratory if the source were at rest. The actual

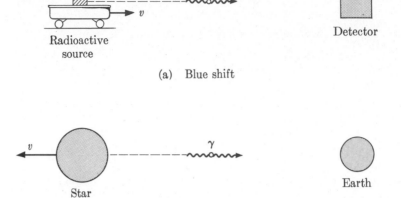

(a)   Blue shift

(b)   Red shift

FIGURE 20.16   (a) For a source approaching a detector, the measured frequency is increased (a "blue shift"). (b) For a receding source, the measured frequency is decreased (a "red shift").

measured frequency in this example is greater than v_0, a so-called "blue shift."*

If the wave in Figure 20.15 were replaced by a wave propagating to the left, the only change required in the results would be a change of sign of β in Equations 20.47 and 20.48.   Then

Light wave propagating opposite to the direction of the moving frame

$$\frac{v}{v'} = \sqrt{\frac{1 - \beta}{1 + \beta}} = \frac{1 - \beta}{\sqrt{1 - \beta^2}}, \qquad (20.50)$$

$$\frac{\lambda}{\lambda'} = \sqrt{\frac{1 + \beta}{1 - \beta}} = \frac{1 + \beta}{\sqrt{1 - \beta^2}}. \qquad (20.51)$$

■ EXAMPLE: A star, receding from the earth at speed v [Figure 20.16(b)], emits a photon opposite to its direction of motion, of intrinsic frequency $v' = v_0$.   What is its measured frequency on earth?   Equation 20.50 is relevant. It gives

$$v = v_0 \sqrt{\frac{1 - \beta}{1 + \beta}}. \qquad (20.52)$$

The frequency v is less than v_0, a so-called "red shift."   If, as an example, $\beta = 0.1$, then $v = 0.905 v_0$, enough to shift a visible photon from green to yellow or from orange to red.   ■

Both of the effects illustrated in Figure 20.16 have been measured.   For

---

* For a visible photon, an increase of frequency and decrease of wavelength shifts it toward the blue end of the spectrum.   A decrease of frequency and increase of wavelength shifts it toward the red end of the spectrum.   From these facts are derived the phrases "blue shift" and "red shift".   Now, however, these phrases are used to designate increase or decrease of frequency in any part of the spectrum.

certain nuclear gamma rays, the Doppler shift for velocities of 1 mm/sec or less can be observed. At an opposite extreme of speed, distant quasars display frequencies red-shifted by a factor of three or more. For $v/v_0 = \frac{1}{3}$, Equation 20.52 gives

$$\beta = 0.8, \qquad v = 2.4 \times 10^8 \text{ m/sec.}$$

Quasars show large red shifts

Such is the speed relative to earth of the more remote parts of the universe.

20.10   Intervals, spacetime, and world lines

The Lorentz transformation provides a rational account of the *relativity* of observation. Hidden within itself, it also contains an unexpected statement of *invariance*. If each of the transformation Equations 20.26 to 20.29 is squared and if the squares are combined in the following particular way,

$$(c \, \Delta t)^2 - (\Delta x)^2 - (\Delta y)^2 - (\Delta z)^2,$$

the equations reveal that this combination is exactly equal to

$$(c \, \Delta t')^2 - (\Delta x')^2 - (\Delta y')^2 - (\Delta z')^2.$$

This combination of length and time measurements is something on which the observers agree in spite of their disagreement about length and time separately. It is natural to attach significance to an invariant quantity, and this combination is named the square of the "interval," for which we use the symbol I:

$$I^2 = (c \, \Delta t)^2 - (\Delta x)^2 - (\Delta y)^2 - (\Delta z)^2, \qquad (20.53)$$

$$I^2 = (c \, \Delta t')^2 - (\Delta x')^2 - (\Delta y')^2 - (\Delta z')^2. \qquad (20.54)$$

The interval: an invariant measure of the separation between events

Between two *simultaneous* events in one frame of reference, the interval is proportional to the spatial separation of those events. In this frame, $\Delta t = 0$, and

$$I^2 = -(\Delta x)^2 - (\Delta y)^2 - (\Delta z)^2 = -(distance)^2. \qquad (20.55)$$

I^2 if $\Delta t = 0$

In a frame moving with respect to this one, $\Delta t'$ is not zero—the events are not simultaneous—and $\Delta x'$ is not equal to Δx, but the combination on the right side of Equation 20.54 remains equal to the combination on the right side of Equation 20.55. Two events occurring in the same *place* ($\Delta x = \Delta y = \Delta z = 0$) but at different times in one frame of reference are separated by an interval that is proportional to the elapsed time between the events in that frame:

$$I^2 = (c \, \Delta t)^2. \qquad (20.56)$$

I^2 if $\Delta \mathbf{r} = 0$

The interval is a generalization and a combination of the ideas of spatial and temporal separation. It may seem odd that the square of a physically meaningful quantity can be negative, as in Equation 20.55. This causes no difficulty in practice. It comes about because we choose to call the defined quantity I^2 rather than I. The directly measurable quantity is I^2 (Equation 20.53 or 20.54), and it is measured by a real number. Only because we arbitrarily define I to be the square root of this quantity do we encounter imaginary quantities. In applications, it is sufficient to work with I^2. If I^2 is positive, the interval is said to be "time-like." If I^2 is negative, the interval is "space-like." A "null" interval is one for which $I = 0$.

■ EXAMPLE 1:   Observer A sees two events as simultaneous and 4 m apart. Observer B sees the same two events separated by 5 m. What is the time separation of the events according to B? The answer to this question could be found from the Lorentz transformation equations, but the invariance of the interval provides an easier route to the answer. Calculated with A's measurements, the square of the interval is

$$I^2 = 0 - (4\text{ m})^2 = -16\text{ m}^2.$$

In B's frame of reference, the interval equation is

$$I^2 = (c\,\Delta t')^2 - (5\text{ m})^2 = -16\text{ m}^2.$$

Therefore, $c\,\Delta t' = 3$ m, so B's time difference must be

$$\Delta t' = 10^{-8}\text{ sec}.$$

It is left as an exercise to find the relative speed of A and B.   ■

■ EXAMPLE 2:   What is the interval between Events 1 and 2 in Figure 20.7? Since the interval is invariant, it may be calculated in whatever frame is convenient. In the train-based frame, the spatial separation of the events is $\Delta x' = L$, the length of the car, and $\Delta y' = \Delta z' = 0$. Their temporal separation is $\Delta t' = L/c$ since a photon flies the distance L at speed c. The square of the interval is, therefore,

$$I^2 = (c\,\Delta t')^2 - (\Delta x')^2 = L^2 - L^2 = 0. \tag{20.57}$$

The interval between any two events joined by a propagating photon is a null interval.   ■

The Lorentz transformation has already showed that space and time have to be thought of as being mixed together. Now the invariance of the interval further strengthens that view of a kind of "interchangeability" between space and time. Space and time are still not quite equivalent because in the definition of the interval the space terms are preceded by minus signs and the time term by a *The idea of spacetime*   plus sign, yet it is possible and useful to think of a four-dimensional spacetime labeled by the four coordinates x, y, z, and t, just as ordinary space is three-dimensional and can be labeled by three coordinates x, y, and z. For dimensional uniformity, the fourth coordinate of spacetime may be chosen to be ct, with *The interval is a spacetime*   the dimension of length.* The interval may be thought of as a distance in *"distance"*   four-dimensional spacetime,† an invariant quantity on which all observers agree in spite of their disagreements about distances in space and time separately.

Although four-dimensional spacetime defies visualization, it is still quite instructive to picture a slice of spacetime and examine simple events in that

---

* Often the unification of space and time is further emphasized by the following notation: $x_0 = ct$, $x_1 = x$, $x_2 = y$, $x_3 = z$. However, in this text, we do not use the subscript notation.

† Because of the opposite signs preceding the space and time terms in the definition of the interval, spacetime is non-Euclidean. In a Euclidean four-dimensional spacetime, distance would be defined by $L^2 = (c\,\Delta t)^2 + (\Delta x)^2 + (\Delta y)^2 + (\Delta z)^2$.

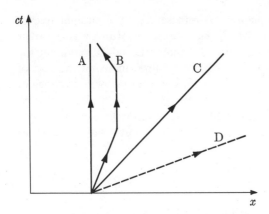

FIGURE 20.17   World lines in a Minkowski diagram. The speed of the woman (B) is greatly exaggerated relative to the speed of light (C). Line D corresponds to a speed greater than *c*.

slice. For example, consider the "Minkowksi diagram" in Figure 20.17, with one spatial dimension plotted horizontally and the time dimension plotted vertically. The complete history of any object restricted to move only in the *x* direction can be represented by a line in this diagram. A man at rest is represented by the straight vertical line A. A woman who walks to the right, stops for awhile, and walks to the left leaves the trace B. A light wave traveling to the right has a history represented by C. Such lines are called *world lines*, and any point on a world line is an event. The most interesting events are those in which two or more world lines intersect. The dashed line D could not qualify as the world line of any known physical entity because it corresponds to a speed greater than the speed of light.

The Minkowski diagram plots t vs x

World lines are spacetime trajectories

■ EXAMPLE 3:   What are the world lines of the locomotive and observation car of a train moving in the *x* direction with speed *v*? How do lines of fixed position in the train ($\Delta x' = 0$) and lines of fixed time in the train ($\Delta t' = 0$) appear in the Minkowski diagram? Figure 20.18 provides the answers. Motion at

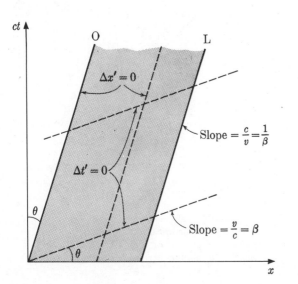

FIGURE 20.18   Lines L and O are world lines of the locomotive and observation car of a train moving with constant speed *v*. Lines of fixed position in the train ($\Delta x' = 0$) are parallel to L and O, with slope equal to $1/\beta$. Lines of fixed time in the train ($\Delta t' = 0$) are straight lines of slope β. How would you place *x'* and *ct'* axes in this diagram?

constant velocity in a spacetime diagram is represented by a straight line of slope $dt/dx = 1/v$. If, as in Figure 20.17, the time-axis coordinate is ct rather than t, the slope is c/v, or $1/\beta$. Such lines, designated L and O, represent the ends of the train; the shaded region between these lines indicates the rest of the train. The lines L and O and any other lines parallel to them are lines of

Lines of constant x': slope $1/\beta$

fixed position in the train, along which $\Delta x' = 0$. This could be demonstrated formally by setting $\Delta x' = 0$ in Equation 20.31. To find the lines of fixed time in the train, set $\Delta t' = 0$ in Equation 20.30. This substitution leads to $\Delta t = v\,\Delta x/c^2$, or, if $\Delta t = t - t_0$ and $\Delta x = x - x_0$, to

$$c(t - t_0) = \frac{v}{c}(x - x_0).$$

This is the equation of parallel straight lines (for different choices of x_0 and t_0), all with slope

Lines of constant t': slope β

$$\frac{d(ct)}{dx} = \frac{v}{c} = \beta.$$

Two such lines are shown in Figure 20.18. Note that the two angles marked θ are equal. ∎

World lines depict particle transformations

In the submicroscopic world, elementary-particle transformations can be conveniently represented by world lines. The decay of a pion at rest is illustrated in Figure 20.19(a). The world line of the motionless pion is a straight vertical line until the moment of its annihilation. Then the massless neutrino that is created moves off in one direction at the speed of light, while the newly created muon moves away in the other direction at a lesser speed. Fascinating world lines also result from the annihilation and creation of positron-electron pairs. In the diagram of Figure 20.19(b) a positron-electron pair is created at A as

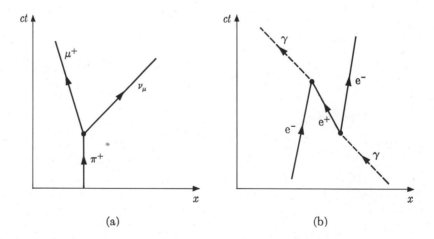

(a)   (b)

FIGURE 20.19   World-line diagrams of elementary-particle transformations. These are called Feynman diagrams. (a) Decay of a positive pion at rest: $\pi^+ \to \mu^+ + \nu_\mu$. (b) One process that contributes to photon-electron scattering, $\gamma + e^- \to \gamma + e^-$. An intermediate positron appears.

two new world lines come into existence. At a later time at point B the positron encounters another electron, both annihilate, and two world lines terminate. But dare we take a more radical view of these events? Does the electron at B perhaps not annihilate at all, but merely turn around and move backward through time until it reaches point A, where once again it turns around and resumes its course forward through time? An answer to this question was given in 1949 by Richard Feynman. He showed that either view of the events is equally acceptable and that an entirely consistent mathematical theory of positrons can be constructed in which they are regarded as electrons moving backward in time. World-line portrayals of particle transformations, such as those in Figure 20.19, are called Feynman diagrams. They will receive more attention in Chapter 27.

Time-reversed trajectories

Feynman diagrams defined

20.11   The twin paradox*

So contrary are the ideas of relativity to ordinary ways of thought that numerous puzzles and "paradoxes" have been proposed over the years, some of the best of which provide challenging tests of one's ability to think in relativistic terms. Probably the most famous of these, one which has excited a great deal of interest and even stirred up considerable controversy, is called the "twin paradox." Anton (twin A) stays at home on earth, while Bertram (twin B) cruises about the universe at nearly the speed of light. Since Bertram's rapid motion has slowed down his clocks and his life processes along with them, he (1) returns home to find himself much younger than Anton. But from Bertram's point of view, it is Anton who was traveling and therefore living more slowly. Could we not with equal justification say that (2) Anton should be younger than Bertram when they rejoin? Or, in view of the reciprocity of observation, (3) should they instead still be equal-aged twins when they reunite? The first of these three possibilities is the correct one. Bertram *will* be younger than Anton. The problem is to reconcile this result with the principle of reciprocity and the absence of preferred frames of reference. We shall first discuss a more mundane version of the twin paradox involving trains and automobiles and then demonstrate mathematically the unequal aging of the twins.

The space-travelling twin is younger. Why?

Suppose that Anton is standing motionless on the ground as Bertram speeds past in a train. Both note as they pass that their watches point to the same time, but each makes rapid observations, and concludes that the other's watch is running slow. Each, therefore, predicts that later the other's watch will be behind his own. Can they both be right? Oddly enough, they can. It depends on how they go about checking up on their watches later.

Let us suppose that the twins pass each other in this manner on two occasions (Figure 20.20). On the first occasion, Bertram leaves the train at the next station, catches the next train back, and rejoins Anton to find his watch behind Anton's. "That's odd," says Bertram, "I could have sworn it was your watch that was slow. Oh, well," he adds philosophically, "at least I haven't

(a) A remains at rest; he ages more

---

* Several interesting articles on the twin paradox (also called the clock paradox) are contained in *Special Relativity Theory, Selected Reprints* (New York: American Institute of Physics, 1963). This booklet also contains a useful bibliography on relativity theory.

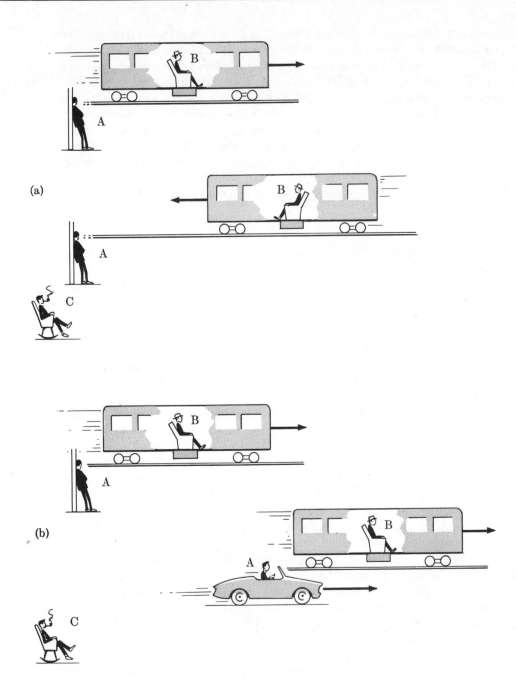

FIGURE 20.20   The twin paradox. (a) Anton waits for Bertram to return. Bertram is younger when they meet. (b) Anton overtakes Bertram, who waits patiently in his inertial frame. Anton is younger when they meet. Charles understands this because he sees Bertram moving more rapidly than Anton in case (a) and Anton moving more rapidly than Bertram in case (b).

aged as much as you." On the second occasion, Anton rents a fast car, over-takes the train and boards it at the next station. Now it is Anton's turn to be surprised but to take what comfort he can from his lower rate of aging. Each observer's prediction has been borne out provided that he remains patiently in his own inertial frame of reference and lets the other observer come to him. "All quite simple," says an impartial observer, Charles, who takes the human point of view that the earth is really *the* frame of reference. "Bertram's watch was of course running slowly because he was moving, as was proved when he came back to Anton. But if Anton is so foolish as to travel even faster than Bertram in his effort to overtake him, small wonder that Anton's watch slowed down even more than Bertram's."

(b) B remains on the train; he ages more

PROPER TIME AND THE AGING OF THE TWINS

To calculate the aging of the twins, it is useful to introduce the concept of *proper time*. The proper time associated with the displacement of an object is defined as the time measured in an inertial frame of reference moving with the object. If the object is accelerated, an inertial frame can keep pace with it only for an infinitesimal time, so the increment of proper time $d\tau$ is defined by

$$d\tau = dt' \qquad (d\mathbf{r}' = 0). \qquad (20.58)$$

Proper time defined in a frame moving with an object

The condition $d\mathbf{r}' = 0$ indicates that during this infinitesimal time, the object is at rest in the moving frame. Because of the invariance of the interval, proper time may be defined more generally in any frame:

$$d\tau = \sqrt{(dt)^2 - \frac{1}{c^2}\left[(dx)^2 + (dy)^2 + (dz)^2\right]}. \qquad (20.59)$$

Proper time defined in any frame

In case the object is moving with constant velocity, the elapsed proper time may be defined for a finite interval (see Equation 20.53) as

$$\Delta\tau = \sqrt{\frac{I^2}{c^2}} = \sqrt{(\Delta t)^2 - \frac{1}{c^2}\left[(\Delta x)^2 + (\Delta y)^2 + (\Delta z)^2\right]}. \qquad (20.60)$$

The significance of proper time is that it is the time that would be recorded by a clock moving with an object. For each of the twins, therefore, the proper time gives the elapsed time by his watch and the extent of his aging.

With the help of the Minkowski diagrams in Figure 20.21, we may easily calculate the aging of the twins for each of the situations depicted in Figure 20.20 (for both diagrams in Figure 20.21, x and t are the coordinates of the earth-based observer C):

(a) *A remains at rest; B travels out and back.* In time T, B moves a distance vT. He then starts back and reaches $x = 0$ again at $t = 2T$ [Figure 20.21(a)]. His world line is OPQ. A's world line is the straight vertical line OQ. Between Events O and Q, the elapsed proper time for A is simply

Analysis of case (a)

$$\Delta\tau_A = 2T. \qquad (20.61)$$

For B, Equation 20.60 must be applied separately to the two legs of his journey. His elapsed proper time is (we use $\Delta x = \pm vT$ and $\Delta y = \Delta z = 0$)

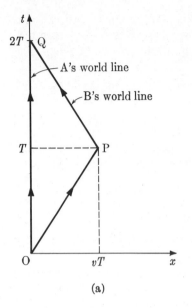
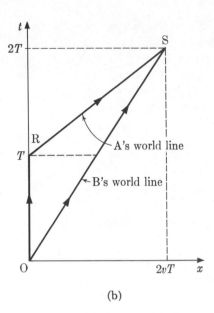

FIGURE 20.21   World-line diagrams for the two histories illustrated in Figure 20.20.

(a)   (b)

$$\Delta\tau_B = \sqrt{T^2 - \frac{v^2 T^2}{c^2}} + \sqrt{T^2 - \frac{v^2 T^2}{c^2}}$$

$$= 2T\sqrt{1 - \beta^2}. \tag{20.62}$$

The ratio of times is

$$\frac{\Delta\tau_B}{\Delta\tau_A} = \sqrt{1 - \beta^2} < 1. \tag{20.63}$$

Proper time is less along the longer spacetime path

Bertram is younger than Anton when they rejoin. Note, in Figure 20.21(a), that although B's world line is longer than A's, his elapsed proper time is less. The more indirect route in spacetime is "shorter."

Analysis of case (b)

(b) *B continues at constant velocity; A rests for a time and then overtakes B.* Suppose that A waits a time T and then moves with speed $2v$, overtaking B at $x = 2vT$ and $t = 2T$ [Figure 20.21(b)]. A's world line is ORS; B's world line is the straight line OS. For A, the elapsed proper time is T while he remains at rest and $\sqrt{T^2 - 4v^2 T^2/c^2}$ while he is moving, for a total of

$$\Delta\tau_A = T(1 + \sqrt{1 - 4\beta^2}). \tag{20.64}$$

For B, the elapsed proper time is

$$\Delta\tau_B = 2T\sqrt{1 - \beta^2}. \tag{20.65}$$

The ratio of times is

$$\frac{\Delta\tau_B}{\Delta\tau_A} = \frac{2\sqrt{1 - \beta^2}}{1 + \sqrt{1 - 4\beta^2}} > 1. \tag{20.66}$$

This time it is Anton who is younger when they rejoin. Again the longer path in spacetime is the path of less proper time. To show that the ratio on the right side of Equation 20.66 is indeed greater than 1 is left as a problem.

The general rule to cover these experiments is that any observer who leaves an inertial frame, moves with respect to it, and then rejoins it will find that his time is behind the time of observers who remained in the frame. There is actually nothing paradoxical about the twin paradox. Indeed, the differential aging has been verified—not with human twins, to be sure, but with twin nuclei and even with twin clocks (a reference to the latter verification appears in the footnote on page 1008).

Time lags more for the observer who experiences acceleration

MACH'S PRINCIPLE

Even though it is both explained and tested, the twin paradox does raise some fundamental questions to which no satisfactory answers have yet been provided. Why are there any inertial frames at all? Given that there are inertial frames, what determines *which* frames of reference are inertial? We can at best define an inertial frame operationally. It is one in which Newton's first law holds true—objects on which no force acts are unaccelerated. The most appealing hypothesis about the "true nature" of inertial frames is due to Ernst Mach; it is usually called Mach's principle. Mach suggested that the distribution of matter in the universe determines preferred frames of reference and that any frame unaccelerated with respect to the "fixed stars"—that is, with respect to the average distribution of matter in the universe—is an inertial frame.* This would mean that matter throughout the universe would determine the properties of spacetime at the earth—a challenging idea indeed. (Actually, the more modern view would replace Mach's "matter" by matter plus energy. We do not yet know what fraction of the energy in the universe is in the form of matter.)

Why are inertial frames special?

Is it because of the distribution of mass and energy in the universe?

20.12   Significance of the speed of light

The special theory of relativity applies to all parts of nature, including phenomena that have nothing to do with light or other electromagnetic radiation. Why, then, does the speed of light play such a central role in the theory? Its constancy, adopted as a fundamental postulate, leads to the Lorentz transformation and to all of the strange attributes of this transformation, including the relativity of time. The speed of light turns out to be nature's speed limit, and it makes its appearance in nearly every equation of relativity.

In fact, the speed of light plays two distinct roles in relativity theory. It is a conversion factor, and it is a speed limit. In its first role, it is, in a sense, of no fundamental significance at all. We can gain insight into this role of the speed of light if we consider, by analogy, the mechanical equivalent of heat, which is equal to 4.18 J/cal. By historical accident, the unit of energy (the joule) and the unit of heat (the calorie) were defined separately before it was known that there was a relation between heat and energy. Had it been known soon enough that

Two roles for c

---

* Mach actually suggested even more, that inertial mass exists at all only because of the presence of the rest of the matter in the universe. According to this principle, a body alone in an otherwise empty universe would possess no mass.

heat is itself a form of energy, heat would have been measured in joules and there would have been no need even for the idea of a mechanical equivalent of heat. The number 4.18 is just a way of correcting past error and joining together two ideas that were believed to be different but are not.

The idea of spacetime leads us to a similar view of the speed of light. Space and time are really parts of a single entity, spacetime. Properly, they should have the same unit of measurement. Because the meter and the second were independently defined before any connection between space and time was known, the speed of light appears as the correction factor relating the two different units, which should have been the same. According to this view, the numerical value of c has no particular meaning.

(1) It is a units conversion factor

The analogy with the mechanical equivalent of heat should not be pressed too far. While it is true that with "properly" chosen units, the numerical value of c would be 1, we cannot dispense with the *idea* of the speed of light. Whatever its numerical value, it is important in setting a speed limit in nature (its second role). Even to a cosmic creature not bound by time who could take in the full panorama of spacetime at a glance, to whom human history is a mere map before him, the idea of the speed of light would be important because it would provide a boundary line between possible and impossible world lines in the spacetime map.

(2) It is nature's speed limit

Granted that there *is* a limiting speed in nature, why is it light that sets this limit and not something else? The modern answer is to be found in the particle concept of light. It is the masslessness of photons that enables them—indeed requires them—to move at nature's greatest speed. This means that light, although special, is not unique. Neutrinos and the hypothetical gravitons, also massless particles, move at the same speed as light. When the theory of relativity was formulated, neutrinos were unknown and unsuspected. The theory developed primarily from studies of electromagnetism. Contributing to the point of view about nature that helped stimulate its development were experiments with light such as the Michelson-Morley experiment. For these reasons, light was regarded as the special radiation of special relativity. In bare outline, the chain of reasoning about the speed of light that approximates the actual historical development is this:

An approximately historical sequence

(1) Because of the desire to extend the Galilean type of invariance from the laws of mechanics to the laws of electromagnetism, it is postulated that the speed of light is the same for all observers (in inertial frames of reference). This postulate is backed by experiments with light that failed to reveal the ether.

(2) The postulate of constant light velocity (together with the idea of reciprocity) leads to the Lorentz transformation equations, which supplant the Galilean transformation equations.

(3) The Lorentz transformation equations become difficult or impossible to interpret for speeds greater than the speed of light, suggesting that light sets the speed limit for nature.

This reasoning should be capped by an experimental finding:

(4) Nothing has ever been observed to move faster than light.

An alternative chain of reasoning, which from the modern point of view has a little more appeal than the historical sequence outlined above, runs like this:

(1) Suppose there exists in nature a maximum speed v_{max}, which is the same for all observers.*

(2) The existence of the constant speed v_{max} leads to the Lorentz transformation equations and to other consequences of the theory of relativity.

(3) Massless particles, if any, will achieve the speed v_{max}. Massive particles will move more slowly.

A reconstructed logical sequence

This logic does more than merely replace the symbol c with the symbol v_{max} because it leaves open the possibility that nothing actually achieves the limiting speed. Suppose there were in nature no massless particles to move at the greatest speed. Would there be a theory of relativity? If so, could it have been discovered? The answer to both questions is emphatically yes. Its discovery might have been delayed a few years but surely for not very long, for the behavior of high-energy electrons would have provided ample evidence for the inadequacy of previous theory. It is a bit of luck that light achieves nature's greatest speed. However, the careful study of any high-speed particle motion would have led physicists inescapably to the same theory of relativity.

If nothing in nature achieved the speed c, relativity would be no different

* If the speed v_{max} were not the same for all observers, there would be one observer with the largest v_{max}; his would be a "maximum maximum speed." According to the other fundametal postulate of the theory of relativity (Section 19.7), all inertial frames of reference are equivalent and there are no such privileged observers.

Summary of ideas and definitions

The idea of reciprocity: If A and B are in relative motion and carry out the same experiment, A's description of B's experiment is the same as B's description of A's experiment (except for a change of sign of their relative velocity).

Reciprocity must apply if all inertial frames of reference are equivalent.

Because of reciprocity, observers agree about (1) distances measured perpendicular to their relative velocity and (2) the magnitude of their relative velocity.

Clocks in one frame of reference can be consistently synchronized by means of light signals. Synchronization is a relative concept.

The Lorentz transformation may be derived from thought experiments using only two ideas: the constancy of the speed of light and reciprocity.

The Lorentz transformation equations are linear equations relating the space and time measurements of observers in relative motion. For the frames of reference defined in Figure 20.6,

$$c\,\Delta t = \frac{c\,\Delta t' + \beta\,\Delta x'}{\sqrt{1 - \beta^2}}, \qquad c\,\Delta t' = \frac{c\,\Delta t - \beta\,\Delta x}{\sqrt{1 - \beta^2}},$$

$$\text{(20.28)} \qquad\qquad\qquad \text{(20.30)}$$

$$\Delta x = \frac{\Delta x' + \beta(c\,\Delta t')}{\sqrt{1 - \beta^2}}, \qquad \Delta x' = \frac{\Delta x - \beta(c\,\Delta t)}{\sqrt{1 - \beta^2}},$$

$$\text{(20.29)} \qquad\qquad\qquad \text{(20.31)}$$

$$\Delta y = \Delta y', \qquad \text{(20.26, 20.32)}$$

$$\Delta z = \Delta z'. \qquad \text{(20.27, 20.33)}$$

Time dilation: If $\Delta x' = 0$ (a fixed point in the moving frame),

$$\Delta t = \frac{\Delta t'}{\sqrt{1 - \beta^2}}. \qquad \text{(20.3, 20.34)}$$

Moving clocks run slow.

The Lorentz contraction: If $\Delta t' = 0$ (simultaneous measurements in the moving frame),

$$\Delta x = \frac{\Delta x'}{\sqrt{1 - \beta^2}}. \qquad (20.37)$$

An object moving with respect to the observer is contracted in its direction of motion.

The relativity of simultaneity: If $\Delta t = 0$ (simultaneous events in the stationary frame),

$$\Delta t' = -\frac{v\,\Delta x'}{c^2}. \qquad (20.38)$$

The events are not simultaneous in the moving frame.

The addition of velocities: If Frame 3 has x component of velocity v_2 with respect to Frame 2 and if Frame 2 has x component of velocity v_1 with respect to Frame 1, the x component of velocity of Frame 3 in Frame 1 is

$$v = \frac{v_1 + v_2}{1 + (v_1 v_2/c^2)}. \qquad (20.40)$$

Particle decay tests time dilation; particle acceleration tests the addition of velocities.

Frequency and wavelength are relative concepts. The difference in frequency and wavelength between different frames is called the Doppler shift (Equations 20.47–20.52).

The interval, defined by

$$I^2 = (c\,\Delta t)^2 - (\Delta x)^2 - (\Delta y)^2 - (\Delta z)^2, \qquad (20.53)$$

is an invariant quantity.

The invariance of the interval and the symmetry of the Lorentz transformation equations support the idea of a four-dimensional spacetime.

Minkowski diagrams display world-line trajectories in the t-x plane. Such diagrams for particle transformations are called Feynman diagrams.

The proper time associated with a moving object is the time measured in a frame moving with the object (Equations 20.58–20.60). The elapsed proper time between two events is greatest along a straight world line connecting the events.

A twin who leaves an inertial frame and later returns to it will be younger than a twin who remained in the inertial frame.

Perhaps inertial frames are special because they are unaccelerated with respect to the average distribution of mass and energy in the universe (Mach's principle).

The speed of light plays two important roles in relativity theory: (1) It is a units conversion factor for space and time. (2) It is nature's speed limit.

If there were no massless particles and if nothing achieved the speed of light, the theory of relativity would be exactly the same.

QUESTIONS

Section 20.1

Q20.1   Make up a thought experiment other than those mentioned in Section 20.1 that shows the "paradoxical" nature of the postulate $c = constant$. Does your experiment imply a relativity of time? or of space? or of both? Does it violate common sense?

Q20.2   In a rocket car similar to the one shown in Figure 20.2, the ceiling light (C) is slightly closer to the front (F) than to the rear (R) of the car. According to the driver of the car, the light emitted by C therefore reaches F before it reaches R. Is it still possible that the observer on the ground will say that the light reaches R before it reaches F?

Section 20.2

Q20.3   A hypothetical experiment depicted in Figure 20.3 is used to derive Equation 20.3, which relates the time differences between two events in spacetime measured by observers in different inertial frames of reference. (1) What are the two events? (2) Which observer places the two events at the *same* point in space? (3) Which observer places the two events at *different* points in space?

Section 20.3

Q20.4   Give a statement of the reciprocity principle in your own words.

Q20.5   Two clocks are located a fixed distance apart in a certain frame of reference. Suggest a method to test for their synchronization that does not use light or other electromagnetic signals.

Q20.6 In what way does the Lorentz contraction discussed in Section 20.4 differ from the FitzGerald contraction mentioned in Section 19.6?

Section 20.4

Q20.7 Stationary observers measure the shape of an object passing at high speed to be exactly circular. What is the shape of the object according to observers traveling with it?

Q20.8 (1) Which of the Galilean transformation equations "mixes" space and time? (2) Why do the Lorentz transformation equations appear to "mix" space and time in a more fundamental way?

Section 20.6

Q20.9 Under what conditions can the Lorentz transformation equations (Equations 20.24–20.27) be applied without the Δ symbols—i.e., Δt replaced by t, $\Delta t'$ replaced by t', etc?

Q20.10 In a frame of reference moving at speed v, two events are separated by finite space and time intervals $\Delta x'$ and $\Delta t'$. What happens to Δx and Δt as $v \rightarrow c$?

Q20.11 According to the first part of Equation 20.36, the difference in measured time intervals for two observers moving with a low relative speed is $\Delta t - \Delta t' \cong \frac{1}{2}\beta^2 \Delta t'$. Why is it permissible to replace $\Delta t'$ by Δt on the right side of this equation (thereby obtaining the last part of Equation 20.36) but not permissible to set $\Delta t' = \Delta t$ on the left side?

Section 20.7

Q20.12 The figure shows an observer O looking at a long, thin object that is in high-speed motion. To the observer the object does not appear to be contracted; it actually appears to be stretched (that is, the angle α is greater than it would be if the object were stationary). Explain why. [A full analysis shows that in fact the apparent stretching is better described as an apparent *rotation* of the object (counterclockwise in this instance). See Victor Weisskopf, "The Visual Appearance of Rapidly Moving Objects," *Physics Today* **13**, No. 9, 24 (1960).]

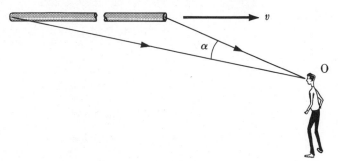

Q20.13 (1) In one frame of reference, events A and B occur simultaneously at different points in space. There are other frames in which A occurs before B and others in which B occurs before A. Refer to Equation 20.38 in order to explain this fact. (2) Events C and D are simultaneous in *all* frames of reference. What additional fact about these events can you infer?

Q20.14 (1) Is it possible for an observer in frame of reference 1 to consider the relative speeds of frames 2 and 3 to be greater than the speed of light c? (2) Is it possible for an observer in frame 2 to consider his speed relative to frame 3 to be greater than c?

Q20.15 Is it possible to make an electron beam sweep across the face of a cathode-ray tube at a speed greater than the speed of light? Why or why not?

Q20.16 Examining Equation 20.3, a student argues as follows: For observer B, A's clock (which records a time interval Δt) is the moving clock. Since the equation implies $\Delta t > \Delta t'$, B must conclude that A's clock is running *faster* than his own. This violates the principle of reciprocity, according to which *each* observer should consider the other's moving clock to be running slow. Bring in the idea of clock synchronization to explain qualitatively the insufficiency of the student's reasoning. (See also Problem 20.1.)

Section 20.8   Q20.17 Explain in your own words why we are unaware of relativistic effects in our everyday lives. Can you draw any conclusion about the probable relation between human perceptions and the fundamental theories of nature?

Q20.18 Extremely energetic pions are created near the top of the atmosphere. Those moving nearly horizontally are likely to decay into muons (and neutrinos). Those moving nearly vertically are likely to strike and react with nuclei before they have a chance to decay. (1) Why does the fate of these high-energy pions depend on direction in this way? (2) Why do lower energy pions created near the top of the atmosphere almost all decay into muons, regardless of their direction of motion?

Section 20.9   Q20.19 Can a classical wave (one for which relativistic effects are negligible) exhibit a Doppler effect?

Q20.20 The simple formula $\lambda v = c$ was well known for electromagnetic waves before the theory of relativity was devised. What new thing did relativity have to say about this equation?

Q20.21 Are the wavelength and frequency of light changed if the light is reflected from a moving mirror?

Q20.22 A certain source of light is vibrating with an average velocity that is zero and a root-mean-square velocity that is not zero. Is the average frequency of the light that it emits Doppler shifted? If so, is it red-shifted or blue-shifted? (HINT: Compare Equations 20.47 and 20.50.)

Section 20.10   Q20.23 The square of a four-dimensional interval may be negative (see, for instance, Equation 20.55). The square of a speed cannot be negative and still be physically meaningful. Explain this difference by discussing the difference in the way a speed is measured and the way an interval is measured.

Q20.24 The interval (defined by Equation 20.53) is said to be "invariant under a Lorentz transformation." This means that it has the same value in different inertial frames if the Lorentz transformation connects space and time measurements in these frames. Is the interval invariant under a Galilean transformation? (Refer to Equations 19.11–19.14.)

Q20.25 Cite pairs of events that are separated by (1) a time-like interval, (2) a space-like interval, and (3) a null interval.

Q20.26 If two events are separated by a time-like interval in one frame of reference, they are separated by a time-like interval in all frames of reference. Why?

Q20.27 The distance between two points in a plane is expressed in terms of Cartesian coordinates by $L = \sqrt{(\Delta x)^2 + (\Delta y)^2}$. (1) For what kinds of change (transformation) of the coordinates is L an invariant? (2) Is L invariant under a Lorentz transformation?

Q20.28 Pick any two simple occurrences, either in the elementary particle world or in your own life, and sketch the world-line diagrams for these occurrences.

Q20.29 Which runs slower in a sun-fixed frame of reference, a clock on Earth or a clock on Mars? (Consider only the effect of orbital motion, not of spin motion.)

Section 20.11

Q20.30 A relativistic couple live on planet X and work on planet Y. They synchronize their watches over breakfast. (1) She goes to work first and he follows later at the same speed. Do their watches agree when they meet for lunch? (2) In the evening she goes straight home and he makes a side trip to planet Z to shop before going home. Do their watches agree when they meet for dinner? Give reasons for both answers.

Q20.31 Proper time is defined in terms of a square root (Equation 20.59). Why can we be confident that the elapsed proper time for a moving material particle will always be real, never imaginary?

Q20.32 Experimenters on Earth observe the motion of a high-speed space vehicle enroute from Titan to Icarus, and calculate the proper time for the trip. (1) How does this proper time compare with the time recorded by passengers on the space vehicle? (2) How does this proper time compare with the time of the trip recorded on Earth clocks?

Q20.33 Do you consider it likely that during the next half century the speed of manned space vehicles will become so great that the "twin paradox" will become a familiar reality for astronauts returning from lengthy space missions? Give a reason for your answer.

Q20.34 Every elevator ride gives evidence that absolute acceleration has meaning and absolute velocity does not. Discuss the sensations you might experience in an elevator ride if (a) absolute velocity had meaning or (b) absolute acceleration had no meaning.

Q20.35 Suppose that at some future date photons are discovered to have a small non-zero mass. (1) Would all photons travel at the same speed? (2) Would any entity in nature travel faster than photons of light? (3) Would relativity theory need to be corrected to take account of this discovery?

Section 20.12

EXERCISES

Section 20.2

E20.1 Fill in the algebraic details after Equation 20.2 in order to derive the time-dilation formula, Equation 20.3.

E20.2 A passenger on an interplanetary express bus catnaps for 5 min by his watch. If the bus is maintaining a speed of $0.99c$ through the solar system, how long do observers fixed on the planets judge the nap to be?

E20.3 The driver of a relativistic rental car returns his car after what he measures to be 1 hr of driving. The rental agent says the car has been out for 2 hr. At what speed was the car driven? Express the answer both as a fraction of the speed of light and in m/sec.

E20.4 A roadside observer A sends a light beam vertically upward a distance D, where it is reflected back to its starting point. He measures the round-trip time to be t_A. A moving observer B measures its round-trip time to be t_B.

Draw a diagram analogous to Figure 20.3 to help analyze this example, and derive an equation analogous to Equation 20.3 relating the two time measurements.

Section 20.3 E20.5 Anthony states: "At 12:01 precisely two photons simultaneously struck the same point in my frame of reference. One microsecond later, an electron was emitted from this same location." Helene, in high-speed motion relative to Anthony, observed the same events. With which parts of Anthony's description does she agree, and with which parts does she disagree?

E20.6 A clock C_3 is placed next to clock C_1 in Figure 20.4 and is synchronized with C_1. Then C_3 is moved at speed v through distance d until it is close to clock C_2. By how much must the reading of C_3 then be advanced to bring C_3 into synchronism with C_2? Give the answer (a) algebraically and (b) numerically for $v = 0.6c$ and $d = 300$ m.

Section 20.4 E20.7 Electrons in a certain TV picture tube are accelerated to a speed of 10^8 m/sec ($\frac{1}{3}c$). As measured in the living room, the length of the tube is 12 in. What is its length in a frame of reference moving with the electron at its final speed?

E20.8 A light plastic balloon in orbit around the earth is moving at a speed of 5 mile/sec. In its rest frame, it is a sphere 20 m in diameter. Describe its shape and calculate the extent of its "flattening" in a frame fixed with respect to the earth.

Section 20.5 E20.9 Give explicit expressions for Δx, Δt, $\Delta x'$, and $\Delta t'$ for the experiment shown in Figure 20.3. Event 1 is a light beam leaving the floor of the rocket car; event 2 is the light beam reaching the floor after its reflection from the ceiling.

E20.10 Obtain Equations 20.14 and 20.15 from Equations 20.12 and 20.13.

Section 20.6 E20.11 Show that if the Lorentz transformation Equations 20.24 and 20.25 are applied to the hypothetical photon experiment depicted in Figure 20.7, they lead to Equations 20.14 and 20.15.

E20.12 Regard Equations 20.24 and 20.25 as two equations for two unknowns, $\Delta x'$ and $\Delta t'$. (1) Solve for these unknowns. (2) Explain how the resulting formulas for $\Delta x'$ and $\Delta t'$ support the principle of reciprocity.

E20.13 Write Equations 20.30 and 20.31 in a completely symmetric form like Equations 20.28 and 20.29.

E20.14 Two of the Galilean transformation equations (Equations 19.14 and 19.11) are

$$\Delta t = \Delta t', \qquad \Delta x = \Delta x' + v\,\Delta t'.$$

Compare these with the corresponding Lorentz transformation Equations 20.24 and 20.25. (1) What condition must be satisfied in order that the Lorentz transformation equations be accurately approximated by the Galilean transformation equations? (2) For $v = 0.1c$, what percentage error results from using the Galilean equation to calculate Δx?

E20.15 A frame of reference with primed coordinates is moving in the negative z direction with speed $v = \beta c$ relative to a "fixed" frame with unprimed coordinates. (1) Give the two Lorentz transformation equations that make it possible to calculate Δt and Δz, given $\Delta t'$ and $\Delta z'$. (2) Give the inverse transformation equations that make it possible to calculate $\Delta t'$ and $\Delta z'$, given Δt and Δz.

E20.16   Equation 20.35, $(1 - \beta^2)^{-1/2} \simeq 1 + \frac{1}{2}\beta^2$, follows directly from the binomial   Section 20.7
expansion (see page A19). (1) Improve the approximation by adding a third
term to the right side (a term proportional to β^4). (2) What fractional error
results from setting $1/\sqrt{0.98}$ equal to 1.01? (3) What fractional error results
from using Equation 20.35 when $\beta = 10^{-6}$?

E20.17   For $\beta \ll 1$, the Lorentz-contraction factor, $\sqrt{1 - \beta^2}$, is approximately
equal to $1 - \frac{1}{2}\beta^2$. (1) What is the next term in this series expansion (a term
proportional to β^4)? (2) Evaluate $\sqrt{1 - \beta^2}$ for $\beta = 0.6$ in each of three ways:
(a) using the approximation $1 - \frac{1}{2}\beta^2$, (b) using the better approximation of
part 1, and (c) exactly.

E20.18   (1) Prove that for speeds near the speed of light, the square-root factor that
appears in many of the equations of relativity may be approximated as
follows:
$$\sqrt{1 - (v^2/c^2)} \simeq 1.41\sqrt{(c - v)/c}.$$
(2) Use this result to determine the Lorentz-contraction factor for an object
moving at the speed of a 20-GeV electron, a speed that is 0.1 m/sec less than
the speed of light.

E20.19   Rocket taxis of the future move about the solar system at half the speed of
light. Drivers receive $10 per hour as measured by clocks in the taxis. The
taxi drivers' union demands that the pay be based on Earth time instead of taxi
time. If their demand is met, by what fraction will their wages rise?

E20.20   Before taking off in Tokyo, a pilot checks his watch and finds that it agrees
exactly with one of a synchronized network of clocks. When he lands 8 hr
later after having covered 8,640 km at a speed of 300 m/sec, he checks his
watch with another clock in the network and finds (if he can detect extraordinarily small time differences!) that his watch is now slow. By how much
does it lag?

E20.21   Relative to Earth, a fictional spacecraft moves at a speed that is only 3 m/sec
less than the speed of light. According to observers on Earth, the craft takes
1.3 sec to travel from a point near the moon to a point near the earth. (1)
How much time is required for this trip according to the occupants of the
spacecraft? (2) What is the distance from the moon to the earth according to
the occupants of the spacecraft? (NOTE: A useful approximate formula
appears in Exercise 20.18.)

E20.22   Meter stick A moves at half the speed of light past meter stick B at rest in the
laboratory (see the figure). At the instant of time in the laboratory when the
front of the moving meter stick is even with the front of the stationary meter
stick, where, according to the laboratory observer, is the rear of the moving
meter stick?

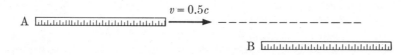

E20.23   A fictitious, relativistic railroad car, when at rest, has a length of 14 m. To
measure its length as it streaks by at 99 percent of the speed of light, observers
on the ground note the position of its front at a particular time and the position

of its rear at the same time. (1) Show that observers on the train consider 46 nsec to have elapsed between these two measurements. (2) What is the length of the moving car measured by the ground-based observers?

E20.24   Ant and Bee are stationed 50 cm apart. As a meter stick flies by, they find that they are opposite its two ends simultaneously. (1) What is the speed of the meter stick? (2) According to observers in the frame of reference of the meter stick, how far apart are Ant and Bee?

E20.25   A spaceman in a satellite traveling at a speed of 6,000 m/sec sees events in Los Angeles and New York (4×10^6 m apart) that he judges to be simultaneous. How much time elapses between these events according to earth-bound observers?

E20.26   (1) Show from Equation 20.40 that the "sum" of c and any other speed v is c. (2) Find the relativistic velocity sums for these pairs: (a) $v_1 = v_2 = 0.5c$; (b) $v_1 = v_2 = 0.9c$; (c) $v_1 = 0.99c$, $v_2 = 0.10c$.

E20.27   An observer on Earth detects two space ships headed directly toward one another on opposite paths, each with a speed of $0.5c$. What do the occupants of the space ships measure their relative speed to be?

E20.28   A rocket ship cruising from Earth to Jupiter passes by Mars at a relative speed of $0.4c$. Experimenters on the ship observe two unidentified spacecraft, one moving toward Jupiter, the other moving toward Earth, both at a speed of $0.8c$ relative to the rocket ship. What speed do colonists on Mars assign to these other two craft? (Keep in mind that the symbols v_1, v_2, and v in Equation 20.40 refer to components of velocity in a given direction.)

Section 20.8   E20.29   Charged pions at rest have a mean lifetime of 2.6×10^{-8} sec. Charged pions emerging from a certain accelerator have a speed of 2.4×10^8 m/sec ($0.8c$). (1) What is the measured mean lifetime of the moving pions in the laboratory frame of reference? (2) What is the mean distance covered by the pions in the laboratory before they decay? (3) What is the mean distance from the accelerator to the points of decay in the rest frame of the pions? (NOTE: This is the distance moved by the accelerator in the pion-frame, not the zero distance moved by a pion in its own rest frame.)

E20.30   A 10-GeV muon experiences a time-dilation factor of 95. By how much does the speed of the muon differ from the speed of light?

Section 20.9   E20.31   A certain galaxy is receding from the earth at 1 percent of the speed of light. (1) By what percentage are its spectral wavelengths shifted compared with wavelengths of corresponding light sources on earth? (2) Is this a red shift or a blue shift? (3) A prominent radiation of hydrogen on earth has a wavelength of 6,563 Å. What is the wavelength of this radiation observed in the light of the galaxy?

E20.32   The intrinsic wavelength of the so-called Lyman alpha line of hydrogen is 1,216 Å (far in the ultraviolet). In the light of the quasar 3C9, this line appears at 3,660 Å (the edge of the visible region). If this enormous shift arises from the motion of the quasar, what is the quasar's speed of recession from the earth?

E20.33   Quasars are often characterized by a "red-shift parameter" Z defined by $Z = \Delta\lambda/\lambda_0$, where λ_0 is the wavelength of a certain spectral line observed in light emitted by a terrestrial source and $\Delta\lambda \, (= \lambda - \lambda_0)$ is the shift in wavelength of this line observed in light from a quasar. Show that if the quasar red shift is a Doppler shift, the quasar's speed of recession is related to Z by the formula

$$\frac{v}{c} = \frac{(Z + 1)^2 - 1}{(Z + 1)^2 + 1}.$$

E20.34 With the help of the so-called Mössbauer effect (see Section 22.4), changes in the frequency of nuclear gamma rays of less than 1 part in 10^{14} can be detected. With what speed must a radioactive source be moved in order that its gamma rays be Doppler-shifted by 1 part in 10^{14}? Is this "fast" or "slow"?

E20.35 Show that for speeds much less than the speed of light, the fractional change of frequency in the Doppler effect is given by $\Delta v/v \cong \pm v/c$, where the positive and negative signs refer to motion of the source toward and away from the observer, respectively.

E20.36 According to the rocket-car driver in Figure 20.2, the interior light in his car emits orange light of wavelength 6,000 Å. Relative to a roadside observer, the speed of the car is $\frac{1}{3}c$. (1) Does the roadside observer measure the forward-going light to be in the visible part of the spectrum? If so, what is its color? (2) Does he measure the backward-going light to be in the visible part of the spectrum? If so, what is its color?

E20.37 Use the Lorentz transformation equations to derive the following equation of invariance for the spacetime interval:

$$(c\,\Delta t)^2 - (\Delta x)^2 - (\Delta y)^2 - (\Delta z)^2 = (c\,\Delta t')^2 - (\Delta x')^2 - (\Delta y')^2 - (\Delta z')^2.$$

Section 20.10

E20.38 (1) Show that any two events between which a physical particle moves are separated by a time-like interval. (2) Does this mean that space-like intervals are physically meaningless? Why or why not?

E20.39 Find the relative speed of observers A and B in Example 1 of Section 20.10.

E20.40 If two events are simultaneous in one frame of reference, their spatial separation is less in this frame than in any other. Use the interval concept to explain this fact.

E20.41 A light in the center of a rocket car is switched on. According to the driver, the front and rear of the car are each at a distance L from the light. The car moves with speed v. (1) What is the square of the spacetime interval between the events of photons reaching the front and rear of the car? (2) Evaluate this quantity numerically for $L = 1$ m and (a) $v = 0$ or (b) $v = 0.99c$.

E20.42 Event 1: A photon leaves a point on the floor of a rocket car, starting vertically upward in the car's frame of reference. Event 2: The photon is reflected from the ceiling of the car 1.2 m above the floor. Event 3: The photon reaches the point on the floor from which it started. (1) Find the intervals between (a) Events 1 and 2, (b) Events 2 and 3, and (c) Events 1 and 3. State whether each interval is space-like, time-like, or null. (2) Find the space and time differences, Δx and Δt, between Events 1 and 3 for a ground-based observer who sees the car moving at 70.7 percent of the speed of light. Verify that his calculated interval for this pair of events is the same as the interval determined by the driver.

E20.43 Within a relativistic railroad car moving over the earth at 80 percent of the speed of light, a relativistic baseball is thrown forward at half the speed of light relative to the car. Event E_1: The ball is thrown from $x' = 0$ at $t' = 0$. Event E_2: The ball is caught at $x' = 6$ m at $t' = 4 \times 10^{-8}$ sec. (1) Is the interval between events E_1 and E_2 time-like or space-like? (2) Is there any frame of reference in which the ball appears to be caught before it is thrown? (3) Is there any frame of reference in which the ball appears to be moving toward negative x instead of toward positive x?

E20.44   A space ship moving at constant speed v passes near the earth at $t = 0$. Later, it beams back a radio message. In a Minkowski diagram, show the world lines of the earth (ignore its finite size), the rocket ship, and the radio wave. Label points where world lines intersect.

E20.45   Draw the Minkowski diagram that corresponds to Figure 20.2. Include world lines for the point F near the front of the car, the point R near the rear of the car, the light C at the center of the car, and the two photons that fly from C to F and R when the light is turned on. Label the significant points where world lines meet. (Let the axes of the diagram be the ground-based observer's x and t.)

Section 20.11   E20.46   A particle moves at a speed of $0.99c$ for a time of 7×10^{-8} sec on laboratory clocks. What is the elapsed proper time for this motion?

E20.47   An object moves at speed v relative to some reference frame. Show that $d\tau$, the object's increment of proper time, and dt, the time increment measured in the reference frame, are related by $d\tau = dt\sqrt{1 - (v^2/c^2)}$.

E20.48   In the lower part of Figure 20.20, Anton is shown driving at speed $2v$ in order catch up with Bertram, who is riding at speed v (both speeds being measured in Charles's frame of reference). (1) What do Anton and Bertram measure their relative speed to be? (2) Charles says that the time Anton spends driving is equal to the time he spent waiting. (a) Does Anton consider one of these times to be longer than the other? If so, which one? (b) Does Bertram consider one of these times to be longer than the other? If so, which one?

E20.49   While Arthur remains on Earth, his twin sister Barbara journeys at 60 percent of the speed of light to a nearby star and back. Both were 20 years old when the trip began and Arthur is 40 when it ends. (1) How old was Barbara when her spacecraft turned and headed for home? (2) How old is she at the end of the trip?

E20.50   Angela remains on Earth for 10 years while her twin brother Benjamin journeys away at half the speed of light. Then she boards a super space cruiser that travels at the speed of light (actually *almost* at the speed of light) and catches up with Benjamin after 10 more Earth years. If Angela and Benjamin were 20 when they parted, how old is each of them when they rejoin?

Section 20.12   E20.51   (1) Consider a system of units in which $c = 1$ and time is measured in meters. Express (a) 1 sec and (b) 1 yr in meters. (2) Consider a system of units in which $c = 1$ and distance is measured in seconds. Express (a) 1 m and (b) the distance to the moon in seconds.

E20.52   In a system of units in which $c = 1$, what is the speed of (a) sound in air, (b) the earth in its orbit, and (c) a neutrino?

E20.53   In working with the equations of relativity theory, physicists routinely set $c = 1$ as a matter of convenience. At the end of a calculation, factors of c

can be restored if need be by considering dimensional consistency. Put factors of c wherever they are needed in the following equations: (1) $v = (v_1 + v_2)/(1 + v_1 v_2)$, (2) $I^2 = (\Delta t)^2 - (\Delta x)^2$, (3) $E = m$, and (4) $p = hv$. (Symbols have their standard meanings: E is energy, p is momentum, h is Planck's constant, m is mass.)

PROBLEMS

P20.1 In the example at the end of Section 20.2, the driver of a rocket car sees a time difference of 10 μsec between two ground-based clocks when his own clock ticks off 6 μsec. Yet the driver finds that a *single* clock on the ground runs *slow*, showing an elapsed time of only 3.6 μsec during 6 μsec of rocket-car time. (1) What is the distance between the two ground-based clocks in the rocket-car frame of reference? (2) What is the distance between these two clocks measured on the ground? (3) According to the rocket-car driver, the two clocks on the ground are not synchronized. Which one is set ahead, and by how much is it set ahead, according to the driver? *Optional:* Generalize part 3: Obtain a formula for the amount of *a*synchronization attributed to ground-based clocks by the driver as a function of the distance $\Delta x'$ that he measures between the clocks.

Clock synchronization and the reciprocity of time dilation

P20.2 A beacon light on a certain planet flashes once per μsec as measured by clocks on that planet. In the frame of reference of a passing armada of Martians, the light moves 400 m between successive flashes. (1) What is the speed of the armada relative to the planet? (2) What is the time between flashes as measured by the passing Martians?

Transformation of space and time intervals

P20.3 A right triangle has sides of lengths x and y, a hypotenuse of length r, and an interior angle θ, as shown in the figure. To an observer moving parallel to side x with speed $v = \beta c$, the triangle has sides of length x' and y', a hypotenuse of length r', and an interior angle θ'. (1) Why does the moving observer agree with a stationary observer that the triangle is a right triangle? (2) Prove that the angles θ and θ' are related by

Lorentz contraction of a triangle

$$\tan \theta' = \frac{\tan \theta}{\sqrt{1 - \beta^2}}.$$

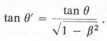

(3) Prove that the lengths r and r' are related by

$$r' = r\sqrt{1 - \beta^2 \cos^2 \theta}.$$

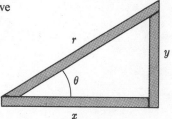

P20.4 Expand Equations 20.28 and 20.29 as a power series in β through terms of third order (keep terms containing β^3; discard terms containing β^4 and higher powers of β). Identify the terms that give the Galilean transformation and the terms that give the leading correction to the Galilean transformation.

Relation of Lorentz and Galilean transformation equations

P20.5 Measured on the ground, the distance from pole A to pole B is L_1, the distance from pole B to pole C is L_2, and the distance from pole A to pole C is L_3 (see the figure). The homogeneity of space implies that $L_3 = L_1 + L_2$. A moving observer, making measurements at a fixed time in his frame of reference, finds these distances to be L_1', L_2', and L_3'. Show that if the Lorentz transformation Equation 20.18 were nonlinear—that is, if it contained terms

Linearity of the Lorentz transformation

proportional to $(\Delta x)^2$ or $(\Delta x')^2$—the distance L_3' would *not* be equal to $L_1' + L_2'$. To the moving observer, space would appear inhomogeneous. What general principle of relativity would this violate?

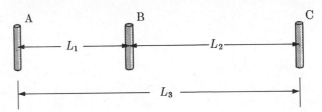

Time dilation of "stationary" clock

P20.6 Complete Example 5 in Section 20.7 by analyzing the time-keeping qualities of the ground-based clock 2 from the viewpoint of observers on the train. The train-based observers first see clock 2 opposite their clock 4 (Figure 20.11). Later, clock 2 has "moved" to be opposite their clock 3 (Figure 20.12). Show that observers on the train conclude that clock 2 is running more slowly than their own clocks and that the ratio of the rates is $\sqrt{1 - \beta^2}$.

Reciprocity of Lorentz contraction

P20.7 Exercise 20.23 describes an experiment in which ground-based observers measure the length of a moving railroad car. Show that if observers in the car measure the distance between the two ground-based observers, they find it to be the same as the ground-based observers find the length of the car to be. (SUGGESTION: Carry out this demonstration algebraically rather than numerically.)

Temporal order of events

P20.8 In a certain frame of reference, two events occur at the same place but not at the same time. Show that if event 1 precedes event 2 in this frame of reference, it precedes event 2 in *all* frames of reference: the temporal order of the events in invariant. *Optional:* Comment briefly on the relationship of this result to the idea of cause and effect.

P20.9 In a certain frame of reference, two events occur neither at the same place nor at the same time ($\Delta x \neq 0$ and $\Delta t \neq 0$). (1) Show that (a) if $|\Delta x| \leq c|\Delta t|$, the temporal order of the events is the same in all frames of reference, and (b) if $|\Delta x| > c|\Delta t|$, the events may occur in the opposite temporal order in some other frame of reference. (2) It is sometimes said that if two events can be "connected" by a light signal or other physical signal, the temporal order of the events is invariant, whereas if they cannot be so "connected," their temporal order is not invariant. Explain this statement in terms of the results of part 1.

Spacetime transformations

P20.10 Clocks in Baltimore and San Francisco, 4,000 km apart, are synchronized by setting both to $t = 0$ at the instant when they receive a radio signal radiated from a point in Kansas halfway between them. As this synchronization is being carried out, a Tralfamadorian fleet is passing over the United States from west to east at 60 percent of the speed of light. (1) Do the alien space-people consider the transmitter to be located midway between Baltimore and San Francisco? Why or why not? (2) What is the distance from San Francisco to Baltimore according to the cruising Tralfamadorians? (3) Which of the two clocks on Earth do they consider to be set ahead, and by how much? (4) If the visitors from space transmit their own message when they are directly over the Kansas transmitter, will their message be received in San

Francisco and Baltimore (a) at the same Earth time? (b) at the same Tralfamadore time?

P20.11 Prove that if v_1 and v_2 both lie between 0 and c, their relativistic "sum" as given by Equation 20.40 is less than c. (SUGGESTION: Write Equation 20.40 in the form

Addition of velocities

$$\frac{1}{\beta} = \frac{1 + \beta_1\beta_2}{\beta_1 + \beta_2}$$

and seek to show that the right side of this equation exceeds 1.) *Optional:* Extend the proof to include negative values of v_1 and/or v_2.

P20.12 Let the runner in Figure 20.13 be replaced by a tachyon (a hypothetical particle that moves faster than light). (1) Use Equation 20.40 to prove that if $0 < v_1 < c$ and $v_2 > c$, the speed v of the tachyon relative to the ground is also greater than c. (2) Repeat the proof for a tachyon flying to the left: If $0 < v_1 < c$ and $v_2 < -c$, then $v < -c$. This means that a tachyon in one frame is a tachyon in any other frame provided that the relative speed of the two frames is less than c.

P20.13 In Figure 20.14, rocket ship 2, with coordinates x'', t'', moves at speed v_2 relative to rocket ship 1, with coordinates x', t'. Rocket ship 1, in turn, moves at speed v_1 relative to an Earth-fixed frame with coordinates x, t. The following Lorentz transformation equations relate measurements in these frames of reference:

Successive Lorentz transformations

$$c\,\Delta t'' = \frac{c\,\Delta t' - \beta_2\,\Delta x'}{\sqrt{1 - \beta_2{}^2}}, \qquad \Delta x'' = \frac{\Delta x' - \beta_2 c\,\Delta t'}{\sqrt{1 - \beta_2{}^2}},$$

$$c\,\Delta t' = \frac{c\,\Delta t - \beta_1\,\Delta x}{\sqrt{1 - \beta_1{}^2}}, \qquad \Delta x' = \frac{\Delta x - \beta_1 c\,\Delta t}{\sqrt{1 - \beta_1{}^2}},$$

Eliminate $\Delta t'$ and $\Delta x'$ from these equations in order to express $\Delta t''$ and $\Delta x''$ in terms of Δt and Δx. Show that the resulting equations are equivalent to a single Lorentz transformation to a frame of reference moving at a speed given by Equation 20.40. Although the algebra is complicated, the result is important, for it shows that two successive Lorentz transformations can be replaced by a single Lorentz transformation, and it yields the relativistic law of addition of velocities.

P20.14 Brakes can be applied individually to the wheels of a relativistic railroad train. The wheels are spaced equally along the length of the train. (1) Braking method 1: The brakes are applied simultaneously in the train's frame of reference. What do ground-based observers say about the timing of the activation of the brakes? (2) Braking method 2: The brakes are applied simultaneously in the ground-based frame. What do the train crew members say about the timing of the activation of the brakes? (3) Suppose that each brake exerts an essentially infinite force and brings the part of the train on which it acts instantaneously to rest. Which, if either, of the above methods of braking causes the train to be (a) crushed to less than its normal length? (b) pulled apart to more than its normal length? (c) stopped at its normal length?

Braking a relativistic train

P20.15 When the locomotive of the train pictured in Figure 20.10 reaches the far end of the tunnel (point B), the locomotive is suddenly stopped. At the same instant, the engineer sends a distress signal by radio. As the signal passes each part of the train, that part is also suddenly stopped. (1) Show that when the entire train is finally stopped, it is compressed to a length of only 100 m (and thus occupies only 40 percent of the length of the tunnel). (2) Draw world lines for the locomotive L and observation car O in a ground-based x-ct diagram, including times before L stops and after O stops. Shade the region between these world lines in order to indicate the bundle of world lines that represents the train as a whole.

Speed of a particle in an accelerator

P20.16 A particle moving at speed v in an accelerator experiences a momentary force and acquires an infinitesimal increment of speed dv. In a frame of reference moving at speed v, the added speed is greater; it is dv_0. (1) Using the velocity-addition formula (with appropriate approximations for small dv and dv_0), show that

$$dv_0 = \frac{dv}{1 - (v^2/c^2)}.$$

(2) Starting from rest, a particle is accelerated to speed v_f. If a classical law of velocity addition were valid, its final speed would be v_{cl}. Integrate both sides of the above equation in order to obtain the result

$$\frac{v_f}{c} = \frac{e^{2v_{cl}/c} - 1}{e^{2v_{cl}/c} + 1} = \tanh\left(\frac{v_{cl}}{c}\right).$$

Discuss this result in the limits $v_{cl} \ll c$ and $v_{cl} \gg c$.

Brehme diagram

P20.17 The figure shows a version of a spacetime diagram known as a Brehme diagram. To form the diagram, think of starting with a pair of perpendicular axes (the dashed lines). First swing each of these axes inward through an angle $\frac{1}{2}\alpha$ to form the x and ct axes; then swing each of these axes outward through an angle $\frac{1}{2}\alpha$ to form the x' and ct' axes. The angle α is defined by $\alpha = \arcsin(v/c)$. An event is represented by a point such as E. Its space and time coordinates in the two frames of reference are found by dropping perpendiculars (the dotted lines) to the four axes. Prove from the geometry of the diagram that x and t are related to x' and t' by a Lorentz transformation (Equations 20.24 and 20.25 or 20.30 and 20.31). This diagram makes the special assumption that $x = x' = 0$ when $t = t' = 0$.

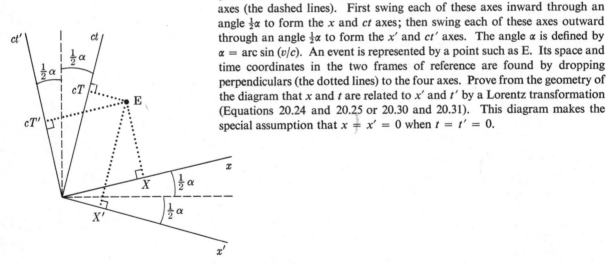

P20.18 The Brehme diagram is defined in the preceding problem. (1) In such a diagram, show the world lines of clock 1 fixed at the origin of the unprimed system and clock 2 fixed at the origin of the primed system. (2) From a simple geometric construction, derive the time-dilation formula. Point out how the reciprocity of time dilation is reflected in the diagram. (3) From another simple geometric construction in the Brehme diagram, derive the Lorentz-contraction formula. [For applications of the Brehme diagram, see F. W.

Sears and R. W. Brehme, *Introduction to the Theory of Relativity* (Reading, Massachusetts: Addison-Wesley Publishing Co., 1968) and John S. Rigden, *American Journal of Physics* **40**, 1831 (1972).]

P20.19 Figure 20.21(b) gives the world lines of Anton and Bertram for the case in which Anton waits for time T and then catches up with Bertram at speed $2v$ while Bertram continues at speed v. Prove that Anton is younger when they meet by proving that the ratio of their proper times, $\Delta\tau_B/\Delta\tau_A$, given by Equation 20.66, is greater than 1. (HINT: If you can prove that a function is monotonic, you can establish a limiting magnitude for it by evaluating it at one end of its range.)

Twin paradox

P20.20 In both of the cases illustrated in Figure 20.20, David rides on the train moving to the right (in the first case he remains on that train after Bertram leaves it). For each of these cases, sketch a Minkowski diagram with world lines of Anton and Bertram as seen in *David's* frame of reference. For each case, give a careful *qualitative* discussion of the aging of the twins from David's perspective.

P20.21 A particle moves with constant velocity from its point of creation to its point of decay. Prove that there is no frame of reference in which the elapsed time between these events is less than the proper time. For what frame is the elapsed time *equal* to the proper time?

Extremal character of proper time

P20.22 The figure shows a parallel-plate capacitor bearing charges q and $-q$ on its plates. In the rest frame of the capacitor, its plates are squares of side L separated by distance d, and the electric field between the plates has magnitude E. Charge is a scalar quantity (the same for all observers in inertial frames). (1) Ursula moves horizontally (parallel to E) and measures an electric field $\mathbf{E}'$ between the plates. (a) Show that $\mathbf{E}' = \mathbf{E}$. (b) Name one quantity that is *not* the same in Ursula's frame and in the rest frame. (2) Victor moves upward (perpendicular to E) and measures an electric field $\mathbf{E}''$ between the plates. (a) Show that $E'' = E/\sqrt{1 - (v^2/c^2)}$. (b) Name one quantity other than electric field that is not the same in Victor's frame and in the rest frame. (3) Using the shaded box in the figure as a Gaussian surface, prove that Gauss's law is valid in the frames of reference of both Ursula and Victor.

Lorentz invariance of Gauss's law

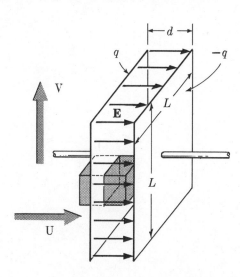

Electric field of a moving charged particle

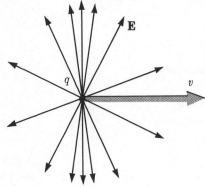

P20.23   (This problem should be attempted only after completing the preceding problem.) A charged particle moves at high speed v through the laboratory. In the rest frame of the particle, the electric field is a standard Coulomb field: it is directed radially and its magnitude is

$$E' = \frac{1}{4\pi\epsilon_0} \frac{q}{r'^2}.$$

In the laboratory frame, the field has the appearance shown in the figure; it is directed radially and its magnitude is

$$E = \frac{1}{4\pi\epsilon_0} \frac{q}{r^2} \frac{1 - \beta^2}{(1 - \beta^2 \sin^2 \theta)^{3/2}},$$

where θ is the angle between the velocity vector and a radial line. Using the results of the preceding problem and the transformation properties of length scales, verify the correctness of this formula for E in two special cases: (1) $\theta = 0$ and (2) $\theta = \frac{1}{2}\pi$. (NOTE: The laboratory frame in the preceding problem corresponds to the particle's rest frame in this problem.)

21

Relativistic Energy and Momentum

Underlying the work in Chapter 20 was Einstein's second postulate, the constancy of the speed of light. To this we must now add his first postulate, the Principle of Relativity, in order to find out what the theory of relativity has to say about mass, momentum, and energy. Rather than attempting a superficial survey of the whole of relativistic mechanics, we shall concentrate on these few concepts and their conservation (energy and momentum) or lack of it (mass).

21.1 Energy

In this section we encounter relativity's most famous formula, $E = mc^2$. From the contemporary point of view, it is easiest to say that the equivalence of mass and energy is an experimental fact. Numerous experiments have demonstrated that mass is convertible to energy, and energy to mass, and that the conversion factor between the two is the square of the speed of light. However, it is of interest to see how the mass-energy equivalence can be deduced directly from the postulates of relativity. Recall that Einstein established this link long before there was any experimental evidence for it.

DERIVATION OF $E = mc^2$

In his first paper on mass and energy, Einstein based his argument on a thought experiment in which an object at rest in the laboratory emits oppositely directed light waves of equal energy [Figure 21.1(a)]. To modernize and simplify his treatment without losing its essence, we consider instead the decay of a neutral pion into two oppositely directed gamma rays of equal energy [Figure 21.1(b)].

In the laboratory frame, let us call the energy given up by the pion E_0 and the energies of the two resulting gamma rays E_1 and E_2. According to the

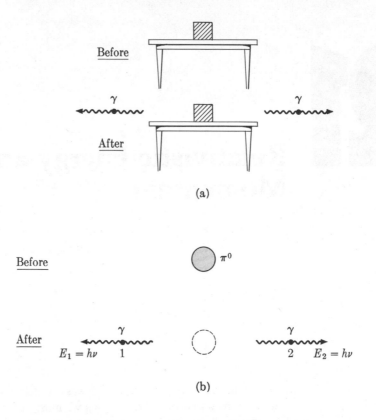

FIGURE 21.1   (a) Einstein's original thought experiment. A massive object emits two equal pulses of light in opposite directions. (b) A modernized version of the same experiment. A pion, at rest in the laboratory, decays into two photons of equal energy.

given conditions, $E_1 = E_2$. The law of energy conservation can therefore be written

$$E_1 + E_2 = 2E_1 = E_0. \tag{21.1}$$

For a photon, energy is proportional to frequency. If we let v represent the frequency of either of the photons in the laboratory frame, we can write

$$E_1 = E_2 = hv, \tag{21.2}$$

Energy conservation in laboratory frame of reference

$$E_0 = 2hv. \tag{21.3}$$

These equations are, by themselves, not very interesting because they do not relate E_0 to any property of the pion. To gain new insight, we must examine the same decay event from the point of view of an observer moving through the laboratory with speed v.

To be definite, let this observer be moving to the left. In his frame of reference, the pion is moving to the right with speed v before its decay (Figure 21.2). After its decay, photon 1 with energy E_1' and frequency v_1' flies off to the left; photon 2 with energy E_2' and frequency v_2' flies off to the right. The

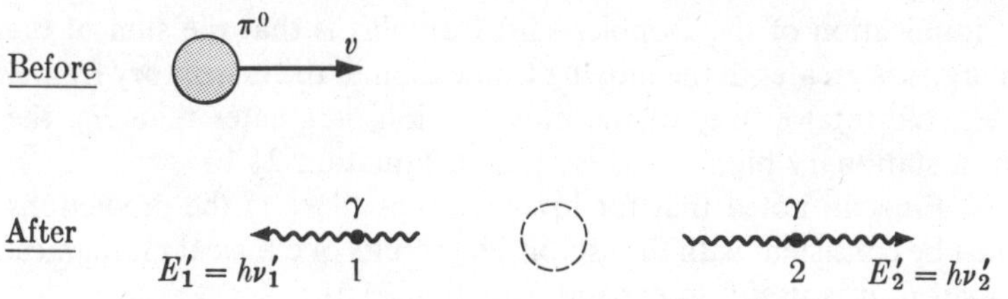

Before

After

$\overset{\gamma}{\sim\!\!\!\!\bullet\!\!\!\!\sim}$ 1   2 $\overset{\gamma}{\sim\!\!\!\!\bullet\!\!\!\!\sim}$

$E_1' = h\nu_1'$ $E_2' = h\nu_2'$

FIGURE 21.2 Pion decay in moving frame of reference. The photon energies are Doppler-shifted.

Doppler-shift formulas, Equations 20.47 and 20.50, relate the frequencies ν_1' and ν_2' to the frequency ν of the photon in the laboratory frame:

$$\nu_1' = \nu\,\frac{1-\beta}{\sqrt{1-\beta^2}}, \qquad (21.4)$$

Photon frequencies in moving frame

$$\nu_2' = \nu\,\frac{1+\beta}{\sqrt{1-\beta^2}}, \qquad (21.5)$$

where $\beta = \nu/c$. The frequency ν_1' is less than ν (a red shift); the frequency ν_2' is greater than ν (a blue shift). It is through these two equations that the properties of spacetime enter the discussion. The invariance of physical laws enters in two ways. First, we assume the energy-frequency relation for photons to be valid in all inertial frames, with h as a universal constant. This means that the photon energies in the moving frame are*

Doppler shift rests on Einstein's second postulate ($c = $ constant)

$$E_1' = h\nu_1', \qquad (21.6)$$

$$E_2' = h\nu_2'. \qquad (21.7)$$

Second, we assume the law of energy conservation to be valid in both frames of reference. In the moving frame, the law reads

Energy equations rest on Einstein's first postulate (invariance)

$$E_\pi = E_1' + E_2', \qquad (21.8)$$

where we use E_π to designate the total energy of the moving pion—the same as the energy it releases since it ceases to exist. With the help of Equations 21.6 and 21.7, the energy conservation equation in the moving frame reads

$$E_\pi = h\cdot(\nu_1' + \nu_2').$$

Substituting from Equations 21.4 and 21.5 gives

$$E_\pi = \frac{2h\nu}{\sqrt{1-\beta^2}}. \qquad (21.9)$$

Finally, because of Equation 21.3,

$$E_\pi = \frac{E_0}{\sqrt{1-\beta^2}}. \qquad (21.10)$$

Energy of moving pion

---

*Einstein did not use the relation $E = h\nu$ in his original work on mass and energy. However, he used the fact that electromagnetic wave energy is Doppler shifted in exactly the same manner as frequency, a result that was known before the photon was proposed.

An important implication of the Doppler-shift formulas is that the sum of the two photon energies is greater in the moving frame than in the laboratory frame. Accordingly, E_π, the total energy of the moving pion, is greater than E_0, the total energy of a stationary pion. This is clear in Equation 21.10.

To find E_0, Einstein noted that for low velocities ($\beta \ll 1$) the predictions of relativity must be consistent with the established results of classical mechanics. To consider small β, it is useful to expand Equation 21.10:

$$E_\pi = E_0[1 + \tfrac{1}{2}\beta^2 + \tfrac{3}{8}\beta^4 + \cdots]. \tag{21.11}$$

For $\beta = 0$, $E_\pi = E_0$, which is a consistency check on the work, but provides no new information. For β small but not zero, terms proportional to β^4, β^6, etc., are negligible compared with the term proportional to β^2, so it is a good approximation to write

Low-speed approximation

$$E_\pi \cong E_0 + \frac{1}{2}\frac{E_0}{c^2}v^2. \tag{21.12}$$

The second term on the right side can be identified as the nonrelativistic kinetic energy if E_0/c^2 is set equal to m, the mass of the pion. Indeed, it must be so identified if classical mechanics is to be correct at speeds much less than the speed of light. Therefore,

$$E_0 = mc^2. \tag{21.13}$$

Note that this is an exact result, not an approximate result, since the term $\tfrac{1}{2}(E_0/c^2)v^2$ in Equation 21.12 must be precisely equal to $\tfrac{1}{2}mv^2$ in the limit of small v. The constant term on the right side of Equation 21.12 is not predicted by classical mechanics. However, it is perfectly acceptable since in classical mechanics any constant may be added to energy. One of the significant aspects

Zero of energy is meaningful

of Equation 21.13 is that it establishes an absolute energy, removing the classical arbitrariness of the zero of energy.

In order to generalize these results to any particles or material objects, we drop subscripts in Equations 21.10 and 21.13, and write

$$E = mc^2 \quad \text{(stationary particle),} \tag{21.14}$$

Total energy of an object

$$E = \frac{mc^2}{\sqrt{1 - \beta^2}} \quad \text{(moving particle).} \tag{21.15}$$

In the example just discussed, the speed v was both the relative speed of the two frames of reference *and* the speed of the pion in one frame. Therefore, in Equation 21.15, β may be taken to refer to the speed of the particle in any chosen frame of reference. What these extraordinarily important equations tell us is that a particle at rest has an intrinsic energy, an "energy of being," equal to mc^2. In motion, its energy is greater; it is mc^2 divided by the ubiquitous factor $\sqrt{1 - \beta^2}$. The quantity m is the rest mass of the particle. Since in this text we use no other kind of mass, we usually call it simply the mass. It is an invariant constant for a given particle, independent of the speed of the particle, and must not be confused with the "relativistic mass" or "dynamic mass" used by some authors.*

■ EXAMPLE 1: A neutral pion, with a rest energy of 135 MeV, is moving through a laboratory at 60 percent of the speed of light. If it decays in the manner shown in Figure 21.2, what are the energies of the two photons that are emitted? By what factor does the pion's total energy exceed its rest energy? Using Equation 21.4 to, substitute for v_1' in Equation 21.6 gives

$$E_1' = h\nu \frac{1 - \beta}{\sqrt{1 - \beta^2}} = h\nu \sqrt{\frac{1 - \beta}{1 + \beta}}. \tag{21.16}$$

From Equation 21.3, $h\nu = 67.5$ MeV. Using this value together with $\beta = 0.6$, we find

$$E_1' = (67.5 \text{ MeV}) \sqrt{\frac{0.4}{1.6}} = 33.75 \text{ MeV}.$$

In a similar way, Equations 21.5 and 21.7 give

$$E_2' = h\nu \frac{1 + \beta}{\sqrt{1 - \beta^2}} = h\nu \sqrt{\frac{1 + \beta}{1 - \beta}}. \tag{21.17}$$

In this example,

$$E_2' = 2 \times 67.5 \text{ MeV} = 135 \text{ MeV}.$$

The sum of these two energies is 168.75 MeV, which agrees, as it must, with the total pion energy calculated from Equation 21.15:

$$E = \frac{135 \text{ MeV}}{\sqrt{1 - (0.6)^2}} = \frac{135 \text{ MeV}}{0.8} = 168.75 \text{ MeV}.$$

Even at its very great speed of 1.8×10^8 m/sec, the pion has a total energy only 25 percent greater than its rest energy:

$$\frac{E}{mc^2} = 1.25.$$

This is a reminder of the enormous energy of matter locked up in its mass.   ■

MASS-ENERGY CONVERSION

Mass changes less drastic than that of pion decay often occur. When they do, Equation 21.14 implies that energy change and mass change in the rest frame are related by

$$\Delta E = \Delta m \, c^2. \tag{21.18}$$

---

* The relativistic mass m_r is defined by $m_r = m/\sqrt{1 - \beta^2}$. In terms of this concept, Equation 21.15 takes the form $E = m_r c^2$. Because of its invariance, m is a more significant quantity than the variable mass m_r.

Einstein cannot be faulted for lack of boldness. Yet, in 1905 not even he was prepared to suggest the total conversion of mass to energy. More cautiously, he suggested that mass changes accompanying radioactive transformations might be large enough to measure. Finally, in 1932, Equation 21.18 was verified in a nuclear reaction. In the same year, the discovery of the positron opened the way to observation of the complete annihilation of matter.

■ EXAMPLE 2:   Nuclear physics has provided extensive experimental support for the mass-energy equivalence. A good example is afforded by the deuteron, the nucleus of "heavy hydrogen" (^2_1H), composed of one neutron and one proton. As the following numbers show, the mass of the deuteron is not equal to the sum of the masses of its constituents (the mass unit is the amu, defined in Section 13.3):

$m_d < m_p + m_n$

Mass of proton	= 1.00728
Mass of neutron	= 1.00866
Mass of proton + mass of neutron	= 2.01594
Mass of deuteron	= 2.01355
Difference between mass of system and mass of its parts	= 0.00239

This difference, amounting to about one part in a thousand of the deuteron mass, means that an energy change must accompany the transformation of a deuteron into a proton and a neutron. A simple calculation shows the energy equivalent of 0.00239 amu to be 2.23 MeV, and experiment verifies that this much energy must be added to a deuteron to separate it into its components.

Concept of binding energy   This is called the binding energy of the deuteron.   ■

■ EXAMPLE 3:   When 2 moles of hydrogen and 1 mole of oxygen unite to form 2 moles of water vapor ($2H_2 + O_2 \rightarrow 2H_2O$), the energy released is 115.6 kcal. By how much does the mass of the material decrease in this chemical reaction? Including the mechanical equivalent of heat as a conversion factor, we obtain, from Equation 21.18,

$$\Delta m = \frac{\Delta E}{c^2} = -\frac{115.6 \text{ kcal} \times 4{,}184 \text{ J/kcal}}{(3 \times 10^8 \text{ m/sec})^2}$$

$$= -5.37 \times 10^{-12} \text{ kg.}$$

Mass = constant, an adequate   This change of mass, about 1 part in 10^{10}, is below the threshold of measurability.
approximation for chemistry   Therefore mass conservation is a reliable law in chemical change.   ■

KINETIC ENERGY

Kinetic energy is, by definition, energy of motion, or the difference in the energy of a particle when moving and its energy when at rest. It is

Definition of kinetic energy
$$K = \frac{mc^2}{\sqrt{1 - \beta^2}} - mc^2 \quad \text{(relativistic).} \quad (21.19)$$

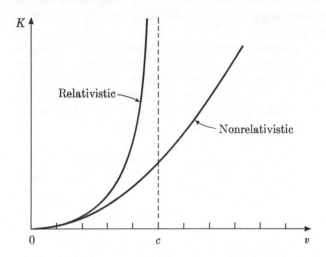

FIGURE 21.3   Graphs of kinetic energy vs speed according to the relativistic definition, Equation 21.19, and the nonrelativistic definition, Equation 21.20. The nonrelativistic curve is a parabola. The relativistic curve approximates a parabola at low speed, but curves more rapidly upward to approach infinity at the speed-of-light barrier.

At first glance this bears no resemblance to the classical definition of kinetic energy, but from the expansion in powers of β^2 discussed above (Equation 21.11), we know that for small β it does, in fact, reduce to

$$K = \tfrac{1}{2}mv^2 \qquad \text{(nonrelativistic).} \tag{21.20}$$

It is in the realm of high-speed motion that the relativistic kinetic energy diverges completely from the Newtonian formula. This divergence is illustrated in Figure 21.3. At the "speed-of-light barrier" the energy of a material particle approaches infinity. No input of energy, however great, can push the speed past the speed of light. In this domain, with v near c, all similarity between Newtonian mechanics and the facts of nature disappears.

■ EXAMPLE 4: By how much does the actual kinetic energy of the pion considered in Example 1 differ from the kinetic energy calculated nonrelativistically? Its true kinetic energy is

$$K = 168.75 \text{ MeV} - 135 \text{ MeV} = 33.75 \text{ MeV.}$$

The nonrelativistic formula for K may be written $K = \tfrac{1}{2}mc^2(v/c)^2$. This gives

$$K(\text{nonrelativistic}) = \tfrac{1}{2}(135 \text{ MeV})(0.6)^2$$

$$= 24.3 \text{ MeV.}$$

As indicated in Figure 21.3, the nonrelativistic formula underestimates the kinetic energy.   ■

No concept of physics has weathered more winds of change than the concept of energy. And from every storm it has emerged stronger and broader, with its branches now extending into every field of physical and biological science. First potential energy was added to work and to kinetic energy. Then came electrical energy, chemical energy, heat energy, electromagnetic energy, and nuclear energy. To the list of the manifold forms of energy the theory of relativity added mass, the most fundamental form, other than kinetic energy, because at the deepest level every energy is manifested as either energy of motion or energy of being.

The speed of light, which appeared as the link between the unit of distance and the unit of time, appears again (or rather its square appears) as the link between mass and energy. In the equation $E = mc^2$ the factor c^2 is not fundamentally important (of course, this is not to say that it can be omitted!). The essential physical idea is the proportionality of energy to mass. The constant c^2 is merely a conversion factor to align the discrepant units of mass and energy: $c^2 = 9 \times 10^{16}$ J/kg. Because this number is, by macroscopic standards, a very large number, ordinary changes of energy produce negligibly small changes of mass (see Example 3 in this section). For this reason alone, the mass-energy equivalence escaped man's notice until this century.

21.2   Momentum

The relativistic definition of momentum may be derived from analysis of the same pion decay experiment considered in the previous section,

$$\pi^0 \to \gamma + \gamma$$

(see Figures 21.1 and 21.2). We need add only one more fact about electromagnetic waves, the relation between their energy and momentum:

$$E = pc. \tag{21.21}$$

Well before the theory of relativity was developed, it was known that electromagnetic radiation carried momentum as well as energy and that these two quantities were simply related by Equation 21.21. This relation remains valid for photons. Hence the momentum of a single photon is

$$p = \frac{h\nu}{c}. \tag{21.22}$$

In the laboratory frame of reference (Figure 21.1), the momentum is conserved: It is zero both before and after the decay. We need not know the relativistic definition of momentum to reach this conclusion. At low speed, the classical definition, $p = mv$, must be valid. In particular, therefore, $\mathbf{p} = 0$ if $\mathbf{v} = 0$; the initially motionless pion has no momentum. After the decay, the two photons of equal energy have equal and opposite momentum, $\mathbf{p}_1 = -\mathbf{p}_2$. The sum is zero.

In the moving frame of reference (Figure 21.2), we may work with magnitudes since all momenta are directed along the same straight line. The conservation of momentum in this frame implies

$$p_\pi = p_2' - p_1', \tag{21.23}$$

where p_π is the momentum of the moving pion, and p_1' and p_2' are the momenta of the two photons. With the help of Equation 21.22, Equation 21.23 becomes

$$p_\pi = \frac{h}{c}(\nu_2' - \nu_1').$$

From the Doppler-shift formulas, Equations 21.4 and 21.5, we get

$$v_2' - v_1' = \frac{2v\beta}{\sqrt{1 - \beta^2}}.$$

The pion momentum may, therefore, be written

$$p_\pi = \frac{2hv}{c^2}\frac{v}{\sqrt{1 - \beta^2}}. \tag{21.24}$$

In these equations, v is the frequency of either photon in the laboratory frame of reference. From Equations 21.3 and 21.13, we may conclude that the combination $2hv/c^2$ is m, the mass of the pion. (This could also be concluded from the requirement that the right side of Equation 21.24 approach mv when v is much less than c.) The final result for the momentum of a particle of mass m is (we now drop the subscript π)

$$p = \frac{mv}{\sqrt{1 - \beta^2}}. \tag{21.25}$$

This defines the magnitude of momentum. As a vector quantity, it is   *Momentum of a particle*

$$\mathbf{p} = \frac{m\mathbf{v}}{\sqrt{1 - \beta^2}}. \tag{21.26}$$

We re-emphasize that m is the rest mass of the particle, an invariant constant.

Since the denominator in Equation 21.26 is always less than 1, the magnitude of the relativistic momentum is always greater than the product mv: it is only slightly greater at low speed but very much greater as the speed nears the speed of light. This behavior of the relativistic momentum is illustrated in Figure 21.4. Appearing there is the same "speed-of-light barrier" preventing motion at   *Again a speed-of-light barrier* speeds greater than the speed of light. No matter how much momentum a particle acquires, its speed can never quite reach the limiting speed c (unless its mass is zero, a special case that will be discussed in the next section).

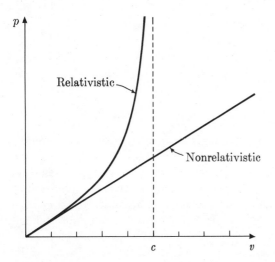

FIGURE 21.4   Graphs of the magnitude of momentum of a particle according to the relativistic definition, Equation 21.25, and according to the nonrelativistic definition, $p = mv$.

In this section and the last, we have used *known* properties of electromagnetic waves and photons in order to arrive at formulas for the unknowns: the energy and momentum of a material particle. In the logic of this development, the inclusion of both mechanical and electromagnetic quantities in the conservation laws is crucial. There are other ways to deduce the relativistic formulas for energy and momentum, in which this interplay between mechanics and electromagnetism is less evident, but it is still present in the background because the properties of light determine the nature of the Lorentz transformation. Another aspect of the logic requires comment. Equations 21.15 and 21.26 are *definitions* of E and **p**. As such, why are they not arbitrary? Because energy and momentum are conserved quantities. *Only* with these definitions do we have invariant conservation laws of energy and momentum.

*E and **p** are defined (1) to match classical mechanics at small v and (2) to be conserved in all frames*

■ EXAMPLE: What is the expression for the energy of a particle as a function of its momentum? To find out, we need only eliminate the speed v between Equations 21.15 and 21.25. If Equation 21.25 is written $p = mc\beta/\sqrt{1 - \beta^2}$, it may be solved for β. The result is

$$\beta = \frac{p}{\sqrt{p^2 + m^2c^2}}.$$

From this it follows that

$$\sqrt{1 - \beta^2} = \frac{mc}{\sqrt{p^2 + m^2c^2}}.$$

Substituting this expression for $\sqrt{1 - \beta^2}$ in Equation 21.15 leads to

Energy as a function of momentum

$$E = \sqrt{m^2c^4 + p^2c^2}. \tag{21.27}$$

For $p = 0$, this formula reduces to $E = mc^2$, as it should. Let us consider its approximate form for small p. Then

$$E = mc^2\sqrt{1 + \frac{p^2}{m^2c^2}} \cong mc^2\left(1 + \frac{1}{2}\frac{p^2}{m^2c^2}\right)$$

$$\cong mc^2 + \frac{p^2}{2m} \quad (p \ll mc). \tag{21.28}$$

The right side is the rest energy plus the nonrelativistic kinetic energy.   ■

21.3   Massless particles

In classical mechanics, a particle without mass has neither energy nor momentum, nor any other measurable characteristic. It is nothing. This is not the case in relativity theory; a measurable physical entity can exist without mass. As pointed out at the end of Chapter 20, there is no reason known why massless particles *must* exist, yet several are known in nature. There is excellent experimental evidence that the photon and the electron's neutrino are totally lacking in rest mass.

Consider what happens to Equations 21.15 and 21.25 if the mass m is

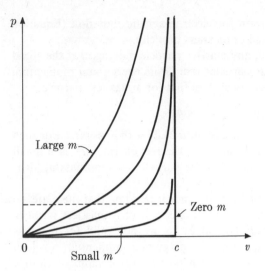

FIGURE 21.5   Momentum graphs depend on particle mass. For a given momentum, as indicated by the horizontal dashed line, less mass means more speed. Massless particles, regardless of their momentum, move at the maximum speed c.

allowed to approach zero. The numerator of both expressions approaches zero. The denominator too may be allowed to approach zero ($\beta \rightarrow 1$) in such a way that energy and momentum remain finite. To think of this limiting process in more physical terms, imagine a set of particles 1, 2, 3, . . . of successively smaller mass ($m_1 > m_2 > m_3 \ldots$). We may accelerate each of these particles until it has a predetermined fixed energy. The speed required to achieve this energy is determined by

$$\sqrt{1 - \frac{v^2}{c^2}} = \frac{mc^2}{E}$$

As $m \rightarrow 0$, $v \rightarrow c$

for each particle. For the successively smaller masses, the speeds get closer and closer to the speed of light. It is then consistent to postulate the existence of a particle of finite E, with $m = 0$ and $v = c$. Further insight into this limiting process is afforded by the momentum vs speed graphs of Figure 21.5. A particle with very little mass need acquire only a small momentum in order to move near the speed of light. Thereafter, further increases in its momentum increase its speed only slightly as it strains toward the limiting speed. For a massless particle, the momentum "curve" becomes the backward-L indicated by the heavy lines in Figure 21.5.

For m exactly zero, the right sides of Equations 21.15 and 21.25 become mathematically undetermined (0/0). However, the ratio of the two expressions remains well defined in the limit:

$$\frac{E}{p} = \frac{c^2}{v} .$$

(21.29)

E-p relationship for any particle

This equation is valid both for finite mass and for zero mass. For massless particles, with $v = c$, it simplifies to

$$E = pc,$$

(21.30)

Exact equation for massless particle

the relation that was already known for electromagnetic radiation (Equation 21.21) before anyone had conceived of massless particles.

According to Equation 21.29, any massive particle moving near the speed of light behaves "like" a massless particle; that is, its energy and momentum satisfy approximately the same relationship as that for a massless particle:

Approximate equation for
superrelativistic particle

$$E \cong pc \qquad (E \gg mc^2). \qquad (21.31)$$

(The same approximation follows from Equation 21.27 with $p \gg mc$.) For such a particle, which we may call superrelativistic, the rest energy mc^2 is a small fraction of the total energy. The fact that the particle has any mass at all is then unimportant.

Often, the beginning student of relativity finds it puzzling that there are no separate formulas defining the energy and momentum of a massless particle. He wants to ask, "If Equations 21.15 and 21.26 are not valid for massless particles, what *are* the defining equations of energy and momentum for such particles?" There are none. As Figure 21.5 makes clear, the momentum of a photon is not a function of its speed. Its speed is fixed at one value; its momentum may have any value. The *only* general equation governing the energy and momentum of a massless particle is the relation between the two, $E = pc$. Operationally, we measure the momentum of a photon not by measuring its speed but by measuring changes of momentum that accompany its emission and absorption. To give an example: If a kink in a bubble chamber track indicates that a charged particle has lost energy and changed its momentum and if these changes are related by $\Delta E = \Delta p\, c$, an experimenter may infer that a massless particle was emitted at that point. This interpretation might be confirmed by the appearance, elsewhere in the chamber, of an electron-positron pair whose total energy and momentum match the energy and momentum lost by the first particle. (See Figure 3.1(b), in which two photons are revealed in this way.)

No functions E(v) or p(v) if
m = 0

21.4   An example of particle decay

To apply the relativistic definitions of energy and momentum, and test their consistency with the velocity-addition formula, we consider a particular example, the decay of a neutral kaon into two pions, indicated by

$$K^0 \rightarrow \pi^+ + \pi^-.$$

Call the mass of the kaon M and the mass of each pion m. In the laboratory frame, where the kaon is at rest (Figure 21.6), the total momentum is zero; the pions therefore fly apart with equal speed v. In this frame, the initial energy is Mc^2, and the final energy of each pion is (with $\beta = v/c$)

$$E_\pi = \frac{mc^2}{\sqrt{1 - \beta^2}}.$$

Energy conservation requires the equality of energies before and after the decay:

Energy conservation in
laboratory frame

$$Mc^2 = \frac{2mc^2}{\sqrt{1 - \beta^2}}. \qquad (21.32)$$

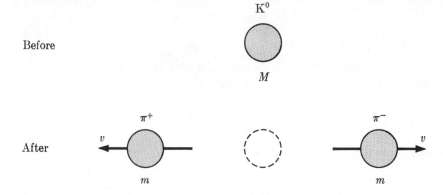

FIGURE 21.6   Decay of stationary kaon in the laboratory frame. The total momentum is zero. The product pions are of equal energy.

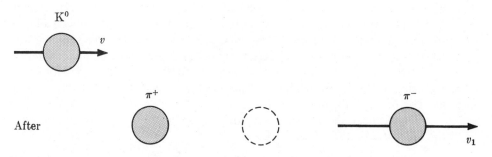

FIGURE 21.7   Kaon decay in moving frame of reference. In this frame, the positive pion is at rest. Momentum conservation requires that the initial momentum of the kaon be equal to the final momentum of the negative pion.

Now let us examine the same decay process in a frame of reference moving to the left at speed v. In this frame (Figure 21.7), the kaon before its decay moves to the right with speed v and possesses momentum

$$p'_K = \frac{Mv}{\sqrt{1 - \beta^2}}.$$

After the decay, the pion that moved leftward in the laboratory frame is at rest in the moving frame so that all of the initial momentum of the kaon in this frame must be acquired by the right-going pion. Its speed is v_1 (*not* twice v), and its momentum is

$$p'_\pi = \frac{mv_1}{\sqrt{1 - \beta_1^{\ 2}}},$$

where $\beta_1 = v_1/c$. The conservation of momentum in this frame can be written

Momentum conservation in
moving frame

$$\frac{Mv}{\sqrt{1 - \beta^2}} = \frac{mv_1}{\sqrt{1 - \beta_1{}^2}}.$$ (21.33)

From the two conservation laws, as expressed by Equations 21.32 and 21.33, we can solve for v_1 in terms of v. For instance, from Equation 21.32, write

$$M = \frac{2m}{\sqrt{1 - \beta^2}},$$

and substitute this in Equation 21.33, obtaining

$$\frac{2mv}{1 - \beta^2} = \frac{mv_1}{\sqrt{1 - \beta_1{}^2}}.$$

The factors m cancel on the two sides, and the algebraic solution for v_1 (left as an exercise) is

Velocity-addition formula is
derived

$$v_1 = \frac{2v}{1 + (v^2/c^2)}.$$ (21.34)

This is exactly what would have been predicted by the velocity-addition formula of Chapter 20. The speed v_1 is the relativistic "sum" of v (the speed of the right-going pion with respect to the laboratory) plus v again (the speed of the laboratory with respect to the observer). So we reveal the mutual consistency of (a) the relativistic definition of energy, (b) the relativistic definition of momentum, and (c) the relativistic equation for the addition of velocity. From any two of these, the third may be derived.

To complete the example numerically, we need only one input number, the ratio $M/2m$. From Table 3.1 it is

$$\frac{M}{2m} = \frac{497.8}{2 \times 139.6} = 1.783.$$

Equation 21.32 gives $\beta = 0.828$ ($v = 2.48 \times 10^8$ m/sec), and Equation 21.34 gives $\beta_1 = 0.982$ ($v_1 = 2.95 \times 10^8$ m/sec). Relativity is clearly very important even though the decay particles are not energetic enough to be superrelativistic.

21.5   Four-vectors

In Chapter 20, the invariance of the interval and the mixing together of space and time in the Lorentz transformation led us to introduce the idea of a four-dimensional spacetime, filled with world lines and events. Each event is a point in spacetime located by three space coordinates and one time coordinate, and any pair of events is separated by a spacetime "distance," the interval. With this image of spacetime, we may quite naturally think of the four coordinates locating an event as being the four components of a single vector, which, to avoid confusion with old-fashioned three-dimensional vectors, we shall call a four-vector. This spacetime four-vector is a generalization of the idea of a *"Position" vector in spacetime* position vector in ordinary space. Rather than locating a point in space, it locates an event in spacetime. Its components are ct, x, y, and z, and the square of its "length" is $(ct)^2 - x^2 - y^2 - z^2$. The length of the four-vector is a constant for all observers because it is the interval under a new name.

THE MOMENTUM-ENERGY FOUR-VECTOR

In Newtonian mechanics, several different vector quantities appeared: position, velocity, acceleration, momentum, force. We have been able to extend the idea of the position vector to the four-dimensional world by appending ct to it as a fourth component. This extension has several technical advantages in the theory of relativity, the most important of which, for our present purpose, is that the "length" of the four-vector is an invariant quantity, whereas the ordinary three-dimensional length is not invariant but depends on the state of motion of the observer. This process of generalizing vectors from three to four dimensions can be carried out not only for the position vector but for all of the vectors of mechanics, and some unexpected and interesting partnerships turn up. Next in interest to the joining together of space and time is the union of energy and momentum.

Momentum, because it is a three-dimensional vector, may be expressed in component form:

$$p_x = \frac{mv_x}{\sqrt{1 - (v^2/c^2)}}, \tag{21.35}$$

$$p_y = \frac{mv_y}{\sqrt{1 - (v^2/c^2)}}, \tag{21.36}$$

$$p_z = \frac{mv_z}{\sqrt{1 - (v^2/c^2)}}. \tag{21.37}$$

Note, in these equations, that individual components of v appear in each numerator, whereas the total speed v appears in each denominator. Since space has acquired a fourth dimension—time—momentum needs a fourth component, or "time component." It is easy to guess what the form of this fourth component should be. Since

$$p_x = \frac{m(dx/dt)}{\sqrt{1 - (v^2/c^2)}}$$

and since p_y and p_z are similarly proportional to dy/dt and dz/dt, for the time component we may postulate

$$p_t = \frac{m[d(ct)/dt]}{\sqrt{1 - (v^2/c^2)}}.$$

This reduces to

$$p_t = \frac{mc}{\sqrt{1 - (v^2/c^2)}} = \frac{E}{c}. \tag{21.38}$$

The time component of momentum, $p_t \sim E$

As noted after the second equal sign, the fourth component of momentum is, to within a factor c, the same as the total energy E. This merger of two of the

Other mergers

key concepts of mechanics into a single four-dimensional entity was achieved by Hermann Minkowski in 1908. Other mergers of importance, which we shall not pursue, include electric charge with electric current and electric field with magnetic field. Not long after Einstein's pioneering work, all of classical physics became imbedded in the new spacetime.

In the following two subsections, we verify, in two ways, the correctness of the choice of p_t given by Equation 21.38.

LENGTH OF THE MOMENTUM-ENERGY FOUR-VECTOR

The four-dimensional momentum-energy vector has a length, whose square is defined in much the same way as the square of the spacetime interval. It is

$$p_t{}^2 - p_x{}^2 - p_y{}^2 - p_z{}^2.$$

This combination, as a little algebra reveals, is exactly equal to the simple constant

$$m^2 c^2,$$

the same for all observers. Although both the energy and momentum of a particle depend on the state of motion of the observer, here is a certain invariant combination on which all observers agree. Its invariance supports the idea that $p_t, p_x, p_y,$ and p_z are indeed components of a four-vector.

Although spacetime vectors connecting pairs of events may be either space-like or time-like, the momentum-energy vector of a material particle is always time-like, as indicated by the positive value of the right side of the equation

Energy-momentum: a time-like vector of invariant length

$$p_t{}^2 - p_x{}^2 - p_y{}^2 - p_z{}^2 = m^2 c^2. \tag{21.39}$$

For a massless particle, always standing apart as a special case, the momentum-energy vector is a null vector of zero length (although momentum and energy are of course not separately zero). A briefer and often useful way to write Equation 21.39, valid for particles with or without mass, is

$$E^2 = p^2 c^2 + m^2 c^4. \tag{21.40}$$

This is equivalent to Equation 21.27 expressing the energy of a particle in terms of its momentum and its mass.

■ EXAMPLE 1: A particle moves with constant speed v along the x axis. Show that its momentum vector in the p_x-p_t plane is parallel to its displacement vector in the x-ct plane. The two Minkowski diagrams are shown in Figure 21.8. In the x-ct plane, we have

$$\tan \theta = \frac{c \, \Delta t}{\Delta x} = \frac{c}{v}.$$

In the p_x-p_t plane, the angle is the same since

$$\tan \theta = \frac{p_t}{p_x} = \frac{mc}{\sqrt{1 - \beta^2}} \cdot \frac{\sqrt{1 - \beta^2}}{mv} = \frac{c}{v}.$$

The fact that $\tan \theta > 1$ confirms that the two vectors are time-like.   ■

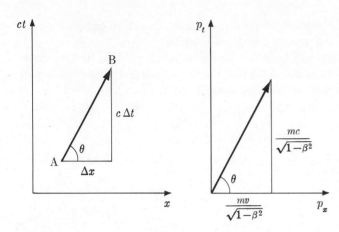

FIGURE 21.8   For a particle moving with constant speed, the displacement vector in spacetime is parallel to the momentum-energy four-vector. Both vectors are time-like.

TRANSFORMATION OF THE MOMENTUM-ENERGY FOUR-VECTOR

To relate the viewpoints of different observers about the components of the four-dimensional "position" vector, or event vector, we use the Lorentz transformation. It should not be surprising that the components of the momentum-energy four-vector transform in exactly the same way. In fact, they *must* do so, since the technical *definition* of a four-vector is a set of four components that follow the same transformation law that space and time follow.

Definition of a four-vector

Suppose an observer on the ground measures a particle to have momentum components p_x, p_y, and p_z, and energy E. A moving observer, in the frame of reference defined by Figure 20.6, measures the same particle to have momentum components p'_x, p'_y, and p'_z, and energy E'. (The particle may be moving with respect to both observers. Its speed need have no relation to the relative speed v of the frames of reference.) The measurements of the two observers are related by

$$E = \frac{E' + vp'_x}{\sqrt{1 - \beta^2}}, \tag{21.41}$$

$$p_x = \frac{p'_x + (vE'/c^2)}{\sqrt{1 - \beta^2}}, \tag{21.42}$$

Lorentz transformation for energy and momentum

$$p_y = p'_y, \tag{21.43}$$

$$p_z = p'_z. \tag{21.44}$$

These are precisely analogous to Equations 20.24–20.27 respectively. The only difference is in the placement of factors of c in the numerators, a difference required to maintain dimensional consistency. With the correspondence

$$ct \leftrightarrow \frac{E}{c},$$

$$x \leftrightarrow p_x,$$

$$y \leftrightarrow p_y, \tag{21.45}$$

$$z \leftrightarrow p_z,$$

and a similar correspondence for primed variables, spacetime components and momentum-energy components transform identically.

The simplest check of Equations 21.41 and 21.42 is afforded by considering an object at rest in one frame. A crate of mass m, sitting motionless in a boxcar, has, in the train-based frame, momentum and energy given by

$$\mathbf{p}' = 0,$$

$$E' = mc^2.$$

Putting these values into the right sides of the transformation equations gives at once

$$E = \frac{mc^2}{\sqrt{1 - \beta^2}},$$

Definitions of E and p follow from the transformation law

$$p_x = \frac{mv}{\sqrt{1 - \beta^2}}.$$

The transformation yields the definitions of energy and momentum for the crate moving at speed v, a good test of consistency.

■ EXAMPLE 2: Show that the Lorentz transformation equations for momentum and energy lead to the velocity-addition formula. Consider the runner in Figure 20.13. His momentum and energy measured in the train are p' and E'. Measured on the ground, they are p and E. From Equations 21.41 and 21.42, these quantities are related by

$$\frac{E}{c} = \frac{(E'/c) + \beta_1 p'}{\sqrt{1 - \beta_1{}^2}}, \tag{21.46}$$

$$p = \frac{p' + (\beta_1 E'/c)}{\sqrt{1 - \beta_1{}^2}}, \tag{21.47}$$

where the relative speed of the two frames of reference is $v_1 = \beta_1 c$. It is simplest to work with momentum-energy ratios because (from Equation 21.29)

$$\beta = \frac{pc}{E}.$$

Dividing Equation 21.47 by Equation 21.46 gives

$$\beta = \frac{pc}{E} = \frac{p' + (\beta_1 E'/c)}{(E'/c) + \beta_1 p'}$$

$$= \frac{(p'c/E') + \beta_1}{1 + \beta_1(p'c/E')}.$$

Finally, we may set $p'c/E'$ equal to β_2, the speed of the runner (in units of c) in the train-based frame, obtaining

Velocity-addition formula follows from the transformation law

$$\beta = \frac{\beta_2 + \beta_1}{1 + \beta_1 \beta_2}, \tag{21.48}$$

in agreement with Equation 20.40.   ■

What, exactly, does it mean to say that energy is the fourth component of momentum? It seems scarcely adequate to answer that it is a component pointing in the time direction. We can appreciate the meaning of north, south, east, west, up, and down. But which direction is the time direction? Unfortunately, man seems unable to visualize four dimensions, yet that is just what the theory of relativity is asking him to do. The best one can do is to try to extrapolate one's pattern of thought from two dimensions to three and then to four, to form analogies, and to make use of what has already been learned about space and time. By way of analogy, we might think of a two-dimensional bug living out his life in a plane. He would "know" that space has two dimensions. If a more learned bug tried to explain to him the meaning of the third dimension, he might become irritated and exclaim, "But what can you *mean* by a third dimension? It is nothing you can point to; it is nothing we can experience." We three-dimensional creatures must be likewise content to accept the fourth dimension as something at best vaguely visualizable yet vitally important in deepening our view of the world.

The fourth dimension

★21.6 Particles in one dimension

Even in one dimension, the collision and interaction of two particles is somewhat complicated in relativity theory because each particle may alter its mass as well as its momentum and energy, and new particles may be formed. In this section we shall confine our attention to two ideas, the idea of invariant mass and the idea of available energy.

INVARIANT MASS

A pair of particles moving along the same straight line in the laboratory frame of reference are depicted in the upper left diagram of Figure 21.9. Particle 1

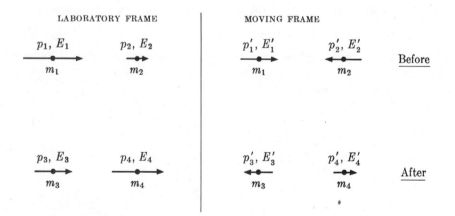

FIGURE 21.9 "Before and after" views of particle collision and transformation in two frames of reference. The moving frame is chosen to be the center-of-momentum frame, with $\mathbf{p}_{total} = 0$. *Conserved* quantities are the same from top to bottom. *Invariant* quantities are the same from left to right.

has mass m_1, x component of momentum p_1, and energy E_1. Particle 2 is characterized by m_2, p_2, and E_2. In a frame of reference in motion relative to the laboratory (upper right diagram), the particles have the same masses, m_1 and m_2, but different momenta* and energies, p_1', E_1', p_2', and E_2'. At some later time, after the particles have collided, interacted, transformed, or decayed, there may be any number of particles present, none of which need be either of the original particles. In the laboratory we might find, for instance, two particles of masses m_3 and m_4 whose momenta and energies are p_3, E_3, p_4, and E_4 (lower left diagram). In the moving frame (lower right diagram), these particles have a different set of momenta and energies, p_3', E_3', p_4', and E_4'.

Invariance and conservation distinguished

A quantity is called *invariant* if it is the same in different inertial frames of reference. The individual rest masses, m_1 to m_4, are examples of invariants. They are the same from left to right in Figure 21.9. A quantity is *conserved* if it remains unchanged in time, the same after interaction as before. The total energy in either frame is an example of a conserved quantity. It is the same from top to bottom in Figure 21.9. Thus in the laboratory frame, the constant total energy is

$$E_T = E_1 + E_2 = E_3 + E_4. \tag{21.49}$$

Note that an invariant quantity, such as the mass of a single particle, need not be conserved, and a conserved quantity, such as energy, need not be invariant. In the moving frame of reference, the conservation of energy is expressed by

$$E_T' = E_1' + E_2' = E_3' + E_4', \tag{21.50}$$

and E_T' is not equal to E_T.

A quantity that is both invariant *and* conserved is the invariant mass M of the system, defined by

Definition of invariant mass

$$M^2 c^2 = \left(\frac{E_T}{c}\right)^2 - p_T^2, \dagger \tag{21.51}$$

where E_T is the total energy in the laboratory frame, given by Equation 21.49, and where p_T is the magnitude of the total momentum in the same frame,

$$p_T = |p_1 + p_2| = |p_3 + p_4|. \tag{21.52}$$

It is invariant and conserved

The *conservation* of M follows at once from the conservation of its defining quantities, E_T and p_T. Its *invariance* is deduced from the Lorentz transformation. From Equations 21.41 and 21.42, we can write

$$\frac{E_1 + E_2}{c} = \frac{(1/c)(E_1' + E_2') + \beta(p_1' + p_2')}{\sqrt{1 - \beta^2}},$$

$$(p_1 + p_2) = \frac{(p_1' + p_2') + \beta(1/c)(E_1' + E_2')}{\sqrt{1 - \beta^2}}.$$

---

* Throughout this section, "momentum" means x component of momentum. It may be positive or negative.

† The definition may be extended to more than two particles and to motion in three dimensions.

Squaring both sides of these equations and taking their difference leads, after some algebra, to the invariance condition

$$\left[\frac{1}{c}(E_1 + E_2)\right]^2 - (p_1 + p_2)^2 = \left[\frac{1}{c}(E'_1 + E'_2)\right]^2 - (p'_1 + p'_2)^2,$$

which is, of course, the same as

$$\left(\frac{E_T}{c}\right)^2 - p_T{}^2 = \left(\frac{E'_T}{c}\right)^2 - p'_T{}^2. \qquad (21.53)$$

Since the left side is, by definition, M^2c^2, the right side is the same:

$$M^2c^2 = \left(\frac{E'_T}{c}\right)^2 - p'_T{}^2. \qquad (21.54)$$

Equations 21.51 and 21.54 demonstrate the invariance of M.

Equation 21.51 (or 21.54) is actually a defining equation for rest mass (see Equation 21.39). The quantity M is, therefore, the rest mass *of the system*, an idea that must be carefully distinguished from the rest masses of constituents within the system. Imagine particles 1 and 2 being held within a hypothetical massless box. In some frame of reference, which we denote by double primes, the total momentum is zero;

$$p''_T = p''_1 + p''_2 = 0.$$

(Such a frame can usually be found.* It is called the center-of-momentum [c.o.m.] frame. In the nonrelativistic limit, it is the same as the center-of-mass frame.) In this frame, the total energy is, because of the invariance of M,

$$E''_T = Mc^2. \qquad (21.55)$$

Energy in center-of-momentum frame

Viewed as a whole, the system behaves like a single motionless object of mass M. If set on a scale, the box containing the two particles would cause the scale to read M (Figure 21.10). In general, M is not equal to $m_1 + m_2$. The particles might, for example, both be photons, with $m_1 = m_2 = 0$. A pair of photons nevertheless form a system that has mass—invariant and conserved.

■ EXAMPLE 1: The mass M might differ from $m_1 + m_2$ because of interaction energy. The deuteron is an example (page 1050). Another example is shown in Figure 21.11. A compressed spring between two cars has potential energy U. When a catch is released, the cars separate, each with energy $mc^2 + \frac{1}{2}U$ and with equal and opposite momentum. The total energy and momentum are $E_T = 2mc^2 + U$ and $p_T = 0$. Substituting these values in Equation 21.51 gives

$$M = 2m + \frac{U}{c^2},$$

FIGURE 21.10 Mass of a system. If the total momentum is zero, the rest mass of the system as a whole is the same as its invariant mass M. In general, M is not equal to $m_1 + m_2$.

---

* An exception would be a pair of photons moving in the same direction. Even when there is no center-of-momentum frame, M is an invariant constant.

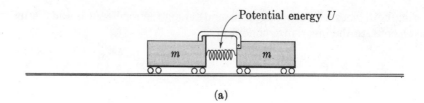

(a)

FIGURE 21.11   The invariant
mass of the two-car system
is $2m + U/c^2$, both before
and after the cars separate.

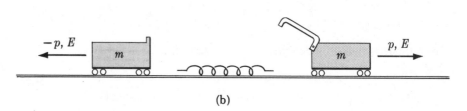

(b)

which is the mass of the system both before and after the catch is released. (For the deuteron, $M < m_1 + m_2$; in this example, $M > m_1 + m_2$.)   ■

■ EXAMPLE 2:   The mass M could differ from $m_1 + m_2$ because of kinetic energy [as in Figure 21.11(b)]. Two oppositely directed photons are an example. Suppose that they are gamma rays, one of energy 0.5 MeV and one of energy 2 MeV. Then $E_T = 2.5$ MeV, $p_T c = 1.5$ MeV, and

$$Mc^2 = \sqrt{(2.5)^2 - (1.5)^2} \text{ MeV} = 2 \text{ MeV}.$$

The mass of this two-photon system is 3.6×10^{-30} kg, about four times the mass of an electron.   ■

AVAILABLE ENERGY

A question of utmost practical importance for the utilization of accelerators is this: In the collision of one particle with another, what part of the total energy of the particles is available for the creation of new mass? This is a question we dealt with nonrelativistically in Section 12.6. Now we examine it relativistically.

Case for analysis: two initial particles of equal mass

For simplicity, let us choose particles of equal mass m, one of which—the target particle—is initially at rest (upper left diagram of Figure 21.12). This is a common situation, covering the important example of projectile protons striking hydrogen nuclei. In the center-of-momentum frame of reference (upper right diagram in Figure 21.12), the two particles have equal and opposite momentum. This frame moves with respect to the laboratory at speed v; other notation is defined in the figure.

In the laboratory frame, the particle or particles resulting from the collision *must* possess kinetic energy. Otherwise, the necessary final momentum would not be provided. In the c.o.m. frame, the final particles *may* possess kinetic energy but they need not. Since the total momentum in this frame is zero, the result of the collision may be a particle or set of particles of total mass M sitting *Maximum rest mass of* motionless (lower right diagram in Figure 21.12). This will be the result of *products when $K = 0$ in* maximum rest mass. All of the available energy has gone into mass, none *c.o.m. frame* into kinetic energy.

The mass M is, in fact, the invariant mass of the system. In the c.o.m. frame after the collision (lower right diagram), it is given by

$$M^2c^2 = \left(\frac{E'_T}{c}\right)^2 - 0 = \frac{E'^2_T}{c^2}.$$

In the laboratory frame before the collision (upper left diagram), it is given by

$$M^2c^2 = \frac{E^2_T}{c^2} - p^2_T$$

$$= \frac{1}{c^2}(E_1 + mc^2)^2 - p_1{}^2. \tag{21.56}$$

This result may be simplified by substituting $(E_1/c)^2 - m^2c^2$ for $p_1{}^2$ (from Equation 21.40). A little algebra then converts Equation 21.56 to

$$M^2c^2 = 2m(mc^2 + E_1). \tag{21.57}$$

As indicated in Figure 21.12, E_1 is the initial energy of the projectile particle. Before the collision, the energy concentrated in the form of rest mass is $2mc^2$. After the collision, the maximum energy in the form of rest mass is Mc^2. The difference between these two is defined to be the available energy,

$$E_{\text{available}} = Mc^2 - 2mc^2. \tag{21.58}$$

This is, from Equation 21.57,

$$E_{\text{available}} = \sqrt{2mc^2(mc^2 + E_1)} - 2mc^2. \tag{21.59}$$

Energy available to make new mass

For a "slow" incident particle, it is useful to write E_1 as the sum of a mass energy and a kinetic energy,

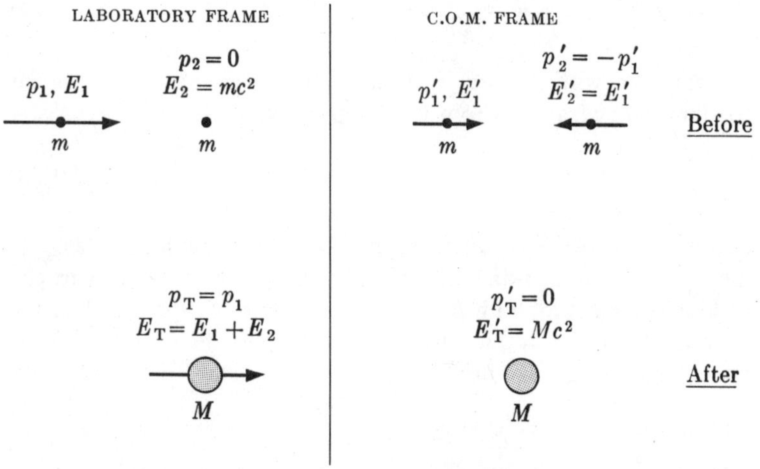

FIGURE 21.12 Collision of projectile particle with target particle of equal mass. The available energy is the greatest energy that can be transformed into mass of the final system. It is equal to $Mc^2 - 2mc^2$ if the mass M has zero kinetic energy in the c.o.m. frame.

$$E_1 = mc^2 + K.$$

It is left as an exercise to show that for $K \ll mc^2$,

$K \ll mc^2$
$$E_{\text{available}} \cong \tfrac{1}{2}K \quad \text{(nonrelativistic)}. \tag{21.60}$$

This confirms Equation 12.96. In the opposite limit of a superrelativistic projectile particle ($E_1 \gg mc^2$), the approximate result is

$K \gg mc^2$
$$E_{\text{available}} \cong 2mc^2 \left(\sqrt{\frac{E_1}{2mc^2}} - 1 \right) \quad \text{(superrelativistic)}. \tag{21.61}$$

Example: Of 300 GeV, only 22 GeV available

For a 300-GeV proton ($mc^2 \cong 1$ GeV) at the National Accelerator Laboratory in Illinois, either Equation 21.59 or Equation 21.61 gives $E_{\text{available}} = 22$ GeV. Unfortunately, relativity conspires to make the available energy much less than the incident energy for large accelerators. The nonrelativistic result for the same proton would be $E_{\text{available}} = \tfrac{1}{2}(300 \text{ GeV}) = 150$ GeV.

It is of some interest to find the speed of the center-of-momentum frame in Figure 21.12. The condition of zero total momentum in this frame provides a way to do so. Equations 20.30 and 20.31 may be translated from spacetime to momentum-energy by means of the correspondence set forth in Formulas 21.45. The transformation from laboratory to c.o.m. frame is then (in part)

$$p_1' = \frac{p_1 - \beta(E_1/c)}{\sqrt{1 - \beta^2}},$$

$$p_2' = \frac{0 - \beta mc}{\sqrt{1 - \beta^2}},$$

the latter because $p_2 = 0$ and $E_2 = mc^2$. If one sets $p_2' = -p_1'$, the solution for β is elementary. The result is

Speed of c.o.m. frame
$$\beta = \frac{p_1 c}{mc^2 + E_1}. \tag{21.62}$$

This may be compared with $\beta_1 = v_1/c$, where v_1 is the speed of the incident particle in the laboratory frame. From Equation 21.29,

Speed of incident particle
$$\beta_1 = \frac{p_1 c}{E_1}. \tag{21.63}$$

For a nonrelativistic particle, $E_1 \cong mc^2$. Then $\beta_1 \cong p_1/mc$, and $\beta \cong p_1/2mc \cong \tfrac{1}{2}\beta_1$. The speed of the c.o.m. frame is half the speed of the incident particle. For a superrelativistic particle, both β and β_1 are close to 1; the speed of the c.o.m. frame is only slightly less than the speed of the particle, which in turn is only slightly less than the speed of light.

21.7   The Compton effect

In 1923, Arthur Compton detected an increase in the wavelength (decrease in frequency) of scattered X rays, presumably as a result of their collision with electrons in a target. Detailed studies of this Compton effect, as it is now called,

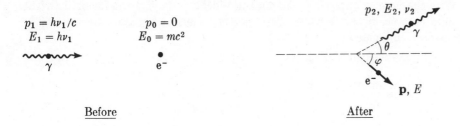

$p_1 = h\nu_1/c$
$E_1 = h\nu_1$

γ

$p_0 = 0$
$E_0 = mc^2$

e^-

p_2, E_2, ν_2

γ

θ

φ

e^-

$\mathbf{p}, E$

Before   After

FIGURE 21.13   The Compton effect. The target electron is approximated as being at rest before the collision.

soon provided solid support for the photon theory of light since the results were successfully described by assigning to the photon an energy $h\nu$ and momentum $h\nu/c$ and treating the scattering as the result of a two-body encounter between a photon and an electron.

It is sufficient to analyze the process in a single frame of reference. Figure 21.13 shows "before" and "after" views of the scattering event in the laboratory frame of reference. For high-energy photons (although not for visible light), the initial motion of the electron may be ignored. The electron is treated as a target particle at rest. The photon approaches with frequency ν_1 and departs with lower frequency ν_2 after being deflected through an angle θ. The momentum $\mathbf{p}$ of the recoiling electron makes an angle φ with the line of direction of the incident photon. If we define x and y directions as shown in Figure 21.13, we may write two conservation equations for momentum and one for energy, as follows:

$$p_x: \qquad \frac{h\nu_1}{c} = \frac{h\nu_2}{c} \cos\theta + p \cos\varphi, \qquad (21.64)$$

$$p_y: \qquad 0 = \frac{h\nu_2}{c} \sin\theta - p \sin\varphi, \qquad (21.65)$$

Conservation equations for photon-electron collision

$$E: \qquad h\nu_1 + mc^2 = h\nu_2 + E. \qquad (21.66)$$

The photon energies before and after are $h\nu_1$ and $h\nu_2$. The photon momenta before and after are $h\nu_1/c$ and $h\nu_2/c$. The sine and cosine factors are necessary to give momentum components in the y and x directions. What we wish to obtain from these equations is an expression for the final frequency ν_2 as a function of the initial frequency ν_1 and the scattering angle θ. This requires eliminating the unknowns φ, p, and E. To do so requires one additional equation, the relationship between p and E for the recoiling electron:

$$p^2 c^2 + m^2 c^4 = E^2. \qquad (21.67)$$

All the physical principles are contained in these four equations. What remains is algebraic manipulation. From Equation 21.64, we may write

$$p^2 c^2 \cos^2\varphi = (h\nu_1 - h\nu_2 \cos\theta)^2.$$

Similarly, Equation 21.65 yields

$$p^2 c^2 \sin^2\varphi = (h\nu_2 \sin\theta)^2.$$

The sum of the left sides of these two equations is $p^2 c^2$, since $\cos^2\varphi + \sin^2\varphi = 1$.

With the help of the same trigonometric identity for θ, the sum of the right sides becomes $h^2(v_1{}^2 + v_2{}^2 - 2v_1 v_2 \cos \theta)$. Thus an equation from which φ has been eliminated is

$$p^2 c^2 = h^2(v_1{}^2 + v_2{}^2 - 2v_1 v_2 \cos \theta). \tag{21.68}$$

From Equation 21.66, we have

$$E^2 = h^2 \left(v_1 - v_2 + \frac{mc^2}{h} \right)^2.$$

The difference of these two equations provides further simplification. The left sides yield $E^2 - p^2 c^2 = m^2 c^4$. The right sides yield

$$2h(v_1 - v_2)mc^2 - 2h^2 v_1 v_2(1 - \cos \theta) + m^2 c^4.$$

When this expression is equated to $m^2 c^4$, a further cancellation occurs, leaving

$$0 = 2h(v_1 - v_2)mc^2 - 2h^2 v_1 v_2(1 - \cos \theta).$$

Finally, collecting the frequencies on one side of an equation, we have

Decrease of frequency

$$\frac{v_1 - v_2}{v_1 v_2} = \frac{h}{mc^2}(1 - \cos \theta). \tag{21.69}$$

This result can be made even simpler if it is expressed in terms of wavelength rather than frequency. Note that

$$\lambda_2 - \lambda_1 = \frac{c}{v_2} - \frac{c}{v_1} = \frac{c(v_1 - v_2)}{v_1 v_2}. \tag{21.70}$$

Using this relationship in Equation 21.69 gives

Increase of wavelength

$$\lambda_2 - \lambda_1 = \left(\frac{h}{mc} \right)(1 - \cos \theta). \tag{21.71}$$

This famous result expresses the increase in wavelength of the scattered photon in terms of its scattering angle θ and a single combination of fundamental constants, h/mc. This combination is called the Compton wavelength, for which the usual notation is $\lambda_C{}^*$:

The Compton wavelength

$$\lambda_C = \frac{h}{mc} = 2.426 \times 10^{-12} \text{ m.} \tag{21.72}$$

The Compton wavelength is intermediate in extent between the size of an atom ($\sim 10^{-10}$ m) and the size of a nucleus ($\sim 10^{-14}$ m). Note that it is the wavelength of a photon whose energy is $mc^2 = 0.511$ MeV. For such a photon,

$$\lambda = \frac{c}{v} = \frac{hc}{hv} = \frac{hc}{mc^2} = \frac{h}{mc}. \tag{21.73}$$

---

* A quantity that is also frequently encountered is the "reduced Compton wavelength" λ_C. It is $\lambda_C = \lambda_C/2\pi = h/mc = 3.86 \times 10^{-13}$ m $= 386$ fm.

However, Equation 21.71 holds true for *all* photons greater than a few tens of eV in energy (a minimum required to make valid the approximation of a stationary target electron).

Any important equation is worth examining in several limiting situations. From Equation 21.71, we note that $\Delta\lambda$ $(= \lambda_2 - \lambda_1)$ is zero if $\theta = 0$—not surprising since the photon is then undeflected—and is equal to $2\lambda_c$ if $\theta = \pi$. The Compton wavelength provides the scale of the wavelength change. For a photon of low energy (low compared with 0.5 MeV), the incident wavelength λ_1 is much greater than λ_c. The change of wavelength is therefore a small fraction of the wavelength:

$$\frac{\Delta\lambda}{\lambda} = \frac{\lambda_c}{\lambda}(1 - \cos\theta) \ll 1 \qquad \text{(low energy).} \qquad (21.74) \qquad h\nu_1 \ll mc^2$$

Correspondingly, the fractional change of energy of the photon is small. This limit is appropriate for the X rays observed by Compton. A sample of his experimental results is shown in Figure 21.14. In an opposite high-energy limit, with $h\nu_1 \gg mc^2$, the incident wavelength λ_1 is much less than λ_c. Then the *change* of wavelength is much greater than the initial wavelength, and Equation 21.71 may be approximated by

$$\lambda_2 \cong \frac{h}{mc}(1 - \cos\theta) \qquad \text{(high energy).} \qquad (21.75) \qquad h\nu_1 \gg mc^2$$

No matter how great the initial energy, the final energy is in the vicinity of 0.5 MeV if the photon is scattered through an appreciable angle. To be more exact,

$$h\nu_2 \cong \frac{mc^2}{1 - \cos\theta} \qquad \text{(high energy).} \qquad (21.76)$$

Although we shall not do so here, it is a simple matter to also find the recoil energy and momentum of the electron and the angle φ of the recoiling electron's track.

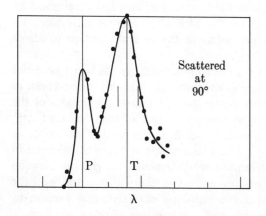

Scattered at 90°

P

T

λ

FIGURE 21.14 Sample of Arthur Compton's experimental results [*Physical Review* **22**, 409 (1923)]. Intensity of X rays is plotted as a function of wavelength for a particular angle of scattering from a graphite target. The line marked P identifies a component of the scattered radiation that has suffered no change of wavelength: $\lambda = \lambda_1 = 0.711$ Å. The line marked T identifies the component of increased wavelength: $\lambda_2 = \lambda_1 + \Delta\lambda = 0.735$ Å. For this particular angle of 90 deg, $\Delta\lambda = \lambda_c = 0.0243$ Å.

21.8   The significance of special relativity

Any successful theory in science contributes to man's understanding in two ways. First, it provides a satisfying explanation of a set of empirical facts of nature and shows how these facts can all be understood in terms of a few simple ideas. Its success in quantitative prediction is the acid test of any theory. But a good theory does more. It alters more or less profoundly man's view of the world around him. It may do so by demonstrating the utility and hence the importance of some new concept. The idea of field, for example, which was provided by the theory of electromagnetism, remains today a central concept of modern physics, having grown enormously in importance during the last hundred years. From relativity has come the idea of invariance, a pillar of nearly every branch of contemporary physical science.

Relativity has introduced new concepts and merged old ones

Besides introducing new concepts, a theory may revolutionize our view of nature by drawing together old concepts or old facts in an entirely new and unsuspected way. The revolution of relativity has come about in large part from syntheses of ideas previously thought to be unrelated. Space and time have been drawn together into a single concept of spacetime; the electric and magnetic fields have been amalgamated into the electromagnetic field tensor; momentum and energy have been united; mass has been shown to be another form of energy. When relativity was joined to quantum mechanics, more unsuspected connections appeared. The spin of the electron and the existence of antiparticles were remarkable consequences of the relativistic invariance requirement.

Relativity as a supertheory constraining other theories

A particular significance of special relativity has been its role in physics as a kind of supertheory. *All* laws of nature, said Einstein, must be the same in all inertial frames of reference. This invariance requirement has been a strait jacket on the free invention of scientists, and a surprisingly strong one. In probing into the unknown world of the interactions among elementary particles, physicists have learned that the rejection of all laws of interaction that do not conform to the Principle of Relativity leaves only few possibilities. Besides the relativistic invariance (in inertial frames), other kinds of invariance principles have been discovered. It remains a challenging open question as to whether all the invariance principles taken together will so rigidly circumscribe the conceivable laws of nature that the actual laws will be uniquely determined by invariance requirements alone. If so, the idea of invariance introduced by special relativity will have been promoted to the central position in all of physics.

Relativity removed the last props of a privileged Earth

More than any other theory since mechanics, relativity has had a powerful impact upon man's view of his place in the universe. This has come about in part because relativity has removed finally the last remaining vestiges of the pre-Copernican view of the privileged status in nature of man and his Earth. When the ether vanished, there vanished with it any hope that the earth, or even our solar system or our galaxy, could be a preferred frame of reference in the universe. The empty space of Einstein which replaced the ether of Newton and Maxwell cast man adrift from any anchor in the world. And with the vanishing of a spatial anchor went the vanishing of a temporal anchor, as absolute time gave way to relative time and to the mixing of space and time.

The other vital aspect of relativity's impact on man's view of his place in the universe can be summed up by the statement: Relativity violates common sense. Common sense, or intuition, or self-evident truth, derives from man's perceptions of the world about him. The lesson of relativity has been that man's perceptions are an inadequate guide to the description of the scheme of nature. Pretwentieth-century physical science, no matter how revolutionary, no matter how unexpected, remained always visualizable and not out of harmony with common sense. The earth swinging around the sun is not hard to picture, even if our more naïve impression is that the sun moves around the earth. A spherical earth is not hard to accept, even if we cannot readily perceive its curvature. Even electric and magnetic fields are visualizable with a little effort, and nothing about them need cause incredulity. But in relativity we encounter both the incredible and the nonvisualizable. The relativity of time, the addition of velocity, the speed-of-light barrier remain incredible because nothing in our experience has ever raised the strange effects of relativity to the threshold of observability. Four-vectors and spacetime remain nonvisualizable because, like it or not, we are three-dimensional creatures.

Relativity violates common sense

In 1920 it was argued that the next generation of school children would learn about relativity at an early age and would come to accept its concepts and its peculiarities as quite everyday matters not out of harmony with common sense. Nearly two generations have passed with no noticeable progress in this direction. This optimistic prediction seems very unlikely of fulfillment at any time, for no amount of early exposure to the theory of relativity can alter the fact that all examples of important application of the theory are outside the domain of human perception. The difficulties of visualization and the non-common-sense aspects of relativity are as real to the trained scientist as they are to the layman. The situation is similar for the other great theory of this century, quantum mechanics. Together they suggest that we may be on the threshold of a complete divergence between the fundamental concepts needed to describe the basic laws of nature and the everyday concepts used to describe the world around us. If this is so, the progress of fundamental science may be slowed as man gropes for the concepts needed to probe deeper. On the other hand, the power of mathematics together with the evidence of new experimental findings may lead man on to the new concepts, no matter how strange. Or— and this seems quite unlikely—physics may be passing through a difficult phase to be replaced again by one featuring concrete and familiar concepts, as still deeper and more general theories evolve.

The intrinsic difficulty of the new concepts

The special theory of relativity has raised a host of questions that for the present must be called philosophical, although they may one day become scientific. Why, for example, does man perceive space and time in such different ways if they are really only parts of the same entity, spacetime? Why, if we can move this way or that in space, do we find ourselves moving inflexibly in only one direction through time? Are there other parts of the universe or other eras in the history of the universe when the direction of motion through time was different? If we are three-dimensional creatures imbedded in a four-dimensional world, are there still more dimensions still further removed from our perception? Such questions, apparently idle today, give some indication of the kinds of questions that might be answerable within the framework of science tomorrow.

Summary of ideas and definitions

The laws of energy and momentum conservation are invariant (valid in all inertial frames of reference).

The magnitudes of energy and momentum are not invariant. They are governed by a Lorentz transformation,

$$\frac{E}{c} = \frac{(E'/c) + \beta p'_x}{\sqrt{1 - \beta^2}}, \tag{21.41}$$

$$p_x = \frac{p'_x + \beta(E'/c)}{\sqrt{1 - \beta^2}}, \tag{21.42}$$

$$p_y = p'_y, \tag{21.43}$$

$$p_z = p'_z. \tag{21.44}$$

One way to derive the relativistic definitions of energy and momentum is by considering π^0 decay in two frames of reference.

For a particle at rest, $\mathbf{p} = 0$, $E = mc^2$.

For a particle in motion,

$$\mathbf{p} = \frac{m\mathbf{v}}{\sqrt{1 - (v^2/c^2)}}, \tag{21.26}$$

$$E = \frac{mc^2}{\sqrt{1 - (v^2/c^2)}}. \tag{21.15}$$

Kinetic energy is defined by

$$K = \frac{mc^2}{\sqrt{1 - \beta^2}} - mc^2. \tag{21.19}$$

The rest mass m of a particle is an invariant.

The quantity c^2 is a mass-to-energy conversion factor, whose large magnitude, 9×10^{16} J/kg, causes the mass change accompanying ordinary energy change to be negligible.

For a massless particle, $E = pc$ (Equation 21.30). For any particle, $$E^2 = p^2c^2 + m^2c^4. \tag{21.40}$$

The momentum-energy four-vector is precisely analogous to a spacetime displacement vector. The exact correspondence is

$$ct \leftrightarrow \frac{E}{c} \quad (= p_t),$$

$$x \leftrightarrow p_x, \tag{21.45}$$
$$y \leftrightarrow p_y,$$
$$z \leftrightarrow p_z.$$

The square of the "length" of the momentum-energy vector is m^2c^2, an invariant (Equation 21.39).

In the center-of-momentum frame of a system, $\mathbf{p}_T = 0$ (this defines the c.o.m. frame), and $E_T = Mc^2$.

The invariant mass of a system is defined in any frame by
$$M^2c^2 = (E_T/c)^2 - p_T^2. \tag{21.51}$$
It is the same as the rest mass of the system as a whole. It may be either greater or less than the sum of the rest masses of particles in the system.

For a particle of mass m and energy E_1 incident on a stationary particle of mass m, the energy available to make new mass is given by

$$E_{\text{available}} = \sqrt{2mc^2(mc^2 + E_1)} - 2mc^2. \tag{21.59}$$

The Compton effect is the increase in wavelength of electromagnetic radiation scattered by electrons. First observed in 1923, it provided strong evidence for photons.

The relativistic treatment of photon-electron scattering leads to the Compton-effect formula,

$$\lambda_2 - \lambda_1 = \left(\frac{h}{mc}\right)(1 - \cos\theta). \tag{21.71}$$

Among the significant features of special relativity are these:
1. Its postulate of the invariance of physical laws makes it a supertheory constraining other theories.
2. It has united various sets of concepts, such as space and time, energy and momentum, electric field and magnetic field.
3. It has shown that at the deepest level, the design of nature violates common sense.

QUESTIONS

Section 21.1   **Q21.1**   (1) Is *energy* an invariant quantity (the same in different frames of reference)? (2) Is the *law* of energy conservation an invariant law? Back up both answers with brief discussions or examples.

Q21.2   Answer in physical terms: *Why* can no material particle be brought from rest to a speed that exceeds the speed of light?

Q21.3   Two identical safety pins are placed in two identical acid baths. One safety pin is latched, the other unlatched. After the acid has dissolved both pins, is there any difference between the acid baths? What happened to the potential energy of the latched safety pin?

Q21.4   The binding energy of a hydrogen atom is 13.6 eV. (1) Is the mass of a hydrogen atom greater or less than the sum of the masses of a proton and an electron? (2) Is it practical to measure the difference between the mass of the atom and the sum of the masses of its constituents?

Q21.5   One way to define "high" energy is by the criterion that kinetic energy exceed rest energy. By this definition, which of the following have high energy: (a) An ion in thermal equilibrium at 10,000 K, (b) a spacecraft moving at 10,000 mile/hr, (c) a neutron with an energy of 10,000 eV, (d) a proton with an energy of 10,000 MeV?

Q21.6   What might be some interesting aspects of a world in which the mass–energy conversion factor c^2 is much smaller than in our world? Suppose, for instance, that $c^2 = 1$ J/kg.

Q21.7   (1) Is the momentum vector of a particle parallel to its velocity vector (a) classically? (b) relativistically? (2) Is the *change* of momentum of a particle ($\Delta \mathbf{p}$) necessarily parallel to its change of velocity ($\Delta \mathbf{v}$) (a) classically? (b) relativistically?   Section 21.2

Q21.8   In Sections 21.1 and 21.2, relativistic definitions of energy and momentum are obtained without explicit reference to time dilation or Lorentz contraction and without use of the Lorentz-transformation equations. How do the properties of spacetime enter the discussion?

Q21.9   A proton of speed v approaches a stationary proton. Classically, the center-of-mass frame for this system moves at speed $\frac{1}{2}v$; in this frame the total momentum of the two protons is zero. Relativistically, there is also a frame of reference in which the total momentum is zero; it is called the center-of-momentum frame. Is the speed of the center-of-momentum frame greater than $\frac{1}{2}v$ or less than $\frac{1}{2}v$? Why?

Q21.10   Does a photon have kinetic energy? Does it have mass energy? Does it have rest energy?   Section 21.3

Q21.11   Is there any way experimentally to tell the difference between a photon and a neutrino?

Q21.12   The y and z components of a certain null vector are zero; only its x and t components are nonzero. What is the slope of this null vector in the x-ct plane?   Section 21.5

Q21.13   (1) Is rest mass an invariant quantity? (2) Is it conserved in particle reactions?

Q21.14   The theory of relativity has brought to our description of nature both more relativity and more invariance. Name (1) two quantities considered invariant in classical physics that turned out to be relative (that is, different for different observers); and (2) two new invariant quantities not recognized in classical physics.

Q21.15   The energy, momentum, and mass of a particle are related by $E^2 = p^2c^2 + m^2c^4$ (Equation 21.40). (1) Under what circumstances is $E = pc$ a good approximation? (2) Under what circumstances is $E = mc^2 + (p^2/2m)$ a good approximation?

Q21.16 Suggest what might serve as the fourth component of the velocity vector in spacetime.

Section 21.6   Q21.17 Often mass energy is considered to be one among several kinds of energy. However, *every* kind of energy in a system can contribute to the mass of the system. Give examples of systems in which (a) kinetic and (b) potential energy contribute to mass.

Q21.18 A chunk of radioactive matter encased in an idealized perfectly insulating blanket gets gradually warmer as its nuclei release energy. (1) Does the mass of the chunk of matter change? Why or why not? (2) Does the sum of the masses of the atoms in the chunk change? Why or why not?

Q21.19 The mass of a system may be (a) greater than or (b) less than the sum of the masses of its constituents. Name one system of each kind (other than those named in the text).

Q21.20 (1) For a given projectile particle, how could a target particle move in order to (a) increase or (b) decrease the *available* energy relative to the available energy for a stationary target? (2) Could the target particle move in such a way as to make the available energy effectively zero?

Q21.21 Suppose that the cost of a very high energy synchrotron (one that accelerates particles into the superrelativistic range) is roughly proportional to its circumference and that its circumference is roughly proportional to the maximum momentum of its particles. What is the approximate relationship between the cost of the synchrotron and its available energy? (Refer to Equation 21.61.)

Section 21.7   Q21.22 Many physicists came to believe in the reality of the photon only after Compton's work on X-ray scattering (1923). Why does the Compton effect lend strong support to the photon idea?

Q21.23 The change of wavelength of radiation scattered by electrons was observed first for X rays. Why had it gone unnoticed for visible light?

Q21.24 (1) When a low-energy photon is deflected by an electron, does the electron gain a small or a large fraction of the photon's energy? (2) When a very high energy photon is deflected by an electron, does the electron gain a small or a large fraction of the photon's energy?

Q21.25 A multi-GeV photon enters a gas and undergoes successive Compton-scattering events. Describe the manner in which it loses energy in its successive collisions.

Q21.26 The most prominent X rays emitted by an element are the so-called K_α X rays. (1) Using an outside reference, find out which element has K_α X rays of wavelength 0.711 Å. (These were the X rays used by Compton to obtain the data shown in Figure 21.14.) (2) To obtain "harder" X rays (higher frequency, shorter wavelength), how should one vary the atomic number of the target in an X-ray tube?

Section 21.8   Q21.27 When relativity theory was younger, some scientists forecasted that its ideas would eventually become familiar and would be accepted by all students as common-sense ideas. Write a paragraph agreeing or disagreeing with this position.

Q21.28 What does it mean to say that relativity theory is a "supertheory"?

Q21.29 Why was mechanics more profoundly altered than electromagnetism by relativity?

Q21.30 Write a brief essay answering the question: What do the theories of electromagnetism and relativity have to do with each other? Consider in particular the historical impact of electromagnetism on relativity and the theoretical impact of relativity on electromagnetism.

EXERCISES

E21.1 How much mass gets converted to energy in the explosion of a 10-megaton H bomb? (See Appendix 4 for a conversion factor.)

Section 21.1

E21.2 An electron emerges from a certain betatron with a total energy of 1 MeV. (1) What is its kinetic energy? (2) What is its speed?

E21.3 In the Berkeley Bevatron, protons reach a speed of $0.99c$. (1) Show that a proton with this speed has a total energy of about 6.6 GeV and a kinetic energy of about 5.7 GeV. (2) If one of these protons were accelerated further until its speed reached $0.995c$, by what factor would its total energy increase?

E21.4 (1) For each of the following, calculate the ratio of the object's kinetic energy to its rest energy: (a) a truck moving at a speed of 15 m/sec; (b) a space vehicle moving at a speed of 7,000 m/sec; (c) an electron moving at 86.6 percent of the speed of light; (d) a cosmic-ray proton with a total energy of 939 GeV. (2) Which of these four is likely to have the greatest kinetic energy?

E21.5 For what speed does the classical formula $K = \frac{1}{2}mv^2$ give an error of 1 percent in a calculation of kinetic energy?

E21.6 (1) For what speed is the total energy of a particle twice its kinetic energy? (2) At this speed, how does the particle's kinetic energy compare with its rest energy mc^2?

E21.7 A "superrelativistic" particle is one for which $E \gg mc^2$. Show that the speed of a superrelativistic particle is given approximately by

$$v \cong c\left[1 - \frac{1}{2}\left(\frac{mc^2}{E}\right)^2\right].$$

E21.8 (1) By how much does the speed of a particle differ from the speed of light if its energy is 1,000 times its rest energy? (2) What is the average lifetime in the laboratory of muons moving at this speed (the average lifetime of muons at rest is 2.2 μsec)?

E21.9 (1) An electron moves at 80 percent of the speed of light. What is its momentum? (2) If you needed to know its momentum only to within 5 percent of the correct value, would the formula $p = mv$ suffice?

Section 21.2

E21.10 A particle of mass m has a momentum equal to mc. (1) Find v/c, the ratio of its speed to the speed of light. (2) Find E/mc^2, the ratio of its total energy to its rest energy.

E21.11 (1) Show that for "low" speeds ($v \ll c$), the approximate fractional error in a calculation of momentum using the classical formula $p = mv$ is $\frac{1}{2}(v/c)^2$. (2) An engineer wants to calculate the momentum of a satellite to 1 part in a million. If the satellite's speed is 7×10^3 m/sec, is the classical formula adequate for his purposes? (3) For what speed is the error of the classical formula about 1 percent? *Optional:* Explain why the answers to Exercise 21.5 and to part 3 of this exercise are not the same.

E21.12 Physicists often express particle momenta in the unit MeV/c (c designates the speed of light). Show that the conversion factor linking this unit to the SI unit of momentum is

$$5.34 \times 10^{-22}\ \frac{\text{kg m/sec}}{\text{MeV}/c}.$$

E21.13 A 20-GeV electron is superrelativistic (see Exercise 21.7); it moves very nearly at the speed of light. (1) What is the momentum of such an electron in kg m/sec? (2) What is its momentum in the unit MeV/c? (3) What is the speed of a 2-gm ping-pong ball with the same momentum as the electron?

E21.14 Just as a gun recoils when fired, a flashlight recoils when it is shining. Consider a flashlight whose mass is 1 kg, initially at rest in an inertial frame of reference, switched on by remote control. What recoil speed does it acquire after 5 sec if, during that time, the power in the narrowly directed light beam is 0.1 W?

E21.15 In relativistic dynamics, it is convenient to define force as the time rate of change of momentum: $\mathbf{F} = d\mathbf{p}/dt$. (1) Express force in terms of mass, velocity, and acceleration. (2) Is force always parallel to acceleration? (3) If a nonzero force acts on a particle, does the particle necessarily respond with a nonzero acceleration?

Section 21.3 E21.16 The wavelength of light from a certain laser is 6,328 Å (6.328×10^{-7} m). What is the momentum of each of its photons?

E21.17 A photon and a proton each have the same total energy, 70 GeV. Which particle has the greater momentum? Greater by what percentage?

E21.18 Sketch curves analogous to those in Figure 21.5 that show total energy E as a function of speed v for particles of large and small mass. Discuss the limit of zero mass.

Section 21.4 E21.19 Fill in the algebraic details that are omitted in the text in order to obtain Equation 21.34 from Equations 21.32 and 21.33.

E21.20 (1) For the decay process $K^0 \rightarrow \pi^+ + \pi^-$, write the energy-conservation equation in the frame of reference in which one of the pions is stationary (see Figure 21.7). (2) Using the values of M/m, β, and β_1 given near the end of Section 21.4, verify the correctness of this equation *numerically*.

E21.21 A neutral pion moving eastward decays into two photons; one flies to the east, one to the west. The eastbound photon has twice the energy of the westbound photon. Prove that the pion moved at one-third the speed of light before its decay. (HINT: Both energy conservation and momentum conservation are relevant.)

Section 21.5 E21.22 From Equations 21.35–21.38, derive Equation 21.39, which expresses the invariance of length of the momentum-energy four-vector.

E21.23 (1) Show that the momentum-energy four-vector of a massless particle is a null vector. (2) What other null vector is associated with a propagating photon or neutrino?

E21.24 A hypothetical tachyon, whose speed always exceeds the speed of light, has a mass that is represented by an imaginary number, not a real number. (1) Show that the tachyon's energy and momentum are then real quantities. (2) Is the tachyon's momentum-energy vector spacelike or timelike?

E21.25 Figures 21.6 and 21.7 illustrate an example of kaon decay. (1) Express each of the following eight quantities in terms of the kaon mass M and the speed v of the moving frame (in which one of the pions is at rest): the total energy E and total momentum p of the system (a) in the rest frame before the decay, (b) in the rest frame after the decay, (c) in the moving frame before the decay, and (d) in the moving frame after the decay. (2) (a) Is the quantity $p^2 - (E/c)^2$ the same before and after the decay? (b) Is it the same in the two frames of reference?

E21.26 From the Lorentz-transformation equations for momentum and energy (Equations 21.41–21.44), derive the equation of invariance

$$p_x{}^2 c^2 - E^2 = p_x'^2 c^2 - E'^2.$$

E21.27 Obtain the inverse Lorentz-transformation equations for energy and momentum. These are equations analogous to Equations 21.41–21.44 that express E', p_x', p_y', and p_z' as functions of E, p_x, p_y, and p_z.

E21.28 In the laboratory frame of reference, a certain particle has an energy $E = 3.2 \times 10^{-10}$ J and a momentum $p = 9.4 \times 10^{-19}$ kg m/sec. (1) What is the mass of the particle? (2) What is the energy of the particle in its rest frame? (3) What is the speed of the particle?

E21.29 The figure shows a meteorite overtaking a rocket ship. Observers on the rocket ship measure the meteorite's energy to be $E' = 10^{17}$ J and its momentum to be $p' = 10^8$ kg m/sec. If the speed of the rocket ship relative to Earth is 2×10^8 m/sec, what are the energy E and momentum p of the meteorite for Earth-based observers?

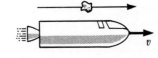

E21.30 The energy of a photon is related to its momentum by $E = pc$ and to its frequency by $E = h\nu$. Use these facts together with the Lorentz-transformation equation for energy (Equation 21.41) in order to derive Equations 20.47 and 20.50 for the Doppler shift of frequency.

E21.31 The figure shows an ordinary vector **a** that lies in the xy plane and a four-vector B that lies in the x-ct plane. (1) What combination of a_x and a_y is invariant under a rotation of axes in the xy plane? (2) What combination of B_x and B_t is invariant under a Lorentz transformation in the x-ct plane (this is a Lorentz transformation joining frames whose relative velocity is in the x direction)? (3) Is a Lorentz transformation equivalent to a rotation of spacetime axes?

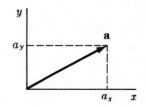

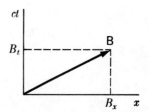

Section 21.6   E21.32   (1) Two 1-MeV photons move in the same direction. What is the invariant mass of this system? (2) Two 1-MeV photons move in exactly opposite directions. What is the invariant mass of this system? (3) What is the *rest* mass of the latter system? (HINT: It is *not* zero.)

E21.33   A photon whose energy is 0.511 MeV approaches a stationary electron, whose rest energy is 0.511 MeV. (1) What is the invariant mass of this system? (2) What is the maximum possible total mass of the products of this photon-electron collision?

E21.34   Show that Equation 21.57 follows from Equation 21.56.

E21.35   (1) A proton whose total energy is $30m_p c^2$ (about 28 GeV) strikes a proton at rest. (a) What is the available energy in the collision in units of $m_p c^2$? (b) What is the maximum total mass of all of the products of the collision in units of m_p (if the original particles survive the collision, they are to be counted as "products")? (2) Answer the same two questions if two protons, each of energy $30m_p c^2$, strike head on in a colliding beam experiment.

E21.36   What is the minimum *kinetic* energy of a projectile proton striking a stationary target proton that makes possible antiproton production in the reaction $p + p \rightarrow p + p + p + \bar{p}$?

E21.37   Equation 21.59 gives the available energy in the collision of a projectile particle of mass m and energy E_1 with a stationary target particle of the same mass m. From this general formula for $E_{\text{available}}$, derive (1) the non-relativistic approximation (Equation 21.60) and (2) the superrelativistic approximation (Equation 21.61).

E21.38   A laboratory has a 30-GeV proton accelerator. The directors have the choice of adding a storage ring that would produce colliding beams of oppositely directed 30-GeV protons or building a new 500-GeV accelerator whose protons would strike stationary target protons. If the laboratory's goal is to maximize the available energy in the particle collisions, which choice should be made? *Optional:* What consideration might make the other choice more attractive?

E21.39   An electron with a total energy of $7m_e c^2$ approaches another electron that is at rest. Show that the speed of the center-of-momentum frame for this pair of electrons is approximately $0.87c$.

E21.40   What is the maximum number of electrons and what is the maximum number of positrons that can emerge from the electron–electron collision defined in the preceding exercise? Include charge conservation as well as energy and momentum conservation in your reasoning.

E21.41   A particle of mass m moves with speed β_1 (in units of c) toward an identical particle that is stationary. (1) Show that the speed of the center-of-momentum frame (in units of c) is given by

$$\beta_c = \frac{\beta_1}{1 + \sqrt{1 - \beta_1{}^2}}.$$

(2) If the energy E_1 of the incident particle greatly exceeds its rest energy mc^2, show that $\beta_c \cong 1 - (mc^2/E_1)$. *Optional:* Extend the answer to part 2 through one more term: $\beta_c \cong 1 - (mc^2/E_1) + \frac{1}{2}(mc^2/E_1)^2$.

E21.42　A photon whose wavelength is 1 Å (10^{-10} m) strikes an electron and is deflected through 90 deg. (1) What is the photon's change of wavelength? (2) What is its fractional change of wavelength?

Section 21.7

E21.43　In being deflected through 60 deg by collision with an electron, a photon doubles its wavelength ($\lambda_2 = 2\lambda_1$). (1) What was the initial wavelength λ_1? (2) Show that the initial energy of the photon was $2m_e c^2$ (about 1 MeV).

E21.44　An experimenter measures the energy of a photon after it undergoes Compton scattering and deduces that the photon's final wavelength is $\lambda_2 = \lambda_c = h/mc$. What upper and/or lower limit can you place on (1) the initial energy of the photon? (2) the angle of deflection of the photon?

E21.45　A 200-MeV photon strikes a stationary proton. If the photon is backscattered ($\theta = 180$ deg), what is the kinetic energy of the recoiling proton? (NOTE: Any event in which a photon scatters from a free charged particle is called a Compton-scattering event because the same theory describes all such processes.)

E21.46　Show that in Compton scattering, the final energy of the photon (E_2) is expressed as a function of its initial energy E_1 and its angle of deflection θ by

$$E_2 = \frac{E_1}{1 + (E_1/mc^2)(1 - \cos\theta)}.$$

E21.47　(1) Show that in Compton scattering, the kinetic energy acquired by the electron is given by

$$K = \left(\frac{\zeta}{1 + \zeta}\right) E_1,$$

where E_1 is the initial energy of the photon and $\zeta = \Delta\lambda/\lambda_1$. (It may be helpful to refer to the answer to the preceding exercise.) (2) Describe the physical conditions that make (a) $\zeta \gg 1$ and $K \cong E_1$, or (b) $\zeta \ll 1$ and $K \ll E_1$.

PROBLEMS

Thought experiments to get mass–energy equivalence

P21.1　In its rest frame, the massive block shown in Figure 21.1(a) emits oppositely directed photons of equal frequency v; its loss of energy in this frame is $\Delta E = 2hv$. In a frame moving at speed $v = \beta c$, the photons have frequencies v_1' and v_2' and the block's loss of energy is $\Delta E' = h(v_1' + v_2')$. (1) Applying the Doppler-shift formulas, show that $\Delta E' = \Delta E/\sqrt{1 - \beta^2}$. (2) In the moving frame, the block suffers no change of speed when it emits the photons. Why? (3) The fact that the block loses more energy in the moving frame than in its rest frame ($\Delta E' > \Delta E$) can be attributed to a loss of *kinetic* energy by the block when it radiates the photons. This kinetic energy loss (in the moving frame) is $\Delta K = \Delta E' - \Delta E$. For $\beta \ll 1$, show that the change of mass required to produce this change of kinetic energy is $\Delta m = \Delta E/c^2$.

P21.2   Identical plates A and B are initially at rest and separated by distance d (see the figure). Plate A emits a photon of energy E and recoils with speed v. At the moment when the photon reaches plate B and is absorbed there, the separation of the plates has increased to $d + x$. If the plates are massive (so that $v \ll c$), they can be described by classical mechanics. This means that the center of mass of the plates, which is stationary at point C before the plates interact, must remain stationary and still be at point C after they inter-act. (1) From this line of reasoning, it follows that plate A must lose mass and/or plate B must gain mass. Why? (2) Assume that plate B gains mass Δm and plate A loses mass Δm. Prove that $\Delta m = E/c^2$. (Note that if $v \ll c$, then $x \ll d$.)

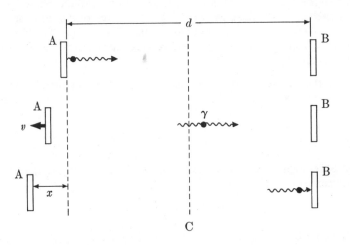

Momentum and velocity   P21.3   From the definition of momentum, it is obvious that if the velocity of a particle is constant, its momentum must be constant. It is not so obvious that if its momentum is constant, its velocity must necessarily be constant. Prove that this is the case. (SUGGESTED METHOD: Set $dp/dt = 0$ and show that this condition can hold only if $dv/dt = 0$.)

Energy and force   P21.4   Show that the equation $dE/dt = \mathbf{F} \cdot \mathbf{v}$ is valid relativistically as well as classically if the force $\mathbf{F}$ is defined by $\mathbf{F} = d\mathbf{p}/dt$.

Recoil red shift   P21.5   A certain nucleus has a rest mass M when it is in its ground state and a rest mass $M + \Delta M$ when it is in an excited state. Consider the example of photon emission (gamma decay) illustrated in the figure. The nucleus is initially in its excited state and initially stationary. Then it emits a photon of energy E and recoils with speed v. If the nucleus did *not* recoil, the energy of the photon would be $E_0 = \Delta M c^2$. (1) Show that because of the nuclear recoil, which is required by momentum conservation, the actual energy of the photon is

$$E = E_0 \left[1 - \frac{E_0}{2(M + \Delta M)c^2} \right].$$

(2) Show that the recoil speed of the nucleus in nonrelativistic approximation is given by $v \cong (\Delta M/M)c$.

P21.6   A neutral pion in flight (with speed $v = \beta c$) decays into two photons whose paths make equal angles θ with the original direction of the pion (see the figure). Prove (1) that the photons have equal energy and (2) that $\cos \theta = \beta$.

Particle decay in two dimensions

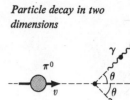

P21.7   (1) A positive pion of mass M is initially at rest. It decays into a muon of mass m and a massless neutrino ($\pi^+ \rightarrow \mu^+ + \nu_\mu$). Using the conservation laws of energy and momentum, show that the speed of the muon is given by

Particle decay in one dimension

$$\frac{v}{c} = \frac{(M/m)^2 - 1}{(M/m)^2 + 1}.$$

(2) Using the known masses of pion and muon, evaluate v/c numerically. (3) If the pion decays instead into a *positron* and a neutrino ($\pi^+ \rightarrow e^+ + \nu_e$), as it may do with a certain small probability, how are the results of parts 1 and 2 (now applied to the positron) changed?

P21.8   A pion moving along the x axis with speed v decays into a muon and a neutrino. As shown in the figure, the x components of velocity of the product particles are v_1 and c, respectively. (1) Write the equations of energy and momentum conservation for this decay process. (2) From these equations, obtain the result

$$\frac{v_1}{c} = \frac{1 - \xi}{1 + \xi},$$

where

$$\xi = \left(\frac{M}{m}\right)^2 \frac{1 - (v/c)}{1 + (v/c)}.$$

(3) Under what circumstances is v_1 (a) nearly equal to c? (b) equal to zero? (c) negative?

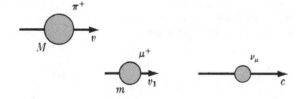

P21.9   A photon has angular frequency ω ($\omega = 2\pi\nu$) and wave vector **k** (the magnitude of **k** is the wave number $k = 2\pi/\lambda$ and its direction is the direction of propagation of the photon). (1) Using the relationships of frequency to energy and wavelength to momentum, prove that k_x, k_y, k_z, and ω/c form the components of a four-vector. (2) What is the length of this four-vector?

Wave vector and frequency form a four-vector

P21.10   (This problem builds on the preceding problem.) (1) Write down the Lorentz-transformation equations that link the wave-vector components k_x, k_y, k_z, and angular frequency ω in a "stationary" frame of reference to the corresponding quantities k'_x, k'_y, k'_z, and ω' in a frame of reference moving in the positive x direction with speed v (as defined in Figure 20.6). (2) Express ω as a function of ω' and v for each of the following cases: (a) $k'_x = k'$, $k'_y = k'_z = 0$ (photon propagating parallel to the x' axis); (b) $k'_x = k'_y = 0$, $k'_z = k'$ (photon propagating parallel to the z' axis). (3) For which of the cases considered in part 2 is the fractional difference of frequencies in the two frames greater?

Four-dimensional scalar product

P21.11   The three-dimensional scalar product is defined by $\mathbf{a} \cdot \mathbf{b} = a_x b_x + a_y b_y + a_z b_z$; it has the property that $\mathbf{a} \cdot \mathbf{a}$ is the square of the length of $\mathbf{a}$. (1) How should the four-dimensional scalar product $A \cdot B$ be defined if $A \cdot A$ is to be the square of the four-dimensional length of A (A and B symbolize four-vectors)? (2) What is the scalar product of (a) a four-dimensional space-time displacement with itself? (b) a momentum-energy four-vector with itself? (c) a spacetime displacement with a momentum-energy four-vector? *Optional:* Prove that the four-dimensional scalar product is an invariant quantity.

Momentum and energy in two dimensions

P21.12   A particle of mass m moves vertically with speed v relative to a railroad car that moves with the same speed v relative to the ground (see the figure). In the train-based frame of reference, the momentum components of the particle are $p'_x = 0$, $p'_y = mv/\sqrt{1 - \beta^2}$, where $\beta = v/c$. (1) What is the particle's energy E' in the train-based frame of reference? (2) Find the momentum components and energy of the particle in the ground-based frame of reference. (3) Show that in the ground-based frame, the path of the particle makes an angle with the horizontal given by $\theta = \arctan\sqrt{1 - \beta^2}$. What is this angle in the limits $\beta \to 0$ and $\beta \to 1$? (4) Verify that your expressions for energy and momentum satisfy the invariance requirement

$$(E/c)^2 - p_x{}^2 - p_y{}^2 = (E'/c)^2 - p'_x{}^2 - p'_y{}^2.$$

P21.13   A particle is initially moving in the x direction with speed v_1 and momentum $\mathbf{p}_1$. An impulsive force in the y direction then adds an increment of momentum $\Delta\mathbf{p}$. The diagram shows the vector addition of momenta: the final momentum is $\mathbf{p}_2 = \mathbf{p}_1 + \Delta\mathbf{p}$. (1) According to classical mechanics, how is the x component of final velocity ($v_{2x} = v_2 \cos\theta$) related to v_1? (2) Show that, relativistically, v_{2x} is *less* than v_1. (3) For the special case $|\Delta\mathbf{p}| = p_1$ ($\theta = \frac{1}{4}\pi$), derive the result

$$v_{2x} = \frac{v_1}{\sqrt{1 + (v_1/c)^2}}.$$

(HINT: Recall that the formulas $E^2 = p^2 c^2 + m^2 c^4$ and $v = pc^2/E$ are valid irrespective of a particle's direction of motion.)

Velocity addition in two dimensions

P21.14   Event 1: A particle leaves point A in a space vehicle. Event 2: The particle reaches point B. In the vehicle's frame of reference (diagram a), the components of the particle's displacement are $\Delta x' = X$, $\Delta y' = Y$, and the components of its velocity are v'_x, v'_y. In an Earth-fixed frame of reference (diagram b), in which the vehicle's speed is v_0, the particle moves from A to B with velocity components v_x, v_y. (1) Use the Lorentz-transformation equations to express Δx, Δy, and Δt in terms of $\Delta x'$, $\Delta y'$, and $\Delta t'$, and from these equations obtain the following laws of velocity addition:

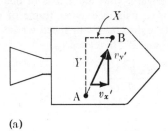

(a)

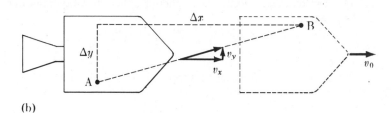

(b)

$$v_x = \frac{v_0 + v_x'}{1 + (v_0 v_x'/c^2)}, \qquad v_y = \frac{v_y' \sqrt{1 - (v_0{}^2/c^2)}}{1 + (v_0 v_x'/c^2)}.$$

(2) Specialize these results to the cases of (a) longitudinal motion ($v_y' = 0$) and (b) transverse motion in the space vehicle ($v_x' = 0$).

P21.15   (1) In a pool-hall frame of reference, two billiard balls collide as shown in the left-hand diagram. Initially, ball A has velocity components v_0, $-v_a$ and ball B has velocity components 0, v_b. In the collision, the x components of velocity are unchanged and the y components of velocity are reversed. Show that the conservation of momentum in this frame requires that v_a and v_b be related by $v_a = v_b \sqrt{1 - (v_0{}^2/c^2)}$. (Note that the classical result would be $v_a = v_b$.) (2) The appearance of the collision in a frame moving to the right with speed v_0 is shown in the right-hand diagram. In this frame the initial velocity components are 0, $-v_b$ and $-v_0$, v_a for balls A and B, respectively. From the velocity transformation laws given in the preceding problem, of the relativistic definition of momentum and the relativistic properties of spacetime. obtain the same result $v_a = v_b \sqrt{1 - (v_0{}^2/c^2)}$. This affords a consistency check

Velocity addition and momentum conservation

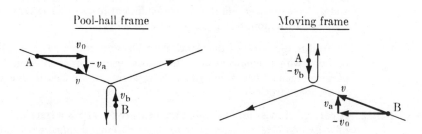

Pool-hall frame   Moving frame

Transformation of photon angle

P21.16 The path of a photon makes an angle θ with the x axis in one frame of reference and an angle θ' with the x' axis in another frame of reference. The second frame is moving in the x direction with speed v relative to the first frame. Show that the angles θ and θ' are related by

$$\cos\theta = \frac{\cos\theta' + \beta}{1 + \beta\cos\theta'},$$

where $\beta = v/c$.

Doppler shift in two dimensions

P21.17 In a frame of reference moving in the x direction with speed $v = \beta c$, a photon has frequency v' and its momentum $\mathbf{p}'$ makes an angle θ' with the x' axis. (1) Show that the frequency of the photon in the laboratory frame of reference is given by

$$v = v'\frac{1 + \beta\cos\theta'}{\sqrt{1 - \beta^2}}.$$

(2) Show that this Doppler-shift formula can also be written

$$v = v'\frac{\sqrt{1 - \beta^2}}{1 - \beta\cos\theta},$$

where θ is the angle between the photon path and the x axis in the laboratory frame. (Note that the Doppler-shift formulas derived in Chapter 20 are special cases of these results with $\cos\theta = \cos\theta' = \pm 1$.)

Mass and energy of a system

P21.18 One nonillion (10^{30}) photons, each of energy 1 MeV, are flying about within an otherwise empty container whose interior walls are perfectly reflecting. (1) The total momentum of the system is zero. (a) What is its total energy in joules? (b) What is its rest mass? (HINT: It is *not* zero.) (2) At what speed should the container be moved in order to add 1 J of energy to the system?

P21.19 Each of the photons in the hypothetical system described in the preceding problem is replaced by an electron whose *kinetic* energy is 1 MeV. The total momentum of the electrons is zero. (1) (a) What is the total energy of this system in joules? (b) What is its mass in kilograms? (2) By how much does the mass of the system differ from the sum of the masses of the constituents? (3) By how much does the bulk kinetic energy of the system differ from the total kinetic energy of the constituents? (4) Some of the electrons in the system lose energy by radiating photons, which are trapped within the system. Which, if any, of the bulk properties of the system are influenced by this process?

Momentum-energy invariant for a system

P21.20 For a system of two free particles, prove that the quantity $(E_1 + E_2)^2 - (\mathbf{p}_1 c + \mathbf{p}_2 c)^2$ is an invariant. What is its significance? (HINT: Although $\mathbf{p}_1$ and $\mathbf{p}_2$ have arbitrary directions, it is sufficient to consider reference frames whose relative motion is along the x axis. Why?)

P21.21 Generalize the result of the preceding problem to n free particles. This can be done with a *minimum* of mathematics, using induction—considering 2 particles, then 3, then 4, etc. (HINT: In what respect are 2 particles equivalent to a single particle?)

Completely inelastic collision

P21.22 A particle of mass m_1 and initial total energy E_1 strikes a stationary particle of mass m_2. The particles stick together, forming a single particle of mass M that moves ahead in the direction of motion of the incident particle. (1) Prove that

$$M = \sqrt{m_1{}^2 + m_2{}^2 + 2m_2(E_1/c^2)}.$$

Verify that this result agrees with Equation 21.57 when $m_1 = m_2 = m$. (2) What is the approximate magnitude of M in the nonrelativistic limit?

P21.23 (1) Prove that the laws of energy and momentum conservation prohibit the decay of an isolated photon into two material particles. Let the particles have arbitrary masses m_1 and m_2, and assume that the photon is adequately energetic: $E_\gamma > m_1 c^2 + m_2 c^2$. (SUGGESTION: Carry out the proof first in one dimension, assuming that the created particles move in the same direction as the photon. The generalization of the proof to two dimensions—arbitrary directions of the final particles—should not be difficult.) (2) Electron-positron pair creation by a photon ($\gamma \rightarrow e^+ + e^-$) is in fact a common process. Explain how it can occur.

Stability of the photon

P21.24 A projectile proton with energy E_1 and momentum p_1 collides with a target proton. If the target proton is inside a nucleus, it is not at rest. Suppose that it is moving directly toward the projectile proton, as shown in the diagram, with energy E_2 and momentum p_2. (1) (a) Show that the invariant mass M of this two-proton system is defined by

Effect of target motion on available energy

$$M^2 c^4 = 2[m^2 c^4 + E_1 E_2 + p_1 p_2 c^2].$$

(b) Verify that this formula agrees with Equation 21.57 when $p_2 = 0$. (2) (a) Consider a limit in which the projectile proton is superrelativistic ($E_1 \gg mc^2$) and the target proton is nonrelativistic ($p_2 c \ll mc^2$). Show in this limit that the invariant mass is $M \cong M_0 + (E_1\sqrt{2mK_2}/M_0 c^3)$, where M_0 is the invariant mass given by Equation 21.57 and K_2 is the kinetic energy of the target proton. (b) Find M_0 and M if $E_1 = 300$ GeV and $K_2 = 50$ MeV (0.05 GeV).

$$\begin{array}{cc} m & m \\ \longrightarrow & \longleftarrow \\ p_1,\ E_1 & p_2,\ E_2 \end{array}$$

P21.25 Prove that for Compton scattering, the angle φ of the path of the recoiling electron is related to the photon scattering angle θ and the initial wavelength λ_1 of the photon by

Electron recoil in the Compton effect

$$\tan \varphi = \frac{\lambda_1}{\lambda_1 + \lambda_c}\ \mathrm{ctn}\ \tfrac{1}{2}\theta,$$

where $\lambda_c = h/mc$. (This expression would be useful in designing a coincidence experiment in which both the recoiling electron and the scattered photon are detected.)

P21.26 Complete the table below for a four-dimensional hypercube (or tesseract). To do this, consider a succession of displacements, first of a point to form a line segment, then of a line segment perpendicular to itself to form a square, then of a square perpendicular to itself to form a cube, and finally of a cube "perpendicular to itself" to form a hypercube. (NOTE: This brain-stretcher has no direct utility in relativity theory.)

Properties of a hypercube

Entity	Dimensionality	Vertices	Edges	Faces	Solids
Point	0	1	0	0	0
Line segment	1	2	1	0	0
Square	2	4	4	1	0
Cube	3			6	1
Hypercube	4				

22 General Relativity

The special theory of relativity, in spite of its all-embracing scope as a theory of theories, is indeed "special" in the sense that it describes transformations of observations only among inertial frames of reference and imposes an invariance requirement on physical laws only in inertial frames. This circumstance need not be regarded as a *defect* of the theory, of course, any more than Newton's laws of motion were regarded as defective for the same reason—that they too apply directly only to motion in inertial frames. Nevertheless, Einstein did regard it as a defect, and his conviction that the laws of nature should be expressed in a form invariant in *all* frames of reference, accelerated or not, was the primary motivating force that led to the general theory of relativity, a structure of magnificent beauty and simplicity from the mathematician's point of view, yet more difficult to understand, interpret, and apply than any other theory in the history of science.

22.1 Inertial forces and gravitational forces

In order to generalize relativity, it is necessary to think about observations in noninertial—that is, accelerated—frames of reference.* In fact we are all experienced observers in noninertial frames, and we know that things are not quite normal when our frame of reference is accelerated. A high-speed elevator

---

* We start with a Newtonian point of view, taking an inertial frame to be a frame in which a body free of all outside influences, including gravity, is unaccelerated. Experimentally, such a frame is found to be one that is itself unaccelerated relative to the average distribution of mass in the universe. This chapter will develop the Einsteinian point of view, in which gravity need *not* be regarded as an outside influence. Then certain accelerated frame—those in free fall—are inertial frames.

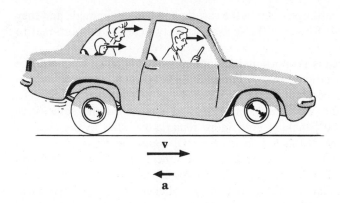

FIGURE 22.1 Inertial force. In a decelerating car, all passengers are thrown forward with equal acceleration. In the car-based frame of reference, each experiences an inertial force proportional to his own inertial mass.

when starting or stopping produces an odd but unmistakable feeling in the passengers. An automobile rounding a corner "throws" the passengers to one side. The same car slowing down throws the passengers forward. The pushing of passengers this way and that inside an accelerated car is brought about by "inertial forces." Being trained in Newtonian mechanics, we know that inertial forces are not real forces at all, but only apparent forces arising from the car's motion.

A formula for inertial force is easy to derive. Consider a passenger in an accelerating car. For him, Newton's second law reads

$$\mathbf{F}_{\text{true}} = m_I\mathbf{a}, \qquad (22.1)$$

where $\mathbf{a}$ is his acceleration relative to an inertial frame and m_I is his inertial mass. We may write

$$\mathbf{a} = \mathbf{a}_{\text{car}} + \mathbf{a}_{\text{rel}}; \qquad (22.2)$$

his acceleration is the sum of the acceleration of the car ($\mathbf{a}_{\text{car}}$) plus his acceleration relative to the car ($\mathbf{a}_{\text{rel}}$). Replacing $\mathbf{a}$ in Equation 22.1 with this sum yields

$$m_I\mathbf{a}_{\text{rel}} = \mathbf{F}_{\text{true}} - m_I\mathbf{a}_{\text{car}}. \qquad (22.3)$$

The combination on the right side is the apparent force in the accelerated frame of reference. The second term is the so-called inertial force,

Inertial forces act in an accelerated frame of reference

$$\mathbf{F}_{\text{inertial}} = -m_I\mathbf{a}_{\text{car}}. \qquad (22.4)$$

Even with no true force acting, the passenger experiences a relative acceleration dictated by this inertial force.

What if we were inside a car with blackened windows and could not watch the driver or hear the engine? Could we distinguish real forces from inertial forces? Before answering this question in the next section, we consider the important similarity between apparent inertial forces and real gravitational forces. Both are proportional to mass. If an adult and a child are in an automobile that is suddenly slowed (Figure 22.1), they will be thrown forward side by side with the same acceleration relative to the car, just as they would fall side by side if they jumped together from a platform. Their equal acceleration relative to the slowing car is no mystery to an outside observer because he sees all the occupants, large or small, tending to continue forward with constant

Inertial force is proportional to mass

velocity. But to the passengers within the car, the force is real enough, and they would decide that this force has the special property that it is proportional to mass.

The inertial force is proportional to inertial mass, the gravitational force proportional to gravitational mass. However, gravitational mass and inertial mass were known to be equal long before the arrival of relativity theory. The experiment of Roland von Eötvös in 1890 had established the equality to within one part in 10^8, making even more remarkable what in prerelativity science had to be regarded as a coincidence. (Of course no one believed that the equality of the two kinds of mass really was a coincidence, but no explanation for the equality had been advanced.) The Eötvös experiment played a role for general relativity similar to that played by the Michelson-Morley experiment for special relativity. In each case the *absence* of a measurable effect or difference was the key result, and in each case the null result was directly related to a central postulate of the theory. The Michelson-Morley experiment was accounted for by the second postulate of special relativity, the constant speed of light. The Eötvös experiment underlies the Principle of Equivalence.

22.2   The Principle of Equivalence

In 1907, after Einstein's relativity had established a link between mass and energy, Max Planck was led to predict a similar link between gravity and energy. Perhaps, said Planck, pure energy, even without mass, should experience gravitational force and exert gravitational force. In the same year Einstein formulated similar ideas in a bolder way. Inertial effects and gravitational effects, said Einstein, are not merely closely related, they are identical and indistinguishable. The observers in the closed car should be unable by any means whatever to ascertain whether the forces they feel are true gravitational forces or apparent inertial forces. This hypothesis of Einstein, called the *Principle of Equivalence*, formed a cornerstone of the theory of general relativity that evolved over the next eight years. An immediate deduction from this postulate is that inertial mass and gravitational mass must be equal*; otherwise the difference between these two kinds of mass would afford a means of distinguishing gravitational from inertial forces.

Inertial forces and gravitational forces are indistinguishable

A few examples may help to clarify the meaning of the Principle of Equivalence. Consider first an elevator falling freely without friction down a very long elevator shaft (Figure 22.2). To observers within the elevator, there are no external forces at all. A ball released from the hand will not fall to the floor of the elevator because it will fall toward the earth just as the elevator itself and the passengers are falling; to the passengers it will appear to float in air. Relative to the elevator the ball satisfies Newton's first law, and the passengers, pursuing this and other experiments as they fall, will conclude that they are in an inertial frame of reference. Not at all, say the ground-based observers. The elevator is an accelerated system. It just happens that upward-

Falling elevator: accelerated frame with gravity or inertial frame without gravity?

---

* Stated more exactly, they must be proportional since it is not necessary that they be expressed in the same unit.

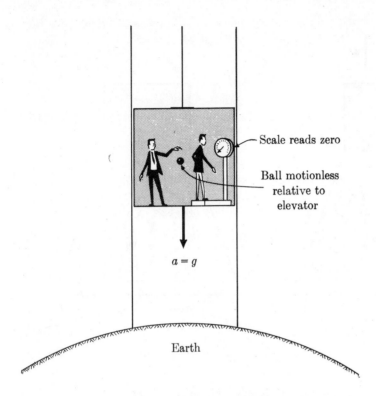

Scale reads zero

Ball motionless relative to elevator

$a = g$

Earth

FIGURE 22.2 To its occupants, a freely falling elevator is an inertial frame. The cancellation of upward inertial forces and downward gravitational forces in the accelerated frame of reference makes it indistinguishable from an inertial frame floating free in gravity-free space.

acting apparent inertial forces cancel the downward-acting real gravitational forces, and the passengers are deluded into believing themselves to be in an inertial frame with no forces acting. The "weightless" condition of astronauts in orbit about the earth arises from just this cancellation of inertial and gravitational forces.

Or consider a space ship, far from any sources of gravitational force, being uniformly accelerated by its rocket engine [Figure 22.3(a)]. This time a ball dropped from the hand will fall with uniform acceleration to the floor of the cabin. From the point of view of an outside observer, the ball remains motionless in space, but the cabin floor is accelerated upward to meet it. He recognizes that there are no real forces acting, only apparent forces arising from the acceleration of the space ship. To observers within the space ship, however, these forces seem quite real. The crew may decide that they are motionless, parked on some planet [Figure 22.3(b)]. According to Einstein's Principle of Equivalence, there is no experiment that the occupants of the falling elevator or the accelerating rocket could carry out that would unambiguously decide in favor of their point of view or the viewpoint of the outside observers. That gravity and acceleration through space produce identical physical effects is the remarkable assertion of the Principle of Equivalence.

One implication of this principle is that a coasting spacecraft, even near the earth or moon, may legitimately be said to define an inertial frame of reference. Since it is equivalent to an inertial frame—according to any experiment performed within it—it *is* an inertial frame.

Thrusting rocket: accelerated frame without gravity or inertial frame with gravity?

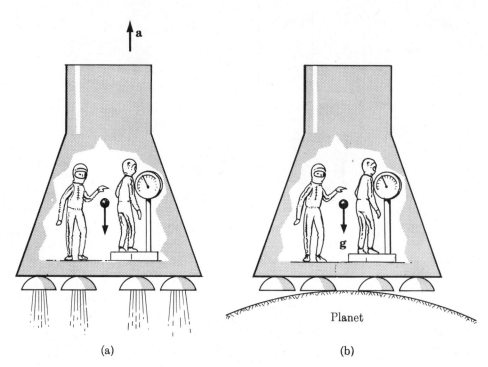

FIGURE 22.3   An accelerated space ship in gravity-free space (a) is, to its occupants, indistinguishable from a space ship sitting motionless in the gravitational field of a planet (b). (The planet, of course, must be chosen so that the acceleration of free fall at its surface, g, matches the acceleration, a, of the first space ship.)

To return to the passengers being thrown forward in the slowing automobile, the Principle of Equivalence means that an enormous mass placed in front of a stationary car would pull the passengers forward in a way indistinguishable from the effect of suddenly slowing a moving car (Figure 22.4). But we know that inertial forces are unreal. They are properties of the motion of our frame of reference. We imagine we are experiencing a force because of

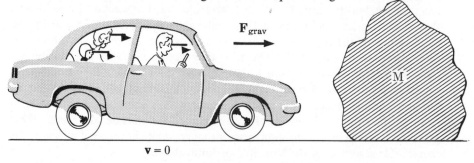

FIGURE 22.4   If a hypothetical enormous mass is placed in front of a stationary automobile, its passengers can be accelerated forward in a way that, to them, is indistinguishable from the effect of decelerating a moving automobile (Figure 22.1).

the acceleration of our frame of reference.   If we accept the Principle of
Equivalence, we must accept the idea that gravitational forces too are "unreal"   *Gravity is an "apparent"*
and are in some way merely properties of space and time.   This is Einstein's   *force linked to spacetime*
point of view, to which we shall return after discussing several implications of
the Principle of Equivalence that have been verified experimentally.

22.3   The bending of light by gravity

Again returning to the example of the elevator that was falling freely down its
shaft (Figure 22.2), let us suppose that the outside observer, in his zeal to
enlighten the elevator passengers and convince them that they are not in an
inertial frame of reference, thinks up a clever experiment.   He arranges with
the passengers to make a pinhole in one side of the elevator and to erect within
the elevator several equally spaced translucent screens that will enable the
passengers to see what route a narrow beam of light follows through the
elevator.   He then shines a narrow beam in horizontally through the pinhole.
It makes its way across the elevator at the speed of light, leaving a visible spot
on each screen as it passes.   Since the elevator is falling with ever-increasing
speed, the distance it falls as the light travels from the second to the third
screen is greater than the distance it falls as the light moved from the first to
the second screen, and so on for the successive intervals.   According to the
outside observer, the light, executing straight line motion through space, should
leave a track within the elevator that seems to be an upward curving parabola
(Figure 22.5).   Since light could hardly travel in a curved path in an inertial
frame, this should convince the passengers that they are in an accelerated frame.
But the Principle of Equivalence allows no physical way for the elevator

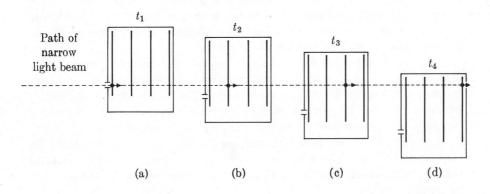

(a)   (b)   (c)   (d)

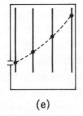

(e)

FIGURE 22.5   Path across translucent screens
in falling elevator predicted by outside
observer who believes that light travels in a
straight line in his frame of reference.
(a) through (d): Successive positions of
elevator at equally spaced time intervals as
light beam crosses screens. (e): Apparent
curved path seen by passengers if the outside
observer's contention is correct.

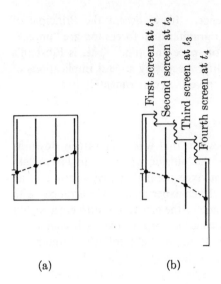

(a)   (b)

FIGURE 22.6   (a) Actual straight path of light seen by elevator passengers is
consistent with other evidence that their frame is an inertial frame.
(b) Superimposed view of elevator position at equally spaced time intervals
shows the downward deflection of the light beam seen by the outside observer.

*An implication of the
Principle of Equivalence:
Light must be attracted by
gravity*

passengers to determine whether their frame is truly inertial or one in which
gravitational and inertial forces are both present but cancel out. The only light
path consistent with the principle is a straight line within the elevator (Figure
22.6). But a straight line to the passengers is a downward-curving arc to the
outside observer. The result of the experiment will not be that the elevator
passengers become convinced of the error of their ways, but that the outside
observer learns to his surprise that his beam of light is attracted by gravity and
follows a curved path rather than a straight line.

This surprising result for the outside observer does not, of course, violate
the Principle of Equivalence. Quite the contrary: It is demanded by the principle.
By the equivalence of gravitational and inertial effects, any effect of the earth's
gravity—observed, for example, within a classroom—could be duplicated by
"turning off" gravity and instead accelerating the whole classroom upward. In
the latter case, a beam of light moving horizontally should appear to be
curving downward. Therefore, in the former case (gravity turned on again)
the light beam should also "appear" to be curving downward; that is, it should
be attracted by gravity.

The gravitational deflection of light was implied by Planck's hypothesis
in 1907 that all energy should experience gravitational force (and exert gravitational force). Yet the phenomenon was apparently not appreciated until 1911,
when Einstein pointed out that on the basis of the Principle of Equivalence,
it was to be expected. Moreover, he suggested a specific method of detecting
the effect. Starlight passing close to the sun should experience some deflection,
and the apparent position of the star should, accordingly, be slightly shifted
relative to its position at some other time of the year when its light received at

*Deflection of starlight by
the sun*

"*Curse Con Edison! Another brownout!*"

Drawing by Lorenz. © 1973 The New Yorker Magazine, Inc.

the earth does not pass near the sun (Figure 22.7). Unfortunately, sunlight itself is so intense that at that time it was impossible to observe stars whose position in the sky was near the sun. Not until 1919 did a total eclipse of the sun make possible the brief but decisive measurements of apparent positions of stars near the sun that verified Einstein's prediction that light (energy without mass) is deflected by gravity. Neither these measurements nor those that followed at later eclipses were accurate enough to test with precision the exact magnitude of the effect. Now at last, after more than half a century, new techniques are available to accurately measure the apparent positions of stars near the sun, even without the benefit of an eclipse. These may soon yield greatly improved data on the bending of light by gravity.

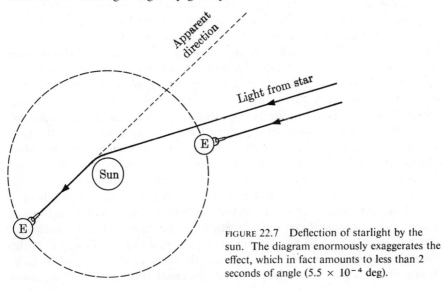

FIGURE 22.7   Deflection of starlight by the sun. The diagram enormously exaggerates the effect, which in fact amounts to less than 2 seconds of angle (5.5×10^{-4} deg).

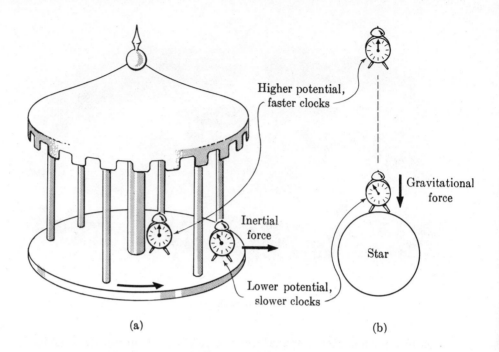

FIGURE 22.8   (a) According to special relativity, the clock near the periphery of the rotating frame runs slower than the clock at the center. An observer in the rotating frame attributes this to the difference in potential of the two locations. (b) Since gravity can duplicate inertial effects, even clocks that are at rest must run slower in regions of lower gravitational potential.

22.4   Gravity and time: the gravitational red shift

Two other famous predictions of general relativity can be approximately understood in terms of the Principle of Equivalence as applied to length and time measurements in accelerated frames of reference. In order to understand these, we will consider a rotating frame of reference (which is, of course, an accelerated frame) rather than a frame uniformly accelerated in a straight line. To stay with familiar objects, let us replace the elevator with a merry-go-round. Consider two clocks on the merry-go-round, one at its center and one at its edge. From special relativity we know that the clock at the center, since it is not moving with respect to the ground, should run at the same rate as ground-based clocks. But the clock at the edge is in motion with respect to the earth and should therefore be observed to be running slower than ground-based clocks. This tells us at once that the two clocks on the merry-go-round, though attached to the same frame of reference, do not run synchronously; the outer clock loses time with respect to the inner clock (Figure 22.8). This difference would be noticeable to observers on the merry-go-round as well as to those on the ground. A ground-based observer attributes the slower rate of the peripheral clock to its motion. To an observer on the merry-go-round, however, neither clock is in motion. He must attribute the difference to something else. In his frame of reference there is one marked difference between the environments

*Clocks are not synchronous
in a rotating frame*

of the two clocks. At the edge of the merry-go-round is a strong "centrifugal force" (an inertial force arising from the accelerated motion), but there is no such force at the center. Therefore, he decides that in a region of stronger force, clocks run slower. Applying the Principle of Equivalence, we must conclude that clocks in strong gravitational fields of force run slower than clocks in weak fields of force. Actually, general relativity shows gravitational potential, rather than gravitational force, to be the significant variable. If we let Δt_1 and Δt_2 be time intervals measured by two clocks located in regions of different gravitational potential, the approximate relationship is

$$\frac{\Delta t_2 - \Delta t_1}{\Delta t} = \frac{u_2 - u_1}{c^2}, \qquad (22.5)$$

The influence of gravitational potential on time

where u is gravitational potential, or gravitational potential energy per unit mass ($u = U/m$). Recall that the dimension of c^2 is also energy per unit mass. The Δt appearing in the denominator on the left side may be taken to be either Δt_1 or Δt_2 or their average since it is assumed that the fractional difference of Δt_1 and Δt_2 is small.

Einstein predicted the effect of gravity on time at the same time he formulated the Principle of Equivalence in 1907, and he suggested a way to observe it. Every atom may be regarded as a clock. The slowing down of clocks—that is, the slowing of all physical processes—is manifested by a slowing down of atomic vibrations. An atom on the surface of the sun, where the gravitational potential is lower (more negative) than on earth, should therefore emit light of lower frequency than that emitted by the same kind of atom on the earth. This effect was indeed observed in sunlight, but various disturbing influences made it hard to measure, and the gravitational red shift, as this effect is called, was in fact never reliably verified until 1960, when an entirely new technique made possible an accurate measurement on earth.

Atoms on the sun have dilated time scales

Usually, when an atom shoots out a photon of light, it recoils like a gun so that some of the energy intended for the photon is drained off by the recoiling atom. But less energy for the photon means less frequency. The act of emitting the photon has lowered the photon frequency, producing a "recoil red shift." In the comparatively weak gravitational field on the surface of the earth, the recoil red shift is so much greater than the gravitational red shift that it was never possible to measure the tiny effect of gravity superposed on the big effect of recoil. In 1957, however, Rudolph Mössbauer in Heidelberg, Germany, discovered a way to entirely eliminate the recoil red shift. Under certain conditions, atoms held within solid crystals at low temperature may be so tightly glued in place that they are unable to recoil when they emit a photon. From deep within such an atom, a nucleus can emit its characteristic photons (gamma rays) at their full frequency, free of any recoil red shift and free of any disturbance from neighboring atoms.

Robert Pound of Harvard, and simultaneously a group in England, realized that this "Mössbauer effect" should at last make possible an accurate test of Einstein's 1907 prediction. If a nucleus identical to the emitting nucleus is used as a receiver of the photon, the receiving nucleus will strongly absorb the photon only if the time scales of the two nuclei, emitter and absorber, are the same and if no effect has altered the photon frequency. An exceedingly minute

Thanks to the "Mössbauer effect," a test on earth

change of frequency (or of time scales) will be at once noticeable because the receiving nucleus will be less well able to absorb the photon. Pound and a student of his, G. A. Rebka, Jr., were the first to achieve reliable results, and announced their findings in the summer of 1960. To within an accuracy of 3 percent, Einstein's prediction was exactly verified. Later experiments reduced the uncertainty to 1 percent.

Near the earth, the change of gravitational potential between points separated by vertical distance h is $\Delta u = gh$. Therefore, the fractional difference of frequency at two levels is, from Equation 22.5,

$$\frac{\Delta v}{v} = \frac{gh}{c^2}. \tag{22.6}$$

For $h = 21$ m,
$\Delta v/v \cong 2 \times 10^{-15}$

Pound and Rebka worked in a shaft within their laboratory, separating the receiving nucleus and the sending nucleus by 21 m (70 ft). The gravitational effect on frequency is then about 2 parts in 10^{15}. This almost inconceivably small effect corresponds to the lower clock falling 1 sec behind the upper clock in 15 million years. At no time before in the history of experimental science had such a small effect been measured.

Two views of frequency shift:
(1) change of time scale;
(2) change of energy

It is interesting that this red shift can be looked at from an entirely different point of view, making use of the equation relating the energy of a photon to its frequency: $E = hv$, where h is Planck's quantum constant. Since a photon has energy, it will be influenced by gravity. A photon leaving the sun will be "retarded" by the sun's gravity and will lose energy as it flies away, just as a ball thrown straight up loses kinetic energy because of the pull of the earth. The photon's loss of energy will be equivalent to a loss of frequency, and it will arrive at the earth with less frequency than a brother photon emitted on the earth. This different viewpoint serves to illustrate the inner consistency of general relativity and the fascinating way the concepts of spacetime, gravity, and energy are linked together.

22.5   Gravity and space: the motion of Mercury

The accelerated merry-go-round of Figure 22.8 implies an effect of gravity on distance measurements quite analogous to the effect on time measurements. A rule laid along the circumference of the merry-go-round will appear contracted to the observer on the ground, whereas a ruler near the center, moving much more slowly, will be nearly unaffected. Again making use of the Principle of Equivalence, we must conclude that distance measurements will be dependent upon the strength of a gravitational field even if no relative motion is involved.

Length also affected by
gravitational potential

Recall that the rotating merry-go-round is equivalent to a stationary merry-go-round with a strong gravitational field near its edge and a weak gravitational field near its center. The dependence of distance scales on gravitational potential has an effect on the motion of planets about the sun. Exactly what the effect is is by no means easy to see, and Einstein was not able to predict the corrections to planetary motion based on the Principle of Equivalence until 1915, when he arrived at a complete mathematical formulation of gravity and of the properties of spacetime. He then found that only the innermost planet Mercury should be measurably influenced. Mercury moves in an elliptical orbit that carries it

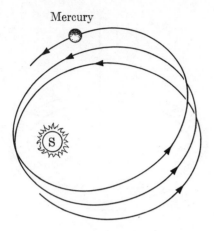

FIGURE 22.9   Precession of the orbit of Mercury. One of the important contributors to the slow rotation of Mercury's orbit is the effect of the sun's gravitational field on the properties of spacetime. In this diagram, both the eccentricity of the orbit and its rate of turning are greatly exaggerated.

periodically into regions of greater and lesser gravitational potential so that, according to the consequences of the Principle of Equivalence that have just been outlined, it experiences periodically varying properties of space and time. The effect on its motion is exceedingly small, but thanks to the great precision of astronomical observation, it is quite easily measurable. It is predicted that the entire ellipse representing Mercury's orbit will itself slowly precess about the sun so that successive trips about the sun will trace out slightly different paths in space (Figure 22.9). Actually, the precession of Mercury's ellipse is caused only in part by the effect of general relativity. Venus, Earth, and other planets also perturb Mercury's motion and contribute to the slow precession of its orbit. The general-relativity contribution amounts to about 0.01 deg per century, or 1 extra revolution in 3 million years. This effect had been known, though unexplained, for many decades, so Einstein's prediction was immediately verified by past observation.

The precession of the orbit of Mercury

Until 1967 the rate of precession of Mercury's orbit was believed to be the most accurate and most crucial test of general relativity. Then a discovery by Robert Dicke and H. Mark Goldenberg at Princeton that the sun is not precisely round introduced a slight blemish in the picture. Because the sun is not quite a perfect sphere, its gravitational field does not follow an exact inverse square law. This in turn contributes to the precession of Mercury's orbit. After adding this new effect to all other known effects and the prediction of general relativity, there remains a tiny discrepancy between theory and observation—about 0.001 deg per century. Perhaps the "known" effects are not well enough known, and improved calculations will wipe out the discrepancy. Perhaps general relativity will require modification. Its important contributions to our understanding of gravity and spacetime will surely not be abandoned, however, nor will the now solid Principle of Equivalence.

A new uncertainty: The sun is not a perfect sphere

Another interesting point appears in considering length measurements on the merry-go-round—geometry itself must be altered in an accelerated frame of reference (or in a fixed frame with a gravitational field). A distance measurement along a radius of the merry-go-round should be unaffected by the motion because the motion is perpendicular to the radius. But distance measurements around the circumference *are* affected. The *ratio* of circumference to diameter

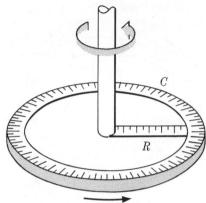

FIGURE 22.10 Rulers in an accelerated frame of reference. The equation of Euclidean geometry, $C = 2\pi R$, is not precisely valid in either a rotating frame of reference or a region of space containing a nonuniform gravitational field.

will no longer be the fixed constant π (3.14159...) but some other number (Figure 22.10). This surprising conclusion is another in the list of violations of common sense that relativity has introduced. It simply means that gravity causes space to be non-Euclidean; the ordinary laws of Euclidean geometry taught in high school are no longer valid. For example, circles need not all have the same ratio of circumference to diameter, and right triangles need not satisfy Pythagoras' theorem. It must be borne in mind, of course, that the deviations from "common sense" predicted by relativity in our everyday world are entirely too small to be observed (if that were not so, common sense might be quite different).

Gravity influences geometry: Space is non-Euclidean

22.6   The new geometry and the new mechanics

Einstein's final formulation of general relativity in 1915 placed geometry in a central role. The mathematics of the theory is too formidable to present here, and we shall have to be content with pointing out a few interesting features of the theory and with indicating some of the implications it holds for the way we think about the world around us and also for possible future theories of nature. But let us first review in logical order (not so very different from the actual historical order) the crucial steps that lead from special relativity to general relativity. First is the desire to extend the Principle of Relativity to embrace invariance of physical laws in all frames of reference, not just inertial frames. This leads to the consideration of accelerated frames, in which apparent forces, or inertial forces, exist. Because of the equality of gravitational mass and inertial mass, inertial forces are indistinguishable from real gravitational forces. The Principle of Equivalence makes of this indistinguishability a fundamental postulate. Applying it to the propagation of light, it is seen that gravity must deflect light, a phenomenon independently suggested by the equivalence of mass and energy. Coupling the equivalence principle with the time-dilation and Lorentz-contraction phenomena of special relativity leads to the conclusion that the properties of spacetime depend on the gravitational potential; it also leads to the prediction of an effect on the motion of Mercury and to the prediction of the gravitational red shift (which is independently

Review of logic, from special to general relativity

suggested by the photon concept of light). Finally, since gravity influences the properties of space and time, it is possible and preferable to regard gravity itself as nothing more than a property of space and time. This reduces gravity to a manifestation of spacetime geometry and provides a rational basis for the Principle of Equivalence since it has always been clear that the "unreal" inertial forces are merely properties of space and time.

Gravity a manifestation of spacetime geometry

General relativity demands of the imagination more than the imagination is able to give. Special relativity had already demanded that we give up the notion of absolute time and that we try to picture a four-dimensional world of spacetime. To these hurdles general relativity adds a "curved" spacetime, asking us to visualize objects not being acted upon by gravitational forces but rather responding in their motion to the "curvature," or "warping," of space in their own neighborhood. In classical physics, space was the stage upon which physical phenomena acted out their parts as absolute time rolled independently on. In special relativity, space and time had to be merged but continued to be the stage, or perhaps better the canvas, upon which phenomena traced out their world-line histories. In general relativity, spacetime is more than the canvas upon which history is painted. It becomes itself an active participant in history, its hills and valleys and warping *being* the phenomena—or at least the phenomena of gravitation. Although the ether was banished by the revolution of special relativity, general relativity has reintroduced a new and subtler "ether"—spacetime itself.* Among the challenging questions raised by relativity are: "Are space and time manifestations of matter and energy? Would space and time have any meaning in an empty universe?"

In order to attempt to visualize curved spacetime, we must retreat from four dimensions to two. The surface of the earth is a good example of a "curved space." In any small region, it seems quite flat, and ordinary geometry works quite well. But if we consider figures of large size, it is obviously non-Euclidean. An equilaterial triangle with sides about 6,000 miles long (Figure 22.11) has three angles of 90 deg instead of three of 60 deg. The Equator is a circle with a circumference that is exactly twice its diameter rather than more than three

Curved space in two dimensions

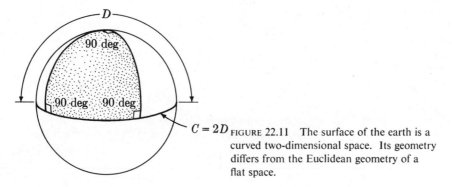

$C = 2D$ FIGURE 22.11   The surface of the earth is a curved two-dimensional space. Its geometry differs from the Euclidean geometry of a flat space.

---

* In 1920 Einstein said: "According to the general theory of relativity, space is endowed with physical qualities; in this sense, therefore, there exists an ether." Compare this statement with the quotation on page 985 from Einstein's 1905 paper.

times its diameter. These are extreme cases, and a surveyor with sufficiently precise measurements could determine the non-Euclidean character of the surface with much smaller figures.

More than 90 years ago, Edwin Abbott, a British clergyman and Shakespearean scholar, invented "Flatland," a two-dimensional realm peopled by squares, triangles, and other two-dimensional figures.* Imagine a group of his squares living on the surface of a large smooth sphere. They would be unable to visualize the curvature of their land because their perspective would not include the necessary third dimension. Nevertheless, with great care they could survey the surface and deduce that it was not a plane because the laws of Euclidean geometry are not precisely correct. Square explorers might journey away from home in a straight line, only to find themselves home again after circling their globe. Man in space is like a Flatlander on a curved surface, able to determine by measurement whether space is "flat" or "curved" but quite unable to visualize a curved space. According to relativity, space is not curved uniformly like the surface of a sphere, but has more curvature near matter and energy and less curvature far away from matter and energy. Yet it probably has an over-all average curvature. It is possible (but has not yet been shown to be so) that space is closed in upon itself, just as the earth's surface is closed, so that the space traveler flying away forever in a straight line would reappear at the earth some billions of years later.

This picture of the space traveler executing a closed circuit without ever turning raises the question: What is a straight line? This is an important question that requires an operational definition for an answer. On the two-dimensional surface of the earth, we can define a "straight line" as the shortest distance between two points. This is usually called a great-circle route. The technical name for it is a geodesic. In three-dimensional space, relativity offers two

Two-dimensional creatures could measure it to be non-Euclidean

A geodesic on Earth

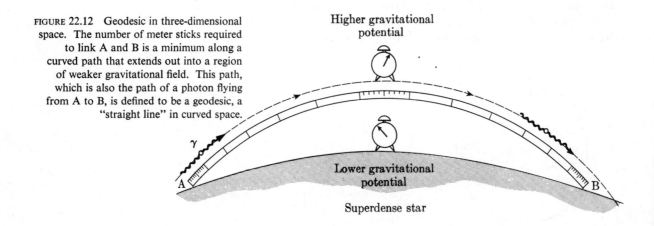

FIGURE 22.12   Geodesic in three-dimensional space. The number of meter sticks required to link A and B is a minimum along a curved path that extends out into a region of weaker gravitational field. This path, which is also the path of a photon flying from A to B, is defined to be a geodesic, a "straight line" in curved space.

Higher gravitational potential

Lower gravitational potential

Superdense star

* Edwin A. Abbott, *Flatland: A Romance of Many Dimensions*, 6th ed. (New York: Dover Publications, Inc., 1952). This classic of science fiction retains its power to instruct and entertain.

equivalent definitions of a geodesic, or straight line (Figure 22.12): It is the path of shortest distance as determined, for instance, by laying out meter sticks end to end, or it is the path followed by a photon. These prove to be the same. As shown in Figure 22.13, the measurements made by Gauss in Germany over a century ago (see Section 5.1) would show space to be non-Euclidean if they were extended to astronomical distances. Because of the observed bending of starlight by the sun, we know that the sum of angles in Figure 22.13, $\alpha + \beta + \gamma$, must be greater than 180 deg.

A geodesic in three-dimensional space: (1) *shortest distance, and* (2) *path of photon*

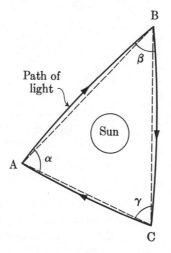

FIGURE 22.13   Surveyors in the solar system who use light paths to define straight lines would find space to be non-Euclidean.

THE LAW OF MOTION

In four-dimensional spacetime, a geodesic is defined not as a path of shortest distance but as a path of greatest proper time. We have already encountered this idea of maximum proper time in considering the twin paradox (Section 20.11). The twin who aged the most was the one who remained in a single inertial frame. It was he who was following a geodesic.

A geodesic in spacetime: maximum proper time

The great importance of the spacetime geodesic is its relation to a relativistic law of motion. If only inertial and/or gravitational forces are considered, the law that replaces Newton's first and second laws is: *All objects follow geodesics in spacetime.* The new law of mechanics is therefore a law of cosmic laziness. In going from one event to another, a body moves in such a way as to maximize the time—as measured by its own clocks—of its spacetime journey.

The new law of motion

The simplest application of this law of motion is to a particle free of gravity or any other outside influence. In an inertial frame of reference, this particle is correctly described by special relativity; in particular, its proper time is given by Equation 20.59:

$$d\tau = \sqrt{(dt)^2 - \frac{1}{c^2}\left[(dx)^2 + (dy)^2 + (dz)^2\right]}$$

$$= dt\sqrt{1 - \frac{v^2}{c^2}}, \tag{22.7}$$

Proper time of body free of any forces

where v is the speed of the particle in the chosen frame of reference [$v^2 = (dx/dt)^2 + (dy/dt)^2 + (dz/dt)^2$]. For the two events A and B in Figure 22.14(a),

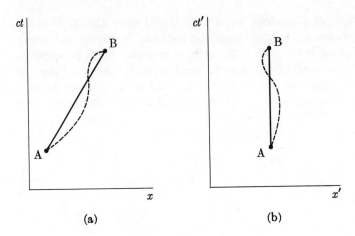

FIGURE 22.14   (a) The world line that maximizes the elapsed proper time
between events A and B is a straight line in the flat space of special relativity.
(b) This is proved by considering a frame of reference in which A and B are at
the same location in space.

we ask what path through spacetime maximizes the proper time of the particle
as it goes from A to B. (We assume the interval between A and B to be time-
like so that it is physically possible for the particle to get from A to B.) Its
elapsed proper time is

Its elapsed proper time

$$\tau = \int_{A}^{B} \sqrt{1 - \frac{v^2}{c^2}} \, dt. \tag{22.8}$$

To show that τ is a maximum if $\mathbf{v} = \textbf{constant}$ is a problem in what is called
the calculus of variations. We can, however, handle this particular problem
without resorting to that branch of calculus. Consider the frame of reference,
with coordinates x', y', z', t', in which events A and B occur *at the same place*
[Figure 22.14(b)]. In this frame the elapsed proper time is

A special frame: end points
at same place

$$\tau = \int_{t'_A}^{t'_B} \sqrt{1 - \frac{v'^2}{c^2}} \, dt'. \tag{22.9}$$

Since the integrand, $\sqrt{1 - (v'^2/c^2)}$, can be no greater than 1, a simple inequality
follows from Equation 22.9:

$$\tau \le t'_B - t'_A. \tag{22.10}$$

In fact, for one possible path—the straight vertical path in Figure 22.14(b)—
$\mathbf{v}' = 0$ (the other two coordinates, y' and z', must be added mentally; they
also do not change). For this path

$$\tau = t'_B - t'_A. \tag{22.11}$$

In this frame, maximum τ
for $\mathbf{v}' = 0$

Since this is the maximum possible value of τ in this frame of reference, the
straight path with $\mathbf{v}' = 0$ must be the actual physical path. The particle remains
motionless in space. Finally, we invoke the invariance of proper time. If we
maximize τ in one frame, we have maximized it in all frames. In any other

frame [such as in Figure 22.14(a)], the transformed world line is a straight line, corresponding to motion with constant velocity.

In any frame, maximum τ for $\mathbf{v}$ = constant

Let us review this reasoning. For a particle free of gravitational or other forces, the geodesic, or path of greatest proper time, in an inertial frame of reference is a straight line in spacetime. According to the new law of motion, this straight world line is therefore the actual spacetime path of the particle. From the condition of maximum proper time follows Newton's first law.

Geodesic path of free particle equivalent to Newton's first law

★MOTION IN A UNIFORM GRAVITATIONAL FIELD

With Einstein's law of motion, we can get a new view of an old problem—motion in a uniform gravitational field, such as that near the surface of the earth. According to Equation 22.5, as we move upward to greater gravitational potential, time runs faster, the fractional change of a time interval Δt being

$$\frac{\Delta(\Delta t)}{\Delta t} = \frac{\Delta u}{c^2} = \frac{g \, \Delta z}{c^2} \, , \tag{22.12}$$

where u is the gravitational potential, defined below Equation 22.5 (here $u = gz + constant$), where g is the acceleration of gravity, and where z is the vertical distance measured upward from any reference level. As suggested by the consideration of a rotating frame (Figure 22.10), length scales are also stretched as one moves to greater gravitational potential.* The amount of the stretching is the same as for time:

$$\frac{\Delta(\Delta s)}{\Delta s} = \frac{g \, \Delta z}{c^2} \, , \tag{22.13}$$

where Δs is a small spatial displacement.

This dilation of both space and time in moving upward is indicated schematically in Figure 22.12. Because of it, the proper time of a particle moving vertically in the gravitational field depends on the position of the particle. It is defined (for $dx = dy = 0$) by

$$d\tau = \sqrt{(dt)^2 - \frac{1}{c^2} (dz)^2 \left(1 + \frac{gz}{c^2}\right)} \, . \tag{22.14}$$

Proper time of particle in uniform gravitational field

This important equation requires some discussion. The coordinates t and z are those of an observer stationed at a reference level $z = 0$. As an object moves upward from this level, its time scale increases in tempo from dt to $dt[1 + (gz/c^2)]$, which follows from Equation 22.12. Similarly, from Equation 22.13, its length scale stretches from dz to $dz[1 + (gz/c^2)]$. This same factor, $[1 + (gz/c^2)]$, multiplying both dt and dz (with $dx = dy = 0$), converts Equation 22.7 to Equation 22.14. It is a general feature of curved spacetime that the definition of proper time deviates from the "flat" spacetime definition, Equation 22.7. Finally, we remark that Equation 22.14 is an approximation, valid for $gz/c^2 \ll 1$.

---

* In the rotating frame, moving from the edge to the center of the disk "against" the centrifugal force is equivalent to moving upward to greater potential in a gravitational field. Length scales in the rotating frame are greatest at the axis, where there is no Lorentz contraction.

Problem: How must a baseball move if it is at the same place at different times?

Armed with this definition of proper time for an object moving along a vertical line in a uniform field, we may apply the new law of motion (τ = maximum) to a simple example of motion. Let Event A be a baseball at $z = 0$ at some time, and let Event B be the baseball at the same point in space at a later time. For convenience, as indicated in Figure 22.15(a), we call these two times $-t_1$ and $+t_1$. Figure 22.15(b) shows possible world lines of the baseball in a Minkowski diagram. The solid curved line is the world line for the actual motion according to Newtonian mechanics:

The Newtonian solution

$$z = z_0 - \tfrac{1}{2}gt^2 = \tfrac{1}{2}g \cdot (t_1{}^2 - t^2). \tag{22.15}$$

(The constant z_0 is equal to $\tfrac{1}{2}gt_1{}^2$ in order that $z = 0$ at $t = -t_1$ and $t = +t_1$.) The dashed lines are other possible world lines. We want to show that the solid curved world line is a geodesic, a path of maximum proper time for the baseball.

From Equation 22.14, we may write, for the elapsed proper time,

Elapsed proper time

$$\tau = \int_{-t_1}^{t_1} \sqrt{1 - \frac{v^2}{c^2}\left(1 + \frac{gz}{c^2}\right)}\, dt, \tag{22.16}$$

with the further condition that $z = 0$ at the end points of the integration. First, a qualitative discussion is in order. In the absence of a gravitational field (set $g = 0$ in Equation 22.16), the baseball moves with constant velocity. If it is to be at the same point in space at different times (Events A and B), this velocity must be zero. The straight line from A to B in Figure 22.15(b) is its world line. This is the conclusion of the previous subsection. Now restore the term containing g. If the world line deviates from a straight line and follows

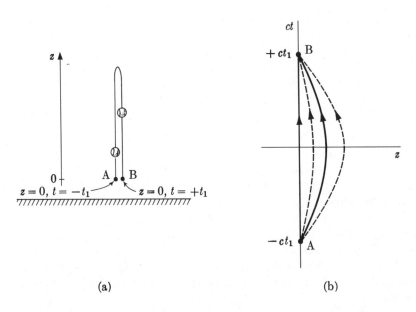

(a)   (b)

FIGURE 22.15   (a) Trajectory of a vertically thrown baseball. It is at $z = 0$ at times $t = -t_1$ and $t = +t_1$. (b) The actual world line of the baseball (heavy curve) is the spacetime path that maximizes the elapsed proper time between Events A and B. The ball rises and falls "in order to" maximize its proper time. Its spacetime path is a geodesic.

one of the dashed lines in Figure 22.15(b), two competing effects occur in the integrand of Equation 22.16. First, the ball has nonzero velocity, so the v^2 term tends to decrease τ. Second, the positive term containing z tends to increase τ. Therefore, we see at least a possibility that the second effect is greater, causing the world line of maximum proper time to be bowed away from a straight vertical line. And this is indeed the case.

Qualitative insight: v = 0 need not maximize τ

To deal with Equation 22.16, we shall make a further approximation, that the motion is nonrelativistic ($v \ll c$). Then

$$\sqrt{1 - \frac{v^2}{c^2}} \cong 1 - \frac{1}{2}\frac{v^2}{c^2},$$

and the integrand is, approximately,

$$\left(1 - \frac{1}{2}\frac{v^2}{c^2}\right)\left(1 + \frac{gz}{c^2}\right).$$

Furthermore, because of the formula

$$(1 - x)(1 + y) \cong 1 - x + y \qquad (x \ll 1, y \ll 1),$$

Equation 22.16 can be approximated by

$$\tau \cong \int_{-t_1}^{t_1} \left(1 - \frac{1}{2}\frac{v^2}{c^2} + \frac{gz}{c^2}\right) dt. \tag{22.17}$$

Low-speed, weak-field approximation

(Recall that $v = dz/dt$.) This time, only the calculus of variations can provide an answer to the question we wish to ask: For what function $z(t)$ does the elapsed proper time, as defined by Equation 22.17, have its maximum value? The answer, which we state without proof, is that, for any pair of physically possible end points of the motion,

$$z(t) = z_0 + v_0 t - \tfrac{1}{2}gt^2;$$

This function maximizes τ

and, in particular, for the end points A and B of Figure 22.15, $z(t)$ is given by Equation 22.15.

We can give a partial proof of the result just stated. Consider a class of motions characterized by constant acceleration a:

$$z(t) = \tfrac{1}{2}a\cdot(t^2 - t_1{}^2),$$

$$v(t) = \frac{dz}{dt} = at.$$

Consider all possible motions with constant a

Putting these expressions into Equation 22.17 gives

$$\tau = \int_{-t_1}^{t_1} \left[1 - \frac{a^2}{2c^2}t^2 + \frac{ga}{2c^2}(t^2 - t_1{}^2)\right] dt. \tag{22.18}$$

The integration is straightforward, to give τ as a function of a for fixed values of g, c, and t_1. What we have then is an extremal problem of elementary calculus, to find the value of a that makes $d\tau/da = 0$. It is left as an exercise to show that the result is

$$a = -g \tag{22.19}$$

For the geodesic, a = −g

and that this is a maximum, not a minimum, of τ.

Strange new view of old familiar motion

In this manner we find that a baseball that is thrown up and falls back down is following a geodesic in spacetime, the nearest thing to a straight line in a curved spacetime. It is remarkable that the ball, although it reverses its course in space, is following as straight a track in spacetime as does a photon that suffers an imperceptible deflection as it passes near the earth. Remarkable too is the fact that the ball makes an excursion up and down, rather than staying put, "in order to" maximize the time* it spends getting from Event A to Event B. Most remarkable of all, perhaps, is the fact that the course of the ball can be attributed to the extraordinarily small term, gz/c^2 (about 10^{-16} for $z = 1$ m), which measures the deviation from "flatness" of spacetime near the earth.

Because of the approximations underlying Equation 22.17, our result for the geodesic of the baseball is the same as the Newtonian prediction. Had the exact integral defining proper time been used instead, the result would have differed very slightly from the Newtonian result.

22.7   The new view of nature

The view of the world to which general relativity has led us was foreseen in 1870 by William Clifford, a British mathematician who displayed the following remarkably prophetic insight:

> I hold in fact (1) That small portions of space *are* in fact of a nature analogous to little hills on a surface which is on the average flat; namely, that the ordinary laws of geometry are not valid in them. (2) That this property of being curved or distorted is continually being passed on from one portion of space to another after the manner of a wave. (3) That this variation of the curvature of space is what really happens in that phenomenon which we call the *motion of matter*, whether ponderable or etherial. (4) That in the physical world nothing else takes place but this variation, subject (possibly) to the law of continuity.†

It remained for Einstein, forty-five years later, to bring this vision to fruition as a successful mathematical theory. Not even Clifford could foresee that this success would require the merging of time with space into a single entity. The view of the world represented by Clifford's vision and by Einstein's interpretation of general relativity has recently been given the name "geometrodynamics" by John Wheeler; the name symbolizes the merging together of geometry and the dynamics of motion—the fusion of actor, stage, and action. Whether *all* physical phenomena can ultimately be described as merely manifestations of the properties of space and time is still an open question. So far only the force of gravity has been simply and convincingly merged with spacetime.

Geometry and dynamics fused

Since the original motivation for the general theory of relativity was the desire to formulate *all* laws of nature in a manner invariant for observers in all frames of reference, accelerated or not, how is it that *one* law—the law of gravitation—assumed such a central role in general relativity? This came about because of the dual nature of mass, on the one hand as inertia, creating apparent

Why is gravity central in general relativity?

---

* This means, of course, the proper time—the time measured by a clock moving with the ball.

† *Proceedings of the Cambridge Philosophical Society* **2,** 157 (1864–76). Clifford's communication is dated February 21, 1870.

forces in accelerated frames of reference, and on the other hand as the source of gravitational force. No other properties of elementary particles seem to have such a dual role. Electric charge, for instance, is a seat of electric force, but it has no "spacetime" property like inertial mass that would lead to a geometrical interpretation of electricity as simple as the geometrical interpretation of gravity. This circumstance troubled Einstein and many other scientists who have sought a "unified field theory" in which electromagnetic and gravitational phenomena would be tied equally simply and directly to the hills and valleys of spacetime. These efforts have not been successful so far. This is not to say that electromagnetism is excluded from general relativity. Spacetime curvature responds to *any* energy, including electromagnetic energy, and a photon will create its little disturbance in spacetime as surely as will a particle with mass. General relativity is indeed general, but in the theory, gravity holds a privileged position.

22.8   The universe in the large

General relativity is undoubtedly the least tested theory of nature that is widely accepted. Its three famous predictions—the correction to the motion of Mercury, the deflection of light by the sun, and the gravitational red shift—have been verified to varying degrees of accuracy, but none to very high precision. A fourth test has recently added support for the theory. Radar waves reflected from Venus and Mercury are slightly delayed—by about 200 μsec in a 25-minute round trip—when they pass close to the sun (Figure 22.16). This effect was first observed in 1967.* The uncertainty of the result, standing at 5 percent in 1973, will undoubtedly be reduced in the future. Another test, involving the precession of a gyroscope in a satellite circling the earth, is scheduled for the 1970s. The beauty and economy of the theory coupled with these few tests have been sufficient to convince most scientists of the correctness of general relativity.

Four tests of general relativity

Will general relativity find more searching tests or new applications in the future? We cannot be sure. One possibility is that at distances much less than the size of an elementary particle, the curvature of spacetime will prove to be significant for the ultimate structure of matter. If this happens (there is no evidence for it as yet), it will probably occur at extremely small distances indeed. If we imagine an electron to be a point mass, the region near this mass within which the spacetime distortions of relativity are important has a diameter of only about 10^{-57} m.†

Little current prospect to see submicroscopic effects of general relativity

Of the effects of general relativity in the universe at large, we can speak with a much higher degree of certainty. Over the enormous distances of inter-galactic space, the cumulative effects of spacetime curvature become large. Various "models" of the universe have been proposed. According to the "big bang" model, the universe is continually expanding away from a highly

Models of the universe

---

* See Irwin I. Shapiro, "Radar Observations of the Planets," *Scientific American*, July, 1968. Later results appear in the paper cited in the caption of Figure 22.16.

† The so-called "gravitational radius" of an electron is $r_G = Gm/c^2 = 6.76 \times 10^{-58}$ m. It is the separation between two point electrons whose gravitational potential energy is equal to mc^2.

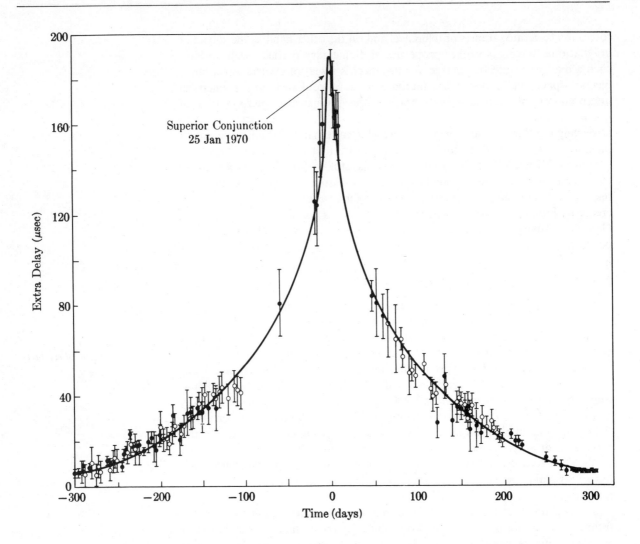

FIGURE 22.16   Extra delay of radar signals reflected from Venus [Irwin I. Shapiro *et al.*, *Physical Review Letters* **26**, 1132 (1971)]. The delay, amounting to nearly 200 μsec when the radiation passes close to the sun, is accounted for by the general theory of relativity. (The open and closed circles represent data from two different antenna systems.)

condensed state that existed some ten or twenty billion years ago.* According to another model, the universe is in a "steady state," with new matter coming into existence to preserve a constant average density despite the recession of visible galaxies from one another. Each of these models is consistent with both general relativity and astronomical observation. Although neither can be definitely ruled out, the weight of evidence currently favors the big bang model.

---

* See P. J. E. Peebles and David T. Wilkinson, "The Primeval Fireball," *Scientific American*, June, 1967.

Besides the overall average curvature of spacetime in the cosmos, there exists the possibility of strong localized curvature in the neighborhood of dense concentrations of mass. A burned-out star could collapse to so small a radius as to make the effects of general relativity quite important near its surface. Pulsars, believed to be rapidly rotating neutron stars, may be such entities. An even more dramatic prediction of general relativity is that stars more massive than the sun, after their fuel is exhausted, may collapse indefinitely into "black holes."* The gravitational field of a black hole is so intense that nothing, not even a photon, can escape from it.

Collapsed stars

Most extreme prediction: black holes that cannot emit light

Many fascinating questions remain unanswered: Is the universe closed or open? Is it finite or infinite? What is the density of energy in the universe? Is energy conserved in the cosmological domain? Are black holes fact or fiction? Is there a connection between the world of the very large and the world of the very small? Man has dared to grapple with these questions—as questions of science—over the past few decades, and answers to them may appear within the coming decades.

---

* See Kip S. Thorne, "Gravitational Collapse," *Scientific American*, November, 1967; also Roger Penrose, "Black Holes," *Scientific American*, May, 1972.

Summary of ideas and definitions

An inertial force is an apparent force that exists in an accelerated frame of reference. The inertial force on a body of mass m is

$$\mathbf{F}_{\text{inertial}} = -m_{\text{I}}\mathbf{a}, \qquad (22.4)$$

where $\mathbf{a}$ is the acceleration of the frame.

Inertial force is proportional to inertial mass; gravitational force is proportional to gravitational mass.

The Principle of Equivalence: Any effect produced by accelerating a frame of reference can be produced identically and indistinguishably by gravity.

Some consequences of the Principle of Equivalence and experimental tests:

Effect Produced by Acceleration	Implication for Gravity	Experimental Test
Inertial force is proportional to inertial mass.	Gravitational force must also be proportional to inertial mass; therefore $m_{\text{I}} = m_{\text{G}}$.	The equality $m_{\text{I}} = m_{\text{G}}$ is tested to very high precision.
Light follows a curved path in an accelerated frame.	Light must be deflected by gravity.	Bending of starlight by the sun observed.
Clocks do not run synchronously in a rotating frame.	Clocks located at different gravitational potentials must not run synchronously.	1. Light from the sun is red-shifted. 2. Frequency of nuclear gamma rays on earth depends slightly on altitude.
Length scales are not uniform in a rotating frame.	Properties of space must depend on the gravitational potential.	The precession of the perihelion of Mercury's orbit agrees with theory.
According to special relativity, geometry is non-Euclidean in an accelerated frame.	Gravity must have an influence on the geometry of spacetime.	Radar waves passing near the sun are slightly delayed.

Different effects of general relativity are intertwined. For example, a red shift reflects both a dilated time scale and a diminished photon energy.

The new view of gravity: It not only influences spacetime, it is itself a manifestation of spacetime.

A three-dimensional geodesic, a path of shortest distance, is the path followed by a photon.

A four-dimensional geodesic is a path of maximum proper time.

The new law of motion: Objects experiencing only inertial and/or gravitational forces follow geodesics in spacetime.

For a free particle in an inertial frame, the spacetime geodesic is a straight world line, the same constant-velocity path as that predicted by Newton's first law.

For a particle in a uniform gravitational field, the spacetime geodesic is a curve corresponding, approximately, to the uniformly accelerated motion predicted by Newton's second law.

In the submicroscopic world, there is little prospect at present that curved spacetime will reveal itself.

In the cosmological world, tests of general relativity may be afforded by the average spacetime curvature of the universe as a whole and by localized curvature near collapsed stars.

QUESTIONS

Section 22.1

Q22.1   To amuse his passengers, a pilot flies his airplane in a pattern of alternating shallow climbs and dives. If the speed of the airplane is held nearly constant, what is the direction of the inertial force acting on the passengers in each part of the flight path?

Q22.2   Does the inertial force acting on a body depend on the frame of reference in which the body is observed? Does the gravitational force depend on the frame of reference?

Q22.3   Can an object experience zero net force in one frame of reference and a nonzero net force in another frame? Explain the reason for your answer.

Q22.4   Walking down the aisle of a moving train, you find yourself pulled to one side of the train with what seems like an approximately constant force. (1) Give *two* possible explanations of this effect. (2) Without looking out the windows of the train, would there be any way for you to decide which of the two possible explanations is the correct one?

Section 22.2

Q22.5   What does it mean to say that an inertial force is a property of space and time?

Q22.6   State the Principle of Equivalence in your own words. What is equivalent to what?

Q22.7   An airplane can perform a maneuver that causes its passengers to experience "weightlessness." (1) What is the general nature of the maneuver? Can it last very long? (2) How does this method of inducing weightlessness illustrate the Principle of Equivalence?

Q22.8   An astronaut in a coasting spaceship forgot to clean up the galley before retiring. He is awakened when all the dirty dishes come crashing into his bed. They might have been thrown by an annoyed fellow astronaut. Give two other possible explanations.

Q22.9   (1) An upward force is applied to the elevator in Figure 22.2 just sufficient to reduce its acceleration to zero; it continues downward at constant velocity. (2) The upward force is then increased for a time to reduce its velocity to zero. (3) Having stopped, the elevator hangs motionless in its shaft. How would passengers in the elevator who believe themselves to remain at rest at all times interpret these three situations?

Q22.10 Figure 22.3 illustrates two states of a spacecraft that produce identical physical effects within the spacecraft. Describe other states of the spacecraft that are equivalent to these two. (There are infinitely many.)

Q22.11 One spacecraft is coasting in orbit. Another is sitting motionless on Earth. One of these vehicles is accelerated relative to the other, yet both can be said to define inertial frames of reference. Explain.

Q22.12 An enormous spacecraft measuring 100 miles from end to end is in orbit around the earth. Does this craft define an inertial frame of reference? To answer the question, consider whether a ball released within the spacecraft would drift with constant velocity relative to the craft.

Q22.13 Sarah and Arthur are riding inside a rotating drum at an amusement park. As shown in the figure, they are opposite one another at the same level, and the floor has been lowered away from their feet. To Sarah, Arthur appears to be at a higher elevation; to Arthur, Sarah appears to be at a higher elevation. Explain how their illusions can be attributed to the Principle of Equivalence.

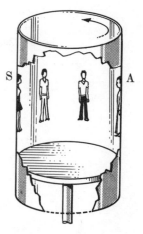

Q22.14 An experimenter inside a closed container floats freely in a state of "weightlessness," yet he finds that a beam of light in the container follows a curved path. Is this observation consistent with the Principle of Equivalence? If so, what can you say about the motion or the location of the container?

Section 22.3

Q22.15 In answering the following two questions, ignore the effect of motion and consider only the effect of gravity. Is the rate of a clock at the center of the earth slower, faster, or equal to the rate of a clock (a) at the earth's surface? (b) at a great distance from the earth?

Section 22.4

Q22.16 A passenger in the rear of a railroad car that is accelerating forward sends photons of a particular frequency in the forward direction. A passenger at the front of the same car measures the frequency of the photons reaching him. If he can measure with unlimited precision, does he measure a frequency that is less than, equal to, or greater than the frequency measured by the passenger at the rear? Why? Invoke the Principle of Equivalence to justify your answer.

Q22.17 In the "Mössbauer effect," a nucleus emits a photon (gamma ray) without recoiling. Does this violate the law of momentum conservation? Explain your answer. (HINT: The nucleus is not isolated.)

Q22.18 Prudence and Charity are twins brought up at the center of a rotating kingdom. (1) If Charity goes to live at the edge of the kingdom for a time and then returns home, which twin will be older? (2) If Charity goes to live at the edge of the kingdom and is later joined by Prudence, which twin will be older? (Ignore any time-dilation effects associated with travel to and from the edge of the kingdom.)

Q22.19 As a photon moves from a region of one gravitational potential to a region of another gravitational potential, its energy and its frequency change by exactly the same factor. What assumption underlies this statement? Is it "automatically" true (that is, true by definition), or does its truth require experimental confirmation?

Section 22.5   Q22.20 Why should the sun's slightly nonspherical shape cause its gravitational field to deviate slightly from an inverse-square field?

Q22.21 Explain why (a) the special theory of relativity is vitally important in understanding elementary particle phenomena, and (b) the general theory of relativity has appeared so far to be irrelevant in the submicroscopic world.

Section 22.6   Q22.22 Figure 22.13 shows an astronomical triangle whose sides are defined by light paths. The sum of its interior angles exceeds π. Is there any astronomical triangle whose interior angles sum to less than π?

Q22.23 In what way does the twin paradox illustrate the law that objects free of external forces follow geodesics (spacetime paths of maximum proper time)?

Q22.24 A photon passing near the earth is imperceptibly deflected. An astronaut near the earth is very perceptibly deflected. If both are following the same law, tracing out a geodesic in spacetime, why are their paths so different? [NOTE: Only a plausible answer to this question is expected. There are two routes to an answer: (1) an argument by analogy, considering low-speed and high-speed motion over a two-dimensional surface that is not flat; (2) a semimathematical argument, based on considering the relative importance of the spatial and temporal parts of the four-dimensional interval for low-speed motion and for high-speed motion.]

Section 22.7   Q22.25 Should it be possible in principle for a photon to execute a circular orbit about a concentrated massive sphere?

Q22.26 Explain in your own words why gravitational force turns out to be the "special" force of general relativity.

Section 22.8   Q22.27 How could a black hole be "observed" if neither matter nor radiation can escape from it?

Q22.28 Based on what you know about the emission and absorption of electromagnetic radiation, suggest how gravitational radiation might be emitted and absorbed.

EXERCISES

Section 22.1   E22.1 A rising elevator stops so suddenly that a 20-kg child is momentarily weightless; during the deceleration, the sum of gravitational and inertial forces on the child is zero. (1) What is the acceleration (magnitude and direction) of the elevator? (2) An 80-kg man in the same elevator is standing on a scale that is capable of reacting instantly to changes of weight. The scale is calibrated to read in kilograms. What does it read (a) as the elevator ascends at constant speed, (b) as the elevator is being stopped, and (c) after the elevator is stopped?

E22.2 Let $\mathbf{F}_i$ designate the inertial force acting on an object and let $\mathbf{F}_g$ designate the gravitational force acting on it. Give examples of motion (either practical or hypothetical) in which (a) $\mathbf{F}_i = 0$ and $\mathbf{F}_g \neq 0$, (b) $\mathbf{F}_i \neq 0$ and $\mathbf{F}_g = 0$, and (c) $\mathbf{F}_i + \mathbf{F}_g = 0$. In each example, specify the frame of reference in which the forces are being measured.

E22.3 "Centrifugal force" is an example of an apparent force or inertial force. If a child of mass m stands a distance r from the axis of a merry-go-round turning with angular speed ω, what is the centrifugal force seeming to act on the child in this accelerated frame of reference? Give its direction and a formula for its magnitude.

E22.4 Imagine a hypothetical world in which the ratio of gravitational mass to inertial mass is not the same for all bodies. Describe an experiment (possible in principle, but not necessarily practical) which would show that the Principle of Equivalence is not valid in this world.

Section 22.2

E22.5 In each of the two rocket-ships depicted in Figure 22.3, the astronauts erect a series of translucent screens and an outsider shines in a narrow beam of light. Apply the Principle of Equivalence and discuss the light path in each of the rocket-ship frames of reference.

Section 22.3

E22.6 A clock suspended in a balloon 10 km above the earth runs faster than a clock below it on the earth. How much time does the balloon-borne clock gain in a year? (Consider only the effect of gravity, not the effect of the earth's rotational motion.) *Optional*: Because the clocks are at different distances from the earth's axis, they move at different speeds in an inertial frame of reference. Prove that the effect of this speed difference is much less than the effect of gravity on the relative rates of the clocks.

Section 22.4

E22.7 In the experiment of Pound and Rebka (Section 22.4), the effect of a 70-ft change of altitude on photon frequency was measured. (1) By what fraction did the frequency change? (2) By what fraction did the photon's energy change?

E22.8 From Equation 22.5, show that the fractional difference in time scales at a great distance from a star and on the surface of the star is equal to $GM/(Rc^2)$, where M is the mass of the star and R is its radius.

E22.9 An astronaut moves slowly away from the earth toward much more massive Jupiter. Before his departure his transmitter and a receiver on Earth are tuned perfectly to the same frequency. Because of the effect of gravity on time scales, he must alter the frequency of his transmitter from time to time in order that its radiation reach Earth with the proper frequency for the receiver. In which part of his trip from the surface of Earth to the surface of Jupiter must he transmit at a slightly increased frequency? In which part at a slightly decreased frequency? In which part at the original frequency? Consider the effects of gravity only, not the effects of motion. (NOTE: In practice the effects considered here would not be large enough to be measurable.)

E22.10 An experimenter on a high-speed merry-go-round measures its radius to be 10.0 m and its circumference to be 60.0 m (for this circle, "π" = 3.0). (1) What is the angular speed of the merry-go-round? (2) What is the value of "g" (the centrifugal acceleration) at the edge of the merry-go-round?

Section 22.5

E22.11 (1) At what separation r does the gravitational potential energy of a pair of electrons $(-Gm^2/r)$ have a magnitude of 1 eV? (2) At what separation is its magnitude equal to $2mc^2$? Answer this part both algebraically and numerically. (3) Compare these distances with characteristic distances now known in the submicroscopic world, and comment.

Section 22.6   E22.12 Explain exactly why the inequality of Formula 22.10 follows from Equation 22.9.

E22.13 Imagine that 40 million meter sticks are laid end to end so that they form a great circle around the surface of the earth. (1) Now the meter sticks are elevated 1 m above the earth's surface. They remain in contact, end to end, except for a gap between the last one and the first one. What is the length of this gap according to nonrelativistic reasoning? (2) According to general relativity, the elevated meter sticks are stretched (Figure 22.12 and Equation 22.13). The gap between the last and first meter stick is therefore less than calculated in part 1. How much less?

E22.14 Suppose that the proper time along the straight world line between events A and B in Figure 22.14 is 1 sec. (1) Sketch and describe spacetime paths between these events whose proper times are (a) slightly less than 1 sec and (b) much less than 1 sec. (2) If these alternate paths are world lines of particles, forces must act on the particles. Why? (See also Problem 22.9.)

E22.15 Carry out the steps suggested between Equations 22.18 and 22.19 to prove that among the world lines characterized by constant acceleration a for a ball near the earth's surface, the world line with $a = -g$ is the one of greatest proper time.

E22.16 (1) If the height to which the baseball in Figure 22.15 is thrown is 1 m, what is ct_1? (2) This calculation indicates that the world line in Figure 22.15(b) is "almost straight." Explain. (Although the path of the ball in *space* is turned through a large angle—180 deg—its path in *spacetime* is only very slightly deflected. Earth's gravity is weak.)

PROBLEMS

Acceleration vs gravity   P22.1 (This is an extension of Problem 19.1.) Discuss the behavior of your accelerometer in a gravitational field. If it is mounted in an airplane, for example, can it distinguish acceleration in level flight from a climb at constant speed? If it is dropped by parachute, can it distinguish constant terminal velocity from free fall with acceleration g? If your accelerometer is unable to distinguish certain effects of gravity from effects of acceleration, can you think of a change in its design that will overcome the problem?

Gravitational deflection of light   P22.2 In passing near a star, a photon experiences so little deflection that the impulse delivered to it can be accurately calculated by approximating its path as a straight line. (1) Making this approximation and taking the effective mass of the photon to be E/c^2, show that the photon's angular deflection is given by

$$\theta = \frac{2GM}{Rc^2},$$

where M is the mass of the star and R is the distance of closest approach of the photon to the center of the star. (2) Evaluate this angle numerically for starlight passing very near the sun. (NOTE: When the effects of space curvature are included, general relativity predicts a deflection twice as great as the deflection calculated here.)

P22.3 A clock of mass M is located a distance r from the axis of a platform rotating with angular speed ω [Figure 22.8(a)]. (1) Give expressions for the potential energy U and potential energy per unit mass u of the clock in the rotating frame of reference. (2) Show that if $\omega r \ll c$, the fractional change in the rate of the clock (relative to a clock at the axis) is given by Equation 22.5. (NOTE: This is an effect of special relativity. Through the Principle of Equivalence it is translated to a prediction about the effect of gravity on time.)

Time scales in a rotating frame of reference

P22.4 (1) A clock is moved from a great distance away and is set on the surface of the earth near the equator. (a) By what fraction does the change of gravitational potential slow its rate? (b) By what additional fraction does the earth's rotation slow its rate (because of the time dilation of special relativity)? (c) For perspective, calculate also the ratio of the first of these effects to the second. (2) Now the clock is raised 2 m in the air and is moved horizontally. With what speed must it be moved in order that it run at precisely the same rate as earth-based clocks beneath it? Show that this speed is the same as the speed the clock would acquire in falling 2 m. (For this calculation, it is legitimate to ignore the acceleration of the earth—that is, to regard the earth-based clocks as being in an inertial frame.)

Effect of gravity on time

P22.5 Machines 1 and 2 in the diagram are hypothetical mass-energy converters of perfect efficiency. Machine 1 absorbs a photon of energy E_1 and from it manufactures a particle of mass $m = E_1/c^2$. The particle, starting from rest, drops a distance h with acceleration g in the earth's gravitational field into machine 2, where its total energy is converted into the energy of a photon. This photon makes its way back to machine 1, where it supplies the energy to make another particle, and so on. Prove that the conservation of energy requires that the photon lose energy on its upward trip, and that its fractional change of energy be given by

Light, gravity, and energy conservation

$$\frac{E_2 - E_1}{E_1} = \frac{gh}{c^2}.$$

Assume that h is small compared with the radius of the earth and that a nonrelativistic description of the fall of the particle suffices.

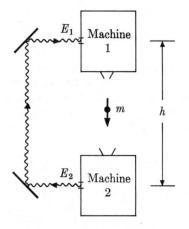

The force on a photon   **P22.6**   The implication of the thought experiment described in the preceding problem is that a photon of original energy E loses an increment of energy $\Delta E = Egh/c^2$ in ascending a distance h near the earth. (1) Express its change of momentum in terms of E, g, h, and c. (2) If force is defined as rate of change of momentum ($F = dp/dt$), what force acts on a photon near the earth? (3) Calculate and compare the earth's gravitational force on a visible photon of energy 2 eV and on an electron.

Acceleration red shift   **P22.7**   The figure shows a rocket-ship in free space far from any stars or planets. It is moving with acceleration g so that conditions inside the ship are the same as if it were standing motionless on earth. A source S at the rear (or "bottom") of the ship emits light of frequency v; a detector D at the front (or "top") of the ship measures the frequency to be $v - \Delta v$. The frequency shift Δv may be regarded as a Doppler shift arising from the fact that the detector D is moving faster when it receives the light than the source S was moving when it emitted the light. Apply the Doppler-shift formula and show that if $gh \ll c^2$, this "acceleration red shift" is the same as the gravitational red shift given by Equation 22.6. (NOTE: Equation 22.6 is also valid only for $gh \ll c^2$. The Principle of Equivalence requires that the acceleration red shift and gravitational red shift are identical more generally.)

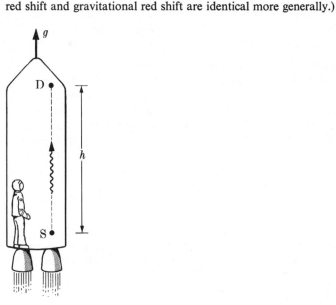

Doppler shift and gravitational shift   **P22.8**   An astronaut circles the earth at an altitude of 200 km and at a speed of 7,000 m/sec. Using a frequency of precisely 3.00×10^8 Hz, he transmits a message in a direction nearly opposite to his velocity (see the figure). Should a receiver on earth be tuned to a frequency slightly lower or slightly higher than 300 MHz? How much lower or higher?

Receiver   Transmitter

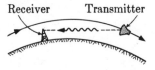

P22.9   Equation 22.8 expresses the proper time τ between two events in a gravity-free region. (1) Show that for a timelike interval between A and B, τ may take on any value between 0 and τ_{max}. What is the nature of the path between A and B for $\tau = 0$? What is the nature of the path for $\tau = \tau_{max}$? (2) (a) Can the path with $\tau = 0$ be the world line of any particle? (b) Can the path with $\tau = \tau_{max}$ be the world line of any particle?

Proper time and world lines

P22.10   (This problem is a generalization of the problem considered in Section 22.6 and illustrated in Figure 22.15.) At $t = 0$, a baseball is at height $z = h$ in the earth's gravitational field (event A); at $t = t_1$, it is at $z = 0$ (event B), Prove that if the baseball moves with constant acceleration along the z axis, its elapsed proper time between events A and B is a maximum if $a = -g$. In a Minkowski diagram analogous to the one in Figure 22.15(b), sketch the actual physical world line and alternative nonphysical world lines.

Motion in a uniform gravitational field

PART SEVEN

Quantum Mechanics

23 Particles and Waves

In December, 1900, Max Planck introduced an idea that was to shake the foundations of physics: the idea that material energy can be transformed into radiant energy only in units of a certain size, or "quantum units." A dozen years later, Niels Bohr generalized Planck's idea into a quantum principle of nature and used the principle with astonishing success to account for the structure of the hydrogen atom. Bohr's principle is this: Some of nature's variables can take on only discrete values and can, accordingly, change only in finite jumps. Building on this principle of discreteness or quantization in nature, in the years 1925–1928 European theoretical physicists created the edifice that we now call the theory of quantum mechanics. The giant stride of physics in those few years has not been equaled since.

23.1 The revolution of quantum mechanics

Like relativity, quantum mechanics is a true revolution in intellectual history. These two theories gave new life to a science that some thought was dying, and their impact on philosophy and literature can be compared only to the similarly strong impact of the Newtonian revolution more than two centuries earlier. Accompanying each of these twentieth-century theories have been a number of new ideas that are completely contrary to those of classical physics and everyday experience.

Quantum mechanics: theory of the submicroscopic world

Quantum mechanics is, in simplest terms, the theory of the submicroscopic world. It is well to remember that every fundamental theory in physics is associated with a particular domain of nature or a particular set of phenomena. Classical mechanics describes the motion of material objects provided, as we now know, that the objects are neither too small nor too swift. Its greatest early triumph was the successful explanation of planetary motion. Electro-

1122

magnetic theory achieved its greatest success in simultaneously accounting for electricity, magnetism, and light. Quantum mechanics scored first in providing an explanation of atomic structure. Describing the motion of particles, the forces between particles, the union of particles to form atoms and molecules, and the processes of creation and annihilation of particles, quantum mechanics has extended man's powers of prediction and quantitative description downward from the molecular to the subatomic and subnuclear domains. Because the submicroscopic world is vitally important within stars, quantum mechanics has, interestingly, also pushed back the frontiers of astronomy. Together, quantum mechanics and relativity have revealed the boundaries of validity of classical mechanics. So far, no definite limit of validity is known for either quantum mechanics or relativity, but in the broad sweep of scientific history, these theories are still young.

It is also relevant to astronomy

In this part of the book, we shall focus our attention more on facts and ideas and somewhat less on general equations and logical organization than we have up to this point. More advanced mathematics is required for quantum mechanics than for relativity or classical physics, mathematics not accessible to most beginning students. Apart from this practical limitation, there is good reason to pay attention to the *facts* of the quantum domain. Most scientists and engineers must understand atomic and nuclear phenomena because it is these phenomena that underlie the structure and properties of all matter.

KEY IDEAS OF QUANTUM MECHANICS

Facts supported by experiment on the one hand and ideas that unify our view of nature on the other hand: these are the two faces of any branch of science. In this chapter and the ones that follow, facts of atoms, nuclei, and elementary particles will be used to illustrate certain key ideas of quantum mechanics. The ideas, in turn, provide a framework that unites the diverse phenomena of the small-scale world. Here we list the ideas. They will be developed later, most of them with some mathematical support.

1. *Granularity.* Much of nature in the small is granular—its physical variables as well as its material pieces.

Key ideas: All are at variance with classical physics

2. *Probability.* The fundamental laws of quantum mechanics are laws of probability, not laws of certainty.

3. *Annihilation and Creation.* Any particle may be annihilated or created; stable matter is a happy chance.

4. *Waves and Particles.* Units of matter and units of radiant energy both share wave properties and particle properties.

5. *Superposition of Wave Amplitudes.* Quantum mechanically, a particle may be in two or more states of motion at one time.

6. *The Uncertainty Principle.* Apart from limitations on human ingenuity, nature imposes fundamental limitations on the precision with which some physical quantities can be measured.

This chapter contains mostly the quantum physics developed from 1900 to 1926. Developments since 1926 are contained (not in historical order) in the four chapters that follow.

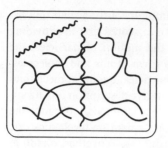

FIGURE 23.1   The *hohlraum*, or hollow cavity, investigated by Planck. Indicated schematically are electromagnetic waves of different frequency. These waves are in thermal equilibrium with the matter in the walls. Radiation emerging from a small hole in the cavity can be studied to reveal the energy per unit volume and per unit frequency interval within the cavity.

23.2   The photon

The photon: an elementary particle

The photon is, from our modern point of view, one of the elementary particles—a rather special particle, to be sure, because it has no mass and no charge, but not a unique sort of entity. It carries one quantum unit of spin (a granular variable, measured in units of $\hbar$); it interacts with all charged particles as well as with some neutral ones; it is the carrier of electric and magnetic forces; and it *is* light—or, more generally, electromagnetic radiation. Every atom emits and absorbs photons of particular energies and frequencies.

Max Planck was led to the quantum idea through studying the way in which energy is distributed among different frequencies of electromagnetic radiation within a closed box (Figure 23.1). The observed distribution (Figure 17.26) is the result of a complex and random interchange of energy between the radiation and the matter in the walls. Planck found that he could account for the distribution, explaining its dependence on both wavelength and temperature, only if he postulated that energy could be transferred from matter to radiation in bundles of a certain size, given by

Planck's hypothesis: quantized energy exchange

$$E = h\nu. \tag{23.1}$$

This is an equation we have already encountered: E is the quantum of energy and ν is the frequency of the radiation. Planck thought only in terms of quantized energy exchange, not in terms of quantized radiation. He continued to believe in a continuous pool of radiant energy.* By adjusting the numerical value of his new constant h to get the best agreement between the calculated and measured distribution of energy among different wavelengths, Planck was able to determine h to remarkable accuracy. His value, 6.55×10^{-34} J sec, differs by only about 1 percent from the modern value,

$$h = 6.6262 \times 10^{-34} \text{ kg m}^2/\text{sec} \quad \text{(or J sec).} \tag{23.2}$$

h is the fundamental constant of quantum mechanics

Planck's constant has turned out to be the fundamental constant of quantum mechanics in much the same way that the speed of light is the fundamental constant of relativity. It determines the entire scale of the submicroscopic world—the energy of photons, the spin of particles, and the size of atoms.

---

* In fact, Planck never accepted the photon idea of Einstein.

Five years after Planck's work, Albert Einstein took the second radical step. He developed a formula for the entropy of high-frequency radiation in a cavity and found it to bear a close resemblance to the formula for the entropy of a collection of particles in a container (see Equations 14.74–14.78). The correspondence was exact if the radiation was imagined to consist of particles with energy given by $E = h\nu$. Einstein dared to suggest that light was indeed corpuscular in nature, and he pointed out that several known phenomena might be accounted for by such light quanta.* One of these was the ionization of atoms produced by radiation†—in particular the fact that a minimum frequency is required to ionize the molecules in a gas. Another was a fact of fluorescence, that the light emitted by a fluorescing substance is always of lower frequency than the light illuminating it. Another phenomenon mentioned by Einstein was the so-called photoelectric effect, to which we now turn.

Einstein's hypothesis: quantized radiation

Early support for the photon idea

THE PHOTOELECTRIC EFFECT

Some years before Einstein's work, it had been noted that when ultraviolet light shone upon the surface of some metals, electrons were emitted from the surface (Figure 23.2). Although a detailed quantitative study of this photoelectric effect was yet to come, it was already known that Maxwell's classical wave theory could not give a satisfactory account of the observations.

The photoelectric effect defined

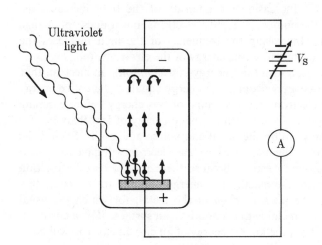

FIGURE 23.2   The photoelectric effect. Ultraviolet light incident upon a metal surface releases electrons. The stopping potential V_s measures the energy of the electrons.

---

* Some years later (1926), the word "photon" came into use to designate Einstein's light quanta.

† Perhaps the first suggestion that radiation has a granular structure was made by J. J. Thomson in 1903. The ionization produced by X rays suggested to him that the energy in a beam of X rays is not spread uniformly but is concentrated in "patches." Einstein, in 1905, was apparently unaware of Thomson's suggestion.

According to the wave theory, the electromagnetic radiation striking the surface set electrons near the surface into motion, and some of these were caused to move so rapidly that they could escape and fly off from the surface. This classical theory had two main predictions to make, and both were in disagreement with the facts. First, more intense radiation should have imparted greater acceleration to the electrons and caused them to fly off with more energy. Instead, the energy of the departing electrons did not vary as the light was made more intense. The only change was that a larger number of electrons escaped. Second, according to the wave idea, the energy should not depend particularly upon the frequency of the light as long as sufficient light intensity shines on the surface. In fact, higher-frequency radiation caused the electrons to fly off more energetically even if the intensity was lowered. Below some particular frequency, no electrons at all escaped. Ordinary visible light was incapable of ejecting any electrons from most metals, however intensely it shone on the surface.

Wave theory fails to fit the facts

The photon theory of light accounts simply and elegantly for these facts. It is only necessary to postulate an all-or-nothing character of photon absorption. An electron either absorbs one whole photon or it absorbs none. The chance that an electron absorbs more than one photon is negligible because the number of photons is much lower than the number of electrons. Having absorbed a photon, an electron either flies from the surface of the metal or dissipates its energy within the metal in a time so short that it has no significant chance to absorb a second photon. Increasing the intensity of the light increases the number of photons and the number of ejected electrons, but it does not change the energy per electron. Increasing the frequency of the light increases the energy of the photons and, therefore, the energy of the electrons, too.

Photon theory accounts for dependence on intensity and frequency

According to the photon idea (and energy conservation), an electron that absorbs a photon of frequency v acquires an energy equal to the entire energy of the photon, hv. The electron may lose some of this energy before escaping from the metal and therefore fly off with a kinetic energy of less than hv. Or it may lose all of its energy within the metal and not escape at all. Even if the photon absorption occurs at the metal surface, the electron will have to expend some of its energy in order to escape because there is a force of attraction holding the electrons within the metal. The energy required to overcome this attractive force is called the *work function* of the metal, for which the usual symbol is W. For a specific metal with a smooth clean surface, W is a constant. Because of the work function, the kinetic energy of an ejected electron will be at most the photon energy minus W:

Work function

$$K_{max} = hv - W. \tag{23.3}$$

If the potential required to stop escaping electrons is measured at each of several frequencies and if the results are plotted as a function of frequency, a straight-line graph should result, as shown in Figure 23.3. This graph shows a "threshold," that is, a minimum frequency below which no electrons escape. The threshold frequency, determined by the condition $hv = W$, is shown for several metals in Table 23.1, along with values of W for these metals. For

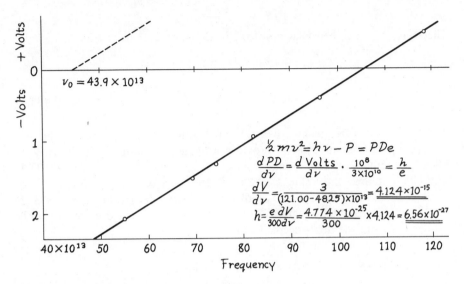

FIGURE 23.3   Photoelectric data and calculation of R. A. Millikan [*Physical Review* **7**, 355 (1916)]. The potential just sufficient to stop electrons ejected from a sodium surface is plotted as a function of the irradiating frequency. Points joined by the solid line do not include the contact potential of about 2.5 V between the emitting metal (Na) and the collecting metal (Cu). The dashed line, which does include this contact potential, shows the threshold frequency to be 43.9×10^{13} Hz.

TABLE 23.1   PHOTOELECTRIC THRESHOLD FREQUENCY AND WORK FUNCTION FOR SEVERAL METALS

Metal	Threshold Frequency (Hz)	Work Function W (eV)
Cesium*	4.6×10^{14}	1.9
Beryllium	9.4×10^{14}	3.9
Titanium	9.9×10^{14}	4.1
Mercury	1.09×10^{15}	4.5
Gold	1.16×10^{15}	4.8
Palladium	1.21×10^{15}	5.0

* The threshold frequency for Cs lies in the visible part of the spectrum. For the other metals, ultraviolet light is required to eject electrons.

comparison with these values, note that the high-frequency end of the visible spectrum (violet light) has a frequency of about 8×10^{14} Hz and a photon energy of about 3.3 eV.

Most thresholds in the ultraviolet

The most significant feature of the graph in Figure 23.3 is the slope of the line, which is Planck's constant h divided by the electron charge e. If a "stopping potential" V_s is applied, as shown in Figure 23.2, that is just sufficient to turn back the most energetic electrons, it satisfies the energy equation,

$$eV_S = K_{max}.*$$

Therefore, K_{max} can be replaced by eV_S in Equation 23.3 to give

$$eV_S = h\nu - W,$$

or

*The experimentally measured
quantity is h/e*

$$V_S = \frac{h}{e}\nu - \frac{W}{e}. \tag{23.4}$$

A graph of V_S vs frequency ν is a straight line with slope h/e. If e is known separately, the measured slope provides a value of h quite independently of Planck's method of determining this constant. As shown in Figure 23.3, Millikan obtained the value $h = 6.56 \times 10^{-27}$ erg sec in this way. If his value of e, 4.774×10^{-10} esu, is replaced by the modern value, $e = 4.803 \times 10^{-10}$ esu, his calculation gives $h = 6.60 \times 10^{-27}$ erg sec, differing by only 0.4 percent from the now-accepted value.

THE PHOTON AND QUANTUM IDEAS

The photon and granularity

The relationship of the photon to the idea of granularity is evident. It replaces continuous wave energy by discrete energy packets, and it replaces gradual emission and absorption of radiation by sudden events of emission and absorption.

Annihilation and creation

Here too is the idea of annihilation and creation. The photon, a particle, comes into and goes out of existence in "explosive" events on the atomic scale.

The photon also introduced the subtler idea of the wave-particle duality, and it implied (although this was not appreciated for a long time) that probability must play a role in elementary processes. Scientists thought that the question of the nature of light, wave vs particle, had long before been settled decisively in favor of waves. That it could be *both* wave and particle was too strange an idea to find ready acceptance. Not until Compton's work in 1923 (Section 21.7) was the photon generally accepted.

Wave-particle duality

An oversimplified characterization of the wave-particle duality is to say that light behaves as a particle when it is emitted and absorbed and behaves like a wave in between. Einstein suggested that the wave aspect of light resulted from the average behavior of a large number of photons. Although this is correct, we now know that even a *single* photon has wave properties. Its wave

Wave aspect of single particle

aspect is demonstrated experimentally by illuminating a double slit with a light source so weak that only one photon at a time reaches the slits. As mentioned in Section 18.3, many such photons acting singly still produce the characteristic interference pattern attributed to waves (Figure 23.4). It is the idea of fundamental probability that explains how the photons "know" where to land. Quantum mechanics attributes to the particles a continuously distributed wavelike probability. Specifically, the *quantum probability* per unit volume that a photon will be detected in a certain region is proportional to the *classical intensity* of the wave in that region:

---

* The potential V_S should include the contact potential difference, if any, between the surface emitting electrons and the surface collecting electrons (see Figure 23.3 caption). However, uncertainty in this added constant potential has no influence on the measured slope.

$$P \sim \frac{1}{2}\,\epsilon_0 |\mathbf{E}|^2 + \frac{1}{2\mu_0}\,|\mathbf{B}|^2, \tag{23.5}$$

Quantum probability ∼ classical intensity

where **E** and **B** are the electric and magnetic field vectors. To convert this proportionality to an equality, it is only necessary to choose the constant of proportionality in such a way that the total probability of finding the photon *somewhere* is 1.

Probability governs photons in a second way. If a hydrogen atom is put into an excited state (a state of greater than normal energy) and the atom is left to itself, after a time it will get rid of its excess energy by spontaneously emitting a photon of light. The length of time the atom remains in its excited state of motion before emitting the photon is entirely uncertain and cannot be calculated. But the *probability* that the photon will be emitted within any particular time interval can be calculated exactly. In this sense—that probabilities are exactly calculable—quantum mechanics is an unambiguous and quantitative theory. Its experimental verification requires that probabilities be measured. For this, a single atom or system will not do. Only by observing the behavior of a collection of many atoms can the probability governing one of them be determined. Similarly, one could never prove with a single toss of a coin that the probability of "heads" is exactly one-half. Verification would require a great many tosses.

Emission probability

The existence of photons gives a granularity not only to the energy but also to the momentum of radiation. From (1) the energy-momentum relationship for a massless particle, $E = pc$, (2) the energy-frequency relationship of a

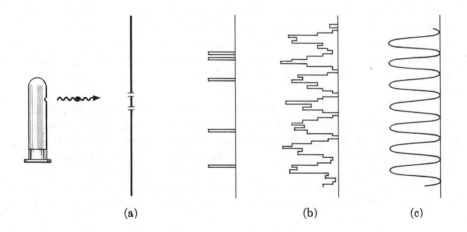

(a)   (b)   (c)

FIGURE 23.4 Interference pattern produced by photons acting singly. (a) The first few photons are detected at seemingly random locations. (b) As more photons are detected, still one at a time, a pattern begins to develop. (c) After a very large number of photons have been detected, the classical two-slit interference pattern is seen. Interpretation: The *probability* that a single photon is detected at a point must be proportional to the classical intensity at that point.

photon, $E = hv$, and (3) the wavelength-frequency relationship of electro-magnetic radiation, $\lambda v = c$, follows a momentum-wavelength relationship for photons,

Momentum of photon

$$p = \frac{h}{\lambda}.$$

(23.6)

This equation is related to the wave-particle duality. Across the equal sign are joined a particle property (p) and a wave property (λ). Planck's constant h is the link between the two.

Given the several ways in which the photon required very unsettling revisions in the physicist's view of nature, it is not surprising that it was a long time in being accepted. In 1913, four of Germany's most distinguished physicists (one of whom was Planck) had this to say about Einstein in their petition support-ing his election to the Prussian Academy of Science: "We may say that there is hardly one among the great problems, in which modern physics is so rich, to which Einstein has not made an important contribution. That he may some-times have missed the target in his speculations, as, for example, in his hypothesis of light quanta, cannot really be held too much against him, for it is not possible to introduce fundamentally new ideas, even in the most exact sciences, without occasionally taking a risk."*

23.3   The electron

CATHODE RAYS AND CHARGE-TO-MASS RATIO

That electrically charged particles reside within atoms had been surmised since the time of Faraday. But not until 1897 was definitive evidence produced for the existence of such a subatomic particle, the electron. In a series of ingenious experiments J. J. Thomson succeeded in proving that cathode rays are beams of negatively charged particles, very probably much smaller in size and considerably less massive than atoms. Even today we often refer to beams of electrons as cathode rays, a name dating from a time when little was known about them except that they emanated from a negatively charged terminal, or cathode.

Cathode-ray tubes

Figure 23.5 shows the main evolutionary steps in the family history of the cathode-ray tube. In the earliest version,† a high voltage applied to terminals in a rarefied gas caused a current to flow and the gas to glow. Later, improved vacuum pumps made it possible to lower the gas pressure to a point such that the gas no longer glowed although current still flowed. Interposition of a metal obstacle between cathode and anode (positive terminal) and alteration of the placement of the anode made clear that something was emanating from the

---

* Max Jammer, *The Conceptual Development of Quantum Mechanics* (New York: McGraw-Hill Book Company, 1966), p. 44. This excellent scientific-historical study (written at a rather advanced level) is available in paperback.

† The glow of rarefied gases stimulated by the passage of electric current through them was observed as early as 1748. Not until the 1850s were gas-discharge tubes used as subjects of serious scientific study. Modern fluorescent bulbs and neon lights are direct descendants of these early gas-discharge tubes.

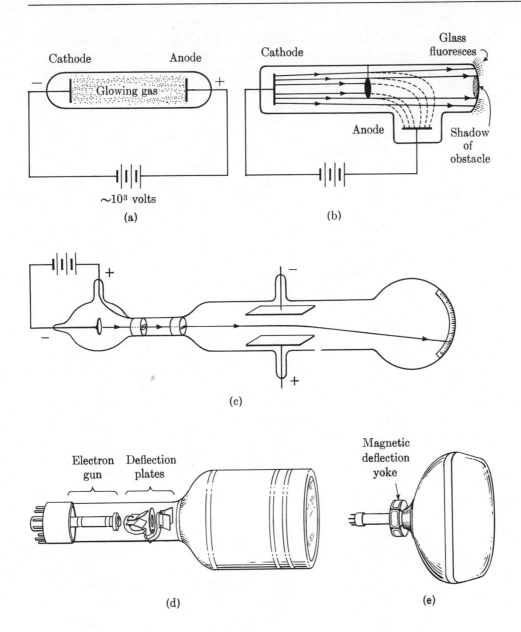

FIGURE 23.5   Evolution of the cathode-ray tube. (a) Gas discharge tube,
within which rarefied gas glows when high voltage is applied to its terminals.
(b) With higher vacuum, residual gas no longer glows, but glass fluoresces.
(Solid lines indicate electron paths; dashed lines indicate lines of electric field.)
(c) Cathode-ray tube of J. J. Thomson, containing anode slits to define narrow
beam and parallel plates to deflect beam electrically. (d) A modern cathode-
ray tube of the type used in oscilloscopes has a more elaborate series of
electrodes to produce a sharply focused beam, two pairs of plates for
deflection both horizontally and vertically, and a phosphor screen. (e) A
television tube uses magnetic rather than electric deflection.

cathode. This "something," which came to be called cathode rays, could be deflected by a magnetic field, but otherwise seemed to move in straight lines, and caused glass to fluoresce. In one of Thomson's cathode-ray tubes [pictured in Figure 23.5(c)], a narrow beam of cathode rays was defined by means of a pair of anodes, each containing a narrow slit. The beam then passed between a pair of parallel plates that could be electrified and struck the end of the tube where a scale permitted deflections to be measured. When charged, the parallel plates could deflect the beam electrically; electromagnets placed near the tube could deflect it magnetically. The modern cathode-ray tube does not differ in principle from Thomson's tube, but it has been refined in many details.

Modern refinements

The cathode is now coated with special materials and heated in order to make it emit electrons copiously. The anode, or pair of anodes, have been replaced by a series of plates and cylinders designed to produce a sharply focused beam of controllable intensity. The glass of the screen is coated with phosphor to make fluorescence more intense. In oscilloscope tubes two pairs of parallel plates permit electric deflection, both vertical and horizontal. In a TV tube, the position of the electron beam on the screen is magnetically controlled by means of coils placed next to the neck of the tube.

Thomson's discovery of the electron

By means of electric deflection, Thomson showed the cathode rays to be negatively charged. He inferred the small size of the negative particles from the ease of their passage through a gas; the distance required for the beam to dissipate its energy was much greater than the distance in which a beam of ionized atoms or molecules of comparable energy would be stopped. Most significant among Thomson's measurements was his approximate determination of the ratio of the charge to the mass of the cathode-ray particles. As outlined in Section 16.5, the charge-to-mass ratio is determined by accelerating electrons through a known potential difference, then deflecting them in a known magnetic field. A modern value of the charge-to-mass ratio of the electron is

$$\frac{e}{m} = 1.75880 \times 10^{11} \text{ C/kg.} \tag{23.7}$$

With appropriate caution, Thomson attributed the large magnitude of his measured e/m ratio to "the smallness of m or the largeness of e, or to a combination of these two." He then went on to argue that the electrons (or corpuscles, as he called them) were very likely much less massive than atoms. He wrote in summary:

His hypothesis of subatomic units

> The explanation which seems to me to account in the most simple and straightforward manner for the facts is founded on a view of the constitution of the chemical elements which has been favourably entertained by many chemists: this view is that the atoms of the different chemical elements are different aggregations of atoms [particles] of the same kind. . . . Thus on this view we have in the cathode rays matter in a new state, a state in which the subdivision of matter is carried very much further than in the ordinary gaseous state: a state in which all matter—that is, matter derived from different sources such as hydrogen, oxygen, &c.—is of one and the same kind; this matter being the substance from which all the chemical elements are built up.*

---

* *Philosophical Magazine* **44**, 293 (1897).

In the decade following Thomson's work, evidence accumulated rapidly in support of the soundness of his conclusions. Now, more than seventy years later, the electron remains the most primordial bit of matter we know; its internal structure, if any, is a complete mystery.

THE MILLIKAN OIL-DROP EXPERIMENT

The charge of the electron was first separately determined with some degree of precision by Robert A. Millikan in 1913. Beautifully simple in conception, Millikan's oil-drop experiment (Figure 23.6) goes right to the heart of the problem by providing a way to measure the force acting on a single electron or a small number of electrons. Tiny droplets of oil are suspended in air between plates that can be charged to provide a known electric field in the region under study. Each droplet, although microscopic in size, contains billions of atoms, yet the net imbalance of charge on a droplet may be equal to the charge of a single electron, or a few electrons, or zero. Since the droplet may have either a slight excess or slight deficiency of electrons, its charge, if any, may be either negative or positive.

The oil-drop experiment to determine e

In the absence of an electric field, a droplet is acted upon by two forces*: a gravitational force,

$$F_g = mg,$$

acting downward; and a frictional force of air drag,

$$F_D = 6\pi\mu rv,$$

acting upward. Here μ is the viscosity of the air, r is the radius of the droplet, and v is its speed. This formula for air drag, known as Stokes's law (Equation 12.78), is valid for spheres of sufficiently small radius and low speed (see Table 12.1). These two forces quickly come into balance as the droplet reaches terminal speed. Then the net upward force acting on the droplet is

$$F_z = 6\pi\mu rv - \frac{4\pi}{3}r^3\rho g = 0. \tag{23.8}$$

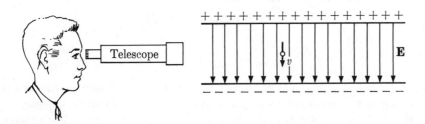

FIGURE 23.6   Schematic diagram of Millikan oil-drop experiment. The terminal speed of a tiny charged droplet is measured as it moves under the combined influence of gravity, frictional air drag, and a known electric field.

---

* A small additional force, the buoyant force of the air, is considered in a problem.

Here we have replaced the mass of the droplet by $\frac{4}{3}\pi r^3 \rho$, where ρ is the density of the oil. The fall of the droplet under these conditions can be watched through a telescope and timed to measure its terminal speed v. With this speed v in hand, one can use Equation 23.8 to find the radius of the droplet:

$$r = \sqrt{\frac{9\mu v}{2\rho g}}.$$
(23.9)

*With **E** = 0, terminal speed determines droplet mass*

From the radius follows at once the mass; then the separate forces F_g and F_D can be calculated.

Now the electric field is turned on. If the droplet has any net charge, a third force is added to the other two:

$$\mathbf{F}_E = q'\mathbf{E}.$$

The droplet responds by accelerating to some new terminal speed. It might reach a higher downward speed or a lower downward speed, or it might reverse direction and move upward. In any case, it settles at a new velocity where the sum of all three forces is zero. If, for example, **E** is directed upward, and the particle moves upward with speed v', we can write

$$F_z = q'E - 6\pi\mu r v' - mg = 0.$$

The charge of the droplet is then given in terms of measured quantities by

*With **E** ≠ 0, terminal speed determines charge*

$$q' = \frac{6\pi\mu r v' - mg}{E}.$$
(23.10)

In a long series of measurements, Millikan produced direct and unambiguous evidence for the quantization of charge. The net charge on a droplet proved always to be an integral multiple (positive or negative) of a smallest unit of charge. This unit he assumed to be the magnitude of the charge on a single electron. A modern value for this fundamental constant is

$$e = 1.6022 \times 10^{-19} \text{ C}.$$

Given e and e/m, the mass m of the electron can, of course, be inferred at once. A modern value for the electron mass is

$$m = 9.1096 \times 10^{-31} \text{ kg}.$$

In energy units, this is

$$mc^2 = 0.5110 \text{ MeV}.$$

The role of aerodynamics in an atomic measurement

An interesting sidelight on the Millikan oil-drop experiment is the essential role played by aerodynamics in the determination of a fundamental property of the electron. In Stokes's law, the viscosity of air is not precisely a constant but depends somewhat on the radius of the sphere. Much of the work required to obtain an accurate value of e went into refining and testing the law of drag force because this was the yardstick against which the electric force had to be measured. As it turned out, the viscosity used by Millikan was in error by about 0.5 percent, and his value of e was in error by about 0.7 percent. After this viscosity correction is made, Millikan's value of e differs from the modern value by only about 0.1 percent.

■ EXAMPLE: The viscosity of air is $\mu = 1.81 \times 10^{-5}$ kg/m sec. A droplet of oil of density $\rho = 850$ kg/m^3 is observed to fall with a speed $v = 10^{-3}$ m/sec. What is the mass of the droplet? If it carries a charge $q' = 10e$, what magnitude of electric field is required to hold the droplet stationary? Is this feasible? From Equation 23.9, the radius of the droplet is

$$r = \sqrt{\frac{9(1.81 \times 10^{-5})(10^{-3})}{2(850)(9.80)}}$$

$$= 3.13 \times 10^{-6} \text{ m} = 3.13 \ \mu\text{m}.$$

Its mass is

$$m = \frac{4\pi}{3} r^3 \rho = \frac{4\pi}{3} (3.13 \times 10^{-6})^3 (850) = 1.09 \times 10^{-13} \text{ kg.}$$

If, with the field on, the drop is stationary, then $v' = 0$ and $q'E = mg$. The required field is

$$E = \frac{mg}{10e} = \frac{(1.09 \times 10^{-13} \text{ kg})(9.80 \text{ m/sec}^2)}{10(1.60 \times 10^{-19} \text{ C})}$$

$$= 6.7 \times 10^5 \text{ V/m.}$$

Although large, this field is not unreasonable. On plates separated by 1 cm, it would require a potential difference of 6,700 V.   ■

Electrons, like photons, have wave aspects as well as particle aspects. The important topic of electron waves will be taken up in Section 23.9.

23.4   Line spectra

Much of what the ancients knew about nature, and a great part of what we now call the classical physics of the seventeenth, eighteenth, and nineteenth centuries, ultimately rests on the quantum mechanics of the submicroscopic world. The quantum nature of atoms dictates the density of ordinary matter; the behavior of solids, liquids, and gases when heated; the transparency, opacity, and color of materials; the existence of physical change such as freezing and boiling; and all aspects of chemical change. Because of the quantum structure of atomic nuclei, nuclear burning lights the sun and stars and nourishes life on earth. The facts that metals are conductors, that chemical cells generate electricity, that a crystal can be doubly refracting, that light travels more slowly in matter than in empty space—all now find their explanation in quantum theory.

Quantum theory underlies much of macroscopic physics

One of the important precursors of quantum theory was the discovery of line spectra. Often, the light emitted by matter is not continuously distributed over a region of the spectrum but rather consists of a definite set of discrete wavelengths (Figure 23.7)—a so-called line spectrum because of its appearance when examined with a spectroscope. Even the sun, which emits a continuous spectrum, reveals certain dark spectral lines arising from selective absorption in its outermost envelope. A portion of the sun's spectrum is shown in Figure 23.8.

Line spectrum defined

When light is emitted by electrons within individual atoms, a line spectrum

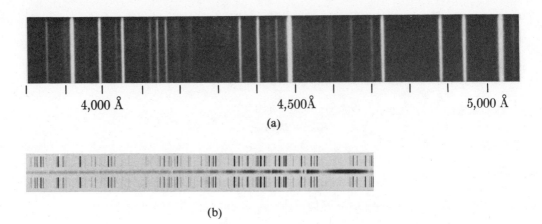

(a)

(b)

FIGURE 23.7   Line spectra. (a) Light emitted by helium in the wavelength
range 3,800 Å (violet) to 5,000 Å (green). (b) The central "belt" shows dark
absorption lines of a stellar spectrum in the range 3,600 Å to 3,800 Å (violet).
Above and below the belt is a comparison spectrum of iron; its numerous
known lines establish an accurate wavelength scale. (Photographs courtesy of
Hale Observatories.)

*Classical explanation of line
spectra*

results because only certain quantum energy changes are permitted and, therefore, only photons of certain definite energies and frequencies are emitted.
Before the photon linked frequency to energy, it was assumed that atoms had
certain preferred modes of vibration at particular resonant frequencies, just as
a violin string, the air in an organ pipe, and the current in an oscillator circuit
have certain characteristic vibration frequencies. Line spectra were taken as
evidence for the existence of atoms with fairly complicated internal structures
containing charged particles; but before the work of Einstein and Bohr, spectra
were not recognized as direct evidence of the quantum structure of atoms.

The first known observation of a spectral line was made in 1752 by Thomas
Melvill, who found that salts of sodium dropped in a flame produce a yellow
light that is of "one determined degree of refrangibility [is refracted through a
specific angle, is not dispersed]; and the transition from it to the fainter color
adjoining is not gradual, but immediate." This momentous discovery went

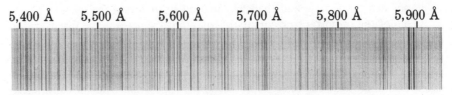

FIGURE 23.8   Portion of the sun's spectrum in the region of green and yellow
light. The strongest pair of dark lines, near 5,900 Å, are contributed by the
absorption of light by sodium atoms   (Photograph from Hale Observatories.)

largely unnoticed and apparently had no impact on the subsequent history of science. Only after Fraunhofer's study of dark lines in the solar spectrum (1814) and his accurate determinations of wavelengths with diffraction gratings (1821–1823) did spectroscopy establish itself as an important branch of experimental physics. The solar lines, seen first by William Hyde Wollaston in 1802, were measured by Fraunhofer and catalogued as the A line, the B line, the C line, and so on. Even after 150 years, we still speak of the Fraunhofer lines. The D line is Melvill's yellow line of sodium, which Fraunhofer found to be a pair of close lines, or doublet (see Figure 23.8). The A line and the B line are red lines of oxygen; the C line is a red-orange line of hydrogen.

History: the Fraunhofer lines

Line spectra afford an interesting example in the history of science of extensive and accurate data having to wait a long time for a theory. Ninety-nine years elapsed between Fraunhofer's first spectral analysis of solar lines and Niels Bohr's theory of the hydrogen spectrum. Meanwhile, thousands of spectral lines were measured to high precision. What kept interest from flagging after many decades of accumulation of data was the practical utility of spectroscopy. As early as the 1820s it was suggested that spectral lines might provide evidence on the composition of materials. This fact was definitively established by Gustav Kirchhoff and Robert Bunsen in the 1850s and 1860s. They made spectroscopy a primary tool of chemical analysis. Since every atom emits a characteristic line spectrum and since the spectra of no two atoms are the same, the line spectrum emitted by any substance provides unambiguous evidence about the atomic constituents of the substance. Through spectral analysis we know much about the distribution of elements in the sun and throughout the universe. One element, helium, was actually "seen" in sunlight before it was discovered on earth. In laboratory measurements, spectroscopy can reveal tiny traces of elements that would be difficult or impossible to recognize by other means. A number of rare elements have been discovered first through their spectra.

Practical utility

Line spectra proved to be the entryway to atoms. They are the visible manifestation of quantized energy levels. They also show us the beautiful unity of nature. We can look at a spectral line from a distant galaxy and know that there, a billion years ago, existed a hydrogen atom, indistinguishable from a hydrogen atom on earth today and restricted in its behavior by the same laws of nature that govern man and his environment now.

23.5   The spectrum of hydrogen

It is an important fact of physics and an agreeable attribute of nature that great insights often come from simple systems or simple experiments. Picture Galileo rolling balls down troughs, Faraday plunging a bar magnet into a coil, or Joule stirring a container of water. In atomic physics, the hydrogen atom, lightest and simplest of all atoms, has been the inspiration and the testing ground for most of the important forward steps, from Bohr's first atomic theory in 1913 to the recent theory called quantum electrodynamics. Even before the first hint of a quantum theory of atoms, the hydrogen atom had made its special simplicity evident through its line-spectrum signature. In 1885 Johann Balmer discovered that the frequencies of the known lines of hydrogen could be

Hydrogen atom a vital testing ground of theory

expressed mathematically by a very simple empirical law.*   Since it is not frequency but wavelength that is measured directly, we divide frequency by the speed of light and write Balmer's law in the form

Balmer series of spectral lines

$$\frac{v}{c} = \frac{1}{\lambda} = \mathscr{R}_{\mathrm{H}} \left(\frac{1}{2^2} - \frac{1}{m^2} \right),\qquad (23.11)$$

in which $\mathscr{R}_{\mathrm{H}}$ is a constant and m is an integer greater than two.   The constant $\mathscr{R}_{\mathrm{H}}$, called the Rydberg constant in honor of Johannes Rydberg, who discovered other approximate spectral formulas a few years later, is an exceedingly accurately known constant, equal to 1.096776×10^7 m^{-1}.   Slightly more fundamental is the value the constant would have if the nucleus of the hydrogen atom were infinitely massive and therefore immobile.   This constant, written $\mathscr{R}_{\infty}$, has the value

Rydberg constant

$$\mathscr{R}_{\infty} = 1.097373 \times 10^7 \text{ m}^{-1}.\qquad (23.12)$$

Even at the time of Balmer's work, the constant $\mathscr{R}_{\mathrm{H}}$ could be determined with considerable precision because spectral wavelengths were among the best-measured quantities in physics.   Even to accurately fit the four visible lines of the hydrogen spectrum with so simple a law was an interesting achievement. Balmer then found that his formula accounted for several more lines in the ultraviolet.   Counting additional lines observed in starlight and attributed to hydrogen, Balmer's formula simply summarized 14 accurately measured wavelengths, all that were known of the hydrogen spectrum at the time.   There could be no doubt of its significance.   Like Kepler's laws of planetary motion, Balmer's law neatly packaged a collection of data, although it did not provide any explanation for the data.

The set of spectral lines expressed by Balmer's law is known as the Balmer series.   Since spectral lines known to Balmer corresponded to every integral value of m from 3 through 16, it was natural to assume that additional lines corresponding to higher m values also existed, only awaiting discovery.   More were soon found.   By the time of Bohr's work in 1913, 33 lines of the Balmer series had been observed (to $m = 35$), all accurately described by Balmer's formula.   The higher members of the Balmer series cluster ever-closer together, as shown in Figure 23.9, with a definite series limit being determined by letting

FIGURE 23.9   The Balmer series of spectral lines emitted by hydrogen.   This photograph spans about one octave of the electromagnetic spectrum, from 6,600 Å on the left (red) to 3,600 Å on the right (near ultraviolet).   [From Gerhard Herzberg, *Atomic Spectra and Atomic Structure* (New York: Dover Publications, 1944).   Reprinted through permission of the publisher.]

* A reference to Balmer's paper appears in Exercise 23.11.

m become infinite in Balmer's formula. It is instructive to calculate the wavelengths of the first few members of the Balmer series*:

$$\frac{1}{\lambda_1} = \mathscr{R}_H \left(\frac{1}{4} - \frac{1}{9}\right) = (6{,}565 \text{ Å})^{-1}, \text{ red}†;$$

$$\frac{1}{\lambda_2} = \mathscr{R}_H \left(\frac{1}{4} - \frac{1}{16}\right) = (4{,}863 \text{ Å})^{-1}, \text{ blue-green};$$

First four Balmer wavelengths in vacuum

$$\frac{1}{\lambda_3} = \mathscr{R}_H \left(\frac{1}{4} - \frac{1}{25}\right) = (4{,}342 \text{ Å})^{-1}, \text{ violet};$$

$$\frac{1}{\lambda_4} = \mathscr{R}_H \left(\frac{1}{4} - \frac{1}{36}\right) = (4{,}103 \text{ Å})^{-1}, \text{ violet}.$$

The angstrom (Å) is 10^{-10} m. The series limit is located in the ultraviolet at about twice the frequency (half the wavelength) of the first line of the series:

$$\frac{1}{\lambda_\infty} = \frac{1}{4} \mathscr{R}_H = (3{,}647 \text{ Å})^{-1}, \text{ ultraviolet}. \qquad (23.13)$$

The series limit

Balmer was sufficiently impressed by the success of his law to speculate that other hydrogen series might exist. His guess for a more general spectral law slightly missed the mark (see Exercise 23.11), but he was correct in imagining that the entire hydrogen spectrum should be characterized by simple numerical regularity. We now know that all the spectral lines of hydrogen are described by the formula

$$\frac{1}{\lambda} = \mathscr{R}_H \left(\frac{1}{n^2} - \frac{1}{m^2}\right), \qquad (23.14)$$

Generalized Balmer formula

in which both n and m are integers ($m > n$). This generalization of Equation 23.11 was first confirmed by Friedrich Paschen, who in 1908 discovered the first two members of a new hydrogen series in the infrared. This series, now called the Paschen series, is characterized by $n = 3$, with $m = 4, 5, 6 \ldots$. The Brackett series ($n = 4$), and the Pfund series ($n = 5$), which, like the Paschen series, lie entirely in the infrared, were first identified in the 1920s.

Other series

The highest frequency (shortest wavelength) series of hydrogen lines, characterized by $n = 1$ (the Lyman series), lies entirely in the ultraviolet, with inverse wavelengths running from $\frac{3}{4}\mathscr{R}_H$ to $\mathscr{R}_H$. Although Theodore Lyman observed the first member of this series in 1906, he did not attribute it to hydrogen until Bohr predicted such a line seven years later.

■ EXAMPLE: Some spectral lines corresponding to values of n as large as 50 have been observed in astronomical studies of hydrogen gas in our galaxy. What is the wavelength corresponding to the values $n = 49$, $m = 50$? In what

---

* These calculated wavelengths are vacuum wavelengths. In practice, wavelengths are usually measured in air, not in vacuum. Because of the index of refraction of air, the Balmer wavelengths in air are about 0.03 percent less than they are in vacuum.

† This is Fraunhofer's C line, also known as the H_α line. Its color is sometimes called red-orange.

part of the spectrum does this line lie? For calculational convenience, Equation 23.14 is best cast in the form

$$\frac{1}{\lambda} = \mathscr{R}_{\mathrm{H}} \frac{m^2 - n^2}{n^2 m^2} = \mathscr{R}_{\mathrm{H}} \frac{(m - n)(m + n)}{n^2 m^2}.$$

Numerical evaluation gives

$$\lambda = \frac{n^2 m^2}{\mathscr{R}_{\mathrm{H}}(m - n)(m + n)} = \frac{(49)^2 (50)^2}{(1.097 \times 10^7)(1)(99)}$$

$$= 5.53 \times 10^{-3} \text{ m} = 0.553 \text{ cm}.$$

This macroscopic wavelength is in the microwave range, the domain of radio astronomy.   ∎

REGULARITIES IN OTHER SPECTRA

The hydrogen spectrum, although the simplest known, is not the only one to exhibit regular series. Figure 23.10 shows two series of sodium lines; many other series are known. The approximate laws developed by Rydberg to describe such series were neither so simple nor so accurate as Balmer's law, but one feature of them proved to be of eventual theoretical significance. All of Rydberg's expressions for inverse wavelength had one thing in common near the series limits: they contained a term approximately equal to the fixed constant $\mathscr{R}$ divided by the square of an integer. Bohr was later able to attribute this common feature to the fact that for all elements, the higher members of spectral series arise from the motion of a single electron far from the atomic nucleus.

Near every series limit,
$1/\lambda \sim constant - (\mathscr{R}/m^2)$

In early work on spectra, $1/\lambda$ was given the name "wave number." To fit modern practice, we define wave number instead as $1/\lambda$. Its symbol is k:

Wave number

$$k = \frac{2\pi}{\lambda} = \frac{1}{\lambda}. \qquad (23.15)$$

Wave number is useful in spectral analysis because, as we know now, it is proportional to photon energy:

$$E = \hbar c k. \qquad (23.16)$$

It is, of course, also simply related to frequency:

$$k = \frac{2\pi v}{c} = \frac{\omega}{c}. \qquad (23.17)$$

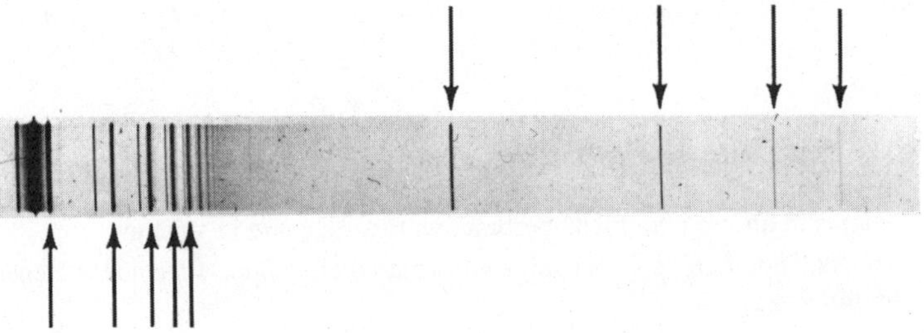

FIGURE 23.10 Series of lines in the spectrum of sodium. One series in the visible region is indicated by arrows below the photograph, another series in the ultraviolet by arrows above the photograph. [From Gerhard Herzberg, *Atomic Spectra and Atomic Structure* (New York: Dover Publications, 1944). Reprinted through permission of the publisher.]

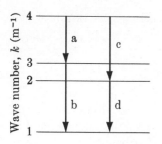

FIGURE 23.11   The Ritz combination principle. An atom is represented by a term diagram. Wave numbers of the characteristic spectral lines are equal to the vertical distances measured between terms. The modern interpretation: The numbered horizontal lines display energy levels, and the vertical arrows indicate quantum jumps.

Another empirical law of spectra discovered in the early part of this century proved to be significant in the development of atomic theory. First noticed by Rydberg and later advanced as a general principle by Walther Ritz (1908) was the fact that the wave numbers of the spectral lines of a particular element could be expressed as differences of a set of "term values" for this element. The way this so-called combination principle works is illustrated in Figure 23.11. The numbered lines are some of the "terms" of a term diagram. Observed wave numbers are measured by the spacing of these terms, which are drawn with a vertical scale expressed in cm^{-1} or m^{-1}. The length of line a is k_a, the length of line b is k_b, etc. This scheme of organization means that simple numerical relationships exist among wave numbers. For the example illustrated,

The Ritz combination principle and term diagrams

$$k_a + k_b = k_c + k_d. \qquad (23.18)$$

Such simple relationships are evident in the spectrum of hydrogen. The wave numbers of the first two lines of the Balmer series, for instance, are

$$k_1 = \frac{2\pi}{\lambda_1} = 2\pi\mathscr{R}_H \left(\frac{1}{4} - \frac{1}{9}\right),$$

$$k_2 = \frac{2\pi}{\lambda_2} = 2\pi\mathscr{R}_H \left(\frac{1}{4} - \frac{1}{16}\right).$$

Their difference,

$$k_2 - k_1 = 2\pi\mathscr{R}_H \left(\frac{1}{9} - \frac{1}{16}\right),$$

is equal to the wave number of the first line of the Paschen series. The Ritz combination principle proved valid for many lines in many elements and greatly helped to organize complex spectra into simple patterns. Note that the principle applies to wave numbers or, equivalently, to frequencies, but *not* to wavelengths. We now recognize the Ritz combination principle as nothing more than a statement of the law of energy conservation. At the time of its discovery, however, the principle was, like Balmer's law, a useful but mysterious fact of nature.

By the time that Ernest Rutherford literally opened up the atom in 1911, atomic spectroscopy was in an advanced state of development. The light coming from atoms had been accurately measured, catalogued, and found to be governed by several empirical laws. It had been used for practical ends, to identify elements and to unravel radioactive decay chains. Yet the mechanism within the atom responsible for this light was entirely mysterious. A wealth of data awaited explanation.

23.6   Key postulates of Bohr's atomic theory

In hundreds of places in the modern world—in books and newspapers, on billboards and television and army uniforms—we see atoms represented symbolically by a small central nucleus surrounded by the intersecting oval orbits of several electrons (Figure 23.12). This is a tribute to the impact of Niels Bohr on the modern world. At the same time it is an unfortunate distortion of the contemporary scientist's conception of the atom. Bohr's planetary model has evolved into what might better be called a nebular model, with electrons spread as waves of probability over the whole volume of the atom. This development notwithstanding, Bohr's original atom model deserves a place in a survey of the fundamentals of physics because, apart from its historical importance as a giant step toward quantum mechanics, it contained several basic ideas that have withstood the test of time and remain as essential aspects of modern atomic theory. In this section and the next two we shall develop the Bohr model of the hydrogen atom.

Bohr united three threads

1. *The energy quantum,*
     $E = h\nu$
2. *Spectral regularities*
3. *The nuclear atom*

In his 1913 paper on atomic structure,* Bohr drew upon three main threads of earlier work, which had not as yet been successfully woven together. First was Planck's conception of the energy quantum, with its energy-frequency relation, $E = h\nu$.† Second was the highly developed empirical science of spectroscopy, particularly the simple regularities of the hydrogen spectrum and the general combination principle of Ritz. Third was the new physical picture of the atom advanced by Rutherford—a heavy, positively charged nucleus of small dimensions surrounded by electrons. Bohr recognized that somehow Planck's quantum constant had to play a role in the mechanics of the atom; only then could the motion of the electrons and the processes of emission and

FIGURE 23.12   An all-too-common contemporary view of the atom. In fact, it is not possible to assign classical trajectories to electrons in atoms.

---

* *Philosophical Magazine* **26**, 1 (1913). This paper can also be found in J. B. Birks, ed., *Rutherford at Manchester* (New York: W. A. Benjamin, 1963). A portion of the paper—with notes that are generally helpful but contain some errors—appears in Morris H. Shamos, ed., *Great Experiments in Physics* (New York: Holt, Rinehart, and Winston, 1959).

† Although Bohr mentions the photoelectric effect in the introduction to his 1913 paper, the body of the paper suggests that he had not yet accepted the photon idea. He needed to use only the fact that the frequency ν of the radiation and the energy change E of the atom are related by $E = h\nu$.

absorption of radiation be drawn together in a unified theory. He was motivated also by the fact that without Planck's constant, there was no rational basis for an atomic scale of length. The combination $4\pi\epsilon_0\hbar^2/me^2$ is a length of the right magnitude (of order 1 Å), whereas without h, no combination of m and $e^2/4\pi\epsilon_0$ can provide a quantity with the dimension of length.* With what one colleague has called daring conservatism, Bohr abandoned only as much of classical mechanics as necessary, holding firm to those classical ideas that still seemed to work within the atom.

Planck's constant needed to establish an atomic length scale

Four of Bohr's ideas deserve special mention, for they have survived to be part of modern quantum mechanics.

1. THE IDEA OF THE STATIONARY STATE

Bohr postulated that electrons in atoms can exist in various states of motion, each state of motion being distinct and characterized by a fixed energy. Such a state is called a stationary state. (Note that the electrons themselves are not stationary in a stationary state.) A corollary of this idea of stationary states is that energy is a quantized variable in atoms, limited to certain discrete values.

Quantized energy

2. THE IDEA OF THE QUANTUM JUMP

It was already known that a quantum principle governed radiation. This led Bohr to abandon all hope of a classical description of the processes of emission and absorption of light. According to classical radiation theory, an electron in a Rutherford atom should radiate continuously; the radiated frequency should change steadily to create spectral bands, not spectral lines; and the atom should collapse finally to the size of the nucleus. None of these things happened. Bohr postulated that an atom undergoes sudden transitions (quantum jumps) from one stationary state to another. He replaced the idea of smooth steady radiation with an idea of occasional tiny explosions, in each of which the electrons suddenly alter their state of motion as they radiate a finite bundle of energy. In a letter to Bohr commenting on a prepublication copy of Bohr's paper, Rutherford wrote, "There appears to me to be one grave difficulty in your hypothesis, which I have no doubt you fully realise, namely, how does an electron decide what frequency it is going to vibrate at when it passes from one stationary state to the other? It seems to me that you would have to assume that the electron knows beforehand where it is going to stop."† Rutherford's question, although a very good one (it had to wait many years for an answer), betrayed one mode of classical thinking that Bohr was willing to abandon. Classically, in order to emit radiation of frequency v, an electron must vibrate at this same frequency v. According to the idea of stationary states connected by quantum jumps, there can be no such simple connection between radiated frequency and electron frequency. An electron may vibrate at one frequency in its initial state and at a different frequency in its final state. The radiation

Radiation sudden, not gradual

A crucial idea: radiated frequency not equal to vibration frequency

---

* In the cgs system of units used by Bohr, the factor $4\pi\epsilon_0$ does not appear. Compare Equations 15.4 and 15.9.

† J. B. Birks, ed., *Rutherford at Manchester* (New York: W. A. Benjamin, 1963), p. 127.

has still another frequency, determined by the energy change of the electron. Fortunately, Bohr let neither the unpredictability nor the nonvisualizability of the quantum jump deter him from advancing the idea. Quantum mechanics subsequently made possible calculations of the *probability* of transitions (the problem that worried Rutherford). These transitions, or quantum jumps, remain as nonvisualizable as they were to Bohr, and any particular one remains nearly as unpredictable.

3. SUBMICROSCOPIC ENERGY CONSERVATION

A term diagram is an energy-level diagram

We have mentioned already that Bohr held onto as much of classical physics as seemed to work in the atomic domain. In particular, he assumed that the law of energy conservation remained rigorously valid. This assumption made possible a simple explanation of the Ritz combination principle. A term diagram (Figure 23.11) is nothing more than an energy-level diagram. Each term value, multiplied by $\hbar c$, is an energy value; and after multiplication by $\hbar c$, the *difference* of two terms, which is a radiated wave number $(1/\lambda)$, becomes the energy radiated by the atom $(\hbar ck = h\nu)$. Looked at in this new way, a term diagram shows the energies of stationary states and indicates the quantum jumps between pairs of these states. For the transitions shown in Figure 23.11, energy conservation requires

$$h\nu_a + h\nu_b = h\nu_c + h\nu_d.$$

The combination principle expresses energy conservation

This means, of course, that the frequencies satisfy the simple equation,

$$\nu_a + \nu_b = \nu_c + \nu_d,$$

which in turn implies the wave-number relationship of Equation 23.18. Bohr was not the first to assume that energy is conserved in atomic systems, but he was the first to make good use of the assumption. The significance of the Ritz combination principle as a simple manifestation of energy conservation could be appreciated only after Bohr had broken loose from the idea that radiated frequency is equal to electron vibration frequency.

4. THE CORRESPONDENCE PRINCIPLE

The three ideas outlined above—stationary states, quantum jumps, and submicroscopic energy conservation—are evidently intertwined. Together they provide a simple description (not, to be sure, a classically visualizable description) of the processes of emission and absorption of radiation, and they relate atomic spectra to atomic mechanics. Bohr's fourth key idea provided an essential bridge between the classical and quantum worlds. His bridge is the correspondence principle, the idea that quantum mechanics must have a "classical limit." This idea of the classical limit was already a part of relativity theory, in which it took a simple form. When particles move slowly compared with the speed of light, the relativistic description of their motion reduces to the classical description. To put it simply, the new theory (be it relativity or quantum mechanics) must agree with the old where the old is known to be correct.

Idea of the classical limit

In his theory of the hydrogen atom, Bohr used the correspondence principle in the following way. He postulated that classical mechanics should approximately correctly describe an atomic transition when the transition takes place between adjacent stationary states that differ very little in energy, vibration frequency, and other properties. Through the correspondence principle he was able to grasp the mysterious quantum jump. The new and unknown was tied to the old and familiar.

Quantum results $\cong$ classical results when fractional change of discrete variables is small

23.7   The Bohr atom

We turn now to the specifics of Bohr's model of hydrogen. He knew of the Balmer series and the Paschen series, described by Equation 23.14, or, in terms of frequency, by

$$v = c\mathcal{R}_H \left(\frac{1}{n^2} - \frac{1}{m^2} \right) .$$

Multiplication of both sides of this equation by Planck's constant h gives the radiated energy per photon,* hv, which Bohr assumed to be equal to the energy difference, ΔE, between two stationary states:

$$\Delta E = hc\mathcal{R}_H \left(\frac{1}{n^2} - \frac{1}{m^2} \right) . \qquad (23.19)$$

A single set of energy values to account for these energy differences is

$$E_n = -\frac{hc\mathcal{R}_H}{n^2} . \qquad (23.20)$$

Energies to match the term diagram of hydrogen

The integer n identifies a particular stationary state. The first (and lowest) is characterized by $n = 1$, the second by $n = 2$, and so on. The negative sign in Equation 23.20 reflects the fact that the electron is bound to the positive nucleus, like the moon to the earth or the earth to the sun. It is often convenient to use the binding energy W, a positive quantity:

$$W_n = +\frac{hc\mathcal{R}_H}{n^2} . \qquad (23.21)$$

Binding energy: $W = -E$

As shown in Figure 23.13, the Balmer series is produced by quantum jumps ending at the second stationary state, the Paschen series by quantum jumps ending at the third stationary state. Without any evidence for the lowest energy state ($n = 1$), Bohr confidently predicted its existence. Before long, the Lyman series, produced by quantum jumps ending at the first stationary state, was identified, thereby vindicating the prediction.

So far we have used the ideas of stationary states, quantum jumps, and energy conservation, yet Equation 23.21 for the binding energies of the stationary states is still an *empirical* formula, chosen to fit the facts of the

---

* In the remainder of the discussion, we shall use the photon idea, which is convenient although not strictly necessary in the reasoning.

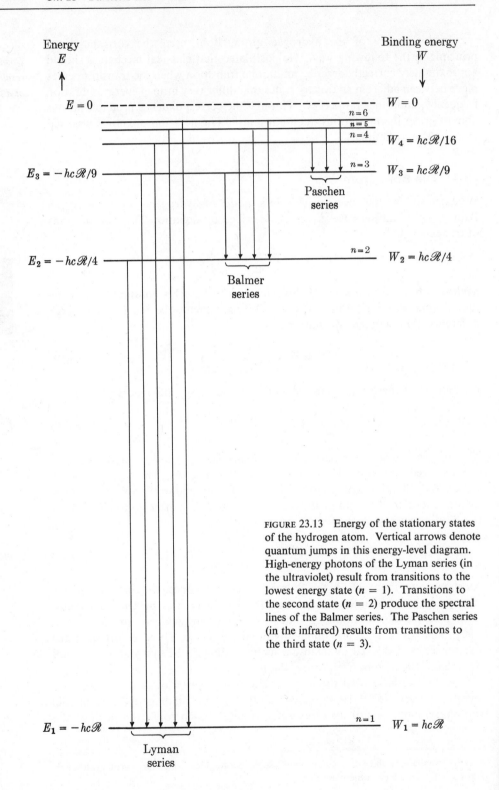

FIGURE 23.13   Energy of the stationary states
of the hydrogen atom. Vertical arrows denote
quantum jumps in this energy-level diagram.
High-energy photons of the Lyman series (in
the ultraviolet) result from transitions to the
lowest energy state ($n = 1$). Transitions to
the second state ($n = 2$) produce the spectral
lines of the Balmer series. The Paschen series
(in the infrared) results from transitions to
the third state ($n = 3$).

spectrum (in the framework of these ideas). The Rydberg constant is a quantity determined by experiment, so far unrelated to other constants in nature. The real triumph of Bohr in his 1913 paper was his "explanation" of the Rydberg constant. He was able to write $\mathscr{R}_\mathrm{H}$ as a combination of other fundamental constants—the electron mass, the electron charge, Planck's constant, and the speed of light. This great achievement required the use of his fourth essential idea, the correspondence principle.

Classically, an electron far from the nucleus radiates continuously at a frequency equal to its own frequency of revolution about the nucleus. It spirals inward, radiating at ever-higher frequencies. Quantum-mechanically, the electron moves in one stationary state, then jumps to a lower state, then to a still lower state, and so on, cascading toward the nucleus while emitting a series of photons that contribute to discrete spectral lines. According to the correspondence principle, these two seemingly very different descriptions of the atom should merge into one when the stationary states are close together in energy and when the successively emitted photons are close together in frequency. The granularity of the quantum description then gives way to the continuity of the classical description. It is evident from Figure 23.13 that this classical limit could be approached in the hydrogen atom only where the energy levels cluster together, at high values of n.

Correspondence principle applicable at high n

To apply the correspondence principle, we need expressions for the mechanical vibration frequency of the electron and for the emitted radiation frequency, expressions that can be equated at high n. For an electron moving at speed v in a circular orbit of radius r about a fixed proton, the centripetal force mv^2/r is equal to the Coulomb force of attraction:

$$\frac{mv^2}{r} = \frac{1}{4\pi\epsilon_0}\frac{e^2}{r^2},$$

where m is the mass of an electron and e is the magnitude of its charge. From this equation it follows that

$$mv^2 = \frac{1}{4\pi\epsilon_0}\frac{e^2}{r} \tag{23.22}$$

and

$$r = \frac{1}{4\pi\epsilon_0}\frac{e^2}{mv^2}. \tag{23.23}$$

The orbital frequency of the electron is

$$v_\mathrm{e} = \frac{v}{2\pi r}.$$

Using Equation 23.23 to eliminate r in favor of v, we get

$$v_\mathrm{e} = 2\epsilon_0\frac{mv^3}{e^2}.$$

This can be rewritten in terms of kinetic energy ($K = \tfrac{1}{2}mv^2$):

$$v_\mathrm{e} = \frac{4\epsilon_0 K}{e^2}\sqrt{\frac{2K}{m}}. \tag{23.24}$$

The left side of Equation 23.22, it should be noted, is twice the electron kinetic energy, and the right side is the negative of the potential energy, so we can write

$$2K = -U. \tag{23.25}$$

The total energy is

Simple energy relationships in Coulomb field

$$E = K + U = -K, \tag{23.26}$$

and the binding energy is

$$W = -E = K. \tag{23.27}$$

Therefore, in Equation 23.24, K may be replaced by W to express the electron's orbital frequency in terms of its binding energy:

$$v_e = \frac{4\epsilon_0 W}{e^2} \sqrt{\frac{2W}{m}}. \tag{23.28}$$

Rotation frequency in terms of energy

Although derived here for circular orbits, this formula is also valid for elliptical orbits. If the unreal condition of a stationary proton is removed and if proton and electron revolve about their center of mass, Equation 23.28 must be altered slightly. The orbital frequency of the electron is then

$$v_e = \frac{4\epsilon_0 W}{e^2} \sqrt{\frac{2W}{\mu}}, \tag{23.29}$$

where μ, the reduced mass of the system (Section 8.11), is given in terms of electron mass m and proton mass M by

$$\mu = \frac{Mm}{M + m}. \tag{23.30}$$

Evidently μ and m differ only slightly (by one part in 1,836).

In order for a quantum description of a cascading electron to correspond to a classical description of a spiraling electron, the cascading electron must pass successively through every stationary state. In a transition from state n to state $n - 1$, the electron emits a photon whose frequency is given by

$$v_r = c\mathcal{R}_H \left(\frac{1}{(n - 1)^2} - \frac{1}{n^2} \right). \tag{23.31}$$

Here the subscript r designates radiation. This equation can be rewritten

$$v_r = \frac{c\mathcal{R}_H \cdot (2n - 1)}{n^2(n - 1)^2};$$

for large n, it can be approximated by

Radiation frequency for $n \rightarrow n - 1$

$$v_r \cong \frac{2c\mathcal{R}_H}{n^3} \qquad (n \gg 1). \tag{23.32}$$

According to the correspondence principle (Figure 23.14), v_r and v_e should be equal at large n. If Equation 23.21 is used to substitute for W in Equation 23.29, the condition $v_r = v_e$ can be written

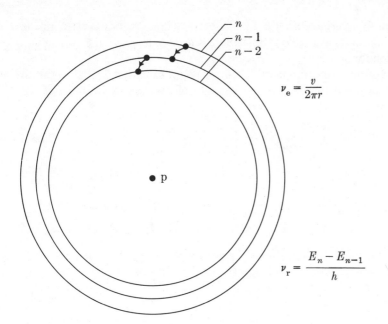

$$\nu_e = \frac{v}{2\pi r}$$

FIGURE 23.14   Application of correspondence principle to distant orbits in hydrogen atom. Classically, the electron rotates at frequency ν_e and emits electromagnetic radiation of the same frequency. Quantum-mechanically, the photon frequency ν_r is equal to the energy difference between successive stationary states divided by Planck's constant. According to Bohr's correspondence principle, these two frequencies must be nearly equal for large orbits of closely spaced energy.

$$\nu_r = \frac{E_n - E_{n-1}}{h}$$

$$\frac{2c\mathscr{R}_H}{n^3} = \frac{4\epsilon_0 hc\mathscr{R}_H}{e^2 n^2} \sqrt{\frac{2hc\mathscr{R}_H}{\mu n^2}}. \qquad (23.33) \qquad \textit{Set } \nu_r \cong \nu_e$$

The most important thing to note first about this equation is that the factor n^3 on the left cancels against an equal power of n on the right. This confirms that the correspondence principle holds generally for all large values of n, not just for a particular transition. It is in fact possible to prove by a somewhat more general argument that the requirement of the correspondence principle can be met *only* if the binding energy varies in proportion to $1/n^2$ at large n, as given in Equation 23.21. Next we notice that Equation 23.33 can be solved for $\mathscr{R}_H$ in terms of other fundamental constants. The result is

$$\mathscr{R}_H = \frac{\mu e^4}{8\epsilon_0^2 h^3 c}. \qquad (23.34)$$

For hypothetical infinite mass of the nucleus, this becomes*

$$\mathscr{R}_\infty = \frac{me^4}{8\epsilon_0^2 h^3 c} = \left(\frac{1}{4\pi\epsilon_0}\right)^2 \frac{me^4}{4\pi\hbar^3 c}. \qquad (23.35) \qquad \textit{The Rydberg constant}$$

This splendid unification of electron constants (e and m), quantum constant (h), and spectral radiation constants (c and $\mathscr{R}$) remains valid today. The Rydberg constant, now known to within 1 part in 10,000,000, helps, through

---

* In his first paper, Bohr did not bother to distinguish between $\mathscr{R}_H$ and $\mathscr{R}_\infty$. Soon afterward, the distinction became important, especially in comparing the spectra of hydrogen and ionized helium, with different nuclear masses. Later, the effect of nuclear mass was important in the discovery of deuterium.

this equation, to determine an accurate value for Planck's constant. With the accuracy of constants available to him, Bohr was able to verify the correctness of his equation for $\mathcal{R}_H$ to within 6 percent.

If we substitute from Equation 23.34 for $\mathcal{R}_H$ in Equation 23.21, we get an alternative expression for the binding energies of the stationary states of the hydrogen atom:

Binding energy in terms of fundamental constants

$$W = \left(\frac{1}{4\pi\epsilon_0}\right)^2 \frac{\mu e^4}{2\hbar^2} \frac{1}{n^2} = \left(\frac{1}{4\pi\epsilon_0}\right)^2 \frac{M}{M+m} \frac{me^4}{2\hbar^2} \frac{1}{n^2}. \qquad (23.36)$$

If the nuclear charge is Ze rather than e (Z = atomic number), the binding energy of the electron is

$$W = \left(\frac{1}{4\pi\epsilon_0}\right)^2 \frac{M_N}{M_N+m} \frac{mZ^2e^4}{2\hbar^2} \frac{1}{n^2} \cong \left(\frac{1}{4\pi\epsilon_0}\right)^2 \frac{mZ^2e^4}{2\hbar^2} \frac{1}{n^2}, \qquad (23.37)$$

where M_N is the mass of the nucleus. The demonstration that Z^2 is the correct factor is left as an exercise. This formula can be applied, for example, to singly ionized helium ($Z = 2$) or doubly ionized lithium ($Z = 3$), whose atoms have but one electron.

■ EXAMPLE 1: Express the Rydberg constant in terms of the permeability constant μ_0 rather than the permittivity constant ϵ_0. The two constants are linked through the speed of light:

$$\mu_0\epsilon_0 = \frac{1}{c^2}.$$

Therefore, in Equation 23.35, $1/4\pi\epsilon_0$ may be replaced by $\mu_0 c^2/4\pi$, giving

$$\mathcal{R}_\infty = \left(\frac{\mu_0 c^2}{4\pi}\right)^2 \frac{me^4}{4\pi\hbar^3 c}.$$

An often-used numerical value is

$$\frac{1}{4\pi\epsilon_0} = \frac{\mu_0 c^2}{4\pi} = 9.0 \times 10^9 \frac{\text{J m}}{\text{C}^2}. \qquad ■$$

■ EXAMPLE 2: What is the minimum energy needed to excite a hydrogen atom? What is its ionization energy? The ionization energy of the atom is the same as the binding energy of its ground state. It is

Ionization energy of hydrogen

$$W_1 = \left(\frac{1}{4\pi\epsilon_0}\right)^2 \frac{\mu e^4}{2\hbar^2} = \frac{(9.0 \times 10^9)^2(9.10 \times 10^{-31})(1.602 \times 10^{-19})^4}{2(1.055 \times 10^{-34})^2}$$

$$= 2.18 \times 10^{-18} \text{ J} = 13.6 \text{ eV}.$$

With less calculation, this number could also be obtained from Equation 23.21: $W_1 = hc\mathcal{R}_H$. Since the binding energy of the first excited state is $W_2 = \frac{1}{4}W_1$, the minimum energy needed to excite a hydrogen atom is

$$W_1 - W_2 = \frac{3}{4}W_1 = 10.2 \text{ eV}.$$

These energies greatly exceed normal thermal energy.   ■

23.8 Bohr orbits

With caution, and with some equivocation, Bohr took a further step and assumed that a classical description of the electron motion might be valid in each stationary state separately.* On this view, the electron moves in a Keplerian ellipse when not engaged in emitting or absorbing radiation. The wave nature of particles has taught us that this picture of sharply defined orbits is wrong. It is nevertheless instructive to examine Bohr's allowed orbits, for they yield the correct order of magnitude for the size of the atom and the speed of the electron. They also suggest a principle of angular-momentum quantization in nature that has proved to be central in quantum mechanics.

RADIUS

Since Bohr orbits are approximate at best, it is appropriate to simplify them to the greatest extent possible by considering only circular orbits. According to Equation 23.23, the radius of a circular orbit is given by $r = e^2/(8\pi\epsilon_0 K)$. Since $K = W$ (Equation 23.27), this can be written

$$r = \frac{1}{4\pi\epsilon_0} \frac{e^2}{2W} . \tag{23.38}$$

Overlooking the slight effect of nuclear motion, we can write, from Equation 23.36,

$$W = \left(\frac{1}{4\pi\epsilon_0}\right)^2 \frac{me^4}{2\hbar^2} \frac{1}{n^2} . \tag{23.39}$$

Substituting this expression for W in Equation 23.38 gives

$$r = 4\pi\epsilon_0 \frac{\hbar^2 n^2}{me^2} . \tag{23.40}$$

Approximate radius of circular orbits

This equation can be written

$$r = a_0 n^2, \tag{23.41}$$

in which a_0, now called the Bohr radius, is a combination of constants with the dimension of length:

$$a_0 = 4\pi\epsilon_0 \frac{\hbar^2}{me^2} = \left(\frac{4\pi}{\mu_0 c^2}\right) \frac{\hbar^2}{me^2} . \tag{23.42}$$

The Bohr radius

The magnitude of the Bohr radius is

$$a_0 = 5.29 \times 10^{-11} \text{ m},$$

or about half an angstrom. This magnitude agreed with what Bohr knew about the size of the hydrogen atom in its normal, or ground, state. According to

---

* Bohr was aware of the fact that he was on less solid ground in postulating classical motion in all stationary states than in applying the correspondence principle to states of large n. He expressed the hope that at least the constants of motion such as energy and angular momentum might be correctly calculated by classical physics.

Equation 23.41, the radius of the orbit of the lowest state, if it is circular, is a_0, the radius of the second orbit is $4a_0$, the radius of the third orbit is $9a_0$, and so on. This rapid growth in the predicted size of the atom with increasing excitation energy nicely explained why very high members of the Balmer series were seen only in starlight, not in laboratory-produced light. In the atmosphere of a star, the density of matter is so low that enormously inflated hydrogen atoms can exist without being seriously disturbed by neighboring atoms.

SPEED AND THE FINE-STRUCTURE CONSTANT

The electron speed in a circular Bohr orbit is also interesting. Since $K = \frac{1}{2}mv^2 = W$, the speed can be expressed in terms of the binding energy by

$$v = \sqrt{\frac{2W}{m}} . \tag{23.43}$$

Substituting for W from Equation 23.39 gives

Approximate speed in circular orbits

$$v = \frac{1}{4\pi\epsilon_0} \frac{e^2}{\hbar} \frac{1}{n} . \tag{23.44}$$

The speed is equal to $e^2/4\pi\epsilon_0\hbar$ in the lowest state ($n = 1$) and successively smaller values in higher states. It is illuminating to cast this equation into dimensionless form by dividing both sides by the speed of light:

$$\frac{v}{c} = \frac{1}{4\pi\epsilon_0} \frac{e^2}{\hbar c} \frac{1}{n} . \tag{23.45}$$

The fine-structure constant shows e^2 in natural units to be small

The dimensionless constant on the right, $e^2/4\pi\epsilon_0\hbar c$, usually abbreviated α, is known as the fine-structure constant.* This constant has fascinated physicists for decades, in large part because it *is* dimensionless. We now recognize it as a "coupling constant," measuring the strength of interaction between an electrically charged particle and the electromagnetic field. It can also be looked upon as the magnitude of $e^2/4\pi\epsilon_0$ measured in "natural" units, that is, in units of $\hbar c$. Numerically, the fine-structure constant is

$$\alpha = \frac{1}{4\pi\epsilon_0} \frac{e^2}{\hbar c} = \frac{\mu_0 c^2}{4\pi} \frac{e^2}{\hbar c} = 0.007297 = \frac{1}{137} . \tag{23.46}$$

Most physicists believe that the fine-structure constant requires an explanation, that there ought to be a deeper reason why three fundamental constants of nature combine to give one particular pure number. (For a time, it was thought that α^{-1} might be exactly the integer 137. It is now known to be 137.036.) So far, the "reason" for the magnitude of α remains a mystery.

---

* In the spectra of many atoms, what appears with coarse observation to be a single spectral line proves, with finer observation, to be a group of two or more closely spaced lines. The spacing of these fine-structure lines relative to the coarse spacing in the spectrum is proportional to the square of $e^2/4\pi\epsilon_0\hbar c$; for this reason the combination is called the fine-structure constant. We now know that the significance of the fine-structure constant goes far beyond atomic spectra.

In Equation 23.45, the fine-structure constant plays the role of "non-relativistic constant." Because α is small compared with 1, the ratio v/c is small compared with 1 in every orbit of hydrogen, and the effects of relativity are small. Relativistic corrections are nevertheless easily measurable in spectra and account for small corrections to Bohr's energy formula, Equation 23.36. In heavy atoms, with highly charged nuclei, the innermost electrons experience a much stronger force, move at higher speed, and are more strongly influenced by relativity.

The atomic electron is nonrelativistic

The quantum number n that has appeared throughout this section and the last is called the *principal quantum number*. It labels the energy values. Since it appears explicitly in many equations, it is, like most quantum numbers, both a label and a variable.

Quantum number: both a label and a variable

Bohr orbits, with properties expressed by Equations 23.41 and 23.45, only roughly approximate the state of the atom for small values of the principal quantum number n. For large n, however, the classical limit is approached, the correspondence principle can be applied, and orbits more nearly portray the true situation. Figure 23.15 compares the modern wave description with the

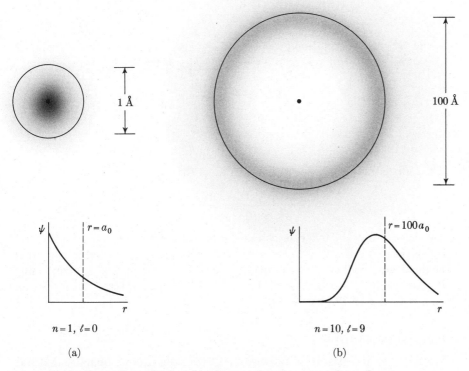

FIGURE 23.15 Comparison of Bohr orbit picture and modern wave picture for electron motion in the hydrogen atom. (a) Lowest stationary state, $n = 1$, with orbital angular momentum zero. (b) Most nearly circular orbit at $n = 10$, with angular momentum $L \cong 9.5\hbar$ (see Equation 24.2). Below each sketch of the atom is a graph of the wave function. The distance scales are not the same in the two graphs, since the atom is 100 times larger at $n = 10$ than at $n = 1$.

Bohr orbit description for $n = 1$ and $n = 10$. For larger n, the electron wave is evidently beginning to collapse into a well-defined ring. At $n = 100$, the classical and quantum correspondence is very close. One reason that Bohr's energy formula, Equation 23.36, remains valid today is that in deriving it he relied on a classical description of the electron motion only at very large n. It should incidentally be remarked that the equations for radius and speed, Equations 23.41 and 23.45, although accurate at large n, tell only part of the story. For simplicity we considered circular orbits; elliptical orbits are also possible.

■ EXAMPLE: Pretend that the Bohr-orbit description is valid even for small values of the principal quantum number (a somewhat shaky assumption, but not completely erroneous). What are the orbital frequencies of the electrons in the lowest two states, and how do they compare with the frequency of the Lyman alpha radiation resulting from the quantum jump between these states? We may substitute from Equations 23.40 and 23.44 in the expression $v_e = v/2\pi r$ to obtain, for the orbital frequency,

$$v_e = \left(\frac{1}{4\pi\epsilon_0}\right)^2 \frac{me^4}{2\pi\hbar^3} \frac{1}{n^3}$$

$$= \frac{2}{n} \frac{W}{h} = \frac{2}{n^3} \frac{W_1}{h},$$

where W is the binding energy of the nth state and W_1 is the binding energy of the lowest state. In terms of W_1, the frequencies of the lowest two states are

$$v_e(n = 1) = 2 \frac{W_1}{h},$$

$$v_e(n = 2) = \frac{1}{4} \frac{W_1}{h}.$$

The radiated frequency in the quantum jump from $n = 2$ to $n = 1$ is

Lyman alpha frequency

$$v_r = \frac{\Delta E}{h} = \frac{W_1 - W_2}{h} = \frac{3}{4} \frac{W_1}{h}.$$

This lies between the two orbital frequencies but is not their numerical average. The eight-fold difference between the two orbital frequencies and the fact that neither is close to the radiated frequency illustrate the fact that classical reasoning is quite inappropriate for small values of n. The frequency scale that is relevant here is $W_1/h = 3.29 \times 10^{15}$ Hz.   ■

ANGULAR MOMENTUM

We have left until last in this discussion of the Bohr atom a quantity that was peripheral in Bohr's original theory of hydrogen but has become increasingly central in quantum mechanics—angular momentum. Bohr noticed that if (and only if) the electron in the hydrogen atom was assumed to move in a circle, a remarkably simple rule of angular-momentum quantization emerged. To get this condition, we need only combine Equations 23.44 and 23.40:

$$L = mvr = m \left(\frac{1}{4\pi\epsilon_0} \frac{e^2}{\hbar} \frac{1}{n} \right) \left(4\pi\epsilon_0 \frac{\hbar^2 n^2}{me^2} \right),$$

or

$$L = n\hbar. \tag{23.47}$$

For circular Bohr orbits, angular momentum is an integral multiple of $\hbar$

Early and not very successful efforts to explain the structure of atoms heavier than hydrogen made extensive use of this simple quantization rule for angular momentum. The modern rules of angular momentum quantization will be taken up in Chapter 24. As indicated in Figure 23.15(a), the orbital angular momentum in the lowest state of the hydrogen atom is actually zero, not one quantum unit.

23.9 De Broglie waves

Although the remarkable fact that elementary entities can have both wave and particle properties was implied by Einstein's theory of the photon in 1905, twenty years passed before it was recognized as a general principle of nature. In 1924 Louis de Broglie postulated that any particle of momentum p has associated with it a wave of wavelength λ and that the two are related by

$$\lambda = \frac{h}{p}. \tag{23.48}$$

The de Broglie wavelength

Already known to be valid for photons (see Equation 23.6), this equation was soon verified experimentally for electrons, later for neutrons and other particles.

Simple though it appears, the de Broglie equation has consequences as significant as Einstein's famous $E = mc^2$. A comparison of the two equations is instructive. The heart of the Einstein equation is the proportionality of energy to mass, with c^2 the constant of proportionality (a *large* constant by normal standards). The heart of the de Broglie equation is the proportionality of wavelength to the inverse of momentum, with h the constant of proportionality (a *small* constant by normal standards). As Einstein's equation drew together two previously distinct concepts, energy and mass, so de Broglie's equation drew together apparently unrelated ideas, a wave property λ and a particle property p. Because p is in the denominator in Equation 23.48, larger p implies smaller λ. For the enormous momenta of macroscopic objects, the associated wavelength is so small that the wave property is completely unobservable. A man walking at 3 mile/hr has a wavelength of less than 10^{-35} m. If he tried to move slower in order to have a larger wavelength, it would not help much. Progressing at one centimeter per century, he would have a wavelength of less than 10^{-23} m, still 10^8 times smaller than the size of an elementary particle. On the other hand, a single electron moving at 3×10^6 m/sec, approximately its speed in a hydrogen atom, has a wavelength of 2×10^{-10} m, just about the diameter of an atom. This is a readily detectable wavelength.

$\lambda \sim 1/p$; the role of h as a constant of proportionality

★THE DAVISSON-GERMER EXPERIMENT

In 1925, Clinton Davisson and Lester Germer, working in the Bell Telephone Laboratories, discovered by accident (they were not yet aware of de Broglie's work) that the intensity of electrons scattered by a sample of nickel depended in an unexpected way on the angle of scattering. They pursued this topic with

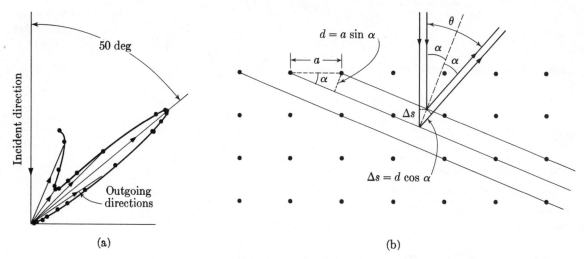

FIGURE 23.16   (a) Sample results of Davisson and Germer. The intensity of 54-eV electrons scattered from a nickel target is shown in a polar plot. (b) Diagram showing reflection of rays by successive planes in the crystal lattice. The condition of constructive interference is $2 \Delta s = n\lambda$. [Graph (a) from *Nobel Lectures, Physics* (Amsterdam: Elsevier Publishing Co., 1965), vol. 2, p. 391. © The Nobel Foundation, 1937.]

pure crystals, and before long they became aware of the relevance of their work to the possible wave nature of matter. By 1927, they had convincingly demonstrated the wave nature of electrons and verified the correctness of de Broglie's equation, $p = h/\lambda$. Similar work was carried out at the same time by George Thomson in England.*

A crystal is a diffraction grating

Because of its regular array of evenly spaced atoms, a crystal acts as an excellent diffraction grating for radiation of appropriate wavelength—a few angstroms. The radiation is reflected from successive planes of atoms in the crystal, and peaks of intensity are observed at certain "Bragg angles," those angles for which the rays reflected from adjacent planes differ by an integral number of wavelengths. In the experiments of Davisson and Germer, an electron beam of well-defined energy and momentum was directed normal to the surface of a crystal. A detector sampled the reflected intensity at various angles. One example of experimental results is shown in Figure 23.16(a), with the electron energy (and therefore wavelength) chosen to produce a well defined maximum at $\theta = 50$ deg.

With the help of the diagram in Figure 23.16(b), we can relate the angle θ to the wavelength λ and the atomic spacing a in the face of the crystal. The condition of constructive interference is

$$n\lambda = 2 \Delta s = 2d \cos \alpha, \qquad (23.49)$$

where n is an integer. Since the spacing between the reflection planes is

---

* Davisson and Thomson shared the Nobel Prize in Physics in 1937.

$$d = a \sin \alpha,$$

Equation 23.49 can be written

$$n\lambda = 2a \sin \alpha \cos \alpha.$$

A simple trigonometric identity converts this to

$$n\lambda = a \sin \theta, \tag{23.50}$$

Condition of constructive interference

where $\theta \, (= 2\alpha)$ is the angle between the incident and scattered beams. (Notice that this equation is identical in form to Equation 18.81 for a grating.)

■ EXAMPLE: The data of Figure 23.16(a) were obtained using 54-eV electrons incident on a nickel crystal with atomic spacing $a = 2.15$ Å (the value of a is separately determined using X rays of known wavelength). How does the theoretical angle of maximum intensity compare with the observed angle, 50 deg? The de Broglie wavelength is

$$\lambda = \frac{h}{p} = \frac{h}{\sqrt{2mK}}. \tag{23.51}$$

Numerical evaluation gives

$$\lambda = \frac{6.63 \times 10^{-34} \text{ J sec}}{\sqrt{2(9.11 \times 10^{-31} \text{ kg})(54 \text{ eV})(1.60 \times 10^{-19} \text{ J/eV})}}$$

$$= 1.67 \times 10^{-10} \text{ m} = 1.67 \text{ Å}.$$

Then, from Equation 23.50,

$$\sin \theta = n \frac{\lambda}{a} = n \frac{1.67 \text{ Å}}{2.15 \text{ Å}} = 0.777n.$$

Only for $n = 1$ is $\sin \theta < 1$. The predicted angle of maximum intensity is therefore

$$\theta = \text{arc sin } 0.777 = 51 \text{ deg}.$$

(The slight discrepancy between the predicted angle, 51 deg, and the observed angle, 50 deg, can be accounted for by the "index of refraction" of the crystal for electron waves. Because the crystal attracts the electrons, their speed in the crystal is slightly greater than in vacuum. Their wavelength in the crystal is therefore slightly less than the 1.67 Å calculated above, and an appropriately refined calculation of θ would give 50 deg instead of 51 deg.)   ■

DE BROGLIE WAVES AND THE BOHR ATOM

Before the wave nature of the electron was proposed, the Bohr quantization rules in hydrogen had seemed exactly that, *rules*—necessary and successful but not derived from any deeper theory. It is true, of course, that any theory, no matter how deep, can ultimately be described as a set of rules. Yet it is pleasing when we have a physical model that makes the rules seem reasonable, or even necessary. That is what the de Broglie waves provided for the Bohr orbits. Consider, most simply, circular orbits. An electron circling with speed v at a

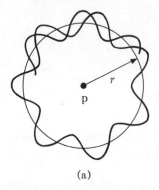
(a)

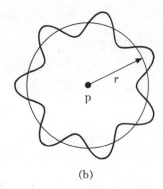
(b)

FIGURE 23.17   The de Broglie wave offers an explanation of quantized Bohr orbits. (a) The wave interferes with itself destructively. (b) The wave satisfies the condition of constructive interference, $n\lambda = 2\pi r$.

distance r from the nucleus has, according to the de Broglie equation, an associated wavelength λ given by

$$\lambda = \frac{h}{p} = \frac{h}{mv}.$$

Suppose we imagine this wave following around the electron orbit and closing on itself (Figure 23.17). Like a snake biting its own tail, the wave may interfere destructively with itself. If the head and the tail of the wave are only slightly out of phase after one revolution, they will be further out of phase after two, and so on. After a very large number of revolutions, the wave will have totally destroyed itself. The sum of all the superposed waves will be zero. On the other hand, if the wave after one revolution is precisely in phase with itself, interfering constructively, it will remain in phase after two or any number of revolutions, and remain alive as a "standing wave." The condition for reinforcement is that the circumference contain an integral number of wavelengths:

A condition of self-reinforcement

$$2\pi r = n\lambda, \tag{23.52}$$

where n is an integer. On the right, λ may be replaced by h/p or h/mv to give

$$2\pi r = n\frac{h}{mv}.$$

This equation may be rewritten

$$2\pi mvr = nh.$$

Since the angular momentum L is equal to mvr, we get

$$L = n\hbar, \tag{23.53}$$

The de Broglie wave "explains" Bohr orbits

exactly the rule found by Bohr for circular orbits. Now the rule is "explained" as the result of a wave closing on itself and interfering constructively only for certain discrete radii.

This de Broglie wave picture of the electron orbits in hydrogen can be described as lying about halfway between the classical orbit theory and the eventual quantum-mechanical theory. It is incomplete in two major respects. First, it still retains the sharply defined Bohr orbit as a guiding line for the wave. Second, it ignores the three-dimensional aspect of the wave, paying attention only to the wavelength along the supposed line of travel. It adds the wave without abandoning the particle. Eventually, in the Schrödinger wave theory of quantum mechanics, the particle and its orbit had to be thought of as spreading out to *be* the wave in a stationary state.

Limitations of de Broglie wave model

Despite these shortcomings of the simple de Broglie description, it contains at least one correct ingredient related to the modern view of energy quantization and angular-momentum quantization. Only those wave distributions are permitted that are finite and satisfy certain *boundary conditions*. For the hypothetical de Broglie wave in Figure 23.17, the boundary condition is a condition of self-reinforcement. For the waves shown in Figure 23.15, the boundary condition is that the wave approach zero as $r \to \infty$.

An important idea: Boundary conditions on waves lead to quantization

23.10   Waves and probability: the wave function

In quantum mechanics, a particle is characterized by a "wave function." Under certain circumstances, the wave function may be a vector quantity or a more complicated mathematical object. We shall consider only *scalar* wave functions, for which the standard symbol is ψ. (Scalar wave functions suffice to describe most material particles, but not photons.) The function ψ, which may depend on both position and time, satisfies a differential equation called the Schrödinger equation, which resembles, but is not the same as, the wave equation satisfied by the electric and magnetic fields, **E** and **B**. We shall examine a simple form of the Schrödinger equation in Section 23.15. Just as one can learn a great deal about electric and magnetic fields without studying their wave equation, so we can explore the meaning and significance of the quantum wave function before studying its Schrödinger equation. Such exploration will be our task in this and the next few sections.

*Scalar wave function ψ analogous to **E** and **B***

The de Broglie equation relates wavelength and momentum. But a wave has a well-defined wavelength only if it is a perfect sine (or cosine) wave. Therefore, if a particle has a precisely defined momentum p, its wave function is a sine wave of wavelength λ, with $\lambda = h/p$. For such a particle moving along the x axis, the wave function can be written

$$\psi = A \sin \frac{2\pi x}{\lambda} = A \sin \frac{x}{\lambdabar} = A \sin kx, \qquad (23.54)$$

For definite momentum and fixed wavelength, ψ is a sine (or cosine) wave

where A is a constant. Although ψ actually depends on time as well as position, this snapshot view of the wave at one time [Figure 23.18(a)] is sufficient for the present discussion. A wave may have many forms other than a sine wave. It might, for instance, appear as in Figure 23.18(b). For such a wave, the wavelength is approximately, but not precisely, defined. Correspondingly, the momentum of the particle is only approximately defined. If the momentum of the particle characterized by this second wave were measured, it might turn out to have any value within a certain range. Here is a manifestation of *probability*,

For other forms of ψ, p has a range of probable values

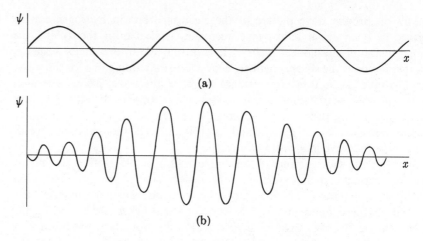

FIGURE 23.18   (a) The wave function of a particle of fixed momentum is a sine wave (Equation 23.54). (b) A wave function may have many other forms. This one describes a particle that is partially localized in space and does not have a precisely defined momentum.

which, as this example indicates, is closely related to the wave nature of particles. A particle may have any of a number of different momenta (or a continuous range of momenta), each with a certain probability. If it does, its wave function is a mixture of many wavelengths. The discussion of uncertain wavelength and momentum is continued in Section 23.14.

Most directly, the wave function is related to probability of position. Consider electrons (or other particles) diffracted by a single slit (Figure 23.19). A narrow slit causes the wave to spread into a broad pattern, exactly as for sound or light. Where, then, is the particle? Until it is measured as a particle, it is nowhere or everywhere. We must think of it not as a particle but as a wave, truly spreading from the slit. This answer will not do indefinitely, however. We may erect a counter, as shown in Figure 23.19, which signals the arrival of a particle at a definite place. Then, according to quantum mechanics, there is a certain probability that the particle will be detected at this place, and this probability is proportional to the absolute square* of the wave function of the particle:

Probability of position

$$P \sim |\psi|^2. \qquad (23.55)$$

Compare this with Formula 23.5. For both, the constant of proportionality is chosen so that the *total* probability to detect the particle somewhere is 1. Thus the wave is, in effect, a wave of probability. Under certain circumstances, as in striking a crystal lattice or passing through a slit, the wave *is* the particle. Under other circumstances, as in the act of detecting a particle, the wave becomes only a ghostly guide whose absolute square provides the relative probability of

---

* The absolute square, rather than just the square, is required because ψ may be a complex quantity.

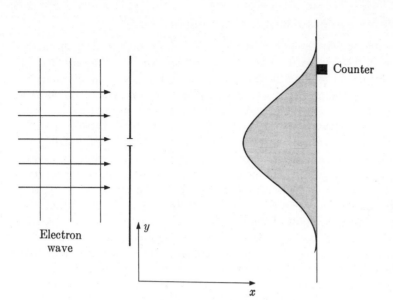

FIGURE 23.19   Diffraction of electrons by a single slit. The square of the wave function at the plane of observation is proportional to the classical wave intensity at that plane. It measures the probability of detection of a particle.

position of the particle. The wave function gives quantitative expression to the idea of the wave-particle duality.

Wave-particle duality manifested through ψ

■ EXAMPLE: The wave function of a particle is

$$\psi = A \sin (kx - \omega t).$$

What is the momentum of the particle? What is the relative probability of detecting the particle at different locations at a single instant of time? What is its relative probability of position averaged over a long time? Since this is a wave of definite wavelength ($\lambda = 2\pi/k$), the particle has definite momentum. It is

$$p = \frac{h}{\lambda} = \hbar k. \qquad (23.56)$$

From Formula 23.55, its relative probability of position is

$$P \sim A^2 \sin^2 (kx - \omega t).$$

For fixed time, this is a function of x that oscillates between 0 and A^2. The particle probability is "bunched," high in some places and low in others. Since the average over a long time of $\sin^2 (kx - \omega t)$ is $\frac{1}{2}$, we have, for the time-average probability,

$$P_{\mathrm{av}} \sim \tfrac{1}{2}A^2 = constant.$$

The special feature of the sine wave is that over a period of time, the particle is equally likely to be found anywhere (at any value of x, in this example).   ■

Wave functions that differ markedly from sine waves are shown in Figure 23.15. In its lowest state of motion, the electron in the hydrogen atom is most likely to be found near the proton ($r = 0$). In a state of large angular momentum, the electron has zero probability of being located at $r = 0$ and a large probability of being located in a doughnut-shaped ring around the nucleus.

Electron probability in the hydrogen atom

23.11   Waves and granularity: a particle in a box

It is surprising at first thought that the wave nature of matter is intimately connected with the granularity of the submicroscopic world. The very fact that a wave is spread out, making the position of a particle uncertain, accounts for some of the quantized properties of the particle. The de Broglie wave model of Bohr orbits illustrated this fact. Here we develop another example.

Consider a particle in a box, bouncing back and forth between parallel impenetrable and perfectly elastic walls (Figure 23.20). Classically, the description of the motion is very simple. The particle has some fixed speed v (any speed is possible), a constant magnitude of momentum, mv, and a constant kinetic energy, $\frac{1}{2}mv^2$. If the walls are separated by a distance d, the particle executes periodic motion, completing one round trip in time $T = 2d/v$. Quantum-mechanically, the description of the motion requires that account be taken of the wave nature of the particle. Classically, since the momentum is constant in magnitude, we expect the quantum wave to have fixed wavelength, that is, to be a sine wave. Not every wavelength is possible, however, because the wave must satisfy certain boundary conditions. Outside the walls, the wave function is zero (there is no chance to find the particle there). We therefore expect the wave function to be zero *at* the walls. This is a requirement that the wave function have no discontinuities, which, at this level of theoretical discussion,

Applicable boundary conditions: $\psi = 0$ at the walls

(a)

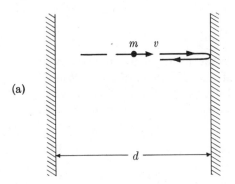

(b)

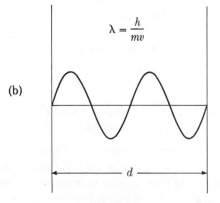

FIGURE 23.20   Particle in a box, moving in one dimension between perfectly reflecting walls. (a) Classical illustration of motion. Any momentum is possible. (b) Quantum wave illustration. The momentum is restricted by the requirement that the wave function be zero at the walls.

we can only suggest as a reasonable requirement. A deeper study of quantum mechanics is needed to justify it. (It is, of course, also justified by the fact that it leads to predictions in agreement with experiment.) If a sine wave is to be zero at both walls, an integral number of half wavelengths must be contained between the walls. This quantization condition is

$$n \frac{\lambda}{2} = d, \tag{23.57}$$

The boundary condition quantizes λ (and p)

where n is an integer—another example of a quantum number. A wave with $n = 4$ is shown in Figure 23.20.

It is interesting that the boundary conditions invoked in this example are equivalent to a principle of self-reinforcement, much like the one illustrated for Bohr orbits in Figure 23.17. If the wave is to reinforce itself after one round trip, the condition of constructive interference is

$$n\lambda = 2d,$$

equivalent to Equation 23.57. To see a physical reason for this condition, imagine a wave of arbitrary wavelength *not* satisfying Equation 23.57. If folded back and forth between the fixed walls, this wave, on each transit, will be out of phase with the wave on other transits, and the sum of all its parts will be zero.

If λ is replaced by h/p in Equation 23.57, the allowed magnitudes of momentum are revealed:

$$p = \frac{h}{2d} n. \tag{23.58}$$

Kinetic energy is also quantized. Assuming nonrelativistic motion, we can write

$$K = \frac{p^2}{2m} = \frac{h^2}{8md^2} n^2. \tag{23.59}$$

Allowed energies of particle in one-dimensional box

The energy diagram in Figure 23.21 shows the set of allowed energies—the stationary states—for the particle in the box. If the particle were electrically charged, it could emit a photon and drop from one of these states to another.

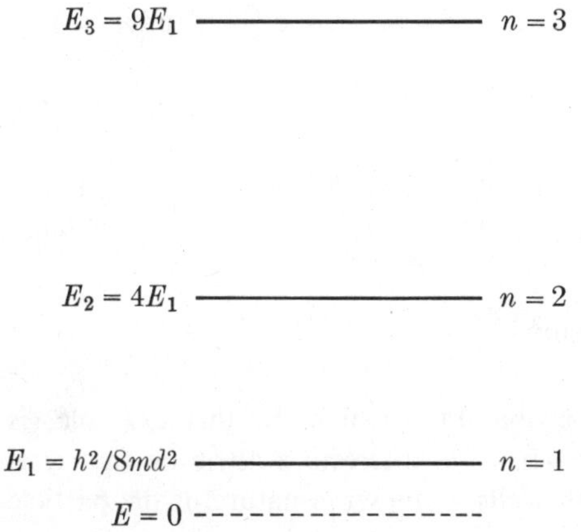

$E_3 = 9E_1$ ——————————— $n = 3$

$E_2 = 4E_1$ ——————————— $n = 2$

FIGURE 23.21   Energy-level diagram for a particle in a box. Because of the boundary conditions on the wave functions, the energies are discrete.

$E_1 = h^2/8md^2$ ——————————— $n = 1$

$E = 0$ - - - - - - - - - - - - -

■ EXAMPLE 1:   The energy unit in Equation 23.59 is $E_1 = h^2/8md^2$. How big is this for typical macroscopic magnitudes? How big is it for typical atomic magnitudes? As the reader may readily calculate, for an object of mass 1 kg moving between walls 1 m apart,

$$E_1 = 5.5 \times 10^{-68} \text{ J} = 3.4 \times 10^{-49} \text{ eV,}$$

a phenomenally small energy, illustrative of the irrelevance of quantum granularity in the macroscopic domain. For an electron held between hypothetical walls 1 Å apart,

$$E_1 = \frac{(6.63 \times 10^{-34} \text{ J sec})^2}{8(9.11 \times 10^{-31} \text{ kg})(10^{-10} \text{ m})^2} = 6.0 \times 10^{-18} \text{ J}$$

$$= 38 \text{ eV};$$

this is the energy of an ultraviolet photon, a "large" energy on the atomic scale.   ■

One special feature of Equation 23.59 deserves mention because it is a common feature of all quantum systems that are restricted in space. This is the absence of a quiescent state. At the very least, the particle in the box has an energy equal to $h^2/8md^2$. This is called its zero-point energy. Like a dollar bill glued to the bartender's wall, the zero-point energy is useless currency. There is no question about its reality, but it cannot be drawn upon. In an isolated atom the electrons move tirelessly and forever after the last photon has been radiated away. In a collection of atoms, a zero-point energy of vibrational motion remains even at absolute zero. These things come about because a wave, restricted in space, cannot take on an arbitrarily great wavelength. Therefore, its associated momentum cannot be zero.

Zero-point energy

■ EXAMPLE 2:   What is the wave function and the probability distribution for the second state of motion of a particle in a box? If we choose $x = 0$ to lie at the left wall and write

$$\psi = A \sin \frac{2\pi x}{\lambda},$$

we have satisfied one of the two boundary conditions: $\psi(0) = 0$. For the second allowed state (put $n = 2$ in Equation 23.57), $\lambda = d$, so the wave function is

$$\psi = A \sin \frac{2\pi x}{d}. \tag{23.60}$$

As a check on the second boundary condition, set $x = d$: $\psi(d) = A \sin (2\pi) = 0$. This wave function appears in Figure 23.22(a). The associated probability distribution is

$$P \sim \sin^2 \frac{2\pi x}{d}.$$

For $n = 2$, $P = 0$ at midpoint

As shown in Figure 23.22(b), this probability—which, in this example, is actually probability per unit distance—has the interesting attribute that it is zero at the midpoint as well as at both walls. The wave nature of the particle

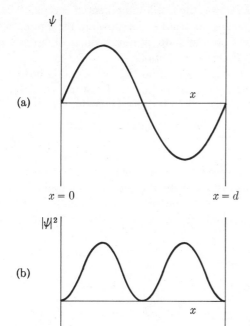

(a)

$x = 0$ $x = d$

(b)

FIGURE 23.22   (a) The wave function of a particle in a box for $n = 2$. (b) The square of the wave function, proportional to the probability per unit distance to find the particle at any distance x from the left wall.

produces a bunching effect, making the particle more likely to be at some places, less likely to be at others. *Classically*, by contrast, the particle would be found with *equal* probability at any point between the walls.   ∎

By suitable stretching of the mind and imagination, many quantum phenomena, such as probability waves, can be adequately visualized. Nevertheless, our usual vocabulary is not quite a match for the nuances of quantum mechanics. It is easy to ask unanswerable questions, such as: If the particle is never to be found halfway between the walls, how can it get from one half to the other half? The only answer that can be given to this question is that the "particle" exists simultaneously in both halves of the available space. Yet, when an external influence causes it to materialize, it shows itself in either one half or the other.

★23.12   Waves and nonlocalizability: the size of atoms

An essential feature of a wave is that it is not localized. It is spread out over a region of space. The less the wavelength, the smaller can be the region of confinement of the wave; but it can never be zero. In terms of this nonlocalizability of waves, we can understand the size of atoms and other quantum-mechanical systems.

A confined wave must execute at least one half-cycle of oscillation; that is, it must rise from a small value to a maximum and back to zero. The wave function of a particle in a box in its lowest state of motion (its "ground state") has this property; it is exactly one half-cycle of a sine wave [Figure 23.23(a)]. The same idea applies to the motion of an electron in a hydrogen atom [Figure

A qualitative guide: at least half a cycle of oscillation for a confined wave

23.23(b)]. The "box" confining the electron is the Coulomb potential energy of interaction between the electron and the central proton. As shown in the figure, the wave function of the electron in its ground state, although quite different from a sine wave, also executes half a cycle of oscillation.

Using the rough analogy of the electron in the atom to a particle in a box, we can obtain an approximate expression for the radius of the atom. From Equation 23.59, the kinetic energy of the electron in its lowest state is

$$K = \frac{h^2}{8md^2} = \frac{h^2}{32mr^2}.$$

We have set $d = 2r$, the diameter of the atom. Actually, the kinetic energy of the electron is variable, depending on its distance from the nucleus; this equation gives only a rough average value. To the same degree of approximation, we can write, for the average potential energy of the electron,

$$U = -\frac{1}{4\pi\epsilon_0} \frac{e^2}{r};$$

and for its total energy, $K + U$,

Approximate energy of electron "boxed" in a hydrogen atom

$$E \cong \frac{h^2}{32mr^2} - \frac{1}{4\pi\epsilon_0} \frac{e^2}{r}. \tag{23.61}$$

The essential way in which the wave nature of the electron has influenced this formula is that it has made the kinetic-energy term a function of radius. The electron cannot, in fact, roll indefinitely down the potential hill in Figure 23.23(b) toward $r = 0$. As the radial extent of its motion gets less, its kinetic energy rapidly gets larger. There is a finite radius that minimizes the total energy. Let us differentiate Equation 23.61 to find it:

$$\frac{dE}{dr} = -\frac{h^2}{16mr^3} + \frac{1}{4\pi\epsilon_0} \frac{e^2}{r^2}.$$

The value of r that makes this derivative vanish is

$$r = 4\pi\epsilon_0 \frac{h^2}{16me^2} = \frac{\pi^2}{4} \frac{4\pi\epsilon_0\hbar^2}{me^2},$$

or, written more simply (see Equation 23.42),

Radius that minimizes energy

$$r = \tfrac{1}{4}\pi^2 a_0. \tag{23.62}$$

Putting this radius into Equation 23.61 gives

$$E = -\frac{4}{\pi^2} \left(\frac{1}{4\pi\epsilon_0}\right)^2 \frac{me^4}{2\hbar^2}. \tag{23.63}$$

The fact that the derivation above is *mathematical* does not, of course, mean that it is *exact*. As Figure 23.23 makes clear, the wave function of the electron in its ground state differs considerably from half a cycle of a sine wave, and the potential energy is anything but constant over the range of motion of the electron. Nevertheless, the results are qualitatively correct. The radius given by Equation 23.62 differs only by a factor of $\pi^2/4$ from the Bohr radius;

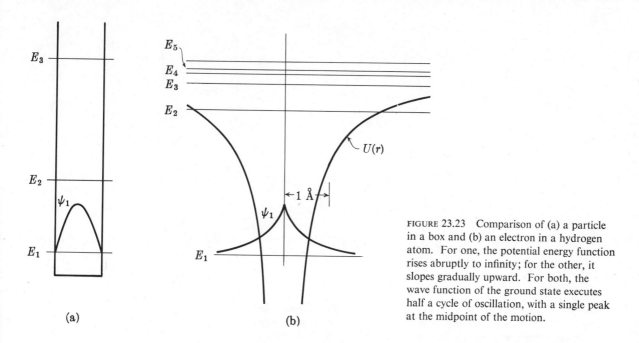

FIGURE 23.23 Comparison of (a) a particle in a box and (b) an electron in a hydrogen atom. For one, the potential energy function rises abruptly to infinity; for the other, it slopes gradually upward. For both, the wave function of the ground state executes half a cycle of oscillation, with a single peak at the midpoint of the motion.

and the energy given by Equation 23.63 is in error by the same factor (compare Equation 23.39). The important thing about the derivation is that in terms of the wave nature of the electron, it shows "why" the radial scale of the atom is $4\pi\epsilon_0\hbar^2/me^2$ and its energy scale is $(4\pi\epsilon_0)^{-2}(me^4/2\hbar^2)$.

Nonlocalizability "explains" the size and energy of the atom

The wave nature of matter explains why a particle can never have all its energy taken from it, and why it can never be localized in space. Were it otherwise, atoms might be inert nuggets 100,000 times smaller than they are.

23.13   Superposition of wave functions

Implicit in the discussion of the last few sections is an analogy between classical and quantum waves. In particular, the quantum wave function ψ may be compared to the displacement A of a sound wave or the electric field E of a light wave (see Section 18.1). Whereas *energy* of the classical wave is proportional to $|A|^2$ or $|E|^2$, it is *probability* of the quantum wave that is proportional to $|\psi|^2$. Another difference is that only $|\psi|^2$, not ψ itself, is a physically observable quantity, whereas both E and $|E|^2$ are observables in the classical domain. However, there are more similarities than differences. The ideas of coherence, superposition, refraction, interference, and diffraction all apply to quantum as well as to classical waves. The following discussion shows that ψ has familiar wave properties. As a matter of nomenclature, we note that wave *function* and wave *amplitude* are used interchangeably in quantum mechanics to designate ψ.

ψ analogous to classical displacement or field

ψ displays all familiar wave properties

Consider a beam of electrons "illuminating" a pair of slits (Figure 23.24). If only slit 1 is open, the probability distribution P_1 for observing electrons at some distance L beyond the slits might be as illustrated in the figure, a broad

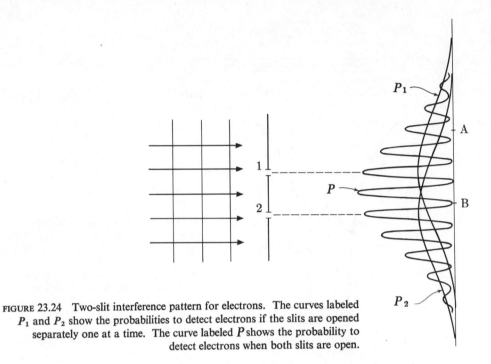

FIGURE 23.24   Two-slit interference pattern for electrons. The curves labeled P_1 and P_2 show the probabilities to detect electrons if the slits are opened separately one at a time. The curve labeled P shows the probability to detect electrons when both slits are open.

pattern with one prominent maximum (see also Figure 23.19). This probability is related to the wave function ψ_1 at the observing screen by

$$P_1 = |\psi_1|^2 = \psi_1{}^*\psi_1 \tag{23.64}$$

($\psi_1{}^*$ being the complex conjugate of ψ_1). If slit 1 is then covered and slit 2 is opened, the electrons will spread out in accordance with a similar broad probability distribution P_2, which is related to the function ψ_2 by

$$P_2 = |\psi_2|^2 = \psi_2{}^*\psi_2. \tag{23.65}$$

Two-slit interference pattern for electrons

With both slits open, the electron probability distribution P at the observing screen shows the characteristic maxima and minima of the two-slit interference pattern, the same as would be observed for light of the same wavelength (see Figures 18.41 and 18.43). The important fact about P is that it is *not* the sum of P_1 and P_2. In quantum mechanics, it is wave amplitudes and not probabilities that add. With both slits open, the wave amplitude ψ at the observing screen is

$$\psi = \psi_1 + \psi_2. \tag{23.66}$$

Since $P = |\psi|^2 = \psi^*\psi$, we have

$$P = \psi_1{}^*\psi_1 + \psi_2{}^*\psi_2 + \psi_1{}^*\psi_2 + \psi_2{}^*\psi_1.$$

This can also be written

$$P = P_1 + P_2 + \psi_1{}^*\psi_2 + \psi_2{}^*\psi_1. \tag{23.67}$$

It is the extra terms $\psi_1{}^*\psi_2 + \psi_2{}^*\psi_1$ on the right side that introduce into P the oscillatory behavior that is not present in P_1 or P_2 (compare Equation 18.14.)

How are these facts to be interpreted? They are clearly not consistent with a classical particle model of electrons. The diffraction of electrons by one slit is puzzling enough if electrons are regarded only as particles; the interference from two slits is even more puzzling. Thinking of electrons as particles, we would have to say that the intensity of electrons observed with both slits open should be the sum of the intensities observed with the slits open one at a time. In fact, for electrons, just as for photons, we must give up the idea that a particle goes through one slit or the other. With both slits open, the electron wave goes through both slits at once, and it is the wave that determines where electrons may be observed as particles. A particular point, such as point A in Figure 23.24, may receive more electrons from both slits together than it would receive from the two slits separately; or, as at point B, the contribution from two slits may vanish where either slit alone would furnish electrons. Although easy to understand for waves, these facts strain our powers of visualization for particles.

Strange quantum fact: An electron goes through slit 1 and slit 2

Another way to interpret the two-slit experiment with electrons is to say that a particle may be in two states of motion at once. Slit 1 alone causes an electron passing through it to go into a certain state of motion that is defined by the wave function ψ_1. Slit 2 alone puts electrons into a different state of motion defined by the wave function ψ_2. The state of motion induced by the pair of slits together is defined by $\psi = \psi_1 + \psi_2$. As the foregoing analysis shows, it is *not* correct to describe this result as an electron in state 1 *or* an electron in state 2. Because it is wave functions rather than probabilities that add, the combined state is an intimate combination of two states. The electron is in state 1 *and* in state 2.

Superposition of quantum states

23.14   The uncertainty principle

One of the most useful insights into nature revealed by quantum mechanics is the Heisenberg uncertainty principle. This is a general principle that takes many forms, one of which is

$$\Delta x \, \Delta p_x \geq \tfrac{1}{2}\hbar, \tag{23.68}$$

One form of the uncertainty principle

with similar relations for y and z components. On the right side of the inequality appears $\hbar$, the ubiquitous Planck constant (here divided by 2π) that turns up in nearly every equation of quantum mechanics. Momentum is represented by p_x, and position (distance) by x. The Δ symbols are used here to mean "uncertainty of" (not "change of"): Δx is the uncertainty of position in the x direction, Δp_x is the uncertainty of the x component of momentum.*

---

* The technical definition of $(\Delta x)^2$ is

$$(\Delta x)^2 = [(x - \bar{x})^2]_{\text{average}},$$

where $\bar{x}$ is the average value of x. Thus Δx is the rms deviation of the x coordinate from its mean value. The quantity Δp_x is similarly defined. The averages are weighted averages using the probability density $|\psi|^2$ for the state of motion in question. For example, for motion in one dimension, the mean value of x is given by

$$\bar{x} = \int_{-\infty}^{\infty} x \, |\psi(x, t)|^2 \, dx$$

if ψ is "normalized" so that $\int_{-\infty}^{\infty} |\psi(x, t)|^2 \, dx = 1$.

The product of these two uncertainties is at least equal to $\frac{1}{2}\hbar$. We shall first discuss the uncertainty principle and then explain it in terms of quantum waves.

Δx and Δp_x can both be near zero on a macroscopic scale

Since on the human scale $\hbar$ is a very small quantity, Δx and Δp_x can be so close to zero in the macroscopic world that there is for all practical purposes no fundamental uncertainty whatever in the position and momentum of large objects. If we wish to specify a man's position to within the size of a single atom, his speed could, in principle, be determined to an accuracy of about 10^{-26} m/sec. Needless to say, the inaccuracies of measurement take over long before the inherent limitation of accuracy implied by the uncertainty relation can play any role. But in the world of particles, this is not so. Masses and distances are so small that the uncertainty principle is of vital importance. An electron, in order to be localized within a distance 10^{-10} m, has an inherent uncertainty of speed of about 10^6 m/sec. In many submicroscopic applications, the actual product of uncertainties is not much greater than the theoretical lower limit. Therefore, it is often a good approximation to replace Formula 23.68 by the approximate equality

Uncertainties are "large" on an atomic scale

This approximation is often valid

$$\Delta x \, \Delta p_x \cong \hbar. \tag{23.69}$$

■ EXAMPLE: Electrons of energy 50 eV are incident on a slit of width $a = 10^{-5}$ m, as shown in Figure 23.19. According to the uncertainty principle, what is a typical angle of diffraction of the electrons? Let the x direction be horizontal, parallel to the original direction of the beam, and let the y direction be vertical, parallel to the screen containing the slit. For the y direction, the uncertainty principle reads

$$\Delta y \, \Delta p_y \cong \hbar. \tag{23.70}$$

The slit, by confining the wave in the y direction, introduces an uncertainty of p_y. A rough value for Δy is $\frac{1}{3}a$. (Since Δy is the rms deviation of y away from its value at the midpoint of the slit, it must be somewhat less than $\frac{1}{2}a$. Even if one chose the cruder guess, $\Delta y = a$, the right order of magnitude would result from this calculation.) As a typical angle of diffraction we may take

$$\theta \cong \frac{\Delta p_y}{p_x},$$

a ratio of transverse momentum to the original horizontal momentum. In Equation 23.70 we set $\Delta y = \frac{1}{3}a$ and $\Delta p_y = \theta p_x$, obtaining

$$\frac{1}{3}a\theta \cong \frac{\hbar}{p_x}.$$

On the right side, $\hbar/p_x$ is, from the de Broglie equation, λ, the reduced wavelength of the electron beam. The typical diffraction angle is, therefore,

The uncertainty principle can account for diffraction

$$\theta \cong \frac{3\lambda}{a} \cong \frac{1}{2}\frac{\lambda}{a}.$$

This slit of less than 0.001 in. scarcely diffracts 50-volt electrons, and would 18.103). The wavelength of 50-eV electrons is about 1.7 Å, or 1.7×10^{-10} m (see the numerical example in Section 23.9). In this example, therefore,

$$\theta \cong \frac{1.7 \times 10^{-10} \text{ m}}{2 \times 10^{-5} \text{ m}} \cong 10^{-5} \text{ radian.}$$

This slit of less than 0.001 in. scarcely diffracts 50-volt electrons, and would diffract higher-energy electrons even less.   ■

The uncertainty principle, when discussed by itself outside the framework of quantum mechanics, is often assigned a profundity that is scarcely justified. It has obvious philosophic implications; and with those who wish to attack science it is especially popular because it shows that even the "exact" scientist is prohibited by nature from measuring things as exactly as he would like. One may also argue that nature is shielding its innermost secrets by allowing man to proceed only so far and no farther in his downward quest. In truth, the uncertainty principle *is* fundamental and presents in capsule form an important part of the physical content of quantum mechanics. Nevertheless, it may be viewed as just one more aspect of the wave nature of matter, in which case it seems considerably less mysterious.

THE UNCERTAINTY PRINCIPLE AND QUANTUM WAVES

To understand the uncertainty principle, one need only grasp a single important idea about the confinement of waves: A wave can be confined, or partially localized, only if different wavelengths are superposed. The "pure" sine wave in Figure 23.18(a) is an unconfined wave. It has a precisely defined wavelength but no boundary in space. If it is a particle wave, it represents a particle with a definite momentum given by $p = h/\lambda$. Where is the particle? It is everywhere, or it is equally likely to be anywhere (along the infinite dimension of the wave). For this wave $\Delta x = \infty$ and $\Delta p_x = 0$. This is an extreme situation that is at least consistent with the uncertainty principle. If the product of two uncertainties is constant, one of the two can become vanishingly small only if the other becomes infinitely great.

> *The key idea: Localization requires a mixture of wavelengths*

The wave shown in Figure 23.18(b) is one formed by superposing many sine waves of different frequency. It is characterized by a finite Δx and a finite Δp_x, with $\Delta x \, \Delta p_x \cong \hbar$. A simpler example, the superposition of just two waves, differing by 10 percent in wavelength, is shown in Figure 23.25. Five cycles from the point of maximum reinforcement, the waves interfere

> *Partial localization with two wavelengths*

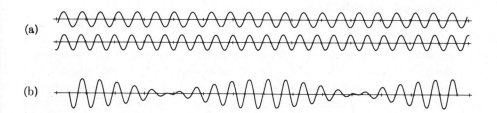

(a)

(b)

FIGURE 23.25 Superposition of two waves differing by 10 percent in wavelength. (a) The two pure sine waves. (b) The wave formed by superposing these two.

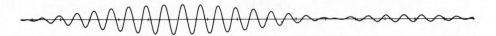

FIGURE 23.26   Superposition of six waves spanning 10 percent in wavelength. The two waves shown in Figure 23.25(a) plus four others intermediate between these two are superposed to form the wave shown here. (The vertical scale is altered.)

destructively. Five cycles further on, they again reinforce. This alternation of constructive and destructive interference produces partial localization of the wave, a bunching together of the wave into regions each about 10 wavelengths in extent.

Greater localization with more wavelengths

Greater confinement is achieved by superposing a large number of different wavelengths. Figure 23.26 shows the result of combining six different pure waves whose wavelengths differ successively by 2 percent. The total spread of wavelengths remains 10 percent, or 5 percent on either side of the average wavelength.   The rms deviation of wavelength is about 3.5 percent of the dominant wavelength: $\Delta\lambda \cong 0.035\lambda$.   The uncertainty of momentum (see footnote on page 1169) has the same relation to the dominant momentum:

$$\Delta p \cong 0.035p.$$

In Figure 23.26, the sixfold superposition produces a better confinement of the wave. (If all possible wavelengths within the given span were superposed, the wave would be fully confined. Outside of a given region of space, its amplitude would fall to zero, never to rise again.) The uncertainty of position is roughly one third of the total spread of the wave—about four wavelengths, according to the figure:

$$\Delta x \cong 4\lambda.$$

The product of position and momentum uncertainties is, in this example,

$$\Delta x\, \Delta p \cong 0.14\lambda p.$$

Since the product λp on the right side is, from the de Broglie equation, approximately equal to Planck's constant h, this equation can be written

$$\Delta x\, \Delta p \cong 0.14h \cong 0.9\hbar,$$

confirming Equation 23.69.

Maximum localization requires
$\Delta p/p_{av} \cong 1$

Since a 10 percent spread in momentum "crushed" the wave packet from infinite extent to a little more than 10 wavelengths, it is a reasonable guess that momenta varying by nearly 100 percent would be required to narrow a packet down to a single cycle. This is true. Maximum confinement requires that wavelengths (and momenta) differing by as much as a factor two be superposed. The electron wave function in Figure 23.23(b) shows such a highly confined wave, completing only one half-cycle of oscillation. The fact that the shape of this wave function differs markedly from the shape of a pure sine wave is a reflection of the fact that it is a superposition of many different wavelengths.

This discussion of wave superposition has demonstrated the essential point that the Heisenberg uncertainty principle is a consequence of the wave nature of particles.* It is no more profound, and in this form says no more and no less, than the de Broglie equation giving the wavelength of material particles. Uncertainty of measurement arises essentially from the nonlocalizability of waves. In a confined state, a particle has a mixture of different momenta. The more narrowly the wave is confined, the greater is the range of momenta.

★23.15   The Schrödinger equation

If particles moved only in force-free regions, with constant kinetic energy and constant magnitude of momentum, there would be no need of a quantum wave equation. Then the wave function of every particle would be a sine or cosine wave, with the wavelength chosen to match the particle's momentum ($\lambda = h/p$), and with the locations of the zeros of the function determined, if necessary, to match appropriate boundary conditions, as for a particle in a box. The need for an equation to govern ψ arises when we consider a particle whose momentum and kinetic energy are not constant but vary in response to forces. In this section we shall specialize to particles moving in one dimension and to forces that can be described by potential energy functions.

A wave equation for ψ is needed when p and K are variable

Let us first review a few equations valid for *constant* momentum p. The de Broglie equation determines a wavelength,

Review of free-particle wave properties

$$\lambda = \frac{h}{p},$$

and the wave function is a sine wave,

$$\psi = A \sin (kx + \varphi), \tag{23.71}$$

in which φ is a phase constant and the wave number k is (repeating Equation 23.15)

$$k = \frac{2\pi}{\lambda} = \frac{1}{\lambda}.$$

Because of the relation between λ and p, the wave number can be expressed simply in terms of momentum or kinetic energy (see Equations 23.51 and 23.56):

$$k = \frac{p}{\hbar} = \frac{\sqrt{2mK}}{\hbar}. \tag{23.72}$$

For large kinetic energy, the wave number is large and the wavelength is small [Figure 23.27(a)]. For small kinetic energy, the wave number is small and the wavelength is large [Figure 23.27(b)].

Large K means large k and small λ

One way to approach variable momentum is to consider a potential energy function that steps from one constant value to another [Figure 23.27(c)]. In one region the wave function is

A two-step potential energy function

---

* Students familiar with Fourier analysis will recognize the relevance of that branch of analysis to the questions of wave superposition considered here.

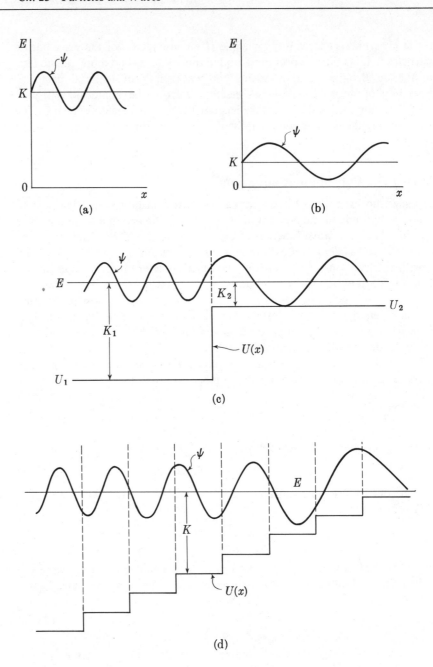

FIGURE 23.27   (a) Large kinetic energy means short wavelength. (b) Small kinetic energy means long wavelength. (c) At a potential-energy step, the wave function changes its wavelength. It may reach a greater maximum value in the region of longer wavelength (less kinetic energy). (d) For a potential of many steps, the wave function consists of many segments of sine waves, which are fitted together to preserve the continuity of ψ and $d\psi/dx$.

$$\psi_1 = A_1 \sin (k_1 x + \varphi_1),$$

where

$$k_1 = \frac{\sqrt{2mK_1}}{\hbar} = \frac{\sqrt{2m(E - U_1)}}{\hbar}.$$

In the other region it is

$$\psi_2 = A_2 \sin (k_2 x + \varphi_2),$$

where

$$k_2 = \frac{\sqrt{2mK_2}}{\hbar} = \frac{\sqrt{2m(E - U_2)}}{\hbar}.$$

For any choice of constants A_1 and φ_1, it is possible to find values of A_2 and φ_2 that cause the wave function and its first derivative to be continuous at the junction between the two regions.

This idea of joining different sine waves can be extended to a situation in which the potential takes many steps [Figure 23.27(d)]. In each narrow region is a small piece of a sine wave, its wave number determined by Equation 23.72. It joins smoothly onto pieces of sine waves of different wave number in adjoining regions. The actual process of choosing magnitudes and phase constants for all these segments of sine waves in order to produce a single smooth wave function ψ would be onerous indeed. However, we have no interest in doing that. Our real concern is with the limit of infinitely many steps in which $U(x)$ becomes a smoothly changing potential energy function. Can we develop an equation governing ψ in that limit? There is an easy way to do so. If we differentiate Equation 23.71 twice with respect to x, we get

A many-step function; many pieces of sine waves must be joined

$$\frac{d^2\psi}{dx^2} = -k^2 A \sin (kx + \varphi),$$

which can be written as

$$\frac{d^2\psi}{dx^2} = -k^2\psi. \tag{23.73}$$

Substituting for k from Equation 23.72 puts this equation in the form

$$\frac{d^2\psi}{dx^2} = -\frac{2mK}{\hbar^2}\psi. \tag{23.74}$$

A differential property of each sine-wave segment

Here is a differential equation for ψ free of all reference to the magnitude A or the phase constant φ. In any one region, $d^2\psi/dx^2$ is proportional to ψ; from one region to another, the constant of proportionality changes. The significance of this equation is that it expresses properties of ψ at each point in terms of the kinetic energy at that same point.

To describe particles moving in one dimension subject to an arbitrary potential energy function $U(x)$, we postulate the validity of Equation 23.74. Since $K = E - U$, we may rewrite the equation in the form

$$\frac{d^2\psi}{dx^2} + \frac{2m}{\hbar^2}[E - U(x)]\psi = 0. \tag{23.75}$$

The time-independent Schrödinger equation in one dimension

This is the *time-independent Schrödinger equation* in one dimension. Its generalization to include time dependence and dependence on three spatial dimensions we leave to more advanced texts. Another instructive way to write this equation is

A form analogous to
K + U = E

$$-\frac{\hbar^2}{2m}\frac{d^2\psi}{dx^2} + U(x)\psi = E\psi. \tag{23.76}$$

This Schrödinger equation may be considered to be the quantum analog of the classical equation of energy conservation,

$$K + U = E.$$

It is the second derivative of the quantum wave that is proportional to kinetic energy. Thus for larger kinetic energy, the curvature of the wave function is greater (more exactly, the ratio $(d^2\psi/dx^2)/\psi$ is greater). This is evident in Figure 23.27.

Our reasoning here should be considered a plausibility argument and not a derivation. Schrödinger's original reasoning, although not the same as presented here, was similar. He sought to replace the algebraic equation of de Broglie, suitable for fixed wavelength, with a differential equation that would be suitable for continuously variable wavelength. The test of the equation is not the logic of its derivation but rather the agreement between its predictions and experiment.

DISCUSSION OF THE SCHRÖDINGER EQUATION

Wavelength and wave number are concepts that appear to be meaningful only for a wave that executes one or more cycles of oscillation, but they can be given meaning in an infinitesimal region and for a wave of any shape. Making the wave number concept meaningful in the small is, in effect, what the Schrödinger equation does. It takes over the de Broglie definition of k, Equation 23.72, and uses it at a point. To say that a wave function such as the one in Figure 23.28 has a wave number (or wavelength) at a particular point is equivalent to saying that if a sine wave is matched to the wave function at that point (same values of ψ, $d\psi/dx$, and $d^2\psi/dx^2$), the sine wave would have a wave number given by Equation 23.72, or a wavelength given by

The Schrödinger equation makes k and λ meaningful in an infinitesimal region

$$\lambda = \frac{h}{p} = \frac{h}{\sqrt{2mK}}. \tag{23.77}$$

Thus the Schrödinger equation joins an infinite number of infinitesimal de Broglie waves into a single smooth wave function that as a whole could differ greatly from a sine wave.

Further insight into the Schrödinger equation can be achieved by considering the role of kinetic energy in determining the curvature of the wave function. We may write Equation 23.74 in the form

$$\frac{d^2\psi/dx^2}{\psi} = -\frac{2mK}{\hbar^2} = -\frac{2m}{\hbar^2}(E - U).$$

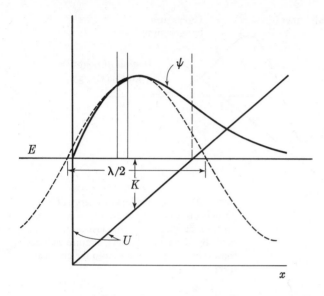

FIGURE 23.28 Graphical demonstration of the meaning of wavelength for the wave function of a particle in a nonconstant potential. A sine wave matched to a small segment of ψ has a wavelength given by Equation 23.77 and a wave number given by Equation 23.72.

For positive kinetic energy, the right side is negative. Therefore, ψ and its second derivative have opposite signs:

$$\psi > 0, \qquad \frac{d^2\psi}{dx^2} < 0, \qquad \text{curvature toward axis;}$$

$$\psi < 0, \qquad \frac{d^2\psi}{dx^2} > 0, \qquad \text{curvature toward axis.}$$

Curvature of ψ for $K > 0$
(classically allowed region)

Whether ψ is positive or negative, its curvature tends to bend it back toward the axis. This behavior is illustrated by the oscillatory part of the wave function in Figure 23.29 and in several earlier figures. The Schrödinger equation admits of an interesting additional possibility: The wave function may penetrate into a "classically forbidden region" of negative kinetic energy. This phenomenon appears to the right of point B in Figure 23.29. Point B, the so-called classical turning point, is defined by $E = U$, or $K = 0$. Classically, it is the limit of the motion. Quantum-mechanically, the particle has a certain probability to be found farther to the right. This probability does, however, diminish rapidly for $x > x_\mathrm{B}$. In this region of negative kinetic energy, the wave function bends away from the axis:

$$\left.\begin{array}{ll} \psi > 0, & \dfrac{d^2\psi}{dx^2} > 0 \\[2em] \psi < 0, & \dfrac{d^2\psi}{dx^2} < 0 \end{array}\right\} \quad \text{curvature away from axis.}$$

Curvature of ψ for $K < 0$
(classically forbidden region)

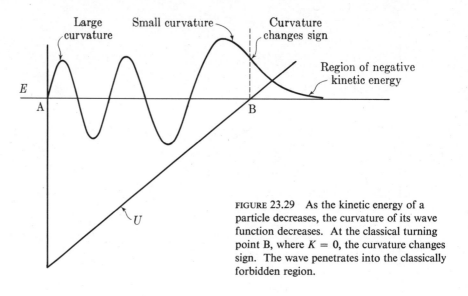

Large curvature — Small curvature — Curvature changes sign

Region of negative kinetic energy

FIGURE 23.29   As the kinetic energy of a particle decreases, the curvature of its wave function decreases. At the classical turning point B, where $K = 0$, the curvature changes sign. The wave penetrates into the classically forbidden region.

At the classical turning point, the second derivative of ψ changes sign.*

The idea of an eigenvalue   The Schrödinger equation is what is called an *eigenvalue* equation.† What this means is that it may have physically acceptable solutions (for instance, giving probabilities that do not change discontinuously and do not become infinite) only for certain values of the energy parameter E. For bound-state problems, only a discrete array of values of E yields acceptable solutions. Thus requirements on the wave function lead to the quantization of energy. The meaning of this eigenvalue property will be illustrated in the discussion of the harmonic oscillator below.

A FREE PARTICLE

The simplest application of the Schrödinger equation is to a free particle. In Equation 23.74, K is constant, so the differential equation tells us that $d^2\psi/dx^2$ is proportional to $-\psi$. This is a now-familiar proportionality, satisfied only by sine and cosine functions. If we insert

$$\psi = A \sin kx$$

as a trial solution into Equation 23.74, we obtain

$$-k^2 A \sin kx = -\frac{2mK}{\hbar^2} A \sin kx.$$

---

* The reason that the wave function in Figure 23.23(b) bends away from the axis for all r is that this is not a one-dimensional wave function but a cross section of a three-dimensional wave function, whose Schrödinger equation is slightly different.

† Eigenvalue is a half-German and half-English word that is sometimes rendered as either "characteristic value" or "proper value."

The equality is satisfied if

$$k^2 = \frac{2mK}{\hbar^2},$$

which is equivalent to Equation 23.72 and, of course, equivalent to the de Broglie equation, $\lambda = h/p$. More generally, a solution of Equation 23.74 for constant k is

$$\psi = A \sin kx + B \cos kx. \tag{23.78}$$

Wave function of a free particle

A PARTICLE IN A HARMONIC-OSCILLATOR POTENTIAL

For a particle experiencing a restoring force proportional to its displacement ($F_x = -kx$), the potential energy is (from Section 10.8)

$$U = \tfrac{1}{2}kx^2.$$

It will prove convenient to express U in terms of the classical "angular" frequency of the harmonic oscillator (Equation 7.32),

$$\omega = \sqrt{\frac{k}{m}}.$$

The classical "angular" frequency is a useful parameter

In terms of the constant ω, the potential energy is

$$U = \tfrac{1}{2}m\omega^2 x^2, \tag{23.79}$$

where m is the mass of the particle. For this example of motion, the Schrödinger equation (Equation 23.75) takes the following form;

$$\frac{d^2\psi}{dx^2} + \left[\frac{2mE}{\hbar^2} - \left(\frac{m\omega}{\hbar}\right)^2 x^2\right]\psi = 0. \tag{23.80}$$

Schrödinger equation for particle in a harmonic-oscillator potential

The general methods of finding the solutions of this differential equation are beyond the level of this text. We shall use only the method of the inspired guess and show that the following wave function,

$$\psi = Ae^{-\alpha x^2}, \tag{23.81}$$

A trial solution

is a solution for appropriate choice of α and E. The first derivative of this function is

$$\frac{d\psi}{dx} = A(-2\alpha x)e^{-\alpha x^2}.$$

Its second derivative is

$$\frac{d^2\psi}{dx^2} = A(-2\alpha + 4\alpha^2 x^2)e^{-\alpha x^2}.$$

Substituting in Equation 23.80 gives

$$Ae^{-\alpha x^2}\left\{[-2\alpha + 4\alpha^2 x^2] + \left[\frac{2mE}{\hbar^2} - \left(\frac{m\omega}{\hbar}\right)^2 x^2\right]\right\} = 0.$$

For this equation to be satisfied at all x, the constant terms and the terms proportional to x^2 must separately sum to zero. This means that

$$2\alpha = \frac{2mE}{\hbar^2}, \tag{23.82}$$

$$(2\alpha)^2 = \left(\frac{m\omega}{\hbar}\right)^2. \tag{23.83}$$

These two simple algebraic equations determine α and E. From Equation 23.83,

$$\alpha = \frac{m\omega}{2\hbar}.$$

Then, from Equation 23.82,

Eigenvalue for the ground state

$$E = \tfrac{1}{2}\hbar\omega. \tag{23.84}$$

Although we have not proved it, this is the energy of the lowest state of the harmonic oscillator—its zero-point energy. The associated wave function is*

Wave function of the ground state

$$\psi = Ae^{-(m\omega/2\hbar)x^2}. \tag{23.85}$$

This is only *one* solution of Equation 23.80. Other solutions, somewhat more complicated in form, describe excited states. The energy diagram and a superposed graph of ψ for the ground state are shown in Figure 23.30(a).

It is of some interest to express the wave function also in terms of the distance a, the coordinate of the classical turning point [Figure 23.30(a)]. The condition $U = E$ that determines this point may be written

$$\tfrac{1}{2}m\omega^2 a^2 = \tfrac{1}{2}\hbar\omega.$$

Therefore,

$$a = \sqrt{\frac{\hbar}{m\omega}}. \tag{23.86}$$

In terms of a, the wave function (Equation 23.85) is

$$\psi = Ae^{-\frac{1}{2}(x^2/a^2)}. \tag{23.87}$$

It is a simple matter to verify that $d^2\psi/dx^2 = 0$ at $x = \pm a$, just as it should.

The fact that the trial function in Equation 23.81 is a solution of the Schrödinger equation only for a particular value of the energy E suggests an eigenvalue condition. Further evidence on this point is shown in Figure 23.30(b). The functions ψ plotted there were obtained numerically. For E slightly less than $\tfrac{1}{2}\hbar\omega$, ψ approaches $+\infty$ at large x. For E slightly more than $\tfrac{1}{2}\hbar\omega$, ψ

Wave-function behavior at large x determines physically allowed energies

approaches $-\infty$ at large x. Only for the exact value $E = \tfrac{1}{2}\hbar\omega$ does the wave function approach zero at large x. All three of these functions are *mathematically* acceptable solutions of the Schrödinger equation, but only one is a *physically*

---

* The coefficient A, determined by the requirement of unit total probability,

$$\int_{-\infty}^{\infty} \psi^2\, dx = 1,$$

proves to be $A = (m\omega/\pi\hbar)^{1/4}$.

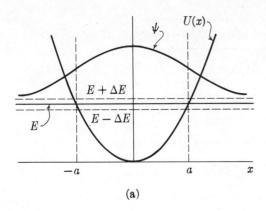

(a)

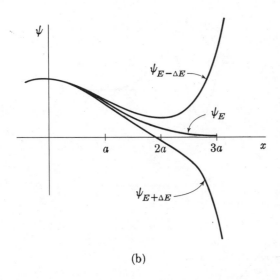

(b)

FIGURE 23.30 (a) Wave function of the ground state of the harmonic oscillator superposed on an energy diagram. (b) Solutions of the Schrödinger equation for E slightly less and slightly greater than $\frac{1}{2}\hbar\omega$ are compared with the physically acceptable solution for $E = \frac{1}{2}\hbar\omega$. The value of E that yields a physically meaningful solution is called an eigenvalue.

acceptable solution. If $\psi \to \pm\infty$, the probability becomes infinite at points remote from the center of the potential, a physically meaningless situation. In fact, nature selects only those energies for which $\psi \to 0$ in the classically forbidden region. As for the particle in the idealized box with impenetrable walls, a boundary condition quantizes the energy.

The spectrum of allowed energies of the harmonic oscillator is especially simple. It is

$$E_n = (n + \tfrac{1}{2})\hbar\omega, \tag{23.88}$$

equally spaced energies separated by an interval

$$\Delta E = \hbar\omega. \tag{23.89}$$

Energies of excited states are equally spaced

This spectrum and several associated wave functions appear in Figure 23.31. Another interesting feature of the oscillator is that if a particle makes a quantum jump from one state to the next lower state, the frequency of the radiated photon is the same as the classical frequency of mechanical oscillation. Classically, a particle in an oscillator potential moves with frequency

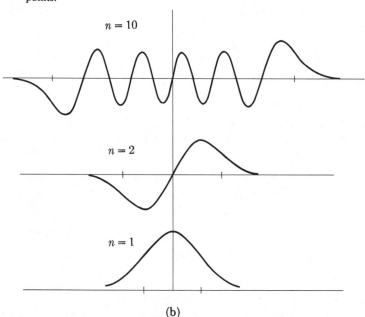

$$E_n = (n - \tfrac{1}{2})\hbar\omega$$

Classical frequency
of oscillation $= \nu = \frac{\omega}{2\pi}$

$$E_3 = \tfrac{5}{2}\hbar\omega$$

$$E_2 = \tfrac{3}{2}\hbar\omega$$

$$E_1 = \tfrac{1}{2}\hbar\omega$$

Frequency of
radiated
photon $= \nu = \frac{\omega}{2\pi}$

(a)

FIGURE 23.31   (a) The equally spaced energy-level spectrum of the harmonic oscillator. (b) Wave functions of first, second, and tenth states. Marks on the horizontal axes show the classical turning points.

$n = 10$

$n = 2$

$n = 1$

(b)

$$\nu_e = \frac{\omega}{2\pi} = \frac{1}{2\pi}\sqrt{\frac{k}{m}},$$

independent of its energy. The frequency of the radiated photon is governed by

$$h\nu_r = \Delta E.$$

A special feature of the harmonic oscillator: Radiated frequency = mechanical frequency

Since $\Delta E = \hbar\omega = h\nu_e$, we have

$$\nu_r = \nu_e. \tag{23.90}$$

This quantum result was known for the harmonic oscillator before Bohr's work on the hydrogen atom (although the wave description of the oscillator came later). The very simplicity of this result, and also its agreement with classical theory, may indeed have delayed the understanding of atomic structure. Before Bohr, no one had thought to break loose from the condition of Equation 23.90. For systems in general, it is valid only as an approximation for large quantum numbers, where the correspondence principle can be applied.

Summary of ideas and definitions

Quantum mechanics is primarily the theory of the sub-microscopic world.

Like relativity, quantum mechanics introduced ideas at variance with common sense and with classical physics. These ideas include (1) granularity of physical variables, (2) fundamental probability, (3) annihilation and creation of matter, (4) the wave-particle duality, (5) superposition of quantum states, and (6) the uncertainty principle.

The photon is a particle with no mass and no charge, with one quantum unit of spin and with energy given by $E = h\nu = hc/\lambda = \hbar ck$.

The photoelectric effect (ejection of electrons from a solid surface by radiation) supports the photon idea and provides a way to measure h/e (Equation 23.4).

Through its emission and absorption processes, its quantum of energy, and its diffraction and interference, the photon illustrates most of the key ideas of quantum mechanics.

By measuring the charge-to-mass ratio of cathode rays, and also in other ways, J. J. Thomson first identified the electron.

The charge of the electron was first accurately measured by Robert Millikan in an experiment in which the electric force on charged oil droplets was calibrated against forces of gravity and frictional air drag.

Line spectra, because they uniquely identify atoms, have great practical utility. In the nineteenth century, they were taken to mean that atoms have characteristic frequencies of vibration (normal modes).

The spectrum of hydrogen is described by the generalized Balmer formula,

$$\frac{1}{\lambda} = \mathscr{R}_H \left(\frac{1}{n^2} - \frac{1}{m^2} \right). \tag{23.14}$$

The first few series in hydrogen are called the Lyman series ($n = 1$), the Balmer series ($n = 2$), the Paschen series ($n = 3$), and the Brackett series ($n = 4$).

According to the Ritz combination principle, every atom is represented by a term diagram. Radiated wave numbers ($k = 2\pi/\lambda = 1/\lambda$) are proportional to the vertical distances between terms in the diagram.

In seeking to explain the spectrum of hydrogen in terms of Rutherford's nuclear atom, Niels Bohr postulated that

1. Electrons normally move in stationary states of quantized energy.

2. Radiation is emitted in sudden quantum jumps between stationary states.

3. Because of energy conservation between matter and radiation, a term diagram is equivalent to an energy-level diagram.

4. When fractional changes of quantized variables are small, quantum results should agree with classical results (the correspondence principle).

A key step in Bohr's reasoning is the equation $\nu_r \cong \nu_e$: Radiated frequency and orbital frequency are approximately equal for large values of the principal quantum number.

Bohr's postulates lead to a formula for the Rydberg constant:

$$\mathscr{R}_\infty = \left(\frac{1}{4\pi\epsilon_0} \right)^2 \frac{me^4}{4\pi\hbar^3 c}. \tag{23.35}$$

The quantity $\mathscr{R}_H$ is the same, with m replaced by the reduced mass μ.

The binding energy of the hydrogen atom is

$$W = \frac{hc\mathscr{R}_H}{n^2} = \left(\frac{1}{4\pi\epsilon_0} \right)^2 \frac{\mu e^4}{2\hbar^2} \frac{1}{n^2}. \tag{23.21, 23.36}$$

The radius, speed, and angular momentum of an electron in a circular Bohr orbit are given by

$$r = 4\pi\epsilon_0 \frac{\hbar^2 n^2}{me^2} = a_0 n^2, \tag{23.40–23.42}$$

$$\frac{v}{c} = \frac{1}{4\pi\epsilon_0} \frac{e^2}{\hbar c} \frac{1}{n} = \frac{\alpha}{n}, \tag{23.45, 23.46}$$

$$L = n\hbar. \tag{23.47}$$

De Broglie assigned a wavelength

$$\lambda = \frac{h}{p} \qquad (23.48)$$

to all material particles as well as to photons. Electron diffraction experiments verified this equation.

The de Broglie equation may also be used to relate wave number to momentum and energy:

$$k = \frac{p}{\hbar} = \frac{\sqrt{2mK}}{\hbar}. \qquad (23.72)$$

Through the condition $2\pi r = n\lambda$, the de Broglie wave provides a partial explanation of quantized Bohr orbits.

The wave function of a free particle is a sine or cosine wave, such as

$$\psi = A \sin kx. \qquad (23.54)$$

The position probability (per unit distance in one dimension or per unit volume in three dimensions) is given by

$$P \sim |\psi|^2. \qquad (23.55)$$

The proportionality is replaced by an equality if ψ is "normalized" to make the total probability equal to 1.

For a particle between rigid walls, the boundary conditions are $\psi = 0$ at both walls; as a result, the energy is quantized and given by

$$K = \frac{h^2}{8md^2} \, n^2. \qquad (23.59)$$

Every system confined in space has a finite zero-point energy in its lowest state.

The finite size of an atom can be attributed to the nonlocalizability of its wave function. The zero-point energy acts as a "repulsive" effect countering the attractive potential.

The wave function is analogous to a classical displacement or field but is itself not an observable quantity.

Wave functions, not quantum probabilities, are additive. If $\psi = \psi_1 + \psi_2$, a particle must be described as existing in two states at once.

One form of the uncertainty principle is

$$\Delta x \, \Delta p_x \geq \tfrac{1}{2}\hbar. \qquad (23.68)$$

It can often be approximated by

$$\Delta x \, \Delta p_x \cong \hbar.$$

An explanation of the uncertainty principle: To produce partial localization of a wave, different wavelengths—therefore different momenta—must be mixed.

The Schrödinger equation is based on the postulate that the differential property of sine waves, $d^2\psi/dx^2 = -k^2\psi$, is valid at every point, for variable as well as for constant k.

For a particle moving in one dimension and experiencing a potential energy U, the time-independent Schrödinger equation is

$$-\frac{\hbar^2}{2m}\frac{d^2\psi}{dx^2} + U(x)\psi = E\psi. \qquad (23.76)$$

The requirement that ψ satisfy certain boundary conditions may limit E (the eigenvalue) to discrete values.

The energies of a particle in a harmonic-oscillator potential are

$$E = (n + \tfrac{1}{2})\hbar\omega. \qquad (23.88)$$

The wave function of the particle in its ground state is

$$\psi = Ae^{-(m\omega/2\hbar)x^2}. \qquad (23.85)$$

QUESTIONS

Section 23.1   **Q23.1**   Name one physical variable that is, so far as we now know, infinitely divisible, free of granularity. Speculate very briefly on the possible alteration of our view of nature that might result, should this quantity later prove to be granular.

Q23.2   On an astronomical scale, the units of matter in the solar system are discrete, or granular (the sun, planets, moons, etc.). Viewed more closely, each such unit appears to be infinitely divisible. Looking still more closely (at the atomic level), one again finds granularity. Does this mean that some form of quantum theory governs the astronomical as well as the atomic realm? In what way do the astronomical and atomic granularities differ?

Section 23.2   **Q23.3**   In what ways does the photon as a particle violate the laws of Newtonian mechanics?

Q23.4   In experiments on the photoelectric effect, what happens if (a) the intensity of the incident light is doubled? (b) the frequency of the incident light is doubled? How does each of these changes support the photon theory of light?

Q23.5   Both the photoelectric effect and the Compton effect involve the interaction of a photon with an electron. In what way do these processes differ?

Q23.6   For each of the following, is it the wave or the particle aspect of light that is more prominent: (a) the photoelectric effect; (b) the Compton effect; (c) diffraction; (d) the emission of light by an atom?

Q23.7   Discuss momentum conservation in the photoelectric effect. (Note in Figure 23.2 that the directions of the incident photons and the emitted electrons are not the same.) (See also Problem 23.1.)

Q23.8   Many phenomena other than the photoelectric effect now support the photon theory of light. Name two such phenomena, either naturally occurring or stimulated by experiment. How does each provide evidence for photons?

Q23.9   If the photoelectric effect takes place in a gas rather than at a solid surface, is there still a threshold frequency below which no photoelectrons are produced?

Q23.10 One of the technical problems that confronted the developers of color television was the design of an image tube (camera) for the red portion of the image. Why was the red tube more of a technical challenge than the green tube or the blue tube?

Q23.11 In an outside reference, look up the term "contact potential." Explain its meaning.

Q23.12 Suggest a reason why gas occupying the space between terminals held at a fixed potential difference [as in Figure 23.5(a)] glows if it is at low pressure, but not if it is at normal atmospheric pressure.   Section 23.3

Q23.13 In a gas-discharge tube, the cathode emits electrons. Why does the anode not emit protons or other charged particles?

Q23.14 Below Equation 23.7 it is stated that the charge-to-mass ratio of the electron is "large." Explain carefully what this means.

Q23.15 In carrying out his experiments to determine e/m for electrons, Thomson used accelerating potentials of 2,000 to 30,000 V. Did the effects of relativity, unknown to Thomson, significantly influence the results of any of his experiments? Explain.

Q23.16 Suggest one or more reasons why magnetic rather than electric deflection is used to direct the electron beam in a television tube [see Figure 23.5(e)]. (Reference to an encyclopedia or other outside reference might be helpful.)

Q23.17 Could the Millikan oil-drop experiment be performed in a vacuum?

Q23.18 A classical system with a discrete set of natural vibration frequencies can be *forced* to vibrate at any of a *continuous* range of frequencies. Illustrate this point with a simple example.   Section 23.4

Q23.19 Hydrogen in a gas discharge tube emits a line spectrum in the visible region. Ionized hydrogen on the sun emits a continuous spectrum in the visible region. What accounts for the difference?

Q23.20 (1) Light from an incandescent source is passed through sodium vapor and then examined with a spectroscope. What is the appearance of the spectrum? (2) Next the incandescent source is switched off and the sodium vapor is heated until it glows. How does the spectrum of the glowing sodium compare with the previously observed spectrum?

Section 23.5   Q23.21 Give the practical reason why the Balmer series was the first among the various series emitted by hydrogen to be identified and quantified.

Q23.22 One table lists all the known spectral wavelengths of a certain element. Another table lists all the known "terms" contained in the term diagram of the same element. Which table is likely to be shorter? Why?

Q23.23 Explain what it means to say that the Ritz combination principle is nothing more than a statement of the law of energy conservation.

Q23.24 Place yourself in the year 1908, armed with all of the facts and theories of that time, but ignorant of all details of atomic structure. If you accepted Einstein's photon and Ritz's combination principle, and believed in the universal validity of the law of energy conservation, what could you conclude about the nature of an atom?

Section 23.6   Q23.25 What is a "normal mode"? (Consult an outside reference if necessary.) A normal mode of a classical system is the analog of a stationary state of a quantum system.

Q23.26 If the electron in a hydrogen atom obeyed classical mechanics instead of quantum mechanics, would it emit a line spectrum or a continuous spectrum? Explain your answer.

Q23.27 Particles within atoms are attracted to one another by gravitational forces. Why did Bohr ignore these forces in his effort to construct a new mechanics for atoms?

Section 23.7   Q23.28 Equation 23.20 gives an energy formula that accounts for the spectrum of hydrogen. Another formula that works equally well is $E_n = A - (hc\mathscr{R}/n^2)$, where A is any constant. Explain why Bohr assumed $A = 0$. Is it *necessary* to assume $A = 0$?

Q23.29 The ionization energy of a hydrogen atom is 13.6 eV. (1) Can a hydrogen atom in its ground state absorb a photon of energy *less* than 13.6 eV? If so, what is the final state of the system? (2) Answer the same questions for a photon of energy *greater* than 13.6 eV.

Q23.30 (1) Can a hydrogen atom in its third state of motion ($n = 3$) emit an infrared photon? (2) Can it absorb an infrared photon?

Section 23.8   Q23.31 Astronomers have identified states of motion in hydrogen with quantum number n greater than 50. Why are such states of motion not identifiable in radiation from hydrogen on earth?

Q23.32 (1) The speed of light c does *not* appear in the formula for the Bohr radius (Equation 23.42). (2) It *does* appear in the formula for the Rydberg constant (Equation 23.35). Give physical "reasons" for these two facts.

Q23.33 Does a theorist have to take relativity into account if he is seeking a reasonably accurate description of the states of motion of the innermost electrons in the uranium atom ($Z = 92$)?

Q23.34 If an international commission increased by a factor of 10 the standard unit of measurement of mass and left the units of length and time unchanged, by what factor would the numerical value of the fine-structure constant α change?

Q23.35 Why are we unaware in everyday life of (a) the wave nature of particles? (b) the particle nature of electromagnetic radiation?   Section 23.9

Q23.36 Explain briefly in your own words why high-energy projectile particles are needed in order to probe the interior of atomic nuclei.

Q23.37 A high-energy neutron interacts with a nucleus only if it strikes the nucleus. The "cross section" of the nucleus is then equal to the projected area of the nucleus (see the figure). For low-energy neutrons, however, the effective cross section of the nucleus may be much greater than its projected area. A low-energy neutron can interact with a nucleus even if its classically calculated trajectory misses the nucleus by a substantial margin. The lower the energy of the neutron, the greater the effective nuclear cross section can be. Explain these facts.

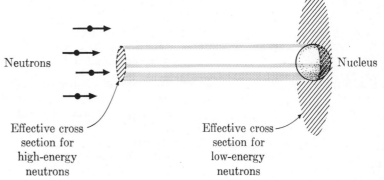

Q23.38 Suggest a reason why electron microscopes are preferred to light microscopes for the study of extremely small entities.

Q23.39 A particle in a box occupies a specific quantum energy state (Figure 23.21 and Equation 23.59). (1) Is the particle's vector momentum $\mathbf{p}$ constant? (2) Is its momentum component p_x constant (x is the coordinate of the one-dimensional motion)? (3) Is its magnitude of momentum p constant?   Section 23.11

Q23.40 As the quantum number n of a particle in a box becomes larger, the successive energy levels get farther apart, not closer together (see Figure 23.21). How can this behavior of the particle's quantum states be reconciled with the correspondence principle, which requires that as the quantum number gets larger, the granularity of the quantum world should give way to the continuity of the classical world? (HINT: Think of the *fractional* change of energy from one state to the next.)

Q23.41 As illustrated in Figure 23.22(b), there are points at which the probability of finding a particle in a box is *zero*. As the quantum number n grows larger, the probability function $|\psi|^2$ executes more cycles of oscillation and the number of points of zero probability increases. How can this behavior of the probability function be reconciled with the correspondence principle, which requires a gradual transition to classical behavior at large values of the quantum number? According to classical reasoning, a particle observed at a random time has an *equal* probability to be found anywhere in the box. (HINT: Imagine the box to be divided into many observation cells, each of small but nonzero dimension.)

Section 23.12   Q23.42   The wave nature of matter is irrelevant in the macroscopic world, yet the whole structure of the macroscopic world depends upon the wave nature of matter. Interpret this statement and discuss it briefly.

Q23.43   Wave functions may be nonzero in classically forbidden regions of negative kinetic energy (regions beyond the classical turning points). (1) Which of the two wave functions in Figure 23.23 is nonzero in a classically forbidden region? (2) Suggest a reason why the other wave function does not penetrate into the classically forbidden region.

Section 23.13   Q23.44   If the intensity of the electron beam in Figure 23.24 were made so low that one electron propagated from the slits to the screen before the next electron reached the slits, would an interference pattern show itself after many single electrons had been detected?

Q23.45   In Figure 23.24, if only slit 1 is open, the intensity of electrons reaching point B is relatively large. Explain in your own words how it can happen that opening slit 2 (with slit 1 remaining open) can cause a sharp *decrease* in intensity at point B.

Q23.46   An experimenter tries to "outwit" the wave-particle duality of electrons. He places a thin sheet of scintillating material across the two slits shown in Figure 23.24 in order to identify the slit through which each electron passes. He is successful in marking the passage of every electron through a specific slit, but then he finds that the interference pattern is destroyed—a broad, smooth pattern of intensity replaces the pattern of alternating maxima and minima. Explain how the observation of the electrons as they pass through the slits can "perturb" the electrons in such a way as to eliminate the interference.

Section 23.14   Q23.47   Explain the connection between the concept of zero-point energy and the uncertainty principle.

Q23.48   The uncertainty principle can be said to "prevent" the collapse of an atom. Explain the connection between the uncertainty principle and the size of atoms.

Q23.49   Any physical quantity is large or small only in a comparative sense, relative to something else. (1) Why do we usually call the speed of light "large"? (2) Why do we usually call Planck's constant "small"?

Q23.50   According to the strict mechanistic determinism embraced by some scientists and philosophers in the eighteenth and nineteenth centuries, a knowledge of the position and velocity of every particle in the universe at one time would make possible (in principle!) the exact prediction of the future in every detail. In the framework of quantum mechanics, is such a calculation of future events possible in principle?

Q23.51   In a theoretical or mathematical sense, classical physics is obtained from quantum physics by allowing Planck's constant h to approach zero. Pick any two equations in this chapter that contain h, and explain how setting $h = 0$ leads to classically expected behavior rather than quantum behavior.

E23.1 (1) Approximately how many photons of an AM radio wave are required to equal in energy one photon of visible light? (2) Convert to photons/sec a power of 1 W of (a) radio waves of frequency 10^8 Hz, and (b) gamma rays of frequency 10^{20} Hz.

E23.2 (1) What is the momentum of a 2-eV photon of visible light? (2) If this momentum were transferred to a 1-gm pellet, what would be the speed of the pellet?

E23.3 (1) What is the maximum wavelength of light that can eject photoelectrons from a beryllium surface (see Table 23.1)? (2) If light of half this wavelength illuminates a beryllium surface, what is the maximum kinetic energy of the ejected electrons?

E23.4 Suppose that the work function of the photosensitive surface in Figure 23.2 is 2 eV and that the photons of ultraviolet light each have an energy of 4 eV. Sketch graphs of electron speed vs x/L, where x is the distance measured upward from the lower plate and L is the distance between the plates, for stopping potentials V_S of (a) 1 V and (b) 4 V. (Assume that the electric field between the plates is uniform.)

E23.5 In being accelerated from rest through a potential difference V, an electron gains kinetic energy eV. (1) Show that the final speed of the electron is given (relativistically) by

$$v = \frac{c \sqrt{\chi(2 + \chi)}}{1 + \chi}, \qquad \text{where} \qquad \chi = \frac{eV}{mc^2}.$$

(Note that the charge and mass of the electron appear only in the combination e/m.) (2) Show that the nonrelativistic expression for the electron's speed is $v = c\sqrt{2\chi}$. (3) What is the percentage error of the nonrelativistic expression for $\chi = 0.1$ ($V \cong 50$ kV)?

E23.6 In a Millikan oil-drop experiment, a droplet is observed to fall with a terminal speed $v = 1.44$ mm/sec when no electric field acts on it. Then a vertical field of 4.9×10^5 V/m is switched on and the droplet is observed to continue downward at a new lower terminal speed $v' = 1.21$ mm/sec. The density of the oil is 750 kg/m^3 and the viscosity of air is 1.81×10^{-5} kg/m sec. (1) How must Equation 23.10 be modified to cover this case? (2) How many quantum units of charge does the droplet possess?

E23.7 A tiny plastic sphere bearing a net charge of just 1 quantum unit is held motionless by an electric force that balances its weight. (1) If the electric field is 8×10^5 V/m, what is the mass of the sphere? (2) If the average molecular weight of the material is 1,000, how many molecules does the sphere contain?

E23.8 (1) Prove that if a pair of spectral lines have a wavelength difference $\Delta\lambda$, their frequency difference is given approximately by $\Delta\nu = -(c/\lambda_{av}^2) \Delta\lambda$, where λ_{av} is the average wavelength of the pair. (2) Use this formula to find the frequency difference in Hz and then the photon energy difference in eV of the yellow D lines of sodium, whose wavelengths are $\lambda_1 = 5,890$ Å and $\lambda_2 = 5,896$ Å.

E23.9 A spectral doublet radiated by potassium has wavelengths $\lambda_1 = 7,665$ Å and $\lambda_2 = 7,699$ Å. (1) In what part of the spectrum does this doublet lie? (2) Are the photons radiated by potassium to make these spectral lines of greater or less energy than the photons of the sodium D lines, whose wavelengths are stated in the preceding exercise? (3) Is the difference in the two potassium photon energies greater or less than the difference in the two sodium photon energies? By about what factor?

Section 23.5 **E23.10** The index of refraction of air for red light is approximately 1.00028. Accordingly, light propagates somewhat more slowly in air than in vacuum, but with no change in frequency. Calculate the wavelength difference of the red line of the Balmer series as observed in air and in vacuum.

E23.11 For the wavelengths of the hydrogen spectrum, Balmer postulated the following general formula:

$$\lambda = b \, \frac{m^2}{m^2 - n^2} \, ,$$

where m and n are positive integers ($m > n$) and b is a constant ($b = 3,646$ Å in air or 3,647 Å in vacuum). (1) Show that this formula is correct for $n = 2$ (the Balmer series) but not correct for other values of n. (2) Balmer's formula can be "patched up" by allowing the multiplier b to be a function of n. Express b in terms of n and the Rydberg constant $\mathscr{R}$. [A translated excerpt from Balmer's first paper can be found in W. F. Magie, *A Source Book in Physics* (Cambridge, Mass.: Harvard University Press, 1935), pp. 360–365.]

E23.12 (1) What is the wavelength of the *longest* wavelength line of the Lyman series? (This calculation shows that the entire Lyman series lies in the ultraviolet.) (2) What is the wavelength of the *shortest* wavelength line of the Paschen series (the series limit)? (This calculation shows that the entire Paschen series lies in the infrared.)

E23.13 The following wavelengths are among those observed in the spectrum of atomic hydrogen: $\lambda_a = 1,026$ Å, $\lambda_b = 1,216$ Å, $\lambda_c = 4,863$ Å, $\lambda_d = 18,756$ Å. Verify that these radiations satisfy the Ritz combination principle. Write a simple formula linking the four inverse wavelengths.

Section 23.6 **E23.14** (1) Verify that the dimension of the combination $4\pi\epsilon_0\hbar^2/m_e e^2$ (the Bohr radius) in length. (2) Another combination of constants with the dimension of length is $\hbar/m_e c$ (the reduced Compton wavelength). Find the ratio of the Bohr radius to the reduced Compton wavelength, algebraically and numerically.

Section 23.7 **E23.15** The ionization energy of a hydrogen atom in its ground state ($n = 1$) is 13.6 eV. What is its ionization energy if it is in its first excited state ($n = 2$)? In what part of the spectrum is a photon of this energy?

E23.16 What energy is required to excite a hydrogen atom from the state with $n = 3$ to the state with $n = 4$? Is this greater or less than a typical energy of thermal motion for an atom in a gas at room temperature?

E23.17 Beginning at its tenth stationary state ($n = 10$), an electron in a hydrogen atom makes 9 successive quantum jumps as it cascades downward through every lower energy level. How many of the 9 photons emitted are in the visible region? Identify the visible photon(s) by color.

E23.18   It is obvious from visual inspection of the hydrogen term diagram (Figure 23.13) that the binding-energy differences ΔW between successive energy levels get small as the quantum number n gets large. It is *not* obvious that the *fractional* change of binding energy, $\Delta W/W$, also gets small. Prove that $|\Delta W/W| \ll 1$ if $n \gg 1$. This condition is a requirement for the validity of the correspondence principle. (Keep in mind that ΔW is the binding-energy difference between *adjacent* energy levels.)

E23.19   Given that the binding energy of the electron in its lowest state of motion in the hydrogen atom is $W_1 = 13.6$ eV, use Equation 23.28 to find its classical orbital frequency in this state. How does this frequency compare with the frequency of visible light?

E23.20   Classically, an electron moving in an elliptical orbit about a proton obeys Kepler's third law: $T^2 = \kappa a^3$, where T is the period of the motion and a is the semimajor axis of the ellipse. (1) Show that for circular orbits, $\kappa = 16\pi^3 \epsilon_0 m/e^2$. (This result is in fact valid for elliptical orbits as well.) (2) Explain why Equation 23.28 is equivalent to Kepler's third law.

E23.21   (1) Verify that the dimension of the Rydberg constant as expressed by Equation 23.35 is inverse length. (2) The inverse of the Rydberg constant is approximately 911 Å. What is the significance of this length?

E23.22   Explain carefully why the binding energy of an electron moving in the field of a nucleus of charge Ze is proportional to Z^2 (see Equation 23.37). Reason in terms of the *changes* that would occur in Equations 23.22–23.36 if the proton of charge e at the center of a hydrogen atom were replaced by a nucleus of charge Ze.

E23.23   (1) An electron in a hydrogen atom moves in a circular orbit with quantum number $n = 50$. Give (a) the speed of the electron, (b) the radius of its orbit, and (c) the frequency of its rotation in this orbit. (2) What is the frequency of radiation emitted by hydrogen in a transition from $n = 50$ to $n = 49$? In what part of the spectrum does this radiation lie?

Section 23.8

E23.24   In intergalactic space, an electron orbits about a proton; the electron's orbital radius is 1 m. (1) What is the quantum number n of this state of motion? (2) What is the electron's speed?

E23.25   If the electron in a hydrogen atom is replaced by a negative muon ($m = 207m_e$), what changes, if any, occur in (a) the size of the atom, (b) the speed of the negative particle, and (c) the binding energy of the atom? (Such "muonic atoms" have been identified and studied—see Section 27.2.)

E23.26   (1) If the nucleus of a hydrogen atom is replaced by a nucleus of charge Ze, how are the electron's (a) orbital radius (Equation 23.41) and (b) speed (Equation 23.44) affected? (2) A single electron is bound to a sodium nucleus ($Z = 11$) and occupies the lowest state of motion ($n = 1$). According to the Bohr-orbit approximation, what are the electron's (a) orbital radius in units of a_0 and (b) speed in units of c?

E23.27   (1) For a hypothetical gas of hydrogen *atoms* (not molecules) at standard conditions of temperature and pressure, what is the approximate mean distance l between the centers of the atoms? (2) To what excited state n would all the atoms have to be raised to bring the atoms into "contact" (such that $r \cong \frac{1}{2}l$)?

E23.28   Find an algebraic expression for the dimensionless product $\mathscr{R}_\infty a_0$ (Rydberg constant times Bohr radius). Express the answer in terms of the fine-structure constant α.

E23.29   The binding energy of the ground state of a hydrogen atom can be written

$$W_1 = \tfrac{1}{2}mc^2\alpha^2.$$

(1) Show that the quantity α appearing in this formula is the same as the fine-structure constant defined by Equation 23.46. (2) What is the implication for atomic structure of the fact that $\alpha \ll 1$?

E23.30   (1) A 1-kg rock is swung in a circle of radius 1 m with a speed of 2.1 m/sec. How many quantum units of angular momentum does it possess relative to the center of its circle? (2) A proton with a speed of 6.3×10^6 m/sec misses a nucleus by a distance of 3.0×10^{-13} m as it flies by. What is the angular momentum of the proton with respect to the nucleus in units of $\hbar$?

Section 23.9   E23.31   (1) Write the de Broglie wavelength of a particle as a function of its kinetic energy K and its mass m (work relativistically). (2) From the answer to part 1 obtain the following approximate formulas:

$$\text{(a)}\quad \lambda \cong \frac{h}{\sqrt{2mK}} \quad \text{if} \quad K \ll mc^2;$$

$$\text{(b)}\quad \lambda \cong \frac{hc}{K} \quad \text{if} \quad K \gg mc^2.$$

E23.32   Using the approximate formulas given in the preceding exercise, calculate the de Broglie wavelength of (a) a 1-MeV proton and (b) a 200-GeV proton. Express the answers in fm.

E23.33   (1) Neutrons are cooled by passing them through liquid helium at 3 K. If they emerge with kinetic energy equal to $\tfrac{3}{2}kT$, what is their wavelength? (2) Ordinary thermal neutrons have 100 times as much kinetic energy ($T = 300$ K). What is their wavelength?

E23.34   (1) Calculate the wavelength of an automobile of mass 1.5×10^3 kg (a) traveling at 60 mile/hr, and (b) traveling at 1 angstrom per century. (2) What is the wavelength of the automobile if its velocity is zero? Compare this answer with the answer to part 1b and discuss.

E23.35   A neutron, an electron, and a photon all have the same wavelength, $\lambda = 10^{-10}$ m (1 Å). (1) Find the speed of the neutron in m/sec. Is this "slow" or "fast"? (2) Find the energy of the neutron in eV. (3) Find the energy of the electron in eV. (4) Find the energy of the photon in eV. In what part of the electromagnetic spectrum does this photon lie? (For neutron and electron, nonrelativistic formulas suffice.)

E23.36   Arrange the following in order of increasing wavelength: (a) an electron with a total energy of 10 GeV, (b) a proton with a total energy of 10 GeV, and (c) a proton with a kinetic energy of 10 GeV. (NOTE: It should not be necessary to calculate the individual wavelengths in order to decide their relative magnitudes.)

E23.37   The de Broglie wavelength of a certain particle is equal to its Compton wavelength. (1) What is the particle's momentum? (2) What is the ratio of its speed to the speed of light?

E23.38 The wavelength of a de Broglie wave is $\lambda = h/p$; its frequency can be written $v = E/h$. Both of these expressions are valid for material particles as well as photons. (1) Write a particle's energy E as a function of its angular frequency ω. (2) Write a particle's momentum as a function of its wave number k. Note the close parallelism of these two formulas.

E23.39 Electrons are directed normal to the surface of a crystal whose atomic spacing is $a = 2.0$ Å. A peak of scattered intensity is observed at only one angle, $\theta = 38$ deg. Show that the kinetic energy of the electrons is approximately 100 eV.

E23.40 Below are listed quantum numbers and wave functions for three of the lower states in the hydrogen atom:

$$n = 1, \ell = 0 \qquad \psi = e^{-r/a_0};$$

$$n = 2, \ell = 1 \qquad \psi = re^{-r/2a_0};$$

$$n = 3, \ell = 2 \qquad \psi = r^2 e^{-r/3a_0}.$$

(The quantum number ℓ identifies the angular momentum of the state; the quantity a_0 is the Bohr radius, 0.53 Å. For simplicity, constants of proportionality are omitted in the formulas for ψ.) For the first of these states—the ground state—a graph of ψ vs r appears in Figure 23.15(a). For the second state, sketch graphs of (1) ψ vs r and (2) ψ^2 vs r. In each graph, identify the Bohr orbital radius, $4a_0$. How well is the electron "confined" to this radius? (The third wave function is provided only for information, or for optional attention.)

Section 23.10

E23.41 The wave function of a beam of electrons propagating in the x direction can be represented by the wave function $\psi = Ne^{ikx}$, where N and k are constants. (1) How does the position probability of the electrons depend on x? (2) What is the wavelength associated with this beam? (NOTE: The full wave function also depends on time; the time dependence is omitted here.)

E23.42 Inside a one-dimensional box, a particle has a constant potential energy V_0. Write a formula for E_n, its total energy (kinetic plus potential) as a function of the mass m of the particle, the dimension d of the box, and the quantum number n.

Section 23.11

E23.43 A proton is held between walls separated by 10^{-14} m (this simulates a nucleus). (1) What is the zero-point energy of the proton in MeV? (2) In a quantum jump from the $n = 2$ state to the $n = 1$ state, what is the energy of the gamma-ray photon emitted by the proton?

E23.44 A marble whose mass is $m = 0.01$ kg rests at the bottom of a glass tumbler of diameter $d = 0.05$ m. According to quantum mechanics, the marble cannot be precisely at rest; it has a zero-point energy. (1) What is the magnitude of the marble's zero-point energy? (2) With this kinetic energy, how long would it take the marble to move across the bottom of the glass?

E23.45 (1) Write an expression for the wave function $\psi(x)$ for a particle in its lowest state of motion in a one-dimensional box. (2) Sketch graphs of (a) ψ vs x and (b) ψ^2 vs x for this state. (3) (a) In this state, where is the particle most likely to be found? (b) At what point(s) is the probability of finding the particle half of the maximum probability?

E23.46   Examine Equation 23.59 for the energy of a particle in a box. Discuss the dependence of the energy on the three quantities h, m, and d (for purposes of this discussion, pretend that the magnitude of Planck's constant h can be changed). Explain "why" an increase in h increases the energy and an increase in m or d decreases the energy.

E23.47   The total area under the curve in Figure 23.22(b) should be equal to 1, for it represents the total probability to find the particle *somewhere*. Apply the condition $\int_0^d |\psi(x)|^2 \, dx = 1$ to the wave function given by Equation 23.60 in order to find the constant A. With this value of A, the wave function is said to be "normalized." (This exercise is generalized in Problem 23.19.)

Section 23.12   E23.48   An electron moves in the field of a nucleus of charge Ze; the potential energy is

$$U(r) = -\frac{1}{4\pi\epsilon_0} \frac{Ze^2}{r}.$$

Adapt the treatment in Section 23.12 in order to show that (1) the radial scale of the motion is proportional to Z^{-1} and (2) the energy of the ground state is proportional to Z^2.

E23.49   A particle of mass m moves in the field of force of a three-dimensional harmonic oscillator; its potential energy is $U(r) = \frac{1}{2}m\omega^2 r^2$. Use the approximate method developed in Section 23.12—minimizing the quantum energy E of the ground state—to show (1) that the particle's kinetic and potential energies are approximately equal, (2) that the order of magnitude of the ground-state energy is $\hbar\omega$, and (3) that the radial scale of the motion is approximately $\sqrt{\hbar/m\omega}$.

E23.50   A particle is pulled toward a fixed center by a force of constant magnitude: $F_r = -f$. (1) What is the potential energy $U(r)$ if $U(0) = 0$? (2) Use the approximate method developed in Section 23.12 (see also the preceding exercise) to find an expression for the order of magnitude of the energy of the lowest quantum state.

Section 23.13   E23.51   Consider the central point on the observing screen in Figure 23.24, where the probabilities P_1 and P_2 associated with the separate slits are equal. What is the maximum possible value of the combined probability P at this point with both slits open?

Section 23.14   E23.52   The uncertainty of momentum of an electron moving in one dimension is $\Delta p_x \cong 10^{-25}$ kg m/sec. What is the approximate dimension of the smallest container within which the electron might be confined?

E23.53   (1) An electron has an approximate speed of 10^6 m/sec. What is its approximate wavelength? (2) Its uncertainty of speed is 3×10^5 m/sec. What is its approximate uncertainty of position?

E23.54   A proton is known to be located within a spherical region of diameter 1 m. Estimate the minimum speed of the proton that is consistent with its localization within this region.

E23.55   The momentum of a 1-gm pellet is determined to within an uncertainty $\Delta p_x = 10^{-11}$ kg m/sec. To what accuracy could its position in principle be determined? Make an approximate guess of the maximum accuracy to which its position could be determined in practice.

E23.56 An electron in its lowest state in the hydrogen atom has an uncertainty of position of about 10^{-10} m (see Figure 23.15). (1) What is its approximate uncertainty of momentum? (2) What is its approximate uncertainty of velocity? How does this compare with the speed of light?

E23.57 An electron is located in space within an uncertainty $\Delta x = 10^{-6}$ m. Its speed is approximately 10^6 m/sec. It is desired to measure its momentum to an accuracy of 1 part in 10^3. Is this possible? Why or why not?

E23.58 A particle has an equal probability to be anywhere within the interval $0 \le x \le a$ and a zero probability to be outside this interval. Its probability function $P(x)$ is shown in the figure. (1) What is $\bar{x}$, the mean value of the particle's position? (2) What is Δx, the uncertainty of its position? (HINT: In the footnote on page 1169, $P(x)$ may replace $|\psi(x, t)|^2$.)

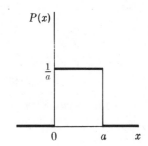

E23.59 About what fractional range of wavelengths must be superposed to produce each of the wave patterns shown in the figure?

(a)

(b)

(c)

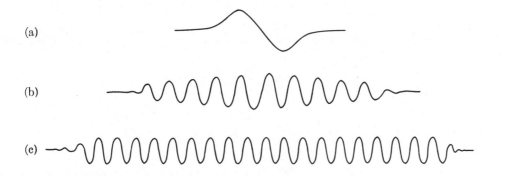

E23.60 At a certain point, the wave function of an electron has the following properties: $\psi = 1$, $d\psi/dx = 0$, $d^2\psi/dx^2 = -10^{20}$ m^{-2}. What is the kinetic energy of the electron in eV at this point?

Section 23.15

E23.61 A particle moves in the potential energy "trough" shown in the figure. The energy of its lowest state is E_1. Sketch the wave function for the lowest state of motion, and indicate in your sketch the points, if any, where $\psi = 0$, where $d\psi/dx = 0$, and where $d^2\psi/dx^2 = 0$. (NOTE: This exercise requires *no* calculation or mathematical manipulation.)

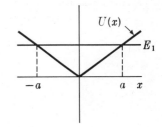

E23.62 A particle moves in a "triangular" potential like the one shown in Figure 23.29. (1) Suppose that the motion is described by classical mechanics and that the location of the particle is observed repeatedly. (a) Where will the particle be found most often? (b) Where will it be found less often? (c) Where will it never be found? The answers define regions of high probability, lower probability, and zero probability *classically*. (2) Discuss the correlation between these classical probabilities and the *quantum* probability distribution implied by the wave function illustrated in Figure 23.29.

E23.63 The wave function for the ground state of a particle moving in a harmonic-oscillator potential is given by Equation 23.87 (or its equivalent, Equation 23.85). Prove that this wave function has an inflection point ($d^2\psi/dx^2 = 0$) at the classical turning point, $x = a$.

E23.64   (1) Show that

$$\psi = Bxe^{-x^2/2a^2} = Bxe^{-m\omega x^2/2\hbar}$$

is a solution to Equation 23.80, the Schrödinger equation for a particle in a harmonic-oscillator potential (B is an arbitrary constant and the other symbols are defined in the text). (2) For which quantum state of the oscillator is this the wave function?

PROBLEMS

No photoelectric effect for free electrons

P23.1   (1) If a free electron at rest could absorb a photon, the electron would have to fly in the direction of the photon's path. Why? (2) Prove that a free electron at rest *cannot* absorb a photon. (SUGGESTED METHOD: Assume that the absorption event does occur and show that it is inconsistent with energy and momentum conservation.) (3) If a free electron at rest cannot absorb a photon, neither can a free electron in motion absorb a photon. Why? (4) Discuss the relevance of these results to the photoelectric effect, which provides an experimental demonstration that electrons *can* absorb photons.

Analysis of photoelectric data

P23.2   In a photoelectric experiment, a student obtains the following values of stopping potential V_S as a function of the wavelength λ of the incident radiation.

λ (m)	V_S (V)
3.60×10^{-7}	1.4
3.00×10^{-7}	2.0
2.40×10^{-7}	3.1

(1) What is the approximate value of h/e deduced from these data? Is it accurate to within 10 percent? (2) What is the approximate magnitude of the work function W? (3) What is the approximate threshold wavelength for ejection of photoelectrons?

Relativistic analysis of e/m experiment

P23.3   In an experiment to measure e/m, electrons are accelerated from rest through a known potential difference V and are then found to execute arcs of radius r in a known magnetic field B. (1) Show that the charge-to-mass ratio of the electrons is given by

$$\frac{e}{m} = \frac{2V}{B^2r^2 - (V/c)^2}.$$

(NOTE: The formula $r = p/eB$, which gives the radius of curvature of an electron moving transverse to lines of a magnetic field, is valid relativistically as well as nonrelativistically.) (2) Show that the result of letting $c \to \infty$ in the expression for e/m above is the same as the result of a nonrelativistic analysis of this experiment.

Role of viscosity in determining e

P23.4   (1) Show that if the assumed viscosity of air is changed by a factor $1 + \varepsilon$, with $\varepsilon \ll 1$, the electron charge determined in an oil-drop experiment is changed by a factor $1 + \frac{3}{2}\varepsilon$. (Refer to Equation 23.10 and equations that precede it.) (2) Using the value $\mu_0 = 1.823 \times 10^{-5}$ kg/m sec for the viscosity of air at 23 °C, Millikan obtained the value $e_0 = 1.591 \times 10^{-19}$ C for the electron charge. An improved value of the viscosity of air at the same temperature is $\mu = 1.833 \times 10^{-5}$ kg/m sec. What is the revised value of e that follows from Millikan's data?

P23.5   Using ideas of buoyant force and Archimedes' principle, explain why the factor ρ in Equation 23.9 should, for greater accuracy, be replaced by $\rho_{oil} - \rho_{air}$.

Buoyancy in the oil-drop experiment

P23.6   Unnoticed by an experimenter who is repeating Millikan's oil-drop experiment, the temperature in the laboratory varies during the course of the experiment. (1) Suggest several ways in which the temperature change might influence the results. (2) For at least one of the effects named in part 1, carry through a semiquantitative analysis in order to estimate the influence of this effect on the value of e for a temperature change of a few kelvins.

Effect of temperature change on oil-drop experiment

P23.7   If you can obtain a small hand-held diffraction grating, use it to examine as many different kinds of lights as you can find in your community: street lights, advertising lights, fluorescent lights, incandescent lights. Which exhibit line spectra? Which exhibit continuous spectra? Which exhibit combined line and continuous spectra? Can you identify the sources of any of the line spectra?

City spectra

P23.8   A spectral series observed in the radiation from atomic hydrogen has inverse wavelengths equal to $0.823 \times 10^7 \, \text{m}^{-1}, 0.975 \times 10^7 \, \text{m}^{-1}, 1.028 \times 10^7 \, \text{m}^{-1}$, $1.053 \times 10^7 \, \text{m}^{-1}, 1.066 \times 10^7 \, \text{m}^{-1}, \ldots$. (1) Write a formula similar to the Balmer series formula that fits these data. (2) What is the name of this series? (3) Higher members of this series cluster closer and closer to a series limit. What is the wavelength of this series limit? In what part of the spectrum does it lie?

Empirical spectral formula

P23.9   In the light emitted by sodium atoms, a spectral series analogous to the Lyman series in hydrogen is described by the formula

$$\frac{1}{\lambda} = \mathscr{R} \left(0.378 - \frac{1}{m^2} \right),$$

where $\mathscr{R}$ is the Rydberg constant and m is an integer. (The formula is valid only for large m.) (1) In terms of the structure of the atom, explain why the second term on the right has the same simple form as in the series of hydrogen. (2) From the formula, calculate the ionization energy of sodium. Express the answer in eV.

Spectral series in sodium

P23.10   Bohr knew that to provide an explanation for the size of atoms, an atomic length scale was required, and he knew that no combination of the constants $e^2/4\pi\epsilon_0$ and m could provide such a scale. For this reason he believed that the constant h must play a role in atomic mechanics. (1) Prove to your own satisfaction, either by trial and error, or by a more rigorous method, that no combination of $e^2/4\pi\epsilon_0$ and m can provide a quantity with the dimension of length. (2) (a) Find a combination of $e^2/4\pi\epsilon_0$, m, and c that has the dimension of length. (b) What is the magnitude of this quantity? (c) This combination can be rejected as a theoretical length scale for atoms because it is not close to the size of an atom. Suggest another reason why Bohr might have rejected it.

Combinations of fundamental constants

P23.11   This problem develops an alternative way to apply the correspondence principle to the hydrogen atom. (1) Let the binding energy of the atom be expressed as a function of an integer n that labels the quantum states— $W = g(n)$—and let ΔW be the energy difference between successive states, the same as the energy radiated in a transition of the kind indicated

The correspondence principle applied to the hydrogen atom

schematically in Figure 23.14. Explain why $\Delta W \cong -dg/dn$ for $n \gg 1$. (2) Equation 23.29 expresses the mechanical frequency of the electron, ν_e, as a function of the binding energy W. Using the facts that $\Delta W = h\nu_r$ and $\nu_r \cong \nu_e$, express ΔW as a function of W (a result that is also valid for $n \gg 1$). (3) Equating the formulas for ΔW obtained in parts 1 and 2 gives a simple differential equation for $g(n)$. Show that the solution to this equation is $g = B/(n + n_0)^2$, where n_0 is an arbitrary constant. What is B? (4) Finally, set $g \, (= W) = hc\mathscr{R}_H/n^2$ (Equation 23.21). Show that the resulting expression for $\mathscr{R}_H$ agrees with Equation 23.34. (A significant feature of this approach: It shows that for highly excited states, W must be proportional to the inverse square of an integer.)

Positronium   **P23.12**   The short-lived positronium atom consists of an electron and a positron. Discuss the term diagram and the spectrum of positronium in detail. Does its spectrum have any lines in the visible region?

Spectrum of ionized helium   **P23.13**   Give a complete discussion of the spectrum of ionized helium (a single electron bound to a nucleus of charge $2e$). Does the spectrum include both ultraviolet and infrared radiation? What is the appearance of the visible part of the spectrum between 4,000 and 7,000 Å? Are any spectral lines of ionized helium identical—apart from center-of-mass-corrections—to lines in the hydrogen spectrum?

"Textbook version" of Bohr atom theory   **P23.14**   In reconstructing Bohr's theory of the hydrogen atom, many texts take the quantization of angular momentum (Equation 23.47) as a basic postulate. Consider circular orbits of an electron moving about a proton, and suppose that the only allowed orbits are those for which the angular momentum is an integral multiple of $\hbar$: $L = n\hbar$. Show that this assumption leads to Equations 23.40, 23.44, and 23.37 for the orbital radius, speed, and binding energy of the electron, respectively. Treat the proton as infinitely massive.

Phase and group velocities of de Broglie waves   **P23.15**   The equations $p = h/\lambda$ and $E = h\nu$ relate a particle's mechanical properties (momentum p and total energy E) to its wave properties (wavelength λ and frequency ν). (1) Find the phase velocity, $v_\varphi = \lambda\nu = \omega/k$, of a de Broglie wave. Show that $v_\varphi = c$ for a massless particle and $v_\varphi > c$ for a particle with mass. (2) Find the group velocity, $v_g = -\lambda^2 \, d\nu/d\lambda = d\omega/dk$, for a de Broglie wave. Show that $v_g = v$, where v is the speed of the particle calculated according to relativistic mechanics. (In a de Broglie wave packet, momentum and energy are transmitted at the group velocity, not the phase velocity. The concept of group velocity is developed in Problem 18.3.)

Electron diffraction by a crystal   **P23.16**   The dots in the figure represent the centers of atoms in a crystal; their horizontal spacing is a and their vertical spacing is b. A beam of electrons is directed vertically downward, normal to the face of the crystal. (1) Show that the condition of constructive interference of electron waves scattered through the angle $\pi - \theta$ by horizontally adjacent atoms (B and E in the figure) is $n\lambda = a \sin \theta$ (the same as Equation 23.50, which was derived in a different way). (2) Show that the condition of constructive interference of electron waves scattered through the angle $\pi - \theta$ by vertically adjacent atoms (E and G in the figure) is $n'\lambda = b(1 + \cos \theta)$, where n', like n, is an integer. (3) If both of these conditions of constructive interference are satisfied, the angle φ shown in the figure satisfies the condition

$$\tan \varphi = \frac{n'a}{nb}.$$

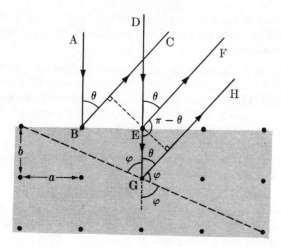

Derive this result and explain why it is a condition that defines Bragg planes in the crystal (that is, it causes the dashed line through point G to pass through other atomic centers).

P23.17 A particle of mass m moves in a circular orbit in a three-dimensional harmonic oscillator potential. Its potential energy is $U = \frac{1}{2}kr^2$; the magnitude of the force is $F = kr$. Show that if the particle's angular momentum is quantized according to the rule $L = n\hbar$, (1) the spectrum of allowed energies is $E = n\hbar\omega$, where $\omega = \sqrt{k/m}$, (2) the orbital radii are $r = r_0\sqrt{n}$, and (3) the orbital speeds are $v = v_0\sqrt{n}$. Give expressions for r_0 and v_0. (4) What is the orbital frequency of the particle in the nth quantum state? (5) What are the emitted frequencies of radiation if the particle cascades in a series of quantum jumps through successive states? (NOTE: An exact quantum treatment of this problem gives $E = (n + \frac{3}{2})\hbar\omega$ for the allowed energies.)

Circular motion in harmonic-oscillator potential

P23.18 The wave function for the $n = 2$ state of a particle in a box is given by Equation 23.60. Generalize this formula; write the wave function $\psi_n(x)$ that is valid for an arbitrary value of the quantum number n. (Like Equation 23.60, your formula may contain an arbitrary constant.) Show that there is a simple relationship between the number of nodes of the wave function and the quantum number n. (A node is a point at which $\psi_n = 0$.)

Particle in a box

P23.19 (This problem makes use of the result of the preceding problem.) For motion in one dimension, the quantity $|\psi|^2$ is probability per unit distance. (1) What is the significance of $|\psi|^2 \Delta x$ if Δx is an infinitesimal distance? (2) What is the significance of the integral $\int_a^b |\psi|^2 \, dx$? (3) A wave function is said to be "normalized" if its integral over the whole domain of the motion is equal to 1. Find the normalized wave functions for a particle in a box by imposing the condition $\int_0^d |\psi(x)|^2 \, dx = 1$ on the wave functions found in the preceding problem.

Normalization of wave functions

P23.20 For motion in three dimensions, the quantity $|\psi|^2$ is probability per unit volume. In case ψ depends only on r (a spherically symmetric wave function), the condition of unit total probability can be written $4\pi\int_0^\infty |\psi(r)|^2 r^2 \, dr = 1$. (1) What is the geometric significance of $4\pi r^2 \, dr$? (2) Normalize the ground-state wave function of the hydrogen atom, $\psi(r) = Ce^{-r/a_0}$—that is, find an algebraic expression for the constant C that causes ψ to satisfy the condition of unit total probability.

Relativistic particle in a box   **P23.21**   (1) Find a relativistic expression for the quantized energies of a particle in a one-dimensional box (let m be the mass of the particle and d be the distance between the walls). (2) Show that in the nonrelativistic limit, Equation 23.59 follows from your answer. (3) Obtain an approximate expression for the energy in the superrelativistic limit ($E \gg mc^2$). (4) Evaluate the zero-point energy of an electron confined to a dimension of 10^{-14} m, comparable to the diameter of a nucleus. Express the answer in eV. Is this electron non-relativistic? Is it superrelativistic?

Complex wave functions   **P23.22**   The figure shows a pair of very narrow slits separated by the distance $2a$, and an observing screen at a distance L from the slits. A beam of electrons of momentum $p = \hbar k$ is incident from the left. If only slit 1 is open, the wave amplitude at points along the screen is $\psi_1 = Ae^{ik(y-a)^2/2L}$, where A is approximately a constant in the central portion of the screen, and y measures vertical distance along the screen. If only slit 2 is open, the wave amplitude at points near the center of the screen is $\psi_2 = Ae^{ik(y+a)^2/2L}$. (1) What is the probability function P_1 if only slit 1 is open? (2) What is the probability function P_2 if only slit 2 is open? (3) Show that if both slits are open, the probability function along the screen is $P = 4|A|^2 \cos^2(kay/L)$. What is the separation Δy between adjacent maxima of the interference pattern?

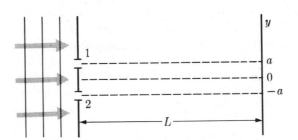

Uncertainty principle for a particle in a box   **P23.23**   The wave function of a particle in a box is

$$\psi(x) = \sqrt{\frac{2}{a}}\cos\left(\frac{\pi x}{a}\right) \qquad \text{for} \qquad -\tfrac{1}{2}a \le x \le \tfrac{1}{2}a$$

and $\psi(x) = 0$ elsewhere. (1) Sketch a graph of this wave function. (2) What is the quantum number n of the particle in this state? (3) Show that the particle's uncertainty of position is

$$\Delta x = a\sqrt{\frac{1}{12} - \frac{1}{2\pi^2}}.$$

(Use the definition in the footnote on page 1169. You will probably need to consult a table of integrals.)

P23.24   For a particle occupying a specific quantum state of motion in a box, the uncertainty of momentum is $\Delta p_x = p = h/\lambda$, where p is the magnitude of the particle's momentum and λ is its wavelength. (1) Explain, at least qualitatively, why there is a momentum uncertainty Δp_x even though the magnitude p is fixed, and why Δp_x is as large as p itself. (2) For the state defined in the preceding problem, express Δp_x as a function of a. (3) What is the uncertainty product $\Delta x\,\Delta p_x$ for the state defined in the preceding problem? How does it compare with the minimum uncertainty product, $\frac{1}{2}\hbar$ (Equation 23.68)?

P23.25 (1) Sketch the approximate appearance of a wave formed by superposing many waves that span a 20 percent range of wavelength: $\Delta\lambda \cong 0.2\lambda_{av}$. (2) If what you have sketched is the wave function of a material particle and $\lambda_{av} = 10^{-11}$ m, what are Δx and Δp_x, its uncertainties of position and momentum? (Only approximate answers are required.)

Superposition and localization

P23.26 The superposition of different wavelengths can localize a wave. Conversely, a wave that is localized must contain components of different wavelengths. Consider the sound wave emanating from one of the long pipes of an organ; the note has a frequency of approximately 30 Hz and it is sounded for 0.33 sec. (1) What is the length of the wave train ($v = 340$ m/sec)? (2) What is the average wavelength? (3) What is the range of wavelengths that must be mixed to form the wave? (4) What is the range of frequencies? *Optional:* Discuss the musical implications. Why do composers never call for short-duration notes of very low frequency?

P23.27 In a world where $\hbar$ is large, the uncertainty principle makes it hard for a croquet player to hit a ball through a wicket. To help alleviate the problem, an inventor designs the device shown in the figure. The ball passes through a cylinder that is permitted to fluctuate in position through the transverse distance Δy. The ball acquires a transverse uncertainty of velocity Δv_y. Influenced by both uncertainties, Δy and Δv_y, the ball misses the center of the wicket by an average distance Y. (1) Show that the optimal design (the design that minimizes Y) is one in which the permitted fluctuation of position of the cylinder is given roughly by $\Delta y \cong \sqrt{\hbar l/mv_x}$ (v_x and l are defined in the figure). (2) Using magnitudes of l, m, and v_x that are reasonable for croquet, evaluate this optimal Δy (a) in a world where $\hbar = 0.01$ J sec and (b) in our world.

Quantum croquet

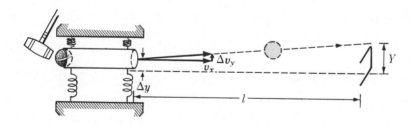

P23.28 In Figure 23.27(c), let the discontinuity of potential energy occur at $x = 0$ and let $K_1 = 4K_2$. For $x \ge 0$, the wave function is

Discontinuity of potential energy

$$\psi_2(x) = \sin(k_2 x + \tfrac{1}{4}\pi)$$

(the unit amplitude and the phase constant $\frac{1}{4}\pi$ are arbitrary). For $x \le 0$, the wave function is

$$\psi_1(x) = A \sin(k_1 x + \varphi).$$

A requirement of quantum mechanics is that both the magnitude and slope of the wave function should be continuous at $x = 0$. Apply these two conditions of continuity in order to find the amplitude A and phase φ of the wave function ψ_1. Are your answers consistent with the visual evidence in Figure 23.27(c)?

Negative kinetic energy   P23.29   Solve the Schrödinger equation (Equation 23.76) in a region of space where the potential energy U is constant and is *greater* than the total energy E (then $K = E - U < 0$). Show that the solution can be written

$$\psi = Ae^{\kappa r} + Be^{-\kappa r}.$$

Express κ in terms of $U - E$.

Sommerfeld-Wilson   P23.30   In 1915, Arnold Sommerfeld and William Wilson proposed the following
quantization rules   equations as quantization conditions for determining the allowed orbits of a particle executing periodic motion in a plane: $\oint L\, d\theta = \ell h$, where L is the particle's angular momentum, θ is its angular coordinate, and ℓ is an integer; and $\oint p_r\, dr = nh$, where p_r is the particle's radial component of momentum, r is its radial coordinate, and n is another integer. The integrals are line integrals carried out around one full cycle of the particle's motion. (1) Show that the first of these equations is equivalent to an equation of angular-momentum quantization, $L = \ell h$. (2) Apply the second equation to the special case of straight-line (one-dimensional) motion in a harmonic-oscillator potential and show that it leads to the equation $E = n\hbar\omega$. This differs by the constant term $\frac{1}{2}\hbar\omega$ from the correct Equation 23.88. (Even in one dimension, the Sommerfeld-Wilson integral is a line integral that follows one full cycle of the motion.)

Qualitative overview of   P23.31   Just as relativity introduced into our description of nature both more
quantum world   relativity and more invariance, quantum mechanics introduced both more discreteness and more fuzziness. (1) Name, and illustrate with a suitable example, a quantity once believed to be continuously variable that proved to be discrete, or granular. (2) Do the same for a quantity once believed to be sharply definable that proved to be "fuzzy." (3) How does the constant h enter into each of your examples?

24

Atomic Structure

Some theories of physics have their roots in particular kinds of phenomena—electrical phenomena, for example—but not in particular physical systems. Electromagnetism and thermodynamics are such theories. Each united data from a wide variety of systems. Other theories, although they too may eventually apply to many systems, have their origins in specific systems of special interest in nature. Newtonian mechanics is such a theory. It brought order and clarity to the solar system. Quantum mechanics is another. It was developed specifically to account for the properties of atoms, and there it had its greatest triumph. In the few years of its major development, 1925–1928, quantum mechanics provided a comprehensive theory of atomic structure and accounted for the regularities of the periodic table. The structure of the atom obviously deserves our careful attention because, apart from its historic role in testing and supporting quantum mechanics, it determines most of the bulk properties of matter and lies at the core of all of chemistry and molecular biology.

Quantum mechanics was developed specifically to explain atomic structure

24.1 The quantization of angular momentum

In his 1913 paper, Niels Bohr suggested that the angular momentum of electrons is quantized in *circular* orbits (see Equation 23.47). Two years later, William Wilson and Arnold Sommerfeld independently advanced arguments in support of a general rule of angular momentum quantization:

The Sommerfeld-Wilson quantization rule (later superseded)

$$L = \ell \, \frac{h}{2\pi} = \ell \hbar,$$

(24.1)

where L designates angular momentum and ℓ is any integer (including zero).* We shall not review their reasoning, because it was superseded later. When quantum mechanics was fully developed, it was learned that the Sommerfeld-Wilson rule gives correctly the maximum *component* of orbital angular momentum **L** along any direction but that the magnitude of **L** is somewhat greater. It is

The modern quantization rule for L

$$L = \sqrt{\ell(\ell + 1)}\, \hbar, \tag{24.2}$$

where ℓ is still an integer. As a matter of shorthand, we usually speak of "orbital angular momentum ℓ," meaning the magnitude given by Equation 24.2. Like Bohr's integer n, the quantity ℓ is called a quantum number.

The discovery by George Uhlenbeck and Samuel Goudsmit in 1925 that the electron has a spin angular momentum whose maximum component is only $\frac{1}{2}\hbar$ was incorporated into quantum mechanics without difficulty. We now understand that the spin quantum numbers s of a particle may be either integral or half-odd-integral, although the orbital quantum number ℓ is restricted to integral values. The allowed values of the magnitude of spin **S** are given by

$$S = \sqrt{s(s + 1)}\, \hbar. \tag{24.3}$$

Magnitudes of **S** *and* **J**

A similar rule applies to the total angular momentum,

$$\mathbf{J} = \mathbf{L} + \mathbf{S}. \tag{24.4}$$

Its quantization of magnitude is expressed by

$$J = \sqrt{j(j + 1)}\, \hbar. \tag{24.5}$$

The quantum number j may be either integral or half-odd-integral. Equations 24.2–24.5 are also valid for systems of particles. Then **J** is the total angular momentum of the system, and **L** and **S** are the total orbital and spin angular momenta of the particles in the system.

■ EXAMPLE: By how much is the approximation $L = \ell\hbar$ in error for $\ell = 1$? for $\ell \gg 1$? For $\ell = 1$, Equation 24.2 gives $L = \sqrt{2}\,\hbar = 1.41\hbar$, which is 41 percent greater than the Sommerfeld-Wilson value, $L = \hbar$. For large ℓ, we write

$$\sqrt{\ell(\ell + 1)} = \ell\sqrt{1 + \frac{1}{\ell}} \cong \ell\left(1 + \frac{1}{2\ell}\right).$$

---

* Probably the first suggestion of a general rule of angular momentum quantization was made by John Nicholson in 1912—on the basis of reasoning and evidence that were at best shaky. The important Equation 24.1 is often attributed to Bohr, but in fact it belongs to Wilson and Sommerfeld. As late as 1915, Bohr wrote, in rebuttal to ideas of Nicholson: "It must be emphasized that only in the case of circular orbits has the angular momentum any connexion with the principles of the Quantum theory. If, therefore, the application of ordinary mechanics to the stationary states of the system does not lead to strictly circular orbits, the assumption [that $L = \ell\hbar$] cannot be applied." [*The Philosophical Magazine*, Series VI, **30**, 394 (1915). The quotation is on page 398.]

The magnitude of **L** in this approximation is

$$L \cong \ell \left(1 + \frac{1}{2\ell}\right)\hbar \qquad (\ell \gg 1).\qquad (24.6)$$

The magnitude $\ell\hbar$ falls short of this value by $\frac{1}{2}\hbar$, a fractional difference of $1/2\ell$. Thus, for $\ell = 10$, the formula $L = \ell\hbar$ is good to 5 percent; for $\ell = 50$, it is good to 1 percent. A much better approximation is $L \cong (\ell + \frac{1}{2})\hbar$. ∎

$L = \ell\hbar$ a fair approximation

$L = (\ell + \frac{1}{2})\hbar$ a better approximation

THE STERN-GERLACH EXPERIMENT: QUANTIZATION OF ORIENTATION

In 1922, Walther Gerlach and Otto Stern published the results of an experiment that demonstrated one of the most fascinating aspects of nature's granularity, the quantization of orientation. Not only is the magnitude of angular momentum quantized, so is its orientation in space. In the ingenious experiment that first revealed this fact, Stern and Gerlach sent a beam of neutral silver atoms through an evacuated space in which pole faces of unusual design produced a very nonuniform field (Figure 24.1). In such a field, an atom experiences a force proportional to the component of its magnetic moment along the field direction.

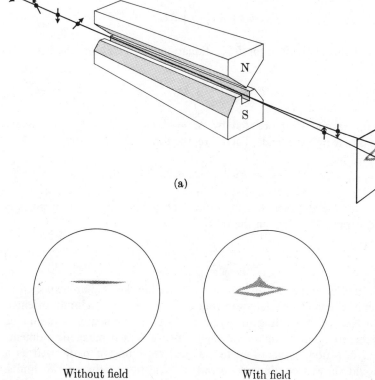

(a)

Without field

With field

(b)

FIGURE 24.1 (a) Apparatus of Gerlach and Stern. Silver atoms emerge from the nonuniform field in two beams. The small arrows indicate the direction of the angular momentum of the atom, which is opposite to the direction of the magnetic moment. (b) Sample experimental results of W. Gerlach and O. Stern [*Zeitschrift für Physik* **9,** 349 (1922)].

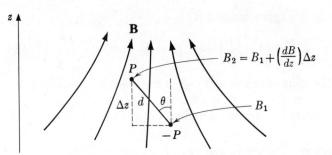

FIGURE 24.2   Idealized dipole
in a nonuniform magnetic
field. In addition to a clock-
wise torque, this dipole experiences a net upward
force.

To see this, consider an idealized magnetic dipole, consisting of poles of strength P and $-P$ separated by distance d, in a nonuniform magnetic field (Figure 24.2). The net force on the dipole is

$$\mathbf{F} = P\mathbf{B}_2 - P\mathbf{B}_1. \qquad (24.7)$$

For simplicity, we assume that the field at the dipole is directed approximately in the z direction ($\mathbf{B} \cong B\mathbf{k}$) and that the inhomogeneity is also in the z direction (this means that $\partial B/\partial x$ and $\partial B/\partial y$ can be ignored in comparison with $\partial B/\partial z$). Then the field B_2 at the upper pole can be related to the field B_1 at the lower pole by means of the following Taylor series expansion carried to first order:

$$B_2 = B_1 + \left(\frac{dB}{dz}\right) \Delta z.$$

Substitution of this expression for B_2 in Equation 24.7 gives, for the net force ($F = F_z$),

$$F = P \left(\frac{dB}{dz}\right) \Delta z.$$

The distances Δz and d are related by $\Delta z = d \cos \theta$, where θ is the angle between the dipole and the field. Therefore, the force can be written

$$F = Pd \left(\frac{dB}{dz}\right) \cos \theta.$$

Finally, we may use the fact that the dipole moment of this pair of poles is $\mu = Pd$ and express the force in the form

$$F = \mu \left(\frac{dB}{dz}\right) \cos \theta. \qquad (24.8)$$

As indicated in Figure 24.1(a), the atoms entering the field are expected to have randomly oriented angular momenta and, therefore, randomly oriented magnetic moments. According to Equation 24.8, different atoms should be deflected differently, depending on the angle θ between their magnetic moments and the field direction. According to classical reasoning, a plate used as a detector should show a continuous spread of deflections between two limits. Instead, Stern and Gerlach observed two well-defined lines on the plate, suggesting that the atoms were emerging from the field with magnetic moments parallel to the field or antiparallel to the field but with no intermediate orientations.

Stern and Gerlach did not know the angular momentum of the silver atom; they probably assumed it to be $j = 1$. Later, quantum mechanics provided the rule for the quantization of orientation, which showed that the silver atom must have angular momentum $j = \frac{1}{2}$. The general rule is this: The component of angular momentum along any chosen direction in space is restricted such that adjacent allowed components differ by exactly $\hbar$. For orbital angular momentum, the allowed components are

$$L_z = m_\ell \hbar, \tag{24.9}$$

where m_ℓ is a positive or negative integer or zero:

$$m_\ell = -\ell, \ldots, +\ell. \tag{24.10}$$

Quantization of L_z: $2\ell + 1$ possible values

The quantum number m_ℓ can take on $2\ell + 1$ different values. It is a standard convention to let the z axis of a coordinate system lie along the chosen direction in space; hence the subscript z in Equation 24.9. Figure 24.3 illustrates the three possible orbital orientations if $\ell = 1$.

For spin angular momentum and for total angular momentum, very similar equations govern the components along a chosen axis:

$$S_z = m_s \hbar; \tag{24.11}$$

$$J_z = m_j \hbar. \tag{24.12}$$

Quantization of S_z and J_z

These orientation quantum numbers, m_s and m_j, may be integral or half-odd-integral. In either case, their successive allowed values differ by 1:

$$m_s = -s, -s + 1, \ldots, s - 1, s; \tag{24.13}$$

$$m_j = -j, -j + 1, \ldots, j - 1, j. \tag{24.14}$$

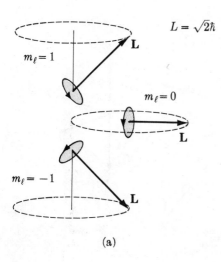

$L = \sqrt{2}\hbar$

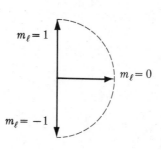

FIGURE 24.3 Quantization of orientation. (a) Three possible orientations of L for $\ell = 1$. (b) Simplified presentation of orientations in terms of the quantum number m_ℓ.

(a)   (b)

An electron or proton, with $s = \frac{1}{2}$, has only two possible orientations [Figure 24.4(a)]. An example with $j = \frac{3}{2}$ is shown in Figure 24.4(b).

Silver atom must have $j = \frac{1}{2}$

One important aspect of the quantization of orientation is that it limits the number of different ways in which a particle or system can move—its number of states, to use the technical term. An atom with angular momentum $\sqrt{j(j+1)}\,\hbar$ can orient itself in just $2j + 1$ different ways. Since, in the Stern-Gerlach experiment, the number of orientations of the silver atoms is observed to be 2, the value of j is at once determined by the condition $2j + 1 = 2$.

Wave boundary conditions can explain quantization of both L and L_z

Most of the results stated in this section are in the form of seemingly arbitrary rules. Their quantum-mechanical derivation is beyond the level of our treatment. However, if we think in terms of wave boundary conditions, the existence of such granularity is not surprising. The simple picture of a de Broglie wave following around a classical orbit suggested the quantization of orbital angular momentum (Figure 23.17). Think now in terms of a three-dimensional wave centered on some point, such as an atomic nucleus. Along any closed path, the wave may oscillate in magnitude. If it does, it must join smoothly onto itself after one trip around the path. The requirements that the wave have neither discontinuities nor regions of infinite probability lead to the quantum conditions on both the magnitude and the component of angular momentum.

By this time, the alert reader may be wondering about a question that we have deliberately avoided: How can the orientation of angular momentum be quantized with respect to one axis and simultaneously be quantized with respect to another axis inclined at some angle to the first? This question will be dealt with in Section 24.2.

★THE MAGNETIC MOMENT OF THE ELECTRON

The force on the silver atom in the Stern-Gerlach experiment is determined by the magnetic moment of the atom (Equation 24.8). Therefore, without knowing

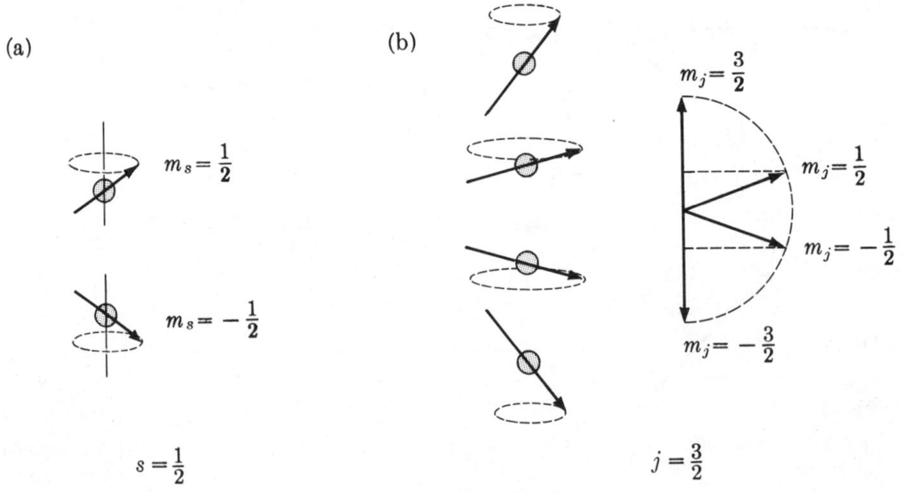

FIGURE 24.4 Quantization of orientation for (a) a particle of spin $s = \frac{1}{2}$, and (b) a system with angular momentum $j = \frac{3}{2}$.

(a)

$m_s = \frac{1}{2}$

$m_s = -\frac{1}{2}$

$s = \frac{1}{2}$

(b)

$m_j = \frac{3}{2}$

$m_j = \frac{1}{2}$

$m_j = -\frac{1}{2}$

$m_j = -\frac{3}{2}$

$j = \frac{3}{2}$

the angular momentum j of the atom, these men could find its magnetic moment —or, more accurately, its maximum component of magnetic moment along the field. With an uncertainty of about 10 percent, they found

$$\mu_z = \frac{e\hbar}{2m}. \tag{24.15}$$

By an odd bit of luck, this value is exactly what one would expect classically for a spinless particle of charge e circling with angular momentum $L = \hbar$. Recall Equation 16.54:

$$\boldsymbol{\mu} = \frac{q}{2m}\mathbf{L}.$$

Using the assumptions of that time, that the electron's magnetic moment arises only from its orbital motion and that $L = \ell\hbar$, we get (for $q = -e$)

$$\mu = -\frac{e\hbar}{2m}\ell. \tag{24.16}$$

Expected magnetic moment of orbiting spinless particle

The quantum unit of magnetic moment in this formula, $e\hbar/2m$, is known as the "Bohr magneton," for which a common symbol is μ_B:

$$\mu_B = \frac{e\hbar}{2m}. \tag{24.17}$$

The Bohr magneton, a convenient unit

Finding experimentally for the silver atom that $\mu = \mu_B$, Gerlach and Stern could reasonably assume that the magnetic moment of the atom was attributable to a single electron with $\ell = 1$.

Only later was it discovered that the intrinsic magnetic moment, or spin magnetic moment, of the electron is twice the classically expected value. It is

$$\boldsymbol{\mu}_s = -2\frac{e}{2m}\mathbf{S}. \tag{24.18}$$

Magnetic moment of the electron (if $L = 0$)

The extra factor 2 is called the g-factor of the electron (see Equation 16.55). Taking the z component of Equation 24.18, we get

$$\mu_{sz} = -2\frac{e}{2m}S_z = -2\frac{e}{2m}m_s\hbar$$

$$= -2\mu_B m_s. \tag{24.19}$$

For $m_s = \frac{1}{2}$, we get $\mu_{sz} = -\mu_B$, the same value predicted by Equation 24.16 with $\ell = 1$. The magnetic moment of the silver atom is indeed contributed (almost entirely) by a single electron, but it arises from the spin of the electron, not from its orbital motion. [The silver atom contains 47 electrons. For 46 of these, the orbital and spin angular momenta sum to zero, which also causes their magnetic moments to cancel. The 47th electron, with $\ell = 0$ and $s = \frac{1}{2}$, accounts for the overall magnetic property of the atom—except for a much smaller contribution by the nucleus.] Magnetic properties of atoms will be considered further in Section 24.10.

FIGURE 24.5 Experiment to show properties of spin states. Atoms of random
spin orientation are incident from the left. Half get through the first spin
polarizer and emerge all identically polarized. Half of these in turn get through
a second polarizer rotated 90 deg from the first. Interpretation: The state of
an atom in the middle region, with spin definitely up, can be regarded as a
superposition of states with spin left and spin right.

★24.2 Superposition of spin states

There is nothing about the Stern-Gerlach apparatus that should change the
orientation of angular momentum. Yet atoms apparently enter the device with
any orientation at all and emerge from it with only two orientations (Figure
24.1). The quantum mechanical interpretation of this behavior is *not* that an
atom changes its orientation as it moves through the nonuniform field. Rather
the field selects orientations that are already present, and—this is the key
point—any orientation whatever can be regarded as a combination (or superposition) of the two orientations selected by the field. Thus quantized orientation bears a close similarity to the polarization of transverse waves. As each
atom enters the apparatus, its state of motion is some superposition of the
two states "spin up" and "spin down." It has to be regarded as existing simultaneously in these two states. With some probability, it will emerge with spin
down.

*The Stern-Gerlach magnet
selects orientations but
does not change orientation*

These ideas can be further illustrated by considering the action of hypothetical spin polarizers on an atomic beam. A spin polarizer is a device that
allows atoms of only one definite spin orientation to pass through it. (It is left
as an exercise to show how such a device could actually be constructed, using
a Stern-Gerlach magnet.) We consider two spin polarizers in tandem, one
rotated 90 deg with respect to the other (Figure 24.5). From the first emerge
atoms with spin up. Classically, we would expect none of these to make
it through the second polarizer since it allows passage only of atoms with spin
to the left. In fact, half of the spin-up atoms appear with spin to the left. The
state "spin up" is the same as a superposition of the states "spin left" and
"spin right." Mathematically, the relation for the wave amplitudes is

Superposition of spin states

$$\psi_{up} = \frac{1}{\sqrt{2}} (\psi_{left} + \psi_{right}). \tag{24.20}$$

*Definite orientation along
one line means probable
orientation along another*

Although the spin of an atom may, at a given time, *definitely* be directed upward,
it has, at the same time, a 50 percent *probability* of being directed to the left.
Similarly, a state with spin definitely directed to the left is an equal mixture of
states with spin up and spin down. More generally, for $j = \frac{1}{2}$, any orientation
whatever is equivalent to some combination of just two orientations, such as
up and down. Paradoxical though they seem, these rules of superposition explain
why an electron spin may point in only two directions along a given line, yet
the line may have any direction at all. For $j > \frac{1}{2}$, the laws of superposition are
somewhat more complicated but the principle is the same.

24.3   The hydrogen atom: quantum numbers and wave functions

In the Bohr theory of the hydrogen atom, each stationary state is characterized by a single quantum number, n. Eventually, four quantum numbers were found to be necessary to describe the state of an atomic electron. We shall consider three of them in this section and the fourth—associated with electron spin—in the next section.

1. PRINCIPAL QUANTUM NUMBER

$$n = 1, 2, 3, \ldots \qquad \text{(all positive integers)}.$$

n identifies the energy

This quantum number and Bohr's energy equation, Equation 23.36, survived in the full theory of quantum mechanics, although the physical picture of the atom underwent radical revision. The principal quantum number specifies the energy, which is quantized because the electron is confined in the radial direction (analogous to the confinement of a particle in a box).

2. ORBITAL-ANGULAR-MOMENTUM QUANTUM NUMBER

$$\ell = 0, 1, \ldots, n - 1 \qquad \text{(n different values)}.$$

For given n, $\ell_{\max} = n - 1$

This quantum number determines the orbital angular momentum, according to Equation 24.2:

$$L = \sqrt{\ell(\ell + 1)}\, \hbar.$$

For the ground state of the atom ($n = 1$), $\ell = 0$.* For excited states ($n > 1$), an interesting multiplicity occurs. For the energy defined by $n = 2$ (the final energy for Balmer transitions), there are actually two distinct stationary states,† one with zero angular momentum and one with 1 unit of angular momentum. These two states are said to be "degenerate," which means that they have equal energy. Therefore, they do not show themselves separately in the spectrum. For $n = 3$, there are three degenerate states of motion, with angular momentum quantum numbers $\ell = 0, 1,$ and 2. These states *correspond* to classical elliptical orbits of equal energy but different eccentricity (Figure 24.6).

States of different ℓ are degenerate in hydrogen

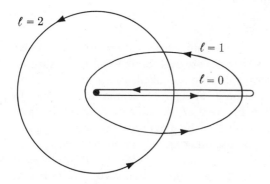

FIGURE 24.6   Three classical orbits that correspond to the three degenerate states of motion in the hydrogen atom with $n = 3$ and $\ell = 0, 1,$ and 2. Classical orbits of equal energy have equal semimajor axes. Actually, of course, the wave functions for these three states of motion are spread out and only roughly correspond to the classical orbits.

* Note that this makes Equation 23.47 incorrect.

† When the multiplicity of orientation is taken into account, there are more than two.

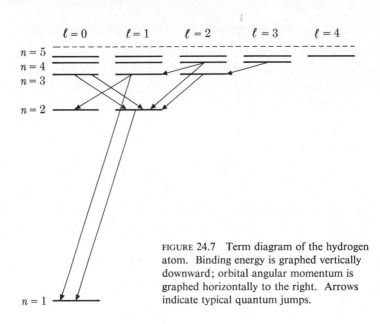

FIGURE 24.7   Term diagram of the hydrogen atom. Binding energy is graphed vertically downward; orbital angular momentum is graphed horizontally to the right. Arrows indicate typical quantum jumps.

In order to display both quantum numbers n and ℓ, a modern term diagram is drawn with energy graphed vertically and angular momentum graphed horizontally. Figure 24.7 shows such a diagram for hydrogen, with arrows added to indicate typical quantum jumps accompanying photon emission. Partly because photons have one unit of angular momentum, most atomic transitions take place between states differing by one unit of orbital angular momentum.

3. ORBITAL-ORIENTATION QUANTUM NUMBER

$$m_\ell = -\ell, -\ell + 1, \ldots, \ell \qquad (2\ell + 1 \text{ different values}).$$

This quantum number determines the component of orbital angular momentum along an arbitrary z axis (Equation 24.9):

$$L_z = m_\ell \hbar.$$

In the absence of magnetic fields or other influences that specify a particular direction in space, differently oriented states are degenerate. This is not surprising. In empty space, with all possible directions equivalent, it should make no difference to the atom in what direction its angular momentum is pointing. In a term diagram such as the one in Figure 24.7, the differently oriented states are not separately displayed. Each rung in the diagram must be imagined to represent $2\ell + 1$ distinct states of motion differing only in orientation.

Single line in a term diagram represents $2\ell + 1$ different orientations

In terms of quantum numbers, the electron in the hydrogen atom is as restricted as a freight car in a switching yard. At the same time, because of its wave nature, the electron ranges free as a cloud over the whole volume of the atom in every one of its restricted states. Figure 24.8 shows cross sections in the radial direction of electron waves for several stationary states in the hydrogen atom. In addition, the waves show oscillation in the angular direction. Pictorial

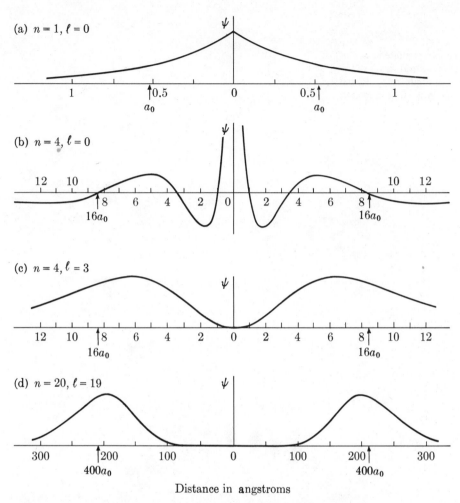

(a) $n = 1$, $\ell = 0$

(b) $n = 4$, $\ell = 0$

(c) $n = 4$, $\ell = 3$

(d) $n = 20$, $\ell = 19$

Distance in angstroms

FIGURE 24.8   Cross sections of electron waves in the radial direction for four states in the hydrogen atom. (a) The ground state, $n = 1$, $\ell = 0$. (b) The state $n = 4$, $\ell = 0$, corresponding to a classical straight-line trajectory through the nucleus. (c) The state $n = 4$, $\ell = 3$, corresponding to a circular orbit. (d) The state $n = 20$, $\ell = 19$, corresponding to a very large circular orbit. Radial scales are not the same in the different graphs.

representations of the three-dimensional waves are given in Figure 24.9 by means of differential shading. The intensity of shading corresponds approximately to the probability per unit volume, or to the square of the wave function.

The four states chosen for pictorial representation illustrate significant features of quantum waves. (a) The most featureless wave is that of the ground state ($n = 1$, $\ell = 0$). Lacking any angular momentum, this state also lacks a preferred direction in space and is characterized by a spherically symmetric wave. In the radial direction the wave behaves in the simplest possible manner, rising to a single maximum at the center of the atom and then falling again. (b) For the higher energy state with $n = 4$ and $\ell = 0$, the absence of angular

Wave functions show the transition from quantum to classical behavior

FIGURE 24.9   Pictorial representation of
probability density for electron waves of the
same four states as in Figure 24.8.   Radial
scales are not the same in the four diagrams.

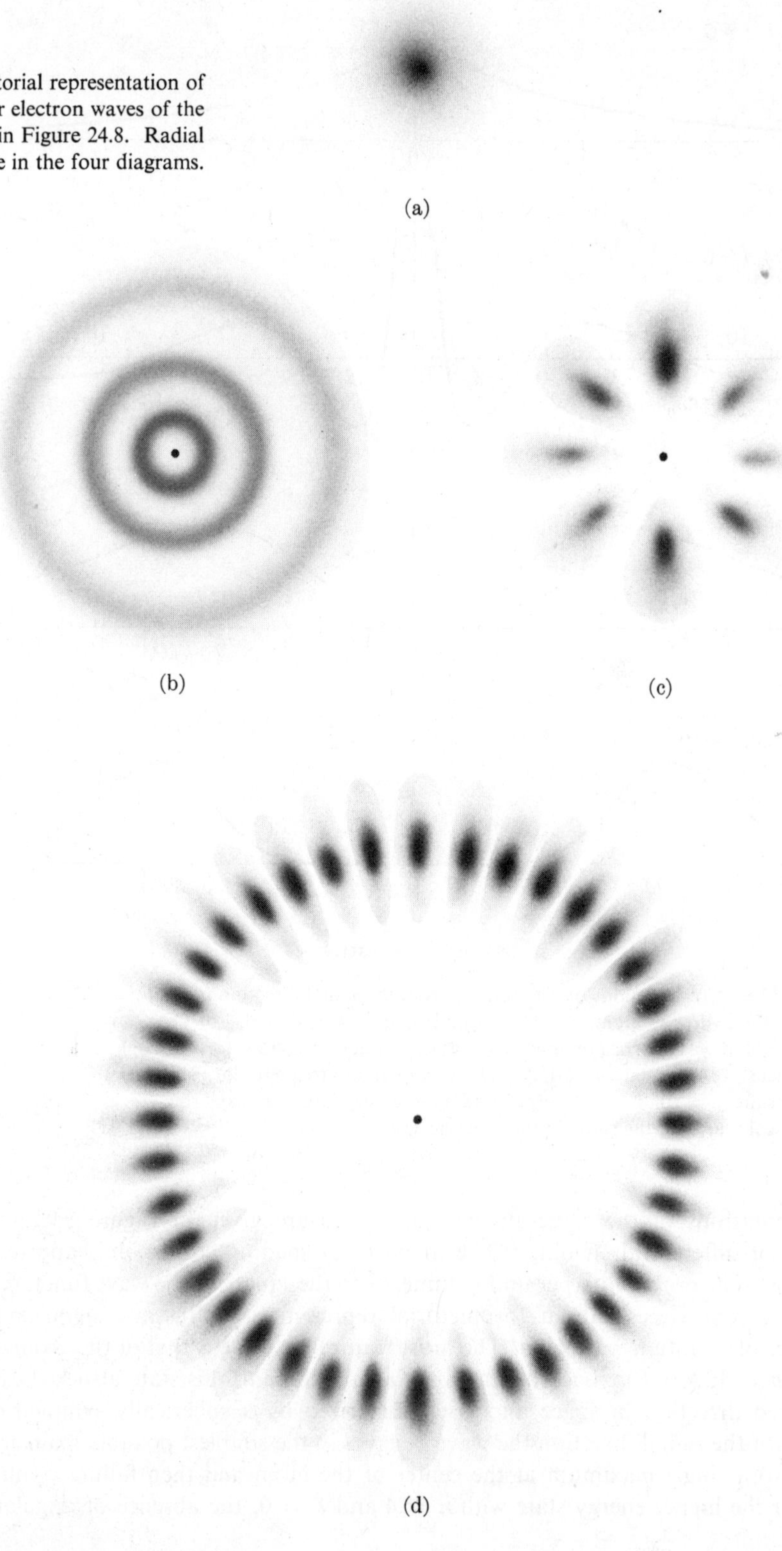

(a)

(b)

(c)

(d)

momentum is again reflected in the spherical symmetry of the wave. The classical analog of this state of motion is a straight-line trajectory back and forth through the nucleus (picture a long, narrow ellipse squeezed so as to become a straight line). In the quantum wave, this to-and-fro motion shows itself in the radial oscillation of the wave. Having a greater distance to cover at $n = 4$ than at $n = 1$, the electron wave undergoes a number of cycles of oscillation from one side of the atom to the other. (c) At the same energy level ($n = 4$), the wave function of a state of higher angular momentum ($\ell = 3$) also shows oscillatory behavior, but it is directed around the nucleus in orbital fashion rather than toward and away from the nucleus. This wave, representing one of Bohr's circular orbits, is concentrated in a doughnut around the nucleus. (d) As quantum numbers increase in magnitude and as the granular effects of quantum mechanics become less significant, the wave picture begins to resemble closely the classical orbit picture. Figures 24.8(d) and 24.9(d) illuminate the correspondence principle. For $n = 20$ and $\ell = 19$, the quantum wave has narrowed into a band with a large hollow center. The wave oscillates as it follows around a circular Bohr orbit, closing upon itself with constructive interference in much the manner visualized by de Broglie (Figure 23.17). The gradual transition from quantum to classical behavior is one of the beautiful aspects of the submicroscopic world.

24.4   Electron spin

Three big discoveries of the year 1925 provided the keys to unlock the mysteries of atoms containing more than one electron. One was the discovery of electron spin. Another was the discovery by Wolfgang Pauli of a most remarkable principle, the exclusion principle (Section 24.7). The third was the first formulation of the new quantum mechanics by Werner Heisenberg (the Schrödinger equation appeared the following year). Together, these developments made possible a grand structural scheme of all atoms. Suddenly, all the facts and knowledge fell into place as the quantum-mechanical theory of spinning electrons provided a simple foundation of understanding for all atoms and, therefore, all of the material world constructed of atoms. It was a victory of the human intellect comparable to Newton's illumination of the solar system. Referring to this giant step, Paul Dirac wrote matter-of-factly in 1929, "The underlying physical laws necessary for the mathematical theory of a large part of physics and the whole of chemistry are thus completely known."* In this and the next few sections, we shall take up the main features of this achievement.

Dirac's bold statement was sound

Because the electron spins, a fourth quantum number is required to classify its states of motion:

4. SPIN ORIENTATION QUANTUM NUMBER

$$m_s = -\tfrac{1}{2}, +\tfrac{1}{2} \qquad \text{(2 different values)}.$$

Two orientations for spin

This quantum number determines the component of the spin **S** along a chosen axis (Equation 24.11):

$$S_z = m_s \hbar.$$

---

* *Proceedings of the Royal Society, London* **123**, 714 (1929).

TABLE 24.1   POSSIBLE VALUES OF FOUR QUANTUM NUMBERS FOR THE LOWEST TWO ENERGY LEVELS IN THE HYDROGEN ATOM

n	ℓ	m_ℓ	m_s
1	0	0	$-\frac{1}{2}$
			$+\frac{1}{2}$
2	0	0	$-\frac{1}{2}$
			$+\frac{1}{2}$
	1	-1	$-\frac{1}{2}$
			$+\frac{1}{2}$
		0	$-\frac{1}{2}$
			$+\frac{1}{2}$
		$+1$	$-\frac{1}{2}$
			$+\frac{1}{2}$

Altogether, the state of motion of a single electron in the hydrogen atom can be characterized by the set of quantum numbers*

Four quantum numbers specify an electron state

$$n, \ell, m_\ell, m_s.$$

At its lowest energy level, the electron has two distinct states of motion, differing only in spin orientation. Both have $n = 1$, $\ell = 0$, and $m_\ell = 0$. The $n = 2$ floor of the Balmer transitions actually consists of eight different states of motion. These are catalogued in Table 24.1, along with the $n = 1$ states. An extension of the table to $n = 3$ shows 18 separate states of motion at the next energy level. Accompanying these quantum numbers is a pictorial scheme, or vector model, showing the orientation of orbital and spin angular momenta [Figure 24.10(a)]. The two angular momenta separately precess about the chosen z axis, each with a fixed component along the axis.

An alternative set of quantum numbers for the electron corresponds more closely to the actual physical situation in the hydrogen atom. Rather than imagining the two angular momenta, orbital and spin, as being separately oriented in space, we can first combine these two into a total angular momentum **J** (quantum number j), this total then being oriented in space, with orientation quantum number m_j [Figure 24.10(b)]. The alternative set of quantum numbers is

An alternative set of quantum numbers

$$n, \ell, j, m_j,$$

with the restriction that j is equal to $\ell + \frac{1}{2}$ or $\ell - \frac{1}{2}$ (unless $\ell = 0$, in which case $j = \frac{1}{2}$ only, since then the total angular momentum is the same as the spin angular momentum). It is one of the peculiarities of quantum mechanics that if m_ℓ and m_s are precisely defined, j and m_j are not; and if j and m_j are precisely

---

* The magnitude of the spin is, strictly speaking, also a quantum number. Since it never changes, there is no reason to keep track of it. It is the same for all states of all electrons in all atoms.

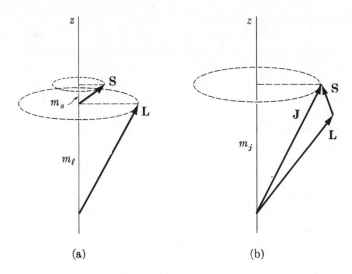

FIGURE 24.10 Two schemes of angular-momentum coupling. (a) **L** and **S** separately precess about the *z* axis. Quantum numbers are n, ℓ, m_ℓ, m_s. (b) **L** and **S** couple to form **J**, which precesses about the *z* axis. Quantum numbers are n, ℓ, j, m_j.

defined, m_ℓ and m_s are not. A state of motion characterized by one set of quantum numbers is a mixture, or superposition, of states of motion characterized by the other set of quantum numbers. These are difficult ideas, although the rules for determining the quantum numbers are easy. At all events, there is one simplifying feature of the two classification schemes for the electron states, a feature that is most important for understanding the structure of heavy atoms. It is that the *number* of distinct states of motion at each energy level is the same for both sets of quantum numbers. This point is illustrated in Table 24.2, which catalogs 2 states for $n = 1$ and 8 states for $n = 2$, using the n, ℓ, j, m_j classification scheme.

TABLE 24.2 ALTERNATIVE CLASSIFICATION OF POSSIBLE STATES OF MOTION FOR THE LOWEST TWO ENERGY LEVELS IN THE HYDROGEN ATOM

In this scheme **L** and **S** are first combined into a total angular-momentum vector **J**, which is then oriented in space.

n	ℓ	j	m_j
1	0	$\frac{1}{2}$	$-\frac{1}{2}$
			$+\frac{1}{2}$
2	0	$\frac{1}{2}$	$-\frac{1}{2}$
			$+\frac{1}{2}$
	1	$\frac{3}{2}$	$-\frac{3}{2}$
			$-\frac{1}{2}$
			$+\frac{1}{2}$
			$+\frac{3}{2}$
	1	$\frac{1}{2}$	$-\frac{1}{2}$
			$+\frac{1}{2}$

24.5   The central-field approximation

The theory of atoms containing two or more electrons is based on the central-field approximation. This idea can best be explained by example. Consider a sodium nucleus, containing 11 protons, alone in space and completely separated from its normal complement of 11 electrons. Surrounding the nucleus is an electric field of magnitude $Ze/4\pi\epsilon_0 r^2$ ($Z = 11$), identical in form to the Coulomb field surrounding a proton in a hydrogen atom but 11 times stronger. If a single electron approaches the sodium nucleus, it will find an available set of allowed states of motion identical to the allowed quantum states in hydrogen except for certain changes of scale. Its ground state ($n = 1$, $\ell = 0$) will be 11 times closer to the sodium nucleus than it would be to the hydrogen nucleus, and its binding energy will be 121 times greater than the binding energy in hydrogen.

Suppose now that the single electron radiates a series of photons and cascades down to the lowest possible energy state about the sodium nucleus. A second electron approaches. It is strongly attracted to the nucleus and weakly repelled by the first electron. The *average* force on the second electron is directed toward the nucleus since the first electron moves in a spherical region centered at the nucleus. The central-field approximation consists of ignoring deviations from the average. The first electron is regarded as a cloud of negative charge surrounding the nucleus. The second electron is then assumed to move in a central field of force created by the nucleus plus the inner electron cloud. The second electron finds an available set of discrete states of motion differing only slightly from those available to the first electron. In fact, the quantum numbers differ not at all. The energies differ somewhat, as do the sizes. Left to itself, the second electron will cascade down to its lowest available state of motion. With the addition of 9 more electrons, the system of sodium nucleus plus 11 electrons becomes a normal sodium atom. According to the central-field approximation, each of the electrons occupies an allowed quantum state in an average central field of force created by the nucleus and the other 10 electrons.

The meaning of the central-field approximation can be clarified by thinking about the solar system. To a good approximation, each planet traces an orbit around the sun as if no other planets were present. Very accurate predictions of planetary orbits require corrections to the central-field approximation arising from the direct forces acting between pairs of planets. In the solar system, the validity of the central-field approximation rests on the great mass of the sun and on the relatively great separation of the planets. Earth is much more strongly attracted to the sun than to Venus, Mars, or Jupiter. A similar pair of factors is at work in atoms. The nuclear charge is greater than the charge on any electron—as much as 100 times greater for the heaviest atoms—making the nucleus the strongest center of force in the atom. Also (for a reason to be clarified shortly), electrons arrange themselves into "shells" at successively greater distances from the nucleus, with wave amplitudes that are only partially interpenetrating.

The most significant difference between the average central field in a heavy atom and the average central field in the solar system results from the opposite sign of the electronic and nuclear charge and the over-all neutrality of the atom. In the solar system, the most distant planet, Pluto, experiences the full force of the sun (at that distance) scarcely modified by the presence of eight other planets between it and the sun. In sodium, by contrast, the force exerted by the nucleus on the most distant electron is greatly reduced by the intervening ten electrons. About ten-elevenths of the attractive nuclear force is canceled by the repulsive force of the inner electrons. The outermost electron "sees" a net charge of $+1$ (in units of the proton charge) and, accordingly, has available a set of quantum states of motion almost exactly the same as the set available to an excited electron in hydrogen. The innermost electron in sodium, on the other hand, "sees" the full nuclear charge of $+11$. It resides in a small, tightly bound state of motion.

The outermost electron is shielded from the nucleus

24.6   The periodic table

In science, explanation sometimes follows hard on the heels of discovery. Sometimes, explanation may even precede discovery; then we call it prediction. At other times, facts or regularities of nature must wait many decades for an explanation. Such was the fate of the set of chemical and physical regularities summarized by the periodic system of the elements. The periodic table, now a fixture in many classrooms and laboratories, was first advanced in a useful form by Dmitri Mendeleeff in 1869. Certain family groups of elements had been recognized earlier—for instance, the chemically similar alkali metals, sodium, potassium, and rubidium; and the halogen family, fluorine, chlorine, bromine, and iodine. Mendeleeff proposed that an arrangement of all the elements in order of increasing atomic weight would reveal regularly recurring properties and lead to family grouping for all the elements. The 62 elements known to Mendeleeff provided considerable evidence in support of such regular recurrence, but they could not be arranged to show a completely orderly periodicity without gaps. Moved by the faith in simplicity that has inspired so much progress in science, Mendeleeff predicted that yet-to-be-discovered new elements would fill in the gaps. Moreover, because of the expected regularities, he could predict in some detail the chemical and physical properties of these unknown substances. Guided by these predictions, during the period 1874–1885 chemists discovered three new elements: scandium, which fitted between calcium and titanium; and germanium and gallium, which filled two gaps between zinc and arsenic. There could be no further doubt about the general correctness of Mendeleeff's periodic system of the elements.

Mendeleeff's classification

A modern version of the periodic table is given in Table 24.3. No gaps remain in the table of 105 presently known elements. Among the numerous atomic quantities showing periodic behavior are: the valence (to be discussed later), which governs the modes of chemical combination of the elements; the size of the atom; the normal phase of the element (solid, liquid, or gas); the properties of its spectrum; and its ionization energy—the energy required to remove a single electron from the atom. Indeed there is scarcely an atomic property that does not vary periodically as atomic number increases, aligning itself with the family groups of the periodic table.

Numerous periodic properties

In the absence of a theory of atomic structure, there could be no hope of

TABLE 24.3   PERIODIC TABLE OF THE ELEMENTS

Group →	I	II					Transition elements							III	IV	V	VI	VII	0
Period 1	1 H 1.00797																		2 He 4.0026
2	3 Li 6.941	4 Be 9.0122												5 B 10.81	6 C 12.011	7 N 14.0067	8 O 15.9994	9 F 18.9984	10 Ne 20.179
3	11 Na 22.9898	12 Mg 24.305												13 Al 26.9815	14 Si 28.086	15 P 30.9738	16 S 32.06	17 Cl 35.453	18 Ar 39.948
4	19 K 39.098	20 Ca 40.08	21 Sc 44.956	22 Ti 47.90	23 V 50.941	24 Cr 51.996	25 Mn 54.9380	26 Fe 55.847	27 Co 58.9332	28 Ni 58.71	29 Cu 63.546	30 Zn 65.38		31 Ga 69.72	32 Ge 72.59	33 As 74.9216	34 Se 78.96	35 Br 79.904	36 Kr 83.80
5	37 Rb 85.468	38 Sr 87.62	39 Y 88.906	40 Zr 91.22	41 Nb 92.906	42 Mo 95.94	43 Tc (97)	44 Ru 101.07	45 Rh 102.905	46 Pd 106.4	47 Ag 107.868	48 Cd 112.40		49 In 114.82	50 Sn 118.69	51 Sb 121.75	52 Te 127.60	53 I 126.9045	54 Xe 131.30
6	55 Cs 132.905	56 Ba 137.34	57–71 *	72 Hf 178.49	73 Ta 180.948	74 W 183.85	75 Re 186.2	76 Os 190.2	77 Ir 192.22	78 Pt 195.09	79 Au 196.967	80 Hg 200.59		81 Tl 204.37	82 Pb 207.2	83 Bi 208.980	84 Po (209)	85 At (210)	86 Rn (222)
7	87 Fr (223)	88 Ra (226)	89–103 †	104 Rf (261)	105 Ha (262)														

*Lanthanide rare-earth elements	57 La 138.91	58 Ce 140.12	59 Pr 140.908	60 Nd 144.24	61 Pm (145)	62 Sm 150.4	63 Eu 151.96	64 Gd 157.25	65 Tb 158.925	66 Dy 162.50	67 Ho 164.930	68 Er 167.26	69 Tm 168.934	70 Yb 173.04	71 Lu 174.97
†Actinide rare-earth elements	89 Ac (227)	90 Th 232.038	91 Pa (231)	92 U 238.03	93 Np (237)	94 Pu (244)	95 Am (243)	96 Cm (247)	97 Bk (247)	98 Cf (251)	99 Es (254)	100 Fm (257)	101 Md (258)	102 No (259)	103 Lr (260)

NOTE: A number in parentheses is the mass number of the longest-lived isotope of an element.

explaining the periodicities of atomic properties. From 1879 to 1911, Mendeleeff's periodic table was extended, corrected, and reinforced as new elements were discovered (including a whole new family, the rare gases), spectral analysis was refined, and atomic-weight measurements were improved. Yet the underlying reason for the periodic system remained nearly as deep a mystery as ever. By exposing the interior of the atom, Rutherford finally cleared the way for an explanation of atomic periodicity. Even then, the explanation was not immediate. In his first paper on atoms in 1913, Bohr made an attempt to account for the structure of atoms heavier than hydrogen in terms of rings of electrons circling the nucleus at various distances. Even earlier J. J. Thomson had proposed an atom model with electrons arranged in successive shells. Although no other aspect of Thomson's model survived, this idea of shell structure persisted, made imperative by the demands of experimental fact. By the early 1920s the following model of heavy atoms was accepted, and later developments proved it largely correct. Orbits of various dimensions are available to the electrons. Each orbit can accommodate only a limited number of electrons. When this limit is exceeded, additional electrons must occupy larger orbits. Periodicity is associated with the capacity of particular orbits. Atoms with the same number of electrons in the outermost shell have similar properties. The alkali metals, for example, have a single electron in their outermost shells. The halogens are one electron shy of a filled shell. Atoms with filled shells are the rare gases, which are particularly stable and almost inert.

Idea of electron shells

24.7   The exclusion principle and atomic structure

Although successful, the shell model of the atom of the early 1920s was perplexing. Why was the capacity of orbits limited? Why would some orbits accommodate more electrons than others? In order to answer these questions, Wolfgang Pauli postulated in 1925 that electrons obey an "exclusion principle." One way to state the exclusion principle is this: *No two electrons can be in identical states of motion at the same time.* Since the state of motion of an electron in an atom is characterized by a set of four quantum numbers, the exclusion principle may also be stated in this way: *No two electrons may have identical sets of quantum numbers.* This rather strange principle, completely at variance with classical reasoning, has a quantum-mechanical basis too subtle for elaboration here. Its basis may be subtle, but its impact on the world could not be plainer. The entire structure of the material world is dictated by the exclusion principle. We now know that electrons, protons, neutrons, and all other particles with half-odd-integral spin ($\frac{1}{2}\hbar, \frac{3}{2}\hbar, \ldots$) obey the exclusion principle, whereas photons and mesons, with integral spin ($0, \hbar, 2\hbar, \ldots$), do not.

The exclusion principle

Not all particles obey it

A good way to understand the impact of the exclusion principle on atomic structure is to take on the Jovian task of building atoms. We start with a stock of bare nuclei, one of each charge—a proton, a helium nucleus, a lithium nucleus, and so on—and a collection of electrons. The nuclei are numbered sequentially by atomic number Z, so that the nuclear charge is $q = Ze$. To work methodically, let us begin with hydrogen ($Z = 1$). An electron brought near to a proton will cascade through successive states of motion to end in the state of lowest

More atom building

energy, the ground state, or the normal state, of the atom. Here the electron's quantum numbers are, in the n, ℓ, j, m_j classification scheme,

$$n = 1, \ell = 0, j = \tfrac{1}{2}, m_j = \tfrac{1}{2} \text{ or } -\tfrac{1}{2}.$$

Consider next helium ($Z = 2$). The first electron will fall into the lowest state, with quantum numbers the same as the ground state of hydrogen. According to the exclusion principle, a second electron cannot join the first with identical quantum numbers. However, there is available at the lowest energy level a second state of motion differing from the first in orientation. The second electron follows the first to a state with principal quantum number $n = 1$ and angular momentum quantum numbers $\ell = 0, j = \tfrac{1}{2}$ but with opposite orientation quantum number m_j. Since these two electrons use up the available two states of motion, this situation is described as a closed shell. Helium is the first closed-shell atom and the first member of the rare-gas family. There are many unique things about helium, all arising from its tightly bound closed-shell structure. To name a few: It is chemically the most inert of all elements; it has the highest ionization energy of any atom; and it has the lowest boiling point of any substance, 4.2 K, because its atoms have so little affinity for each other.

Helium a closed-shell atom

Hydrogen and helium complete the first period. A second period of eight members begins with lithium ($Z = 3$) and ends with the second rare gas, neon ($Z = 10$). In this period electrons fill successively the eight states of motion available at the second principal quantum number, $n = 2$ (see Table 24.2). The first two electrons added about a lithium nucleus can drop into the $n = 1$ state with oppositely directed angular momentum. The third electron is excluded. The lowest state of motion not already occupied is at the $n = 2$ level. The third electron drops down to this level and can go no further. The power of the exclusion principle is evident. Because of it, lithium has one relatively loosely bound electron. The properties of the atom are in every way vastly different than they would be if the exclusion principle did not act to prevent this electron from joining the first two in the lowest state of motion.

Lithium's third electron is excluded from n = 1

When the eight states of motion at the $n = 2$ level are fully occupied, another closed shell results, this one at $Z = 10$, neon. Sodium ($Z = 11$) begins the third period. Its first ten electrons occupy closed shells. Its eleventh electron, excluded from the $n = 1$ and $n = 2$ shells, must stop at the $n = 3$ level. This single eleventh electron can be considered the active agent in sodium. It is responsible for most of the chemical and physical properties of sodium, including its similarity to lithium.

Neon, Z = 10: All states with n = 1 and 2 are occupied

Although it is unnecessary to pursue this atom-by-atom survey further, one important point about atom-building remains to be clarified—the distortion of the energy-level pattern available to one electron by the other electrons in a heavy atom. Consider again the eleventh electron in sodium. It experiences an approximately central force, but this is not a Coulomb force. At a great distance from the nucleus, attracted by a net charge of $+e$, it experiences a force whose magnitude is

$$F = \frac{1}{4\pi\epsilon_0} \frac{e^2}{r^2} \quad \text{(large } r\text{)}. \tag{24.21}$$

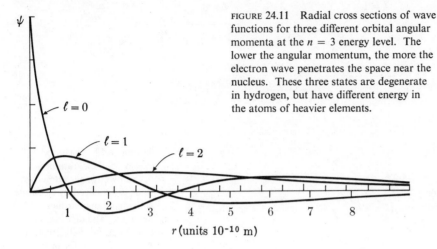

FIGURE 24.11   Radial cross sections of wave functions for three different orbital angular momenta at the $n = 3$ energy level. The lower the angular momentum, the more the electron wave penetrates the space near the nucleus. These three states are degenerate in hydrogen, but have different energy in the atoms of heavier elements.

r (units 10^{-10} m)

If it penetrates close to the nucleus, it experiences the full force of eleven protons,

$$F = \frac{1}{4\pi\epsilon_0}\,\frac{Ze^2}{r^2} \qquad \text{(small } r\text{).} \qquad (24.22)$$

Between these two limits, the form of the law of force varies gradually. Because of this variation, states of motion that would be degenerate in hydrogen are separated in energy in heavier atoms. Occupying the $n = 3$ level in sodium, the last electron could have zero, one, or two units of orbital angular momentum. The state of maximum angular momentum corresponds to a circular orbit, the state of minimum angular momentum to a thin ellipse penetrating close to the nucleus (see Figure 24.6). The different character of these three orbits shows up in the wave functions for $\ell = 0$, 1, and 2 (Figure 24.11). The wave of the $\ell = 0$ state penetrates close to the nucleus into the region of stronger attraction. The $\ell = 2$ wave is concentrated farther from the nucleus. Consequently, the three states, all of the same principal quantum number, are spread apart in energy, the $\ell = 0$ state being lowest (tightest binding), the $\ell = 2$ state being highest (loosest binding). This energy distortion is pictured schematically in Figure 24.12. At $n = 3$, the distortion is sufficient to influence the shell structure in an important way. The "circular" state, with $\ell = 2$, is so loosely bound that it is pushed effectively up into the fourth shell. Rather than the 18 elements that might be expected in the third period (based on counting the total number of states of motion available at $n = 3$), there are only 8 elements—from sodium ($Z = 11$) through argon ($Z = 18$). A period of 18 elements shows itself first in the fourth row of the periodic table.

Shielding depends on ℓ: Distortion of energy levels results

In the distorted energy diagram of Figure 24.12, the individual energy levels are labeled by the largest number of electrons they can hold without violating the exclusion principle. These numbers explain at once the observed lengths of the first five periods of elements (see Table 24.4). For the remainder of the

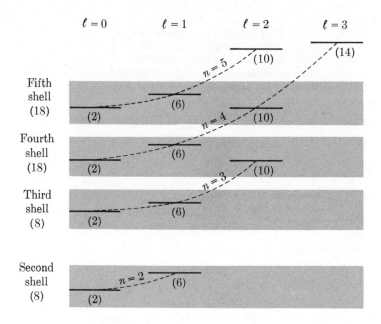

FIGURE 24.12   Distorted energy-level diagram produced by stronger attractive force experienced by electrons with small angular momentum. The distortion influences the shell structure. An $n = 3$ level, for instance, appears in the fourth shell. (This diagram is schematic only, not to scale.)

periodic table, the energy distortion further complicates the pattern. Nevertheless, a very well defined periodicity persists through all the known elements.

The crucial role of spin

The importance of electron spin in shaping atomic structure is worth emphasizing. By itself, spin would have been an interesting discovery since it is a property of an elementary particle. In conjunction with the exclusion principle, it is more than interesting, it is momentous. By doubling the number of states of motion available to the electron, the apparently innocuous fact of electron spin shapes the periodic table and thereby shapes the world.

TABLE 24.4   FIRST FIVE PERIODS OF THE ELEMENTS

Period	Number of Elements	First Element	Last Element
1	2	H ($Z = 1$)	He ($Z = 2$)
2	8	Li ($Z = 3$)	Ne ($Z = 10$)
3	8	Na ($Z = 11$)	Ar ($Z = 18$)
4	18	K ($Z = 19$)	Kr ($Z = 36$)
5	18	Rb ($Z = 37$)	Xe ($Z = 54$)

24.8   Inner and outer electrons

Imagine a set of cards, on each of which an individual atom is represented pictorially by a sketch of the wave function of its innermost and outermost electrons. If these cards are arranged in order of atomic number and are flipped rapidly to produce the impression of motion, what will we see? Drawn inward by the increasing nuclear charge, the wave of the innermost electron shrinks steadily, collapsing from an extension of 1 Å (10^{-10} m) in hydrogen to an extension only about one-hundredth as great (10^{-12} m) in the heaviest elements. The extension of the outermost electron wave varies in quite a different way. It oscillates slightly inward and outward as the cards are flipped, its dimension never straying far from about 1 Å. This outermost electron wave determines the size of the atom. Like most atomic properties, it shows a periodic variation. The periodicity of atomic size was known in Mendeleeff's time and was used by his contemporary Lothar Meyer as supporting evidence for the periodic system of the elements. In Figure 24.13, atomic radii are plotted as a function of atomic number.

Inner electrons: smooth variation with Z

Outer electrons: periodic variation

Just as the radii of the innermost and outermost states of motion vary in a quite different way through the periodic table, so do the energies associated

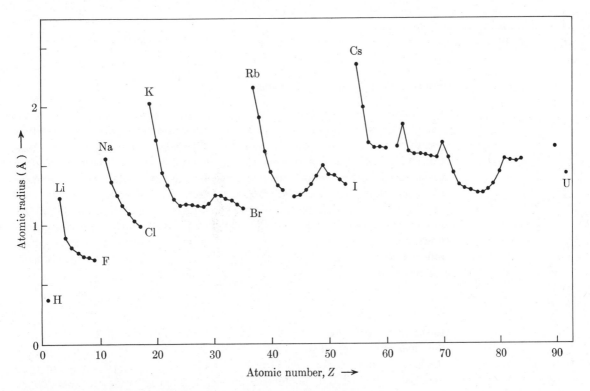

FIGURE 24.13   Atomic radii vs atomic number. Atomic radii cannot be precisely defined. These values are derived from interatomic spacing in covalent bonding and in the solid form of the element. (Data from Figure 2.19, *Chemistry: Principles and Properties*, by M. J. Sienko and R. A. Plane. Copyright 1966, McGraw-Hill Book Company. Used with permission of McGraw-Hill Book Company.)

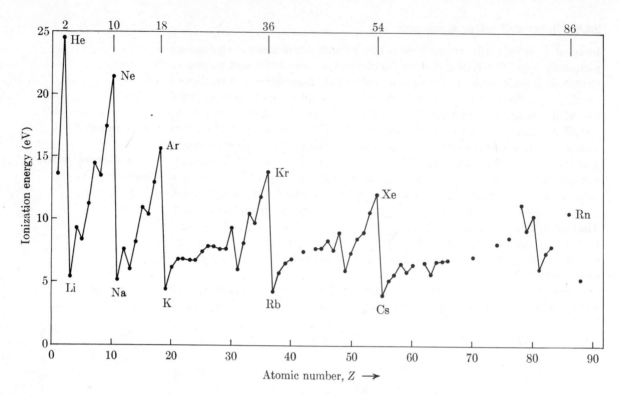

FIGURE 24.14 Ionization energy vs atomic number.

with these states of motion. The ionization energy of the atom, which is the energy required to remove the most loosely bound outer electron, never differs greatly from 10 eV from one end of the periodic table to the other. The ionization energy of hydrogen is 13.60 eV; of radium, 5.28 eV. The cesium atom ($Z = 55$) is most easily ionized, requiring only 3.89 eV to remove its outermost electron. Note in the periodic table that cesium, a member of the alkali-metal family, has a single electron on the outside of closed shells. The largest ionization energy, 24.48 eV, belongs to helium. Figure 24.14 shows the periodicity of ionization energy among the elements. By contrast, the binding energies of the inner electrons vary smoothly, without periodicity, and increase rapidly as Z increases.

X RAYS

Inner electrons produce X rays

In the very early history of modern atomic theory, the regularity associated with the inner tightly bound electrons was used to good advantage in supporting the Rutherford-Bohr model of the atom. Normally, energy absorption and emission by an atom involve only its outer electrons. A sufficiently violent disturbance, however, can excite or remove inner electrons. The photons emitted after such a disturbance, as the atom is settling back to normal, provide a way to get information about the innermost electrons. If an electron is by some means removed from the most tightly bound state of motion (the state with principal quantum number $n = 1$), the atom finds itself with an available unoccupied state of motion at low energy. One of the electrons perched at a higher energy, previously prevented by the exclusion principle from dropping down, is now free to emit a photon and jump to the lower energy. The photon emitted when it does so is called a K X ray. The simplest transition to consider is one in which an electron drops from the $n = 2$ level to the $n = 1$ level. This is called the K_α transition. (Following this transition, another electron will drop into the now empty state of motion left at the $n = 2$ level, and so on, but these successive transitions need not concern us.)

The electron making the K_α transition is moving in a field of force described approximately by the potential energy function

$$U = -\frac{1}{4\pi\epsilon_0}\frac{(Z-1)e^2}{r}.$$ (24.23)

It "sees" the net charge $(Z-1)e$ of the nucleus and the one electron left in the $n = 1$ state. According to Equation 23.37, its transition energy is approximately

$$\Delta E \cong \left(\frac{1}{4\pi\epsilon_0}\right)^2\frac{m(Z-1)^2e^4}{2\hbar^2}\left(\frac{1}{1^2} - \frac{1}{2^2}\right).$$

This can be rewritten as

$$\Delta E \cong \frac{3}{4}\left(\frac{1}{4\pi\epsilon_0}\right)^2\frac{me^4}{2\hbar^2}(Z-1)^2,$$ (24.24)   *Energy of the K_α X ray*

a constant (whose magnitude is 10.2 eV) multiplied by $(Z-1)^2$.

In 1913–1914, Henry G. J. Moseley in England measured with great accuracy the wavelengths of the K_α X rays for a large number of elements. Generating these X rays, it should be mentioned, is not very difficult. It requires only that the element under study be bombarded with a stream of electrons energetic enough to eject atomic electrons from the innermost shells. Then X rays are emitted as the atoms readjust. To measure X-ray wavelengths, Moseley used crystals with known atomic spacing as diffraction gratings. His results beautifully confirmed the Bohr-theory prediction, Equation 24.24. In particular, a graph of $\sqrt{\nu}$ vs Z (ν is the X-ray frequency) was nearly a straight line (Figure 24.15).

Apart from providing support for Bohr's planetary model of the atom, Moseley's measurements had great practical value. They made it possible to ascertain the nuclear charge of almost every known element and, therefore, the   *It reveals the nuclear charge*
proper placement of the elements in the periodic table. Whereas Rutherford could only guess that the atomic number is approximately half the atomic weight, Moseley was able to state confidently the atomic number of gold, for instance (atomic weight 197), as exactly 79. Because of the regular variation of X-ray frequency with atomic number, he was able to pinpoint three missing elements, at $Z = 43$, $Z = 61$, and $Z = 75$. All were later discovered. Finally, he confirmed what had earlier been suspected, that the order of increasing atomic weight and the order of increasing atomic number are not always the same. Some years had to pass before the discovery of the neutron and the theory of nuclear structure made clear the reason for this.

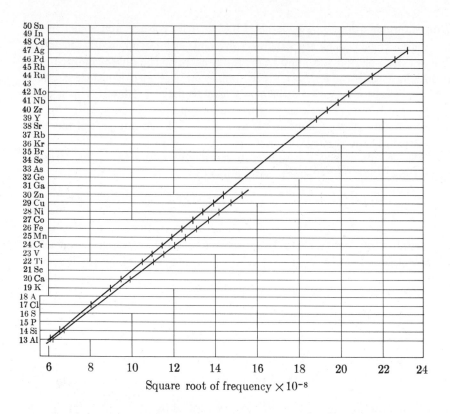

FIGURE 24.15   Measurements of frequencies of K X rays presented by H. G. J. Moseley in 1914 (*Philosophical Magazine* **27**, 703). He plotted Z vs $\sqrt{\nu}$. The upper line connects measured points for K_α X rays ($n = 2$ to $n = 1$ transitions). The lower line is for K_β X rays ($n = 3$ to $n = 1$ transitions). Note the missing element at $Z = 43$.

Although the inner electrons have an appealing simplicity and made important contributions to the understanding of atoms, it is the outer electrons that, quite literally, give life and color to our world. Among the properties of matter that can be attributed to the outer electrons are these: the union of atoms to form molecules; the temperatures of boiling and freezing; electrical resistance; the magnetic properties of materials; ionization energy; spectra in visible and nonvisible regions; the taste, feel, appearance, and color of substances. Because all of these properties are associated with the outer electrons, all show a periodicity as atomic number is increased.

24.9   Fine structure

Even in the hydrogen atom, the different states of motion with the same principal quantum number n are not precisely degenerate. The eight states of motion at $n = 2$, for example, divide into three slightly different energies, contributing to what is called the fine structure of the spectrum. These three levels are shown in Figure 24.16 with an energy scale greatly magnified relative to the scale in

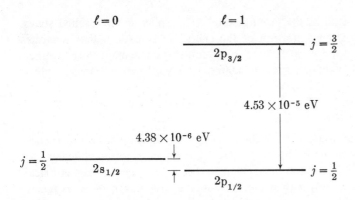

FIGURE 24.16   Fine structure of $n = 2$ levels in hydrogen. The difference between the $2s_{1/2}$ and $2p_{1/2}$ levels, the so-called Lamb shift, is attributed to the transitory existence of virtual particles in the atom—photons, electrons, and positrons—which slightly alter the Coulomb field.

Figure 24.7.   The figure also illustrates the spectroscopic notation that is commonly used to designate electron states of motion. The following letter code is used to specify the orbital angular momentum:

Spectroscopic notation

ℓ	0	1	2	3	4	5 ...
Symbol	s	p	d	f	g	h ...

The letters s, p, d, and f originate with earlier classifications of spectral series as sharp, principal, diffuse, and fundamental. Beginning with the letter f, the code proceeds alphabetically. Preceding the letter is the value of n, and following it as a subscript is the value of j. Thus $2p_{1/2}$ indicates the state with $n = 2$, $\ell = 1$, and $j = \frac{1}{2}$; $3d_{5/2}$ indicates the state with $n = 3$, $\ell = 2$, and $j = \frac{5}{2}$. Since energy does not normally depend on orientation, the quantum number m_j is not included in the shorthand.

The $2p_{1/2}$ and $2p_{3/2}$ levels in Figure 24.16 are referred to as a doublet. Doublet structure is evident in the spectra of hydrogen, lithium, sodium, and many other elements. It is one of the simplest and most direct manifestations of electron spin, for it arises from the two possible relative orientations of spin and orbital angular momentum ($j = \ell \pm \frac{1}{2}$). The most famous spectral doublet, the yellow D lines of sodium, arises from a pair of quantum jumps from the $3p_{1/2}$-$3p_{3/2}$ doublet to the $3s_{1/2}$ state (Figure 24.17). For the outermost

Doublets: a manifestation of spin

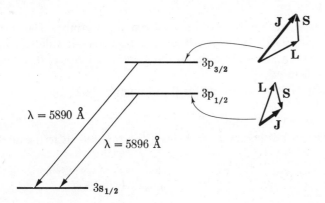

FIGURE 24.17   Transitions from the 3p states to the 3s state in sodium give rise to the yellow D lines, a spectral doublet. (The fine-structure splitting is greatly exaggerated in the diagram.)

electron, the $3s_{1/2}$ state is the ground state. The 3p states are excited states. Despite the heavy-atom distortion of the energy level pattern that separates the 3s ($\ell = 0$) and 3p ($\ell = 1$) states, the 3p doublet states remain close together. The fractional energy difference of the D lines is only 0.1 percent, an example of fine structure.

★SPIN-ORBIT COUPLING

Orbital motion of electron through electric field generates magnetic field

The small energy separation of doublet states, such as those shown in Figures 24.16 and 24.17, is brought about by what is known as *spin-orbit coupling*. An electron, because of its motion through an electric field, "sees" a magnetic field. The energy of the electron then depends on the orientation of its magnetic moment relative to this magnetic field. Since the spin of the electron can orient itself in only two ways relative to the axis defined by **L**, two energy states result.

The exact theory of spin-orbit coupling involves a blend of relativity and quantum mechanics that is beyond the level of this text. However, we can develop an approximate theory that will provide insight into the mechanism of spin-orbit coupling and predict the approximate magnitude of the doublet splitting. The energy of the electron's magnetic moment $\boldsymbol{\mu}$ in a magnetic field **B** is (Equation 16.16)

$$U = -\boldsymbol{\mu} \cdot \mathbf{B}. \tag{24.25}$$

Then the question is: What is the magnetic field **B** experienced by the electron in its rest frame? There are several ways to answer this question. One is to use the law of magnetoelectric induction for a particle moving through an electric field. Another is to regard the nucleus as rotating around the electron and generating a magnetic field at the location of the electron. Both these methods are left to the problems. Here we use a third method. Imagine a particle carrying magnetic pole strength P' moving with velocity **v** through an electric field **E**. According to Equation 16.82, the force acting on this particle is

Force on a hypothetical pole

$$\mathbf{F} = -\mu_0 \epsilon_0 P' \mathbf{v} \times \mathbf{E}.$$

In the rest frame of the particle, this force must be attributed to a magnetic field since magnetic field may be *defined* as force per unit pole strength on a stationary pole. Therefore, the magnetic field in the rest frame of the particle is $\mathbf{B} = \mathbf{F}/P'$, or

$$\mathbf{B} = -\mu_0 \epsilon_0 \mathbf{v} \times \mathbf{E}. \tag{24.26}$$

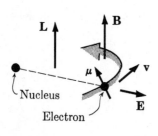

The hypothetical pole may now be dropped from the picture. The result expressed by Equation 24.26—in which P' does not appear—is valid for any particle. It gives the magnetic field "seen" by the particle by virtue of its motion through an electric field.

Using Equation 24.26 to substitute for **B** in Equation 24.25 gives

Magnetic interaction energy

$$U = \mu_0 \epsilon_0 \boldsymbol{\mu} \cdot \mathbf{v} \times \mathbf{E}. \tag{24.27}$$

The electric field **E**, if it is a central field, may be expressed in terms of the potential V by

$$\mathbf{E} = -\frac{dV}{dr}\,\mathbf{i}_r = -\frac{dV}{dr}\frac{\mathbf{r}}{r}.$$

Into Equation 24.27 we put this expression for **E**. Also replacing $\mu_0\epsilon_0$ by $1/c^2$ (Equation 17.77), we obtain

$$U = -\frac{1}{c^2 r}\frac{dV}{dr}\,\boldsymbol{\mu}\cdot\mathbf{v}\times\mathbf{r}. \qquad (24.28)$$

It remains to express this energy in terms of the angular momenta **L** and **S** of the electron. The magnetic moment of the electron is related to its spin angular momentum by (see Equations 16.55 and 24.18)

$$\boldsymbol{\mu} = -g_s\frac{e}{2m}\,\mathbf{S}. \qquad (24.29)$$

μ proportional to **S**

The spin *g*-factor of the electron is found experimentally (and was also predicted by Dirac's theory of the electron) to be twice the classically expected value*:

$$g_s = 2. \qquad (24.30)$$

From the definition of orbital angular momentum, $\mathbf{L} = m\mathbf{r}\times\mathbf{v}$, it follows that

$$\mathbf{v}\times\mathbf{r} = -\frac{\mathbf{L}}{m}. \qquad (24.31)$$

B ~ **r** x **v** ~ **L**

Substituting from Equations 24.29–24.31 in Equation 24.28 gives

$$U = -\frac{e}{m^2 c^2 r}\frac{dV}{dr}\,\mathbf{S}\cdot\mathbf{L} \quad \text{(approximate theory).} \qquad (24.32)$$

The proportionality of this energy to the combination $\mathbf{S}\cdot\mathbf{L}$ gives rise to the phrase "spin-orbit coupling." In the exact theory, a subtle but important additional effect is associated with the fact that the rest frame of the orbiting electron is an accelerated frame, not an inertial frame. To order v^2/c^2, the exact theory yields a spin-orbit energy that differs from Equation 24.32 by a factor of 2. It is

Interaction energy proportional to **S** · **L**

$$U = -\frac{e}{2m^2 c^2 r}\frac{dV}{dr}\,\mathbf{S}\cdot\mathbf{L} \quad \text{(exact theory).} \qquad (24.33)$$

Note that U depends only on the relative orientation of **S** and **L**, *not* on the orientation of either **S** or **L** with respect to an axis in space.

We now specialize to a Coulomb field characterized by the potential,

$$V = \frac{1}{4\pi\epsilon_0}\frac{Ze}{r}.$$

For this potential, Equation 24.33 takes the form

$$U = \frac{1}{4\pi\epsilon_0}\frac{Ze^2}{2m^2 c^2 r^3}\,\mathbf{S}\cdot\mathbf{L}. \qquad (24.34)$$

---

* Modern precision experiments give $g_s = 2.0023192$. One of the triumphs of quantum electrodynamics is its ability to give an exact accounting of this number in terms of the influence of the cloud of virtual particles—photons, electrons, and positrons—that surround a single electron. The physical picture of nature implied by this new theory will be discussed in Section 27.11.

This is still a function of radius. For a particular state of motion, identified by quantum numbers $n\ell j$, we may write

Spin-orbit energy in Coulomb field

$$U_{n\ell j} = \frac{1}{4\pi\epsilon_0} \frac{Ze^2}{2m^2c^2} \overline{\left(\frac{1}{r^3}\right)} \mathbf{S} \cdot \mathbf{L}, \qquad (24.35)$$

in which $\overline{1/r^3}$ is a weighted average of $1/r^3$ over the volume of the atom (the weighting factor is the position probability of the electron, $|\psi|^2$). Of special interest is the difference in this spin-orbit energy for the two states of a doublet, with $j = \ell + \frac{1}{2}$ and $j = \ell - \frac{1}{2}$. It is left as a problem to show, for a single electron, that

$$\mathbf{S} \cdot \mathbf{L} = \begin{cases} \frac{1}{2}\ell\hbar^2, & j = \ell + \frac{1}{2} \\ -\frac{1}{2}(\ell + 1)\hbar^2, & j = \ell - \frac{1}{2} \end{cases}. \qquad (24.36)$$

Thus between the so-called parallel and antiparallel orientations of $\mathbf{L}$ and $\mathbf{S}$ (recall that these vectors are never perfectly aligned—see Figure 24.17), the difference of $\mathbf{S} \cdot \mathbf{L}$ is $\Delta(\mathbf{S} \cdot \mathbf{L}) = \frac{1}{2}(2\ell + 1)\hbar^2$, and the difference of energy is

Doublet splitting

$$\Delta U = \frac{1}{4\pi\epsilon_0} \frac{Ze^2\hbar^2}{2m^2c^2} \frac{1}{2}(2\ell + 1) \overline{\left(\frac{1}{r^3}\right)}. \qquad (24.37)$$

As an approximate way to estimate $\overline{1/r^3}$, we may use the Bohr-orbit model, setting $r = a_0 n^2/Z$. This rather crude approximation gives

$$\overline{\left(\frac{1}{r^3}\right)} = \frac{Z^3}{n^6 a_0^3} \qquad \left(\begin{array}{c}\text{circular Bohr-}\\\text{orbit approximation}\end{array}\right). \qquad (24.38)$$

The exact result in a Coulomb field, which we can only quote without proof, is

$$\overline{\left(\frac{1}{r^3}\right)} = \frac{Z^3}{n^3\ell(\ell + \frac{1}{2})(\ell + 1)a_0^3} \qquad \text{(exact)}. \qquad (24.39)$$

Note that these two expressions are equivalent in the correspondence limit for circular orbits: when $\ell = n - 1 \gg 1$. Equation 24.39 inserted into Equation 24.37 gives

$$\Delta U = \frac{1}{4\pi\epsilon_0} \frac{Z^4}{2n^3\ell(\ell + 1)} \frac{e^2\hbar^2}{m^2c^2a_0^3}. \qquad (24.40)$$

A more compact way of writing this result can be achieved by expressing the Bohr radius in terms of fundamental constants:

$$a_0 = \frac{4\pi\epsilon_0\hbar^2}{me^2}. \qquad (24.41)$$

The reader may verify that this substitution for a_0 leads to

Simplest expression for doublet splitting (in Coulomb field)

$$\Delta U = \frac{(\alpha Z)^4}{2n^3\ell(\ell + 1)} mc^2, \qquad (24.42)$$

where α is the fine-structure constant (Equation 23.46). The coarse structure of the one-electron energy spectrum is of order $\alpha^2 mc^2$. The fine structure, as indicated by Equation 24.42, is of order $\alpha^4 mc^2$.

■ EXAMPLE: What is the energy splitting of the 2p states in the hydrogen atom? of the 3p states in the sodium atom? (See Figures 24.16 and 24.17.) Into Equation 24.42 we insert $\alpha = 1/137$, $Z = 1$, $mc^2 = 0.511$ MeV, $n = 2$, and $\ell = 1$, to obtain, for the 2p states in hydrogen,

$$\Delta U = \frac{5.11 \times 10^5 \text{ eV}}{32(1.37 \times 10^2)^4}$$

$$= 4.53 \times 10^{-5} \text{ eV.}$$

2p splitting in hydrogen

This is an accurate result. The doublet splitting in sodium, on the other hand, can be at best only crudely estimated from Equation 24.42 because the outermost electron in the sodium atom is partially shielded from the nucleus and does not experience a Coulomb field. Rather than making such an estimate, let us work backward to get an effective charge, Z_{eff}. The observed 3p splitting in sodium is

$$\Delta U = 2.1 \times 10^{-3} \text{ eV,}$$

nearly 50 times greater than the 2p splitting in hydrogen. The value of Z needed in Equation 24.42 to give this value is (with $n = 3$ and $\ell = 1$),

$$Z_{\text{eff}} = 3.5.   ■$$

HYPERFINE STRUCTURE

Upon sufficiently close examination, such as with a Michelson interferometer, many spectral lines show themselves to be a set of closely spaced lines with spacings much less even than fine-structure spacings. This hyperfine structure, as it is called, can be accounted for by effects of the atomic nucleus. Many nuclei possess magnetic moments, typically less than atomic moments by a factor of about 10^3 (see the inverse dependence of μ on mass in Equation 24.29). Because of this nuclear magnetism, the energies of atomic states depend slightly on the relative orientation of the angular momenta of the nucleus and the electrons. Another contributor to hyperfine structure is the nonspherical shape of some nuclei. The electric field surrounding a deformed nucleus is not an exactly central field (just as the gravitational field of the slightly deformed earth is not an exactly central field). The energy of an electron (or a satellite) in such a field depends on the orientation of its angular momentum vector relative to the axis of deformation. The spin, the magnetic dipole moment, and the electric quadrupole moment of nuclei can all be measured through observations of hyperfine splittings.

Nuclear effects produce hyperfine structure

Still other hyperfine effects are observed in the light emitted by mixtures of isotopes of the same element. The different reduced mass of the electron in different isotopes separates spectral lines. (As noted earlier, this separation first showed that hydrogen consists of more than one isotope.) In heavy elements, the "isotope shift" (line separation of different isotopes) is caused principally by the finite size of the nucleus. As the radius of the nuclear charge increases, the energies of atomic electrons are displaced upward. Since the effective radius of the nuclear charge is increased either by expanding the nucleus or by deforming it, the isotope shift gives information on both the size and shape of nuclei.

Changes of nuclear mass and nuclear size cause isotope shifts

24.10   Influence of a magnetic field on atomic energy levels

In 1896, Pieter Zeeman discovered that spectral lines are broadened if the emitting atoms are placed in a magnetic field. This Zeeman effect, as it came to be called, was soon discovered to be a splitting of each line into several lines rather than an actual broadening of any line. It is now easy to understand in terms of Equation 24.25. If the atom has a magnetic moment, its energy depends on the orientation of this magnetic moment relative to the magnetic field (now an *external* field). Since the moment, which is parallel to the angular momentum, has a discrete set of possible orientations, the energy of the atomic level splits into a finite set of energies. In the absence of a magnetic field, all directions in space are equivalent, and states that differ only in orientation have the same energy. The magnetic field provides a physically meaningful direction in space—it renders space nonisotropic for the atom—and eliminates the energy degeneracy of different orientations.

In an external field, energy $(-\boldsymbol{\mu} \cdot \mathbf{B})$ depends on orientation

Generalizing Equation 16.55 (or 24.29), for the magnetic moment of an electron we may write

Full magnetic moment of electron

$$\boldsymbol{\mu} = -\frac{e}{2m}(g_s \mathbf{S} + g_\ell \mathbf{L}).\qquad(24.43)$$

As noted by Equation 24.30, $g_s = 2$. The orbital g-factor is the classically expected value,

$$g_\ell = 1.\qquad(24.44)$$

In an external magnetic field $\mathbf{B}_0$, the interaction energy of a single electron with the field is

$$U = -\boldsymbol{\mu} \cdot \mathbf{B}_0 = \frac{e}{2m}(2\mathbf{S} + \mathbf{L}) \cdot \mathbf{B}_0.\qquad(24.45)$$

In general, for an atom, many such terms should be added together. However, we shall give careful consideration only to the example of a single electron. This is not as restrictive as it might appear. In many atoms of odd Z, the angular momenta of all but one of the electrons sum to zero, leaving one electron to contribute the entire angular momentum and magnetic moment of the atom. Even for atoms in which more than one electron contribute, Equation 24.45 may still be used if what is called "Russell-Saunders coupling" prevails in the atom. Then the spins of all the electrons add (or "couple") to a total spin $\mathbf{S}$, and the orbital angular momenta add to a total $\mathbf{L}$. For atoms in which Russell-Saunders coupling is valid, it is necessary only to reinterpret $\mathbf{L}$ and $\mathbf{S}$ in Equation 24.45 as being total angular momenta rather than the orbital and spin angular momenta of a single electron.

Russell-Saunders coupling: Atom has total $\mathbf{L}$ and total $\mathbf{S}$

Whether Equation 24.45 can be directly interpreted as the energy shift of a state depends on whether or not $\mathbf{S} \cdot \mathbf{B}_0$ and $\mathbf{L} \cdot \mathbf{B}_0$ are constants of the motion. If they are not, the energy shift must be deduced as an average value of U. Two limiting cases are of special interest: the strong-field limit, in which the interaction energy of the atom with the external field greatly exceeds the internal spin-orbit interaction; and the weak-field limit, in which the interaction with the external field is much less than the spin-orbit interaction.

THE PASCHEN-BACK EFFECT

Let us choose the z axis to lie along the direction of the external field ($\mathbf{B}_0 = B_0\mathbf{k}$). If B_0 is sufficiently great, the magnetic energy tying $\mathbf{L}$ and $\mathbf{S}$ to the z axis will be greater than the spin-orbit energy linking $\mathbf{L}$ and $\mathbf{S}$ to each other. Then the state of the electron will be as illustrated in Figure 24.10(a); it will be character- *Strong-field quantum* ized by quantum numbers $n\ell m_\ell m_s$. The influence of such a strong field on a *numbers: $n\ell m_\ell m_s$* pattern of spectral lines is called the *Paschen-Back effect*, named after two German physicists who studied such patterns. In a weak field, by contrast, the magnetic interaction energy is not sufficient to break down the spin-orbit coupling that ties $\mathbf{L}$ and $\mathbf{S}$ together to form a total angular momentum $\mathbf{J}$. The *Weak-field quantum* state of the electron in a weak field, characterized by quantum numbers $n\ell jm_j$ *numbers: $n\ell jm_j$* is illustrated in Figure 24.10(b). The effect of a weak field on spectral lines is called the *Zeeman effect*. Previously, we introduced the two diagrams in Figure 24.10 as alternative guides for counting and classifying the states of motion of an electron. We now see that the two classification schemes represent actual physical reality when the atom is placed in strong and weak magnetic fields.

The magnetic energy in a strong field is especially simple. Equation 24.45 may be written

$$U = \frac{eB_0}{2m}(2S_z + L_z).$$

The fact that m_s and m_ℓ are "good" quantum numbers is another way of saying that S_z and L_z are constants of the motion. We may write

$$S_z = m_s\hbar, \qquad L_z = m_\ell\hbar,$$

obtaining for the magnetic energy

$$U = \frac{e\hbar B_0}{2m}(2m_s + m_\ell). \qquad (24.46)$$

Strong-field energy; the Paschen-Back effect

The effect of a strong field on 3p and 3s states (in sodium, for example) is shown in Figure 24.18. The degeneracy is not quite completely removed, because the combination $2m_s + m_\ell$ has the same value for $m_s = \frac{1}{2}$, $m_\ell = -1$ and $m_s = -\frac{1}{2}$, $m_\ell = 1$. Also included in the figure are the small additional energy shifts produced by spin-orbit coupling. States with $\mathbf{L}$ and $\mathbf{S}$ approximately parallel are displaced to slightly higher energy; states with $\mathbf{L}$ and $\mathbf{S}$ approximately antiparallel are displaced to slightly lower energy.

Compare Figures 24.18 and 24.17. Note that the strong field completely wipes out the 3p doublet structure.

THE ZEEMAN EFFECT

In a weak field, it is the total angular momentum $\mathbf{J}$, rather than $\mathbf{S}$ and $\mathbf{L}$ separately, that is coupled to the external field. The electron acts as a single entity with magnetic moment

$$\boldsymbol{\mu} = -g_j\frac{e}{2m}\mathbf{J}, \qquad (24.47)$$

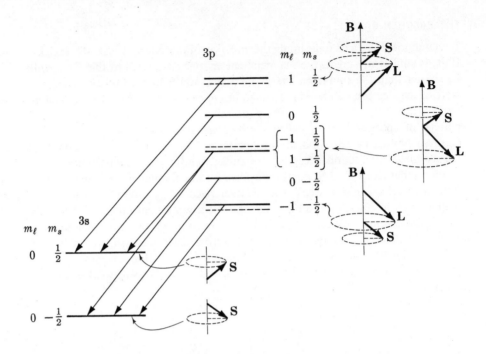

FIGURE 24.18　Energies and transitions of 3s and 3p states of a single electron in a strong field (the Paschen-Back effect). Equation 24.46 predicts 5 equally spaced 3p levels. As indicated by the difference between the dashed and adjacent solid lines, 3 of these are shifted by an additional spin-orbit energy. Vector diagrams show typical orientations of angular momenta. The allowed quantum jumps obey the selection rules, $\Delta m_\ell = 0, \pm 1$ and $\Delta m_s = 0$.

and its magnetic interaction energy is

$$U = -\boldsymbol{\mu} \cdot \mathbf{B}_0 = g_j \frac{e}{2m} \mathbf{J} \cdot \mathbf{B}_0. \qquad (24.48)$$

Compare these two equations with Equations 24.43 and 24.45. The total g-factor g_j depends on the state of the electron. A formula for it is derived in the next subsection.

With $\mathbf{B}_0$ still directed along the z axis, we may rewrite Equation 24.48 in the form

$$U = g_j \frac{eB_0}{2m} J_z.$$

Since J_z is a constant of the motion (in a weak field), given by

$$J_z = m_j \hbar, \qquad (24.49)$$

the magnetic energy for the Zeeman effect takes the form

Weak-field energy; the
Zeeman effect

$$U = g_j \frac{e\hbar B_0}{2m} m_j. \qquad (24.50)$$

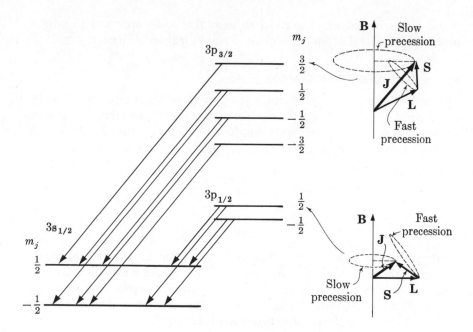

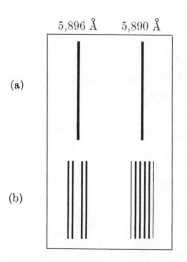

FIGURE 24.19   Energies and transitions of 3s and 3p states of a single electron in a weak field (the Zeeman effect). The level spacing within each multiplet is given by Equation 24.50. Vector diagrams show typical orientations of angular momenta.

FIGURE 24.20   (a) The D lines of sodium in the absence of a magnetic field. (b) The Zeeman pattern of the D lines in a weak field. The $3p_{3/2} \to 3s_{1/2}$ transition splits into six components; the $3p_{1/2} \to 3s_{1/2}$ transition splits into four components. Compare Figure 24.19. [Drawing after photograph in E. Back and A. Lande, *Zeeman Effect and Multiplet Structure* (Berlin: Springer-Verlag, 1925).]

For a given j, this energy splits a level into $2j + 1$ equally spaced levels. Such splitting is illustrated for the 3s and 3p states in sodium in Figure 24.19. Also shown are the allowed transitions from the upper to the lower states. A selection rule, associated with the fact that the photon has unit spin, is

$$\Delta m_j = 0, \pm 1.$$

A selection rule for photon emission

This rule excludes such transitions as the one from $m_j = \frac{3}{2}$ to $m_j = -\frac{1}{2}$. Figure 24.20 compares the sodium D line spectrum in zero field and in a weak field. To calculate and sketch the pattern in a strong field is left as a problem.

It was through analysis of Zeeman patterns that Uhlenbeck and Goudsmit were led to predict the spin of the electron and its magnetic moment.

★DERIVATION OF A FORMULA FOR g_j

The basic expression for the magnetic moment of an electron is given by Equation 24.43. To deduce a formula for g_j, it is necessary to think about how Equation 24.43 must be averaged in order to obtain Equation 24.47. Let us write the two equations together:

Actual moment of electron

$$\boldsymbol{\mu} = -\frac{e}{2m}(2\mathbf{S} + \mathbf{L}),$$

Effective moment in weak field

$$\boldsymbol{\mu}_{\mathrm{av}} = -\frac{e}{2m}g_j\mathbf{J}.$$

To the second, we have added a subscript av to indicate that it is an appropriate average of the first. Reference to Figure 24.10(b) suggests a method of averaging. If $\mathbf{L}$ and $\mathbf{S}$ themselves have no fixed direction in space, but sum to a definite $\mathbf{J}$, the *components* of $\boldsymbol{\mu}$ and $\boldsymbol{\mu}_{\mathrm{av}}$ along the direction of $\mathbf{J}$ should be the same.* We may therefore equate two scalar products:

$\boldsymbol{\mu}_{\mathrm{av}}$ defined by its component along $\mathbf{J}$

$$\boldsymbol{\mu} \cdot \mathbf{J} = \boldsymbol{\mu}_{\mathrm{av}} \cdot \mathbf{J}.$$

From this equality, we obtain

$$2\mathbf{S} \cdot \mathbf{J} + \mathbf{L} \cdot \mathbf{J} = g_j J^2. \tag{24.51}$$

If the good quantum numbers are $n\ell jm_j$, each of these three terms is a constant which can be expressed in terms of quantum numbers. Consider first the term $\mathbf{S} \cdot \mathbf{J}$. If we form the equality

$$\mathbf{L} = \mathbf{J} - \mathbf{S}$$

and take the scalar product of each side with itself,

$$\mathbf{L} \cdot \mathbf{L} = (\mathbf{J} - \mathbf{S}) \cdot (\mathbf{J} - \mathbf{S}),$$

there results an expression for $\mathbf{S} \cdot \mathbf{J}$:

$$\mathbf{S} \cdot \mathbf{J} = \tfrac{1}{2}(J^2 + S^2 - L^2). \tag{24.52}$$

An exactly analogous operation, starting with the equality $\mathbf{S} = \mathbf{J} - \mathbf{L}$, leads to

$$\mathbf{L} \cdot \mathbf{J} = \tfrac{1}{2}(J^2 + L^2 - S^2). \tag{24.53}$$

Therefore, from Equation 24.51,

$$g_j = \frac{3J^2 + S^2 - L^2}{2J^2}.$$

---

* It is true, as suggested by Figure 24.10(b), that $\mathbf{J}$ *also* has no fixed direction in space. However, in the weak-field limit, the slow precession of $\mathbf{J}$ about the field direction may be ignored in first approximation. We may think of the coupling classically in two stages. First, the more important spin-orbit coupling causes $\mathbf{L}$ and $\mathbf{S}$ to precess briskly about their approximately constant sum, $\mathbf{J}$. Second, the weaker magnetic interaction causes $\mathbf{J}$ to precess slowly about the fixed axis defined by $\mathbf{B}_0$.

Finally, we may express the quantum values of J^2, S^2, and L^2 in terms of the quantum numbers j, s, and ℓ, obtaining

$$g_j = \frac{3j(j + 1) + s(s + 1) - \ell(\ell + 1)}{2j(j + 1)}.$$

(24.54)   *g-factor of electron in weak field*

■ EXAMPLE: What are the *g*-factors of an electron in $s_{1/2}$, $p_{1/2}$, and $p_{3/2}$ states? In each of these states (or any other one-electron state), $s = \frac{1}{2}$. Inserting the appropriate values of ℓ—0 or 1—and j—$\frac{1}{2}$ or $\frac{3}{2}$—into Equation 24.54 yields

$$s_{1/2} \text{ state:} \qquad g_j = 2;$$

$$p_{1/2} \text{ state:} \qquad g_j = \tfrac{2}{3};$$

$$p_{3/2} \text{ state:} \qquad g_j = \tfrac{4}{3}.$$

These *g*-factors are reflected in the spacings of levels shown in Figure 24.19.   ■

24.11   Groups of atoms

To deal with groups of atoms in a single section may seem presumptuous, for this is a subject without boundaries. All of chemistry, molecular biology, and the physics of solids, liquids, and plasmas, among other branches of science, are concerned with groups of atoms. We cannot even scratch the surface of these disciplines. In keeping with our emphasis on the fundamental theories of physics and on phenomena that directly illuminate these theories, we must limit our attention to a few of the physical foundations underlying the rich complexity of atomic grouping that make up our world.

VALENCE

A simple and useful characterization of the outer electrons in an atom is the idea of valence. The valence of an atom is equal to the number of electrons in the outermost shell of the atom (positive valence) or to the number of "holes" in the outermost shell, that is, the number of unoccupied states of motion (negative valence). This may be called the theoretical definition of valence. There is also an empirical definition of valence: the number of electrons an atom gains, loses, or shares when it combines with other atoms to form molecules. The empirical valence is not always the same as the theoretical valence, since compounds may be formed without the full participation of the outermost shells of all the atoms. A carbon atom, for example, may unite with one atom of oxygen (CO, carbon monoxide) or with two (CO_2, carbon dioxide). Oxygen has a valence of -2. In one compound, carbon exhibits a valence of 2, in the other a valence of 4. With four electrons in its outer shell, carbon has a theoretical valence of 4.

Concept of valence

Hydrogen, with one electron, is unique in having valence both $+1$ and -1. Helium ($Z = 2$), a closed-shell atom, has zero valence. The next four elements in the periodic table—lithium, beryllium, boron, and carbon—containing respectively 1, 2, 3, and 4 electrons in the $n = 2$ shell, have ascending valences of $+1$, $+2$, $+3$, and $+4$. Lithium, with its single outer electron, is particularly active chemically, combining readily with atoms at the other side of the periodic table that are one electron short of a closed shell. Carbon, in the middle of the second period, is an interesting special case. Since it has four electrons in its outer shell and since it is four electrons short of a closed shell, its valence may be considered either $+4$ or -4. In fact, it never fully gains or loses four electrons in forming a compound but rather shares electrons with other atoms in a kind of union called covalent bonding. Because of its position in the middle of a period and its tendency to share electrons, carbon can form an enormous number of different compounds. Carbon atoms provide the backbone of every organic molecule in every living thing.

Moving on through the second period, we find atoms of negative valence. Nitrogen ($Z = 7$), whose five outer electrons leave three unoccupied states of motion in the second shell, has valence -3. This is reflected in the molecule of ammonia, NH_3. Oxygen ($Z = 8$), two positions short of the closed shell, has valence -2. (Recall oxygen's most familiar compound, H_2O.) Next comes fluorine ($Z = 9$), with valence -1, then neon ($Z = 10$), a closed-shell atom with zero valence. Sodium ($Z = 11$), beneath lithium in the periodic table, also has valence $+1$. Magnesium ($Z = 12$), like boron above it, has valence $+2$, and so on. Evidently valence, like other properties associated with the outer electrons, is periodic.

A periodic property associated with outer electrons

MOLECULAR BONDING

Valence is a simplifying idea, useful for understanding the formation of compounds. Yet the union of atoms to form molecules is rarely simple.* Consider the combination of two hydrogen atoms to form a hydrogen molecule, H_2. When far apart, the two atoms influence each other only very weakly since both are electrically neutral. Nevertheless, a small force acts, called the Van der Waals force. This weak attractive force arises from the phenomenon of polarization. In response to an outside electric field, the electron wave is slightly distorted or displaced, a response that causes the atom in turn to create a dipole electric field that reaches out to other atoms. When two hydrogen atoms come very close together, each greatly distorts the electron wave of the other. The resulting force can cause the atoms to scatter from one another. Or, if the atoms can rid themselves of extra energy, usually by transferring it to another nearby atom or molecule, the force can hold the atoms together as a hydrogen molecule (Figure 24.21). Despite the fact that a hydrogen molecule is indicated symbolically as H_2, it actually bears little resemblance to a pair of hydrogen

Atoms lose individual identity in a molecule

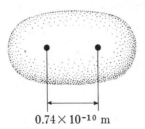

0.74×10^{-10} m

FIGURE 24.21 Schematic representation of hydrogen molecule, H_2. The protons vibrate about a fixed average separation distance; the two electrons spread themselves over the whole shaded region. The molecule bears little resemblance to a pair of adjacent atoms.

* See Arnold C. Wahl, "Chemistry by Computer," *Scientific American*, April, 1970.

atoms side by side. It is an entirely new structure, composed of two protons and two electrons. The protons establish themselves about 0.74 Å apart while the two electrons occupy states of motion spreading around and between the two protons. Since the state of motion of an electron in the molecule is quite different from the state of motion of an electron in a single atom, the molecular spectrum differs greatly from the atomic spectrum. Such a simple series as the Balmer series is not to be found in the hydrogen molecular spectrum.

Every atom, no matter how complicated its electronic structure, has two simplifying features: All of its positive charge is concentrated at its center and so is most of its mass. Obviously, even the simplest molecules do not possess these features. Because the positive charge is distributed over two or more "widely" separated nuclei, the central-field approximation is not valid in molecules. Because the mass is similarly distributed, new kinds of molecular motion are possible that are not found in atoms. In molecules, as in atoms, electrons can jump from higher to lower states of motion, emitting photons, some of which produce visible light. In addition to this kind of transition, molecules can undergo two other kinds of transition, resulting from the vibration and rotation of the nuclei. In the hydrogen molecule, for example, the protons can vibrate along the line joining them. The energies of this mode of motion are quantized. Transitions from higher to lower vibrational states of motion result in infrared spectra. Even lower energy photons, in the far infrared, result from molecular rotational transitions (see the next subsection).

Vibration and rotation

With its completely shared electrons, the hydrogen molecule affords a good example of covalent bonding. Air is composed largely of similarly bound molecules of nitrogen and oxygen, N_2 and O_2. A different kind of binding, ionic binding, occurs when one or more electrons, rather than being shared, are largely transferred from one atom to another. This happens in the molecule of cesium fluoride (CsF), which can be regarded approximately as a pair of ions, Cs^+ and F^-, held together by electrical attraction. Even in ionic binding, however, the closeness of the atoms causes them to lose most of their atomic individuality.

Covalent bonding: Electrons shared

Ionic binding: Electrons largely transferred

MOLECULAR ROTATION

To consider molecular rotation quantitatively, let us specialize to a diatomic molecule whose nuclei have masses M_1 and M_2 [Figure 24.22(a)]. As discussed in Section 13.14, no energy can be associated with the rotation of this molecule about its symmetry axis. However, the molecule can rotate about an axis perpendicular to its symmetry axis. According to Equation 10.108, its rotational energy is

$$K_R = \tfrac{1}{2}I\omega^2,$$

where I is its moment of inertia relative to its center of mass and ω is its angular speed. This is a classical formula. To put it in a form allowing for the application of quantum ideas, we may use the fact that the angular momentum of the molecule is

$$L = I\omega.$$

This means that the rotational energy is

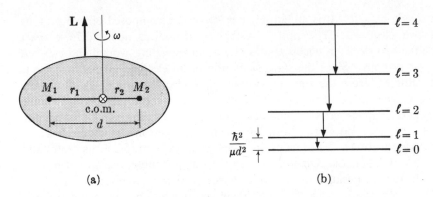

FIGURE 24.22   (a) A diatomic molecule can rotate about an axis perpendicular to its symmetry axis. (b) The rotational energy-level spectrum results from the quantization of angular momentum. If the nuclei are not identical, allowed transitions obey the selection rule $|\Delta\ell| = 1$.

Rotational energy: classical
formula

$$K_R = \frac{L^2}{2I},\qquad(24.55)$$

closely similar to the formula for translational kinetic energy, $K = p^2/2m$. The moment of inertia of the molecule is (from Equation 10.106)

$$I = M_1 r_1{}^2 + M_2 r_2{}^2,$$

where r_1 and r_2 are the distances from the center of mass to the nuclei. It is left as an exercise to show that I can be written more compactly as

$$I = \mu d^2,\qquad(24.56)$$

where $d = r_1 + r_2$, the internuclear spacing, and where μ is the reduced mass of the molecule,

$$\mu = \frac{M_1 M_2}{M_1 + M_2}.\qquad(24.57)$$

Quantum mechanics enters in a simple way. It limits the square of the rotational angular momentum to the set of discrete values

$$L^2 = \ell(\ell + 1)\hbar^2.$$

The allowed energies are, therefore,

Rotational energy of diatomic
molecule: quantum formula

$$E_R = \frac{\hbar^2}{2\mu d^2}\,\ell(\ell + 1).\qquad(24.58)$$

A rotational energy spectrum is shown in Figure 24.22(b).*   It bears a resemblance to the energy spectrum of a particle in a box (Figure 23.21).

---

* For so-called homonuclear molecules (those with identical nuclei, such as H_2, N_2, O_2), a selection rule $|\Delta\ell| = 2$ inhibits the rate at which rotational quantum jumps occur and causes these jumps to link only states of even ℓ or only states of odd ℓ.

■ EXAMPLE: What is the energy spacing between the rotational states with $\ell = 0$ and $\ell = 1$ in the hydrogen molecule? At about what temperature should the rotational degrees of freedom of the hydrogen molecule be excited? For H_2, the reduced mass is $\mu = \frac{1}{2}M$, where M is the mass of a proton. The lowest energy spacing is

$$E = \frac{\hbar^2}{\mu d^2} = \frac{2\hbar^2}{Md^2}.$$

Numerically, it is

$$E = \frac{2(1.055 \times 10^{-34} \text{ J sec})^2}{(1.67 \times 10^{-27} \text{ kg})(0.74 \times 10^{-10} \text{ m})^2}$$

$$= 2.43 \times 10^{-21} \text{ J} = 0.015 \text{ eV},$$

roughly 100 times less than the energy of a visible photon. To estimate the temperature at which rotational excitation becomes important, we may set $\Delta E = kT$, obtaining

$$T = \frac{\Delta E}{k} = \frac{2.43 \times 10^{-21} \text{ J}}{1.38 \times 10^{-23} \text{ J/K}}$$

$$\cong 180 \text{ K}.$$

Is this estimate consistent with the experimental evidence provided by Figure 13.22? Would this characteristic temperature be greater or less for molecules heavier than H_2?   ■

FORCE AND ENERGY

Although atomic and molecular combinations occur in endless variety, the forces acting between atoms and molecules all have certain features in common. Between any pair of atoms or any pair of molecules there acts a weak attractive force if the structures are well separated. As they get quite close together and the electron waves begin to interpenetrate significantly, the force becomes strongly repulsive. This repulsion is created largely by the exclusion principle that prevents more than one electron from occupying any state of motion. Figure 24.23 shows the general character of an interatomic or intermolecular force curve, and the associated potential energy curve. Although the force and energy behave in approximately this way for any pair of atoms, the detailed differences from one pair to another can have enormously important consequences. Atoms of carbon can hold themselves together in graphite up to a temperature of 3,900 K, whereas the force between a pair of helium atoms is so weak that helium does not solidify at all except under high pressure near absolute zero. Hydrogen and oxygen are easily ignited to react explosively. Other atoms combine slowly, even at high temperature. It is important to be aware that the interatomic (or intermolecular) force is quite complicated, depending not only on the electrical forces acting among all of the constituent particles but also on details of the quantum structures of the individual atoms and molecules. It is for this reason that chemistry has developed as a separate discipline of science, with its own techniques and conceptual schemes that have proved useful in classifying, correlating, and controlling the subtle and wonderful variety of atomic and molecular interactions.

Interatomic force: weakly attractive at large r, strongly repulsive at small r

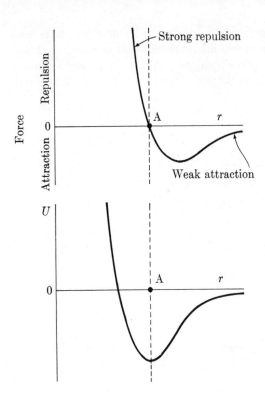

FIGURE 24.23   Approximate form of force and of potential energy between two atoms or molecules. At the point A, where the force changes from attractive to repulsive, the potential energy reaches a minimum.

CRYSTALLINE SOLIDS

Atoms can join together not only in molecules but also in the endless regular arrays of crystalline solids. Some solids are merely frozen molecules, that is, molecules immobilized by intermolecular force and close packing. More often, however, a molecule partially or wholly loses its identity in the solid state because of the powerful effect of its neighboring molecules, much as an atom loses its identity when packed close to other atoms in a molecule. As a result, *A crystal is a "giant molecule"* the crystal as a whole must be looked upon as a single giant molecule. Its size, of course, is no measure of its complexity, since it consists of identical repetitions of a basic pattern.

The types of binding in solid crystals are analogous to the binding in individual molecules. In a crystal of sodium chloride, there is very little sharing of electrons. Ionic bonding is dominant between Na^+ and Cl^- ions, which are situated at alternate corners of a cubic lattice (Figure 24.24). Covalent bonding is to be found in solid elements—such as diamond (carbon), siiicon, and germanium—and in many other substances as well. A metal crystal represents *Metal: extreme covalent bonding* an extreme example of covalent bonding. Electrons are shared not only between adjacent atoms but among all atoms. In a crystal of copper, for example, a sea of conduction electrons, one contributed by each atom, wander without restriction over the whole latticework of copper ions, Cu^+.[*] Although unrestricted in

---

[*] For a more technical discussion, see M. Ya. Azbel', M. I. Kazanov, and I. M. Lifshitz, "Conduction Electrons in Metals," *Scientific American*, January, 1973.

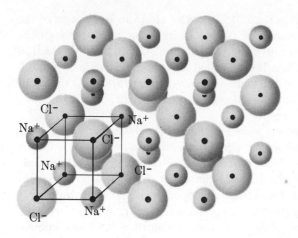

FIGURE 24.24   Ionic binding in sodium chloride crystal. Lines joining nuclei are drawn to show the crystal lattice structure.

position within the crystal, the electrons are not wholly unimpeded. Interacting with imperfections in the lattice, an electron can lose some of its kinetic energy, transferring it to vibrational energy of the ions. This is a process that contributes to the electrical resistance of the metal.

At the heart of transistors and other devices of solid-state circuitry are crystals of semiconducting material, such as silicon or germanium. Usually, these are deliberately made impure by the admixture of a small amount of a different element. The impurity atoms are chosen for their ability either to contribute an electron to the surrounding crystal or to capture an electron from the crystal. In a semiconductor, electrons are not free to wander unrestricted through the crystal, nor are they immobilized in fixed states of motion at ionic sites. They can jump from site to site, hopping through the crystal under the action of an externally applied electric field (Figure 24.25). In n-type semiconductors (n for negative), the electrons contributed by the impurity atoms can jump from atom to atom, carrying negative charge through the crystal [Figure 24.25(a)]. In p-type semiconductors (p for positive), the acquisition of electrons

n-type and p-type semiconductors

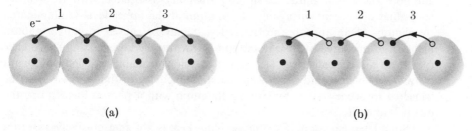

(a)   (b)

FIGURE 24.25   Schematic representation of semiconductors. (a) In an n-type semiconductor, an electron jumps from ion to ion to transport negative charge through the crystal (here to the right). (b) In a p-type semiconductor, an electron jumping from one ion to another leaves behind a hole to be filled by another electron, which in turn leaves a hole to be filled by another. Here the leftward jumps effectively transport positive charge (a "hole") to the right.

by the impurity atoms leaves a slight deficiency of electrons in the rest of the crystal. In these semiconductors, it is the "holes" that move through the crystal, effectively carrying positive charges [Figure 24.25(b)]. If an electron jumps to the left to fill a shell, it leaves behind an unoccupied state of motion. This in turn is filled by an electron jumping into it from further to the right, which in turn relocates the unoccupied state further to the right. In this way the "hole" propagates to the right.

The p-n junction, a diode

The simplest semiconducting circuit element is the diode, or p-n junction, made up of pieces of n-type and p-type semiconductor in contact. Like a vacuum tube diode, this combination conducts current preferentially in only one direction. An applied electric field can easily draw electrons from the n-type to the p-type semiconductor, but an opposite electric field draws very few electrons from the p-type to the n-type semiconductor. Transistors, used for control and amplification of electrical signals, consist of various combinations of n-type and p-type semiconductors.

24.12   Lasers and stimulated emission

By postulating quantum jumps, Bohr created new problems to be solved. How does an electron in an excited state of motion "know" when to jump? How does it "decide" which lower state to choose? Under what circumstances can an electron absorb energy and jump to a state of higher energy? These questions were ultimately answered in terms of transition probabilities, calculable in the theory of quantum mechanics. Even before the theory was developed to make possible these probability calculations, Einstein (in 1917) called attention to certain relationships among the transition probabilities. Associated with any

Three transition probabilities

given pair of energy levels are three transition probabilities (Figure 24.26). One is called the spontaneous-emission probability. This is the chance per unit time that an atom at the higher level will spontaneously emit a photon and jump to the lower level. The second is the absorption probability. This is the chance that an atom at the lower level illuminated by photons of the right frequency and of specified intensity will absorb one of the photons and jump to the higher level. The existence of these two probabilities is not surprising. They account for the excitation of atoms and for the emission of spectra. In addition, there is a third transition probability associated with the pair of levels that does seem surprising. If an atom at the upper level is illuminated by photons of an appropriate frequency, it may be caused to emit a photon identical to one already present and jump down to the lower level. The chance that it does so is called the stimulated-emission probability. The downward transition, which would have occurred spontaneously in time anyway, can be triggered to occur sooner by striking the atom with a photon identical to the one it is to emit.

Stimulated emission: crucial difference between classical and quantum manifestation

Stimulated emission, it should be remarked, is not an exclusively quantum phenomenon. A classically oscillating particle may either emit or absorb energy if accelerated by an electromagnetic wave. However, it emits and absorbs at the *same* frequency—the frequency of its vibration—and, on the average, absorption is more likely than emission when it is exposed to radiation of that frequency. A quantum system in a particular state of motion, on the other

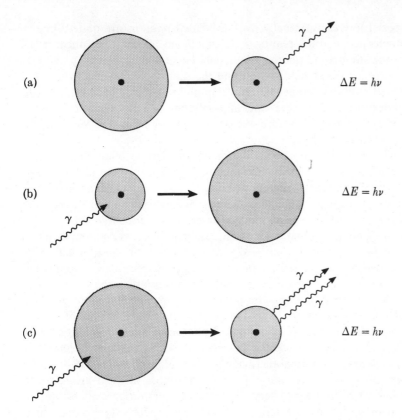

FIGURE 24.26   Types of transition probabilities. (a) Spontaneous emission:
atom jumps to lower-energy state of motion (indicated by smaller size) and
emits a photon. (b) Absorption: atom absorbs a photon and jumps to higher-
energy state of motion. (c) Stimulated emission: incident photon causes
excited atom to emit another photon identical in properties to the incident
photon. In all three cases, photon energy $h\nu$ is equal to the atomic energy
change ΔE.

hand, usually absorbs and emits radiation of *different* frequencies. Therefore,
a photon may be of the appropriate frequency to stimulate emission from a
particular state without running any danger of being absorbed by the system
in that state. Because of this all-important difference, stimulated emission in
the quantum domain has some exceedingly interesting consequences.

   Consider what might happen. Suppose a photon of appropriate frequency
enters a substance containing numerous excited atoms, each one of them in
the same excited state. If it stimulates one of the atoms to emit a photon, the
number of photons grows from one to two. If each of these two stimulates the
emission of another photon, the result is four photons, all identical. The process
could continue so that a single photon entering one side of the substance
produces a flood of identical photons coming out of the other side. It could
be argued that the stimulated emission has only accelerated the emission of
many photons that would have been emitted spontaneously anyway, making

it of no special interest. Actually, the stimulated photons are quite different from spontaneously emitted photons. A stimulated photon is identical in *all* respects to the stimulating photon. Not only has it the same energy and frequency, it also has the same direction and the same polarization. Whereas a million excited atoms spontaneously emitting photons would send them out in a million different directions, the same million atoms in a cascade of stimulated emission would create an intense beam of directed radiation, one million photons in parallel.

Simple in principle, but difficult in practice, a chain reaction of stimulated emission was first achieved for microwaves in 1955 and for light in 1960. The successful devices are called masers and lasers, their names being acronyms for "Microwave (or Light) Amplification by Stimulated Emission of Radiation." Figure 24.27(a) shows a typical modern laser, a gas-discharge tube with a bright pencil of monochromatic radiation emerging from its end. In order to bring into being this marvel of applied physics, a practical question had to be answered: How can atoms be kept in an excited state, receptive to stimulated emission? As we have already emphasized, if all atoms are in the same excited state, one photon can stimulate more photons to stimulate still more photons, all without risk of absorption. Two factors work against this state of affairs. First, whenever an atom emits a stimulated photon, it drops down to a lower energy level and becomes a potential absorber of exactly the kind of photon it just emitted. Second, in normal thermal equilibrium, more atoms will be found at the lower than the higher energy level so that more of them are ready to

A requirement for laser action: more atoms in upper than in lower state

absorb than to emit. In order to keep the stimulated photons free of absorption, so they can in turn stimulate more photons and produce the desired chain reaction, the laser must be designed so that atoms at the lower energy level are promptly elevated back to the upper level by means other than direct photon absorption.

In a helium-neon laser, such as the one pictured in Figure 24.27, the stimulated emission occurs in the neon atoms, and it is the task of the helium atoms to excite the neon atoms back to the upper energy level where they can again emit photons. The laser operates when more neon atoms are maintained at the upper than at the lower energy level.*

Figure 24.28 shows the energies of the relevant states of motion in the two atoms. Energetic electrons, caused by an external power supply to flow through the gas, excite many helium atoms to a metastable (long-lived) state 20.61 eV above the ground state. In this state, one of the electrons in the atom is in the

The role of metastable helium

1s state, the other is in the 2s state. Because of the selection rule $\Delta\ell = \pm 1$ for rapid photon emission, the excited helium atom does not make a quantum jump to its ground state. Instead it prowls through the gas, ready to give up its store of extra energy to any neon atom it finds without energy. In a collision, the energy can be transferred from the helium atom to the neon atom, leaving

---

* The helium-neon laser discussed here is only one among many kinds of lasers. Discussions of some others can be found in the following *Scientific American* articles: C. K. N. Patel, "High-Power Carbon Dioxide Lasers," August, 1968; Morton B. Panish and Izuo Hayashi, "A New Class of Diode Lasers," July, 1971; William T. Silfvast, "Metal-Vapor Lasers," February, 1973.

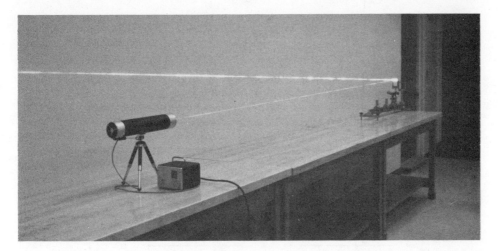

(a)

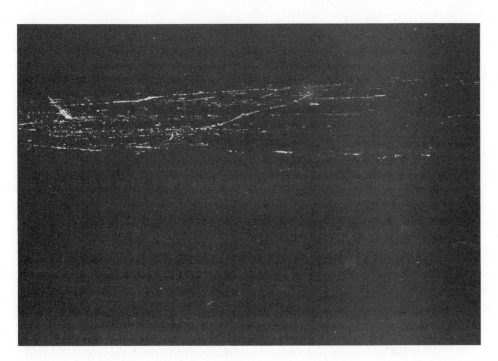

(b)

FIGURE 24.27   (a) A modern laser. Its narrow beam is made visible in this photograph by superimposing on a snapshot of the laser and mirror a time exposure of the beam striking vapor clouds in the darkened laboratory room. (Photograph by Thomas E. Stark and the author.) (b) In this view from Mt. Hamilton in California, the output power of a laser 25 miles away, although only 0.05 watt, is so narrowly directed that the laser stands out clearly amidst the city lights. (Photograph courtesy of Spectra-Physics, Inc.)

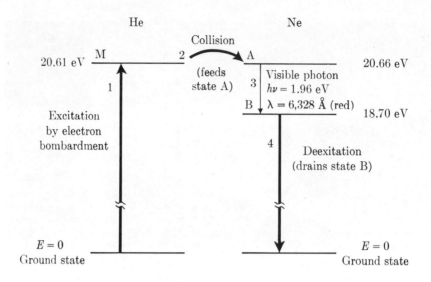

FIGURE 24.28   Partial energy-level diagrams for helium and neon atoms
relevant to laser action. 1. Electrons excite helium atoms to metastable state
M. 2. Helium atom transfers its energy to neon, exciting it to state A.
3. Stimulated emission causes neon atom to jump from state A to state B,
emitting photon of red light. 4. In collision with tube walls, neon dissipates the
remainder of its excitation energy. By this indirect means, more neon atoms
find themselves in state A than in state B at any one time so that a photon of
1.96 eV is more likely to stimulate emission than to be absorbed.

the neon atom at an energy level 20.66 eV above its ground state. (The slight
discrepancy between 20.61 eV and 20.66 eV is made up by kinetic energy of
thermal motion to maintain energy conservation.) By stimulated emission, the
neon atom drops down by 1.96 eV to a state with 18.70 eV of excitation energy,
then dissipates this energy by other means, principally collisions with the wall
of the tube. The laser radiation consists of a narrowly directed beam of red
Because of mirrors, light, of wavelength 6,328 Å and photon energy 1.96 eV. Mirrors at the ends
stimulated emission is narrowly of the tube cause most of this radiation to traverse the tube many times so that
directed every photon has many opportunities to stimulate the emission of other photons
in the same direction. It is only because of these mirrors that the stimulated
emission builds up to a high intensity in one particular direction. The useful
part of the laser beam is the small fraction, about 1 percent, that escapes through
the mirror at the end.

It should be emphasized that the laser is in no sense a *source* of energy.
It is a converter of energy, taking advantage of the phenomenon of stimulated
emission to concentrate a certain fraction of its energy into radiation of a single
frequency moving in a single direction. Because of this concentration, a laser
beam with less total power than an ordinary light bulb can burn a hole through
a metal plate or send a message over hundreds of miles. The light of a more
powerful pulsed laser can be detected after reflecting from the moon.

Summary of ideas and definitions

The early quantum rule of angular-momentum quantization, $L = \ell\hbar$, gave way to the modern rules,

$$L = \sqrt{\ell(\ell + 1)}\,\hbar, \tag{24.2}$$

$$S = \sqrt{s(s + 1)}\,\hbar, \tag{24.3}$$

$$J = \sqrt{j(j + 1)}\,\hbar. \tag{24.5}$$

The Stern-Gerlach experiment, which used an inhomogeneous magnetic field to divide an atomic beam into distinct components, was the first to demonstrate clearly the quantization of orientation.

Angular-momentum components, whether integral or half-odd-integral, are separated by unit steps ($\Delta m = 1$). Allowed components are given by

$$L_z = m_\ell\hbar, \tag{24.9}$$

$$S_z = m_s\hbar, \tag{24.11}$$

$$J_z = m_j\hbar. \tag{24.12}$$

A state of definite orientation relative to one axis is a superposition of states of different orientations relative to another axis.

States of motion of a single electron may be classified with four quantum numbers: either $n\ell m_\ell m_s$ or $n\ell j m_j$, both of which give the same number of states.

The actual physical state of an electron in a strong magnetic field is characterized by $n\ell m_\ell m_s$; in a weak field, its state is characterized by $n\ell j m_j$.

According to the central-field approximation, each electron in an atom experiences an approximately central field produced by the nucleus and the other electrons. Then four quantum numbers label each electron state.

The exclusion principle: No two electrons can be in identical states of motion at the same time. An equivalent version: No two electrons in an atom may have identical sets of quantum numbers.

The exclusion principle accounts for electron shells and the periodic table. Electron spin, by doubling the number of states, is of vital importance.

For given n and for $Z > 1$, electrons of low angular momentum experience a stronger average force than do electrons of high angular momentum. As a result, the energy-level pattern of heavier elements differs from the pattern for hydrogen.

The first few atomic shells:

Number of Electrons	States of Motion
2	1s
8	2s, 2p
8	3s, 3p
18	3d, 4s, 4p
18	4d, 5s, 5p

Outer electrons show periodic variation of radius and energy. Inner electrons show smooth decrease of radius and smooth increase of binding energy as Z increases.

The K_α X ray results from the 2p → 1s transition of an electron in an approximately Coulomb field with central charge $(Z - 1)e$. Its energy is given by Equation 24.24.

Spin-orbit coupling is the interaction between the spin magnetic moment of an electron and the magnetic field generated by its orbital motion. The interaction energy is expressed by Equations 24.32–24.35.

Doublet fine structure results from spin-orbit coupling and the two possible relative orientations of **S** and **L**.

Hyperfine structure results from nuclear magnetic moments, from nuclear deformations (electric quadrupole moments), and from differences of nuclear mass and radius among isotopic mixtures.

The magnetic moment of an electron is

$$\boldsymbol{\mu} = -\frac{e}{2m}(g_s\mathbf{S} + g_\ell\mathbf{L}). \tag{24.43}$$

The g-factors are $g_\ell = 1$ and $g_s = 2$.

In a strong field (Paschen-Back effect), the part of the electron energy depending on its orientation is

$$U = \frac{e\hbar B_0}{2m}(2m_s + m_\ell). \tag{24.46}$$

In a weak field (Zeeman effect), the part of the electron energy depending on its orientation is

$$U = g_j\frac{e\hbar B_0}{2m}m_j. \tag{24.50}$$

The factor g_j is given by Equation 24.54.

Theoretical valence: the number of electrons an atom has beyond closed shells or needs to complete a closed shell. Empirical valence: the number of electrons an atom gains, loses, or shares in a molecule.

In covalent bonding, atoms share electrons. In ionic binding, electrons are largely transferred from one atom to another.

A diatomic molecule exhibits a simple rotational energy spectrum,

$$E_R = \frac{\hbar^2}{2\mu d^2} \ell(\ell + 1). \qquad (24.58)$$

Between every pair of neutral atoms or molecules, there is a weak attractive force at large distance and a strong repulsive force at short distance.

Crystals may be insulators (electrons are held at atomic sites), semiconductors (electrons can jump from site to site), or conductors (electrons range over a large distance).

Stimulated emission: A photon encountering an atom in an excited state causes the atom to emit an identical photon.

When more atoms are kept in an upper than in a lower state, stimulated emission can produce laser action.

QUESTIONS

Section 24.1   Q24.1   How can the correspondence principle be applied to the Stern-Gerlach experiment? What physical variable (or what quantum number) should be changed, and in what way, to make the pattern of discrete deflections of the atomic beam approach the classically expected pattern of a continuous range of deflections?

Q24.2   In atomic-beam experiments of the kind pioneered by Gerlach and Stern, beams of *neutral* atoms pass through an inhomogeneous magnetic field. Could experiments of the same kind be performed with *charged* atoms (ions)?

Q24.3   For $j \gg 1$, are the different possible orientations of an atom separated by approximately equal angles? Why or why not?

Section 24.2   Q24.4   (1) For light polarized along the z axis, there is no meaningful distinction between polarization in the $+z$ direction and polarization in the $-z$ direction. Polarization is specified by a *line* but not by a *direction* along that line. Give the reason for this fact. (2) What about atoms with spin? Is their polarization specified only by a line or by a direction along a line?

Q24.5   (1) If the atoms in Figure 24.5 were replaced by photons of light and the spin polarizers were replaced by light polarizers, would any photons get through the second polarizer? If so, what fraction of the randomly polarized incident photons would get through? (2) How would the second spin polarizer in Figure 24.5 have to be oriented in order to stop all the polarized atoms that enter it?

Section 24.3   Q24.6   How can the straight-line behavior of a classical orbit with $\ell = 0$ (see Figure 24.6) be reconciled with the spherical symmetry of the wave function for $\ell = 0$ [Figure 24.9(a) and (b)]? (HINT: Is the alignment of the orbit for $\ell = 0$ a physically measurable quantity?)

Q24.7   The three orbits shown in Figure 24.6 have the same semimajor axis. Classically, particles moving in these orbits have equal energy. What other feature of the motion is the same classically for these three orbits?

Q24.8   The degeneracy (equality of energy) that exists in the hydrogen atom between states of the same n and different ℓ is a special attribute of the Coulomb field. This degeneracy does not exist in multi-electron atoms. The degeneracy between states of the same ℓ and different m_ℓ, on the other hand, is general for all atoms (and nuclei) that are not subject to external fields. Give a reason for the generality of the latter degeneracy.

Q24.9 The wave function in Figure 24.8(b) can be interpreted as a de Broglie wave whose wavelength increases as r increases. Why does it have this behavior?

Q24.10 (1) If the mass of the sun were comparable to the mass of the earth, would the central-field approximation be valid in the solar system? Why or why not? (2) If a hollow cavity existed at the center of the earth, would the net gravitational force acting on a body moving within the cavity be an approximately central force? Would it be an inverse-square force?

Section 24.5

Q24.11 For a one-electron atom, the quantum numbers n and ℓ enter into the following formulas: $E = E_1/n^2$, where E_1 is the energy of the ground state; and $L = \sqrt{\ell(\ell + 1)}\hbar$. For the states of motion of an electron in a multi-electron atom, one of these formulas remains valid and one does not. (1) Identify the formula that remains valid and explain why it does. (2) Identify the formula that does not remain valid and explain why it does not. (In both atoms the electron experiences a central field. In only one does it experience a Coulomb field.)

Q24.12 Which of the following properties of the elements are periodic: (a) melting temperature, (b) electrical conductivity, (c) atomic mass?

Section 24.6

Q24.13 Discuss hypothetical worlds in which (a) the exclusion principle operates but electrons are spinless; (b) the exclusion principle operates and electrons have spin equal to $\frac{3}{2}\hbar$; and (c) the exclusion principle does not operate.

Section 24.7

Q24.14 In the fourth row of the periodic table, there are 10 "transition elements," scandium ($Z = 21$) through zinc ($Z = 30$). Explain the origin of this number 10 in terms of angular momentum quantum numbers.

Q24.15 In an outside reference (such as an introductory chemistry text), look up the electron orbital assignments for the ground states of the first 54 elements in the periodic table. How do these assignments conform to the pattern of states suggested by Figure 24.12?

Q24.16 The exclusion principle requires that the total angular momentum of a closed-shell atom (such as He, Ne, or Ar) in its ground state must be zero. Explain the reason for this rule.

Q24.17 Figures 24.13 and 24.14 reveal an inverse correlation between atomic radius and ionization energy. Why are these atomic properties correlated?

Section 24.8

Q24.18 The atomic radius of $_{87}$Fr does not appear in Figure 24.13 because it has not been measured. Predict this radius (or predict a range within which you would expect it to lie), and give a reason for your prediction.

Q24.19 Why are s states of electrons not doublets?

Section 24.9

Q24.20 The finite size of a nucleus causes the electric field and the electric potential near the center of an atom to be less in magnitude than would be the case for a point nucleus. An electron is therefore less tightly bound to a nucleus of finite size than it would be to a point nucleus. (1) The effect of finite nuclear size on atomic energy levels is extremely small. Why? (2) Which would you expect to be more strongly influenced by the finite nuclear size, electrons in s states or electrons in p states? Why? (HINT: Examine Figure 24.11.)

Q24.21 Figures 24.16 and 24.17 illustrate the *doublet* structure that is characteristic of atoms with *one* electron outside closed shells. Atoms with *two* electrons outside closed shells ($_{12}$Mg and $_{20}$Ca, for instance) exhibit *singlet* and *triplet* structure. Doublets arise from the two possible orientations of an electron's spin. What gives rise to singlets and triplets?

Q24.22   Equation 24.39 shows that for given n, decreasing the value of ℓ increases the mean value of $1/r^3$. Explain this behavior in terms of the probability distributions of atomic electrons of different orbital angular momentum.

Section 24.10   Q24.23   An electron's spin and its magnetic moment are oppositely directed (Equation 24.18). Why?

Q24.24   (1) Is there any energy degeneracy in the partial term diagram of Figure 24.17—that is, does a single horizontal line in the diagram represent more than one state of motion? (2) Answer the same question for Figure 24.18. (3) Answer the same question for Figure 24.19. (HINT: A single state of motion is specified by a single set of quantum numbers.)

Q24.25   Explain why a magnetic field that is strong enough to produce a Paschen-Back pattern in one set of spectral lines can, at the same time, be weak enough to produce a Zeeman pattern in another set of spectral lines.

Section 24.11   Q24.26   Carbon is the backbone of the organic molecules necessary for life. (1) In terms of the structure of the carbon atom ($Z = 6$) and the concept of valence, explain why carbon is in a favored position to form many complicated molecules. (2) It has sometimes been suggested that silicon ($Z = 14$) might provide a basic element of life on other planets. Why is silicon considered a candidate?

Q24.27   A charged particle approaches a neutral atom. In terms of the idea of polarization, explain why the charged particle, so long as it is well outside the atom, is always attracted, never repelled, by the atom. (HINT: Think of polarization in terms of displacements of the centers of mass of the positive and negative charge in the atom.)

Q24.28   (1) What inhibits the evolution of living matter (a) at very high temperature and (b) at very low temperature? (2) Within roughly what temperature range would you expect the evolution of fairly complex organisms to be possible?

Q24.29   Some organisms can be preserved at very low temperatures for a long time and then revitalized when warmed up. Are the organisms "dead" while they are in cold storage? Discuss this question from a physicist's point of view.

Q24.30   On page 1243 it is calculated that rotational excitation of the hydrogen molecule should become important at a temperature of about 180 K. For molecules heavier than H_2, would rotational excitation become important at temperatures greater or less than 180 K? Give a reason for your answer.

Q24.31   What features of solid-state devices make them preferable to vacuum tubes in most electronic circuits?

Section 24.12   Q24.32   A set of harmonic oscillators are in the same excited state. One of them jumps to a lower state and emits a photon. Is a cascade of photons produced by stimulated emission likely to occur? Why or why not?

Q24.33   In a helium *ion* (a helium nucleus plus one electron), an energy of about 41 eV is needed to excite the electron from the 1s state to the 2s state. In a helium *atom*, only about 21 eV is needed to excite one electron from the 1s state to the 2s state (see Figure 24.28). Why does the atom need less energy than the ion for this excitation?

Q24.34   Many lasers emit coherent beams of more than one wavelength. By reference to Figure 24.28, explain why a helium-neon laser might be expected to emit light of several wavelengths in addition to the prominent wavelength of 6,328 Å. (Keep in mind that many energy levels of neon are not shown in Figure 24.28.)

EXERCISES

Section 24.1

E24.1   A woman idly twists her wedding ring. Its mass is 1 gm and its radius is 1 cm. Show that if she imparts to the ring 1 trillion quantum units of angular momentum ($\ell = 10^{12}$), it would take many years for the atoms in the ring to move as far as the distance to their neighboring atoms.

E24.2   The electron is usually said to be a spin-$\frac{1}{2}$ particle because the maximum measurable component of spin along a fixed direction is $\frac{1}{2}\hbar$. What is the actual magnitude S of the electron's spin in units of $\hbar$?

E24.3   A system of particles has total spin $\mathbf{S}$ and total orbital angular momentum $\mathbf{L}$; the respective quantum numbers are s and ℓ. (1) For fixed s and ℓ, what are the (a) maximum and (b) minimum possible values of the quantum number j? (2) Show that for fixed s and ℓ, the number of different possible values of j is either $2s + 1$ or $2\ell + 1$, whichever is smaller.

E24.4   If the angular-momentum quantum number of the silver atom were actually $j = 1$, as Gerlach and Stern probably supposed, rather than $j = \frac{1}{2}$, what would have been the appearance of the pattern on the detector plate in the Stern-Gerlach experiment [Figure 24.1(b)]?

E24.5   (1) Express the SI unit of the Bohr magneton in terms of the basic units: m, kg, sec, and A. (2) Verify that the product $\mu_B B$ (Bohr magneton × magnetic field) has the dimension of energy.

E24.6   It is convenient to express the z component of an atom's magnetic moment in units of the Bohr magneton through the equation

$$\mu_z = -g\mu_B m_j\ ;$$

here μ_B is the Bohr magneton (Equation 24.17), m_j is the orientation quantum number of the atom, and g is the so-called gyromagnetic ratio, or g-factor (see Equation 24.47). (1) Re-express Equation 24.8 (which gives the force on an atom in an inhomogeneous field) in terms of the quantum number m_j. (2) Explain why, to good approximation, the deflected beams in a Stern-Gerlach experiment will be separated by equal angles.

E24.7   In a Stern-Gerlach experiment, an atomic beam is split into 4 deflected beams. (1) What is the angular momentum quantum number j of the atom? (2) What are the quantum numbers m_j of the atoms in the 4 deflected beams?

E24.8   Design a spin polarizer, a device that allows atoms of only one definite spin orientation to pass through it. (Specify only its essentials, not any details.)

Section 24.2

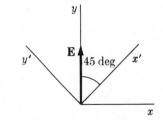

E24.9   An electric field $\mathbf{E}$ is directed along the y axis (see the figure). Express E_y as a linear combination of components $E_{x'}$ and $E_{y'}$ if the x' and y' axes both make an angle of 45 deg with the y axis. In what way are this equation and Equation 24.20 the *same*? In what way are they *different*?

E24.10   In the accompanying figure, the first two spin polarizers are oriented in the same way as in Figure 24.5. A third polarizer has been added that selects atoms with spin directed downward. (1) If the incident beam of spin-$\frac{1}{2}$ atoms at the left has unit intensity, what are the intensities in regions A, B, and C? (2) If the middle polarizer is removed, what happens to the intensity in region C?

Section 24.3   E24.11   There are $2\ell + 1$ different possible values of m_ℓ for a given value of ℓ, and n different possible values of ℓ for a given value of n. (1) How many different combinations of ℓ and m_ℓ are there for a given n? (Because it ignores electron spin, this reckoning yields half of the actual number of distinct quantum states for a given value of n.) (2) Show, either by trial and error or by a more rigorous method, that the number of combinations of n, ℓ, and m_ℓ up to a given n_{max} is $\frac{1}{6}n_{max}(n_{max} + 1)(2n_{max} + 1)$.

E24.12   The average kinetic energy of an electron in a hydrogen atom is the same as the magnitude of the binding energy,

$$\bar{K} = \frac{me^4}{2(4\pi\epsilon_0)^2\hbar^2}\frac{1}{n^2}.$$

(1) Define an approximate average wavelength by means of the de Broglie equation: $\lambda = h/\sqrt{2m\bar{K}}$. Show that this wavelength for an electron in the hydrogen atom is $\lambda = 2\pi a_0 n$, where a_0 is the Bohr radius. (2) How do the "wavelengths" estimated roughly from Figures 24.8(a) and (b) accord with the result of part 1? *Optional:* Why do parts (c) and (d) of Figure 24.8 provide no information on electron wavelength?

Section 24.4   E24.13   Extend Table 24.1 to catalog and count all of the possible states of motion of the electron at the third principal energy level ($n = 3$) in the hydrogen atom using the quantum numbers n, ℓ, m_ℓ, m_s.

E24.14   Use the n, ℓ, j, m_j quantum numbers (as in Table 24.2) to catalog all of the possible states of motion of the electron in the hydrogen atom for $n = 3$. Show that there are 18 such states, the same as the number counted with the n, ℓ, m_ℓ, m_s quantum numbers.

E24.15   (1) Which of the terms depicted in Figure 24.7 represents the largest number of distinct quantum states? How many states? (2) Which term (or set of terms) represents the smallest number of distinct quantum states? How many states? (Include the effect of electron spin.)

Section 24.7   E24.16   (1) What are the two quantum numbers n and ℓ for the outermost, or valence, electron in lithium? If energy is added to excite this electron to the next higher unoccupied state of motion, what are its quantum numbers n and ℓ (refer to Figure 24.12)? (2) Answer the same questions for sodium.

E24.17   (1) What are the occupied states of motion of the 36 electrons in a krypton atom? (2) Why is krypton an unusually stable, chemically inert atom?

E24.18   The total angular momentum of an aluminium atom ($Z = 13$) in its ground state is $j = \frac{1}{2}$. (1) What is the net angular momentum (orbital plus spin) of the most tightly bound 10 electrons in the atom? (2) What are the quantum numbers n, ℓ, and j of each of the least tightly bound 3 electrons in the atom?

E24.19 An electron moving in one dimension between rigid walls makes a quantum jump from its first excited state to its ground state and emits an ultraviolet photon of energy 6 eV. Then 4 more electrons are added, and each moves in the lowest state of motion available to it, consistent with the exclusion principle. (1) What states do the 5 electrons occupy? (Include electron spin in your reasoning.) (2) What is the total kinetic energy of this group of 5 electrons?

E24.20 The energy required to remove one electron from a helium atom is 24.5 eV. What total energy is required to remove both electrons? (HINT: Imagine the electrons to be removed one at a time.)

Section 24.8

E24.21 Compare the approximate speed of an electron in the K shell of a uranium atom with the electron speed in the first Bohr orbit of a hydrogen atom. Is relativity important for either or both of these electrons?

E24.22 The K_α X ray of a certain element has a photon energy of 1.49 keV. If the effective charge experienced by the electron making this transition is approximately $Z - 1$, what is the element?

E24.23 X rays are designated according to the quantum jump that produces them. Here is a partial listing of nomenclature:

$$K_\alpha \quad n = 2 \text{ to } n = 1,$$

$$K_\beta \quad n = 3 \text{ to } n = 1,$$

$$L \quad \text{transitions to } n = 2,$$

$$M \quad \text{transitions to } n = 3.$$

(1) Which X rays correspond to the Lyman series in hydrogen? Which correspond to the Balmer series? (2) (a) Which among the K_α, K_β, L, and M X rays has the highest frequency? (b) Which among these has the lowest frequency?

E24.24 What is the frequency of radiation emitted when an electron in a hydrogen atom makes a transition from the $2s_{1/2}$ state to the $2p_{1/2}$ state (see Figure 24.16)? In what part of the spectrum is this radiation? [NOTE: The small energy difference between the $2s_{1/2}$ and $2p_{1/2}$ states, which is the so-called Lamb shift (after the American physicist Willis Lamb), is produced by subtle effects of virtual electrons, positrons, and photons within the atom.]

Section 24.9

E24.25 As n and ℓ increase, doublet splittings decrease rapidly. What is the ratio of the 2p doublet splitting to the 3d doublet splitting in hydrogen?

E24.26 According to Equation 24.26, the magnetic field **B** "seen" by a particle moving with velocity **v** through an electric field **E** is $\mathbf{B} = -\mu_0\epsilon_0\mathbf{v} \times \mathbf{E}$. (1) Show that for an electron in a circular Bohr orbit in the hydrogen atom, this formula predicts that the magnitude of this magnetic field is

$$B = \frac{\alpha^4 m^2 c^2}{\hbar e n^5},$$

where α is the fine-structure constant, n is the principal quantum number, and the other symbols have their standard meanings. (2) Show that for $n = 2$, $B \simeq 0.4$ T. How does this compare in magnitude with typical laboratory magnetic fields?

E24.27 (1) Show that if shielding effects are ignored, the binding energy of the 2p state in an atom can be written $W_2 = \frac{1}{8}(\alpha Z)^2 mc^2$, where m is the mass of an electron and α is the fine-structure constant. (2) Equation 24.42 shows that the fine-structure splitting, being proportional to Z^4, increases faster with atomic number than the binding energy does. At about what value of Z does the calculated 2p fine-structure splitting become a "coarse structure," comparable in magnitude to the 2p binding energy?

E24.28 The ground state of the hydrogen atom has no fine structure but it does have hyperfine structure. (1) What causes its hyperfine structure? (NOTE: The proton, like the electron, is a spin-$\frac{1}{2}$ particle.) (2) In a transition between the two hyperfine levels of its ground state, the hydrogen atom emits radiation of frequency 1.42 GHz (this is the 21-cm radiation that is an important component of radio emission in the cosmos). How does the ground-state hyperfine splitting compare with the $n = 2$ fine-structure splitting?

Section 24.10   E24.29 As shown in Figure 24.19, the "favored" orientation (the orientation of least energy) of an electron's angular momentum in a magnetic field is the orientation for which **J** is most nearly antiparallel to **B**. Explain carefully the reason for this rule, and relate it to the torque acting on a magnet in a magnetic field.

E24.30 With the help of Equation 24.46, answer the following questions about the strong-field Paschen-Back splittings shown in Figure 24.18. (Ignore the small effect of spin-orbit coupling.) (1) What is the relative spacing of the 3s states and the 3p states? (2) What is the relative total energy spread of the 3s states and the 3p states?

E24.31 (1) Into how many levels is a d state split in a very strong magnetic field? Is there any remaining degeneracy? (2) How do the spacings of the d levels and p levels compare in a very strong field?

E24.32 From observations of the sodium D lines in the spectrum of a certain star, an experimenter deduces that the 3s levels in the atoms (see Figure 24.19) are separated by $\Delta U = 2 \times 10^{-5}$ eV. What magnetic field does he calculate to exist at the surface of the star?

E24.33 A sample of hydrogen is placed in a magnetic field of 100 G (10^{-2} T). Will transitions from the 2p states exhibit a Paschen-Back effect or a Zeeman effect? Justify your answer with an appropriate calculation. (NOTE: The answer is determined by the magnetic interaction energy: Is it greater or less than the energy of the fine-structure splitting? The latter, according to Figure 24.16, is 4.5×10^{-5} eV.)

E24.34 An atom is in a weak magnetic field. (1) What are the g-factors of an electron in $d_{3/2}$ and $d_{5/2}$ states? (2) Is the energy spacing between $d_{5/2}$ levels greater or less than the energy spacing between $p_{3/2}$ levels? (3) Is the total energy spread of $d_{5/2}$ levels greater or less than the total energy spread of $p_{3/2}$ levels?

E24.35 By slowly varying the strength of a magnetic field, an experimenter transforms the Zeeman pattern of a 3p → 3s transition (Figure 24.19) into a Paschen-Back pattern (Figure 24.18). As this happens, the atomic states exhibit two simple properties. 1. The angular-momentum component J_z of each state remains constant (the field is in the z direction). 2. No two states with the same value of J_z "cross." This means that if one state lies higher in energy than another state with the same J_z, it will remain higher in energy than the other state for all values of the magnetic field. Using these two facts, show in a sketch how the 3p levels in a term diagram change in relative position as the applied magnetic field varies from very weak to very strong.

E24.36 What is the valence of (a) potassium ($Z = 19$)? (b) calcium ($Z = 20$)? (c) aluminium ($Z = 13$)? (d) chlorine ($Z = 17$)?

Section 24.11

E24.37 A "radical" is a group of atoms that act as a single unit in combining with other atoms or other radicals to form molecules. (1) The hydroxyl radical, OH, contains one oxygen atom and one hydrogen atom. Explain why its valence is -1. What common compound does it form? (2) The ammonium radical, NH_4, contains one nitrogen atom and four hydrogen atoms. Explain why it has valence $+1$.

E24.38 The nuclei in a diatomic molecule can vibrate as if they were joined by a spring (see the figure). For a carbon monoxide molecule (CO), the measured quantum excitation energy of vibration, $\hbar\omega$, is 0.269 eV. (1) What is the "spring constant" k of the molecule in eV/Å^2? (2) What is the zero-point energy of the vibrational motion in eV? (3) What is the approximate amplitude of the zero-point vibration in Å? [NOTE: The equations of the quantum oscillator (Section 23.15) can be applied to this example if m is taken to be the reduced mass of the two-nucleus system.]

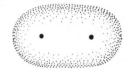

Molecule

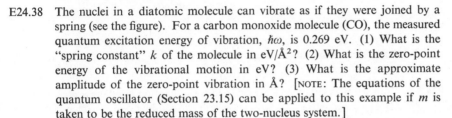

Model

E24.39 At about what temperature would you expect vibrational motion in carbon monoxide to be thermally excited? (A relevant energy is given in the preceding exercise.) Is this temperature greater or less than the temperature required for rotational excitation?

E24.40 The nuclei of a diatomic molecule have masses M_1 and M_2 and are located at distances r_1 and r_2, respectively, from their center of mass [see Figure 24.22(a)]. Show that the moment of inertia of the nuclei relative to their center of mass is $I = \mu d^2$, where μ is the reduced mass (Equation 24.57) and $d = r_1 + r_2$.

E24.41 As indicated in Figure 24.22(b), an infrared line spectrum is produced by quantum jumps between adjacent rotational states in a diatomic molecule. What is the appearance of this spectrum on a photographic plate if distance on the plate is proportional to (a) frequency or (b) wavelength?

E24.42 A certain spectral line produced by a rotational transition in hydrogen chloride (HCl) has a photon energy of 0.00525 eV. Find the initial-state and final-state values of the quantum number ℓ. (NOTE: The spacing between nuclei in HCl is 1.275 Å.)

E23.43 A hydrogen atom is in its first excited state ($n = 2$). (1) What is the energy of a photon that can cause stimulated emission? (2) What is the lowest energy of a photon that can be absorbed? (2) What is the energy of a photon that can be spontaneously emitted?

Section 24.12

PROBLEMS

P24.1 Generalize the treatment given in Section 24.1 of the force on a dipole in an inhomogeneous magnetic field. Show that the force is given by $\mathbf{F} = (\boldsymbol{\mu}\cdot\mathbf{V})\mathbf{B}$, where $\boldsymbol{\mu}\cdot\mathbf{V}$ is the following scalar operator:

$$\boldsymbol{\mu}\cdot\mathbf{V} = \mu_x \frac{\partial}{\partial x} + \mu_y \frac{\partial}{\partial y} + \mu_z \frac{\partial}{\partial z}.$$

Net force on a dipole

Under what conditions is Equation 24.8 a good approximation? (NOTE: The following three-dimensional form of the Taylor series carried to first order may be useful.)

$$f(\mathbf{r} + \Delta\mathbf{r}) = f(\mathbf{r}) + \Delta x \frac{\partial f}{\partial x} + \Delta y \frac{\partial f}{\partial y} + \Delta z \frac{\partial f}{\partial z}$$

$$= f(\mathbf{r}) + (\Delta\mathbf{r}\cdot\mathbf{V})f(\mathbf{r}).$$

Deflection of atomic beam   **P24.2**   The maximum component of the magnetic moment of a silver atom is the same as that of a single electron: $(\mu_z)_{max} = e\hbar/2m_e$. (1) Working from this fact and Equation 24.8, show that the deflection angle of a beam of silver atoms in the Stern-Gerlach experiment is

$$\theta \cong \frac{e\hbar l(dB/dz)}{4m_e K_a},$$

where l is the length of the magnet and K_a is the kinetic energy of an atom. (2) Specify reasonable design parameters to produce a deflection of 0.005 radian.

Superposition of states   **P24.3**   Consider a so-called 2p electron (one with quantum numbers $n = 2, \ell = 1$). (1) The state with $j = \frac{3}{2}, m_j = \frac{1}{2}$ is a linear combination of which two states in the n, ℓ, m_ℓ, m_s classification scheme? (2) The state with $m_\ell = 0, m_s = \frac{1}{2}$ is a linear combination of which two states in the n, ℓ, j, m_j classification scheme? (3) The state with $j = \frac{3}{2}, m_j = \frac{3}{2}$ is exactly equivalent to *one* state in the n, ℓ, m_ℓ, m_s scheme. Give the quantum numbers m_ℓ and m_s of the equivalent state and explain why no "mixture" of different states is possible in this case. (HINT: The equation $J_z = L_z + S_z$ provides a link between the two classification schemes.)

Absorption of X rays   **P24.4**   When X rays of a given wavelength pass through matter, their intensity I decreases exponentially with distance x: $I = I_0 e^{-\mu x}$. The quantity μ, called the absorption coefficient, measures the absorption probability per unit distance for an X-ray photon. The dependence of μ on wavelength λ for the element lead ($Z = 82$) is shown in the figure. (1) Discuss the reason for

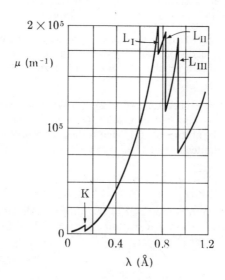

the discontinuities in the function $\mu(\lambda)$. How are these discontinuities related to energy quantization in the atom? Why are there 3 "L-edge" discontinuities and 1 "K-edge" discontinuity? (2) X rays of wavelength near the L_{III}-edge value of 0.951 Å are incident on lead. What thickness of lead is required to produce a 100-fold decrease in X-ray intensity if the wavelength is (a) slightly greater than 0.951 Å or (b) slightly less than 0.951 Å?

P24.5   In the rest frame of a nucleus (diagram a), an electron circles in an electric field. In the rest frame of the electron (diagram b), the nucleus circles and creates a magnetic field **B** at the location of the electron. The spin-orbit energy may be estimated by calculating the energy of the electron's magnetic moment in this magnetic field. (1) Obtain a formula for **B** and show that it can be written

$$\mathbf{B} = \frac{\mu_0}{4\pi} \frac{Ze}{mr^3} \mathbf{L},$$

where m is the mass of the electron and **L** is its orbital angular momentum. (Note that the velocities indicated in diagrams a and b are simply related by $\mathbf{v_N} = -\mathbf{v_e}$.) (2) Putting the above result for **B** into Equation 24.25, obtain the following formula for the spin-orbit energy.

$$U = \frac{\mu_0}{4\pi} \frac{Ze^2}{m^2 r^3} \mathbf{S \cdot L}.$$

Show that this is equivalent to Equation 24.32.

Spin-orbit coupling

(a) Rest frame of nucleus

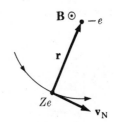

(b) Rest frame of electron

P24.6   The important Equation 24.26, which gives the magnetic field "seen" by a particle moving through an electric field, is derived in the text by considering a hypothetical particle bearing magnetic pole strength. This problem provides another derivation using the law of magnetoelectric induction,

$$\oint \mathbf{B} \cdot d\mathbf{s} = \mu_0 \epsilon_0 \frac{d\Phi_E}{dt}.$$

As shown in the figure, a particle A moves with velocity **v** through a uniform electric field **E**. "Attached" to the particle is a contour ABCDE around which the line integral in the above equation is to be carried out. The quantity Φ_E is the electric flux through the area defined by this contour. (1) Explain why the magnetic field in the frame of reference moving with the particle is nonzero only where **E** is nonzero. (2) Assuming that **B** is directed along the contour (a symmetry argument can justify this assumption), derive the equation for magnitudes, $B = \mu_0 \epsilon_0 Ev$. (3) Show that for the directions of vector quantities in this example, the result of part 2 is equivalent to Equation 24.26.

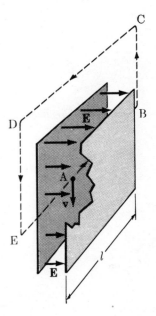

Quantum formula for $\mathbf{L}\cdot\mathbf{S}$ **P24.7**   An atomic system has total spin $\mathbf{S}$ and total orbital angular momentum $\mathbf{L}$; these are combined to form total angular momentum $\mathbf{J}$. (1) Obtain an expression for the scalar product $\mathbf{L}\cdot\mathbf{S}$ as a function of the quantum numbers s, ℓ, and j. (METHOD: Start from the equation $\mathbf{J}\cdot\mathbf{J} = (\mathbf{L} + \mathbf{S})\cdot(\mathbf{L} + \mathbf{S})$; take advantage of known properties of J^2, L^2, and S^2.) (2) Show that for $s = \frac{1}{2}$, the two possible values of $\mathbf{L}\cdot\mathbf{S}$ are $\frac{1}{2}\ell\hbar^2$ and $-\frac{1}{2}(\ell + 1)\hbar^2$. For which of these values are $\mathbf{L}$ and $\mathbf{S}$ most nearly parallel? For which are $\mathbf{L}$ and $\mathbf{S}$ most nearly antiparallel?

Quantum-mechanical cosine   **P24.8**   A so-called quantum-mechanical cosine of the angle between $\mathbf{L}$ and $\mathbf{S}$ may be defined by the formula $\mathbf{L}\cdot\mathbf{S} = LS \cos\theta$. (1) Using the result of the preceding problem, show that

$$\cos\theta = \frac{j(j + 1) - \ell(\ell + 1) - s(s + 1)}{2\sqrt{\ell(\ell + 1)s(s + 1)}}.$$

(2) Prove that $|\cos\theta| \leq 1$. (SUGGESTION: Consider the maximum and minimum possible values of j for fixed ℓ and s.) (3) Show that $\cos\theta$ cannot in fact achieve the value $+1$ (which means that $\mathbf{L}$ and $\mathbf{S}$ can never be exactly parallel), but that it *can* achieve the value -1 (which means that for special circumstances, $\mathbf{L}$ and $\mathbf{S}$ can be exactly antiparallel).

Hyperfine structure   **P24.9**   One contributor to hyperfine energy splittings is the interaction energy $U = -\boldsymbol{\mu}\cdot\mathbf{B}_\mathrm{e}$ of the nuclear magnetic moment with the magnetic field $\mathbf{B}_\mathrm{e}$ created by the motion of atomic electrons. The figure shows a simplified atomic model that can be used to estimate the magnitude of this effect. An electron moves with speed v in a circle of radius r and creates a magnetic field $\mathbf{B}_\mathrm{e}$ at the location of the nucleus. The nuclear magnetic moment can be written $\mu = g(e\hbar/2m_\mathrm{p})$, where m_p is the mass of a proton and g is the dimensionless g-factor, or gyromagnetic ratio, of the nucleus. (1) Show that the energy required to invert the nuclear magnetic moment is (classically)

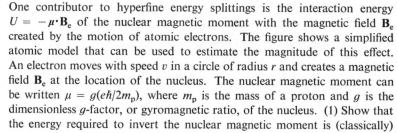

$$\Delta U = g\,\frac{\mu_0}{4\pi}\,\frac{e^2\hbar v}{m_\mathrm{p}r^2}.$$

(2) The speed of the electron is related approximately to its orbital-angular-momentum quantum number by $m_\mathrm{e}vr = \ell\hbar$. Using this relationship and the fact that the nuclear g-factor does not differ greatly from 1, show that the nuclear magnetic energy considered here is smaller than the spin-orbit energy (Equation 24.37) by a factor of about 10^3 for $Z = 1$.

Russell-Saunders coupling   **P24.10**   At a certain instant, one electron in a helium atom is in a 2p state ($n = 2$, $\ell = 1$) and the other electron is in a 3d state ($n = 3$, $\ell = 2$). (1) Show that different orbital and spin orientations permit 60 different combinations of quantum numbers for these two electrons. (2) The two spins couple to a total spin $\mathbf{S}$ with quantum number $\mathscr{S}$, and the two orbital angular momenta couple to a total angular momentum $\mathbf{L}$ with quantum number $\mathscr{L}$. (This is called Russell-Saunders coupling; it is characteristic of the light- and medium-weight elements.) (a) What are the possible values of $\mathscr{S}$? (b) What are the possible values of $\mathscr{L}$? (c) Show that 60 different combinations of orientation of the total $\mathbf{S}$ and total $\mathbf{L}$ are possible. (NOTE: For any number of electrons, $\mathscr{L}$ is an integer. For an even number of electrons, $\mathscr{S}$ is an integer.)

P24.11   The angular momenta $\mathbf{L}$ and $\mathbf{S}$ defined in the preceding problem combine to form a total angular momentum $\mathbf{J}$ with quantum number $\mathscr{J}$. Show that there are 12 different combinations of $\mathcal{L}$, $\mathcal{S}$, and $\mathcal{J}$, and that allowing **J** to take on all possible orientations provides 60 distinct states of motion.

P24.12   Figure 24.20 shows the appearance of the D lines produced by sodium in a weak magnetic field (a Zeeman pattern). Make similar sketches, to scale, of the Paschen-Back pattern of the D lines. First show the pattern for a field so strong that the effect of spin-orbit coupling can be ignored. Then show the pattern for a field in which the spin-orbit shifts have roughly the magnitudes and directions shown in Figure 24.18.

Paschen-Back pattern

P24.13   On the imaginary planet of Halbstark electrons have a *g*-factor of 1 instead of 2. An artist needs instructions on how to modify Figure 24.18 for the use of Halbstarkian students. (1) If spin-orbit coupling is ignored and only the interaction of the electron with the strong external magnetic field is considered, how, if at all, should the artist change (a) the number of 3s levels, (b) the spacing of the 3s levels, (c) the number of 3p levels, and (d) the spacing of the 3p levels? (2) Provide additional instructions to the artist for including the small additional effect of spin-orbit coupling.

Paschen-Back effect in another world

P24.14   (1) Give a careful quantitative discussion of the Zeeman effect for a hypothetical spinless electron. (2) Compare the 3p → 3s Zeeman patterns for an electron without spin and an electron with spin (the latter is shown in Figure 24.20). (3) How do the Paschen-Back and Zeeman patterns differ, if at all, for a spinless electron?

Zeeman effect for spinless electrons

P24.15   A neutral atom moves in the vicinity of an ion whose net charge is $+e$. The atom is polarizable. This means that in an external electric field **E** (such as the one provided by the ion), the atom develops an electric dipole moment **p** given by **p** = α**E**, where α is a positive constant called the *polarizability* of the atom. (1) Show that the atom is attracted to the ion by a force

Atom-ion force

$$F_r = -\frac{2\alpha e^2}{(4\pi\epsilon_0)^2 r^5},$$

where r is the radial distance of the atom from the center of the ion. (2) What potential energy characterizes the interaction of the atom and the ion? (3) Obtain an expression for the ratio of this force to the ion-ion or electron-ion force (the usual Coulomb force) and evaluate the ratio at several distances from 2 Å to 10 Å if $\alpha = 2 \times 10^{-40}$ C^2 m/N. (NOTE: The force between neutral atoms and molecules is weaker than the force considered here and diminishes more rapidly with distance.)

P24.16   In an outside reference, read about the structure and properties of simple transistors. Explain the action of a three-element transistor—especially its action as an amplifier—in terms of the properties of the n-type and p-type semiconductors of which it is composed.

Transistors

25 Nuclear Structure

Twice in history the atomic nucleus has forced itself upon the attention of man. In 1896, Henri Becquerel in Paris was astonished to discover that a salt containing uranium emitted a new kind of radiation powerful enough to darken a photographic plate through its opaque wrapping. In 1945, all mankind came to know and fear the nucleus when the fission of 1 kg of uranium devastated Hiroshima.

These events had something in common. In both, nuclear energy was being released, energy vastly greater *per atom* than the mechanical energy of the most terrifying avalanche, the chemical energy of the most violent combustion, or the electrical energy of the most awesome thunderstorm. The world of science, prepared for the unexpected, could capitalize swiftly on Becquerel's chance discovery. He triggered a world-wide search for the nature of matter, and opened a road of new discovery to Rutherford's nuclear atom and beyond. The world at large was less well prepared for the exploitation of nuclear fission. Man's mastery of nuclear energy on a large scale has produced a state of personal and international tension known as the Atomic Age (more properly, it should be called the Nuclear Age). Of the numerous problems facing the human race in the last third of the twentieth century, none is more urgent than the control of nuclear energy. Numerous other forces in modern society have the potential to alter drastically the nature of human life. Only nuclear energy—in an amount no greater than is already contained in the world's arsenals—clearly has the power to destroy all human life.

It is impossible to study nuclei without having in the back of one's mind a concern for the grave practical implications of nuclear energy. Yet it would be out of place in this text to pursue the politics, sociology, or even the technology of the Nuclear Age. In most of this chapter and the next, the focus will be on the physical principles underlying nuclear structure and nuclear behavior, especially those principles of quantum mechanics that apply to other parts of submicroscopic nature as well. Fission and fusion, the nuclear topics of greatest concern to society, will be treated in Chapter 26.

25.1 Nuclear composition

When the neutron was discovered in 1932,* the world of physics was more than ready for it. Within a few months of its discovery, Werner Heisenberg advanced a theory of nuclear composition, according to which every nucleus is composed only of neutrons and protons. He went on to speculate that these particles, of about equal mass and both strongly interacting, might in some sense be two versions of the "same" particle, differing only in charge. Since then, we have found no reason to correct Heisenberg's theory of nuclear composition, except to further recognize the transitory existence of pions and other mesons within the nucleus. Moreover, his suggestion about the sameness of neutron and proton has borne unexpected fruit. Many different particles have been found to come in groups of nearly equal mass, alike except in charge. For neutron and proton, the masses are, in atomic mass units,

$$m_p = 1.007277 \text{ amu,}$$

$$m_n = 1.008665 \text{ amu.}$$

Neutron and proton: nearly alike in mass and in other properties

Collectively, these two constituents of nuclei are known as *nucleons*.

Light nuclei contain protons and neutrons in about equal number. In heavier nuclei, neutrons outnumber protons (Figure 25.1). Known nuclei range from the single proton in hydrogen to aggregates of more than 100 protons

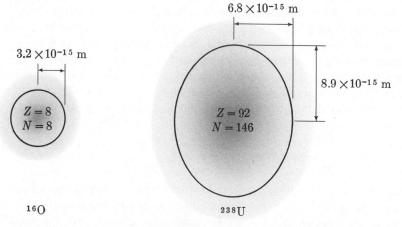

FIGURE 25.1 A light nucleus and a heavy nucleus, drawn approximately to scale. The oxygen nucleus is spherical; the uranium nucleus is not.

* The nuclear reaction that led to this discovery will be discussed in the next chapter.

Nuclear force is a strong interaction

and 150 neutrons at the other end of the periodic table. The nuclear force binding the nucleons together belongs to the class of strong interactions, which is experienced by numerous other elementary particles but not by electrons. Electrons feel only the electrical force of the nucleus and, to a lesser extent, its magnetic force; however, they are immune to the nuclear force that strongly influences nucleons.

CHARGE AND MASS OF NUCLEI

The charge Ze of a nucleus is determined by its number of protons:

$$Z = \text{number of protons in the nucleus,}$$

$$Z = \text{number of electrons in the neutral atom,}$$

$$Z = \text{atomic number.}$$

The atomic number also identifies the name of the element and locates it in the periodic table.

In addition to atomic number Z, a nucleus may be identified by its neutron number N and mass number A:

$$N = \text{number of neutrons in the nucleus;}$$

$$A = Z + N,$$

$$A = \text{number of nucleons in the nucleus,}$$

$$A = \text{mass number.}$$

Isotopes: same Z, different N

All atoms with the same atomic number (the same nuclear charge) belong to the same element. Atoms of the same atomic number but different mass number are called *isotopes* of an element. Evidently, different isotopes of the same element differ only in the number of neutrons in their nuclei. The word "isotope" is used somewhat loosely to mean a particular nucleus, an atom containing that nucleus, or a collection of identical atoms. As an example of typical notation for isotopes, carbon 12 and carbon 14 are designated by $^{12}_{6}\text{C}$ and $^{14}_{6}\text{C}$ (or sometimes just ^{12}C and ^{14}C). Both nuclei contain 6 protons; one contains 6 neutrons, the other 8 neutrons. Their mass numbers are 12 and 14.

Taking account of the nuclear binding energy, we may write for the mass of an atom

Binding energy affects nuclear mass

$$M = ZM_{\text{p}} + NM_{\text{n}} + Zm_{\text{e}} - \frac{B}{c^2}, \tag{25.1}$$

where B is the magnitude of the nuclear binding energy. (Why do we ignore the atomic binding energy of the electrons?) Precision values of atomic masses are measured in a device called a mass spectroscope (Figure 25.2). Ionized (usually singly-ionized) atoms are accelerated electrically through a known potential difference, then deflected in a circular arc by a known magnetic field. The radius of curvature in the magnetic field determines the ratio e/M' in exactly the same manner as in Thomson's experiment to measure e/m for electrons (see Equation 16.33). Since e is known, the mass M' of the ion is

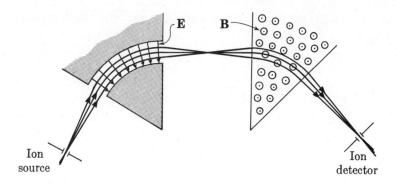

FIGURE 25.2   One version of a mass spectroscope. Ions are accelerated through a known potential difference in the ion source. The radius of curvature in the magnetic field **B** determines the charge-to-mass ratio of the ions. The electric deflection serves to make the instrument double focusing. Ions varying slightly both in angle and energy are brought to a focus at the detector.

determined. It can easily be corrected to give the mass M of the neutral atom. Such measurements provide values for nuclear binding energies (look ahead to Figure 25.17). An average figure, valid to within 10 percent for most nuclei, is

$$B \cong (8 \text{ MeV})A, \qquad (25.2)$$

or 8 MeV per nucleon. In terms of mass, this is

Typical binding energy

$$\frac{B}{c^2} \cong (0.008 \text{ amu})A,$$

representing a binding-energy effect on mass of about 0.8 percent. If, in Equation 25.1, we put $M_p \cong M_n \cong 1.008$ amu, and ignore the effect of electron mass, we get

$$M \cong (Z + N)1.008 \text{ amu} - (0.008 \text{ amu})A,$$

$$M \cong A \text{ amu}. \qquad (25.3)$$

Approximate mass

In atomic mass units, the mass of an atom (which, to this approximation, is the same as the mass of the nucleus) is nearly equal to the mass number A. Equation 25.3 is precisely true by definition for ^{12}C (this defines the amu). Other examples: $M(^{16}\text{O}) = 15.9949$, $M(^{56}\text{Fe}) = 55.935$, $M(^{238}\text{U}) = 238.051$. These are atomic masses (or atomic weights) of specific isotopes. The atomic weight of an *element* (as opposed to an isotope) is the average atomic weight of the normal mixture of isotopes of that element.*

---

* With rare exceptions, the isotopic mixture of an element is independent of the source of the element. (Lead, whose different isotopes are products of different radioactive decay chains, is an exception.) For elements not found in nature at all, the atomic weight of the "normal mixture" of course has no meaning.

■ EXAMPLE: What is the binding energy of the nucleus of ^{12}C? With masses expressed in amu, Equation 25.1 gives

$$\frac{B}{c^2} = ZM_p + NM_n + Zm_e - M$$

$$= 6(1.007277) + 6(1.008665) + 6(0.000549) - 12.000000$$

$$= 0.098946 \text{ amu.}$$

Then use the fact that 1 amu is equivalent to 931.48 MeV, to get

$$B = 92.17 \text{ MeV,}$$

or 7.68 MeV per nucleon.   ■

ELECTRONS IN THE NUCLEUS?

Old idea of nuclear composition: protons and electrons

Before the discovery of the neutron, if nuclei were to be described in terms of known particles at all, it had to be in terms of protons and electrons. No other building blocks were known. An alpha particle, for example, could be described as a closely bound structure of four protons and two electrons. The four protons contributed the necessary mass; the two electrons canceled the excess charge. Similarly, a nucleus of gold 197 could be assumed to contain 197 protons and 118 electrons. Quantum mechanics raised two serious objections against this view of nuclear composition. First, to hold an electron within the confines of a nuclear volume requires an energy larger than is actually associated with nuclear binding. For instance, if an electron is held within the "box" of a helium nucleus, its wave function must undergo at least one half-cycle of oscillation in a distance of about 5×10^{-15} m, the diameter of the nucleus. Its wavelength can be no more than 10^{-14} m. Then the de Broglie equation reveals its least possible momentum:

$$p = \frac{h}{\lambda} = \frac{6.63 \times 10^{-34} \text{ kg m}^2/\text{sec}}{10^{-14} \text{ m}} = 6.63 \times 10^{-20} \text{ kg m/sec.}$$

Is this momentum in the domain of relativistic mechanics or classical mechanics? If we guess it to be classical, we can calculate the speed of the electron to be

$$v_{\text{classical}} = \frac{p}{m} = \frac{6.63 \times 10^{-20} \text{ kg m/sec}}{9.11 \times 10^{-31} \text{ kg}} = 7.3 \times 10^{10} \text{ m/sec.}$$

We have guessed wrong. This speed is 240 times greater than the speed of light, a physical impossibility. Therefore, we must turn to a relativistic equation. Of interest is the electron energy, related to momentum by Equation 21.40:

$$E^2 = (pc)^2 + (mc^2)^2. \tag{25.4}$$

The rest energy of the electron is $mc^2 = 0.511$ MeV. The quantity pc can be calculated for this example (with an appropriate conversion factor):

$$pc = \frac{(6.63 \times 10^{-20} \text{ kg m/sec})(3 \times 10^8 \text{ m/sec})}{1.6 \times 10^{-19} \text{ J/eV}}$$

$$= 1.24 \times 10^8 \text{ eV} = 124 \text{ MeV.}$$

Since pc is so much greater than mc^2, we are in fact discussing a superrelativistic electron, one for which Equation 25.4 takes the approximate form $E = pc$. In round numbers, then, an electron held within a helium nucleus would have a kinetic energy in excess of 100 MeV. This would require, in turn, that its potential energy be negative and still larger in magnitude than its kinetic energy (in order that its total energy be negative). Such a large potential energy creates a severe theoretical difficulty; it leads to the prediction that electron-positron pairs should be spontaneously created in the neighborhood of a nucleus.

First objection: Electron kinetic energy too great

Another difficulty concerns nuclear spin. According to the proton-electron model of nuclear composition, a nucleus of $^{14}_{7}N$ contains 21 particles, 14 protons and 7 electrons. According to the proton-neutron model, the same nucleus contains only 14 particles: 7 protons and 7 neutrons. Since all the particles in question have one-half unit of spin, it makes an important difference whether or not the nucleus contains an odd or an even number of particles. If the number is odd, the total nuclear spin quantum number j must be equal to an integer plus one-half; if even, j must be an integer. Early evidence that the nitrogen nucleus has integral spin was evidence against electrons in the nucleus. Since then, the spins of several hundred nuclei have been determined (by observations of hyperfine structure and in other ways). All are consistent with Heisenberg's theory of neutron-proton composition.

Second objection: Wrong number of spin-one-half particles in nucleus

THE INDEPENDENCE OF ATOMIC AND NUCLEAR PROPERTIES

In studying matter, one of the most important points to keep in mind is the independence of atomic and nuclear properties. The electric charge of the nucleus is the single determining factor of atomic structure. All the other properties of the nucleus are almost irrelevant to the behavior of the electrons. In their atomic properties, for instance, carbon 12 and carbon 14 are nearly identical, yet their nuclei are totally different in structure. One is stable, the other radioactive. The electrons, in turn, have almost no influence on the nucleus. The situation is much the same as for the earth and its satellites. The satellites stay in orbit because of the gravitational pull of the earth, but they are unaffected by a myriad of other interesting properties of the earth. The earth, for its part, does not respond to the presence of the satellites.

Because of this "decoupling" of nuclei and electrons, almost all the properties of matter can be identified as either primarily atomic (meaning attributable to atomic electrons) or primarily nuclear, but not both. The nucleus is the source of the mass of an atom, its position in the periodic table, and its radioactivity, if any. The electrons account for all of the physical and chemical properties of the elements and for their characteristic spectra.

Nuclear and atomic properties are largely decoupled

★25.2 Scattering experiments

Much of what we know about nuclei comes through scattering experiments, experiments in which beams of high-energy particles interact with and are deflected (or scattered) by nuclei. The word "scattering" is now applied also to experiments in which the incident particles are absorbed or transformed and other particles emerge. A few such nuclear reactions will be discussed in the next chapter. Here we consider only examples in which the scattered particles are the same as the incident particles.

In an experiment, a beam of known intensity impinges on a target. The incident flux is

*Flux F_1 constant in a
collimated beam*

$$F_1 = \frac{\text{number of incident particles}}{\text{m}^2 \text{ sec}}.$$

At some angle θ to the direction of the incident beam and at distance R from the target, the outgoing flux is measured:

$$F_2 = \frac{\text{number of outgoing particles}}{\text{m}^2 \text{ sec}}.$$

Flux $F_2 \sim 1/R^2$

Since the scattered particles are fanning out from the target, their intensity diminishes with distance in proportion to $1/R^2$. Therefore, at some angle θ, the product $R^2 F_2$ is independent of R.

To characterize the distribution of outgoing particles, it is useful to introduce the concept of *solid angle*. One way to define an ordinary plane angle is by the formula

$$\theta = \frac{s}{r},$$

where s is the arc of a circle intercepted by the angle and r is the radius of the circle (Figure 5.6). In a similar way, a measure of a conical opening is the solid angle Ω defined by

Solid angle defined

$$\Omega = \frac{A}{R^2}, \tag{25.5}$$

the area intercepted by a cone on the surface of a sphere divided by the square of the radius of the sphere. Figure 25.3 shows an infinitesimal solid angle,

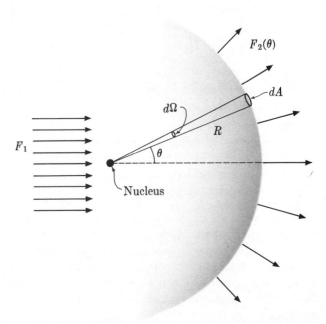

FIGURE 25.3   Geometry of scattering experiment. The incident flux is F_1; the outgoing flux is F_2 (a function of θ). The differential scattering cross section is defined by $d\sigma/d\Omega = R^2 F_2/F_1$.

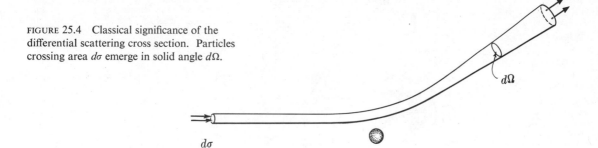

FIGURE 25.4   Classical significance of the differential scattering cross section.   Particles crossing area $d\sigma$ emerge in solid angle $d\Omega$.

$d\Omega = dA/R^2$.   About a point the total plane angle is 2π, and the total solid angle is 4π.   The unit of solid angle is called the *steradian*.

In Figure 25.3, the product $F_2\,dA$ is the number of particles per second crossing the increment of area dA.   Since $F_2\,dA = F_2 R^2\,d\Omega$, we may conclude that

$$F_2 R^2 = \frac{\text{number of outgoing particles}}{\text{steradian sec}}.$$

As noted earlier, this quantity is independent of R.   A useful way to present experimental results is in terms of the ratio $F_2 R^2/F_1$.   This quantity, with the dimension of area, is called the *differential scattering cross section*, for which the notation is $d\sigma/d\Omega$:

$$\frac{d\sigma}{d\Omega} = \frac{F_2 R^2}{F_1} = \frac{\text{outgoing particles per steradian per sec}}{\text{incoming particles per m}^2 \text{ per sec}}. \qquad (25.6)$$

Differential cross section defined

In terms of classical trajectories, the differential scattering cross section has a simple interpretation (Figure 25.4).   It is an increment of area $d\sigma$ normal to the incident beam such that particles crossing this area are scattered into the cone of solid angle $d\Omega$.

SIZE OF THE PROTON

If high-energy electrons impinge on a hydrogen target, they charge through the atomic electrons essentially undeflected.   Only in close encounters with the more massive nuclei—protons, and some deuterons—are the projectile particles significantly deflected.   Determination of the differential scattering cross section in such an experiment therefore provides information about the proton.   An example of an electron-proton differential scattering cross section, obtained by Robert Hofstadter at Stanford University, is shown in Figure 25.5(a).   The actual scattering is much less than the scattering predicted for a point charge, particularly at the larger angles.   This proves that the proton is "soft."   Its charge, rather than being concentrated at a point, is spread over a region of dimension about 10^{-15} m.   The proton charge density ρ is plotted as a function of r in Figure 25.5(b).   For providing this "picture" of the interior of the proton (together with similar information about the neutron, derived from

$\dfrac{(d\sigma/d\Omega)_{\text{obs}}}{(d\sigma/d\Omega)_{\text{pt}}} \ll 1$*; therefore,*

proton charge spread out

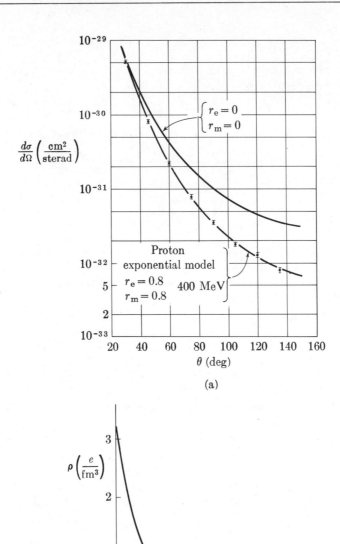

(a)

(b)

FIGURE 25.5   (a) The differential cross section of 400-MeV electrons scattered by protons [E. E. Chambers and R. Hofstadter, *Physical Review* **103**, 1454 (1956)]. The upper curve is the theoretical cross section for scattering by a point charge. The lower curve, passing through the experimental points, is the theoretical cross section for scattering by a proton whose charge and magnetic moment are both spread out, with an rms radius of 0.8 fm. (b) The charge density of the proton (measured in quantum units of charge per fm³), as deduced from electron-proton scattering experiments.

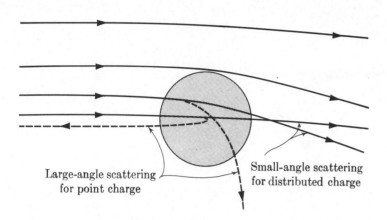

FIGURE 25.6   Effect of a distributed charge on the scattering of electrons by a nucleus, in a classical approximation. (Trajectories are schematic, not to scale.)

Large-angle scattering for point charge

Small-angle scattering for distributed charge

electron-deuteron scattering), Hofstadter was awarded the Nobel prize in 1961.*

The reason why less large-angle scattering is produced by a distributed charge than by a point charge is shown, in a classical approximation, in Figure 25.6. Trajectories that would pass close to a point charge and experience a large deflection instead penetrate the region of the distributed charge, where the particle feels a weaker force and is less deflected. Classically, there would be some angle beyond which no particles at all are scattered. Such sharp cut-offs are unknown in quantum phenomena. The wave nature of the particles permits a few to scatter, by a diffraction mechanism, through large angles.

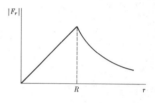

25.3   The size and shape of nuclei

Most nuclei are prolate spheroids (Figure 25.1), slightly deformed from the spherical shape in the direction of a cigar or football shape.† For many purposes, it is sufficient to regard them as spheres, with fairly well-defined boundaries. (The wave nature of matter prohibits sharp boundaries.) Nuclear radii lie between 10^{-15} m and 10^{-14} m (about 10^4 to 10^5 times less than the size of an atom), and follow approximately the formula

$$R = (1.2 \times 10^{-15} \text{ m}) \times A^{1/3}. \tag{25.7}$$

The common length unit in the nuclear domain is the femtometer, more often called the fermi:

$$1 \text{ fm} = 10^{-15} \text{ m}.$$

In this unit, nuclear radii lie between 1 and 10, and the radius formula is

$$R = 1.2A^{1/3} \text{ fm}. \tag{25.8}$$ *Nuclear radius*

The "skin thickness" of a heavy nucleus, the distance over which its density falls rapidly from a high value to a low value, is about 2 fm.

---

* Later experiments, at still higher energies, revealed a "graininess" within the proton; see Henry W. Kendall and Wolfgang Panofsky, "The Structure of the Proton and the Neutron," *Scientific American*, June, 1971.

† See Michel Baranger and Raymond A. Sorensen, "The Size and Shape of Atomic Nuclei," *Scientific American*, August, 1969.

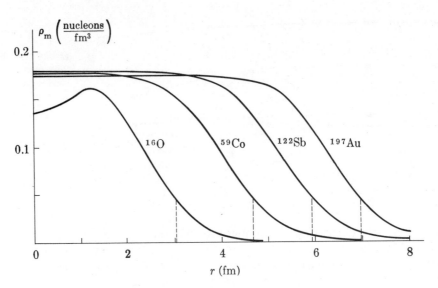

FIGURE 25.7   Density of nuclear matter in four selected nuclei. Dashed lines show the radii given by Equation 25.8.

Information on nuclear radius comes from a variety of sources. One source is "muonic atoms" (Section 27.2). Another is high-energy electron scattering, which reveals the distribution of positive charge in the nucleus. If it is postulated that the neutron density within the nucleus is approximately proportional to proton density (for which there is some evidence), distributions of nuclear matter like those shown in Figure 25.7 result. It is evident that the density in the central part of the nucleus depends very little on mass number. This approximate constancy of density is consistent with Equation 25.8, which implies that nuclear volume ($\frac{4}{3}\pi R^3$) is proportional to the mass number A. It is almost as if every nucleon represents another brick on the structure (but see Section 25.8). This is quite different from the behavior of *atomic* volume, which, except for some periodic variations, remains nearly constant, regardless of the number of electrons.

Central nuclear density is nearly constant

■ EXAMPLE 1: How does the density of nuclear matter compare with the density of normal solid matter? Nuclear density is

$$\rho_m = \frac{M}{\text{volume}} = \frac{(1.67 \times 10^{-27} \text{ kg})A}{\frac{4}{3}\pi(1.2 \times 10^{-15} \text{ m})^3 A}$$

$$= 2.3 \times 10^{17} \text{ kg/m}^3 = 2.3 \times 10^{14} \text{ gm/cm}^3.$$

This is about 10^{14} times greater than the density of a typical solid, a reflection of the fact that normal matter is mostly empty space. A lump of nuclear matter the size of a ping-pong ball would weigh 2 billion tons.   ■

The historic experiments of Rutherford and his collaborators in 1909–1911 were scattering experiments using alpha particles of energy up to 9 MeV. These alpha particles did not have sufficient energy to reach the edge of a gold nucleus, even in a head-on encounter. Therefore, the observed scattering, which was consistent with scattering from a point charge, only showed the nuclear radius to be less than some upper limit. Later experiments, with targets of lower atomic number, showed deviations from point-charge scattering, and therefore gave information on the nuclear radius [Figure 25.8(a)]. Such experiments remain of interest. An example of more recent experimental data is shown in Figure 25.8(b). Note that the differential cross section falls very rapidly at large angles, where, classically, no scattered particles would be expected. Because

Alpha-particle scattering is one source of information on nuclear size

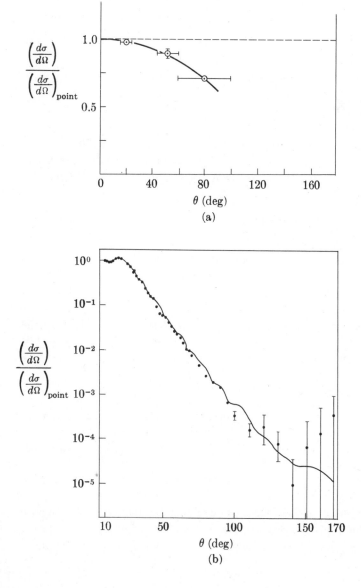

FIGURE 25.8 Differential cross sections for the scattering of alpha particles by nuclei, expressed as a ratio to the cross section expected for a point nucleus. (a) Early measurement of deviation from Coulomb scattering, for RaC alpha particles of energy 5.5 and 7.7 MeV incident on a magnesium target [E. S. Bieler, *Proceedings of the Royal Society, London*, **A105**, 434 (1924)]. (b) More recent data, for 48-MeV alpha particles scattered by lead, showing the cross section at large angles to be 10,000 times less than for a point nucleus [R. Ellis and L. Schecter, *Physical Review* **101**, 636 (1956)].

an alpha particle interacts strongly with a nucleus, its scattering is significantly influenced even by the "tail" of the nuclear surface, at a radius of about $1.4A^{1/3}$ fm.

■ EXAMPLE 2:   A 9-MeV alpha particle approaches a gold nucleus ($Z = 79$) head on. At what distance from the center of the nucleus is it turned back? At its turning point, its kinetic energy is zero, so

$$E = U.$$

If this turning point is outside the nucleus, the potential energy is

$$U = \frac{1}{4\pi\epsilon_0} \frac{2Ze^2}{r}.$$

The point of closest approach of the alpha particle is, therefore,

$$r_{min} = \frac{1}{4\pi\epsilon_0} \frac{2Ze^2}{E}. \tag{25.9}$$

Algebraic juggling can facilitate numerical evaluation

Numerical evaluation of this expression is facilitated by writing it in this way:

$$r_{min} = 2Z \left(\frac{1}{4\pi\epsilon_0} \frac{e^2}{\hbar c}\right) \left(\frac{\hbar}{mc}\right) \left(\frac{mc^2}{E}\right),$$

where m is the mass of an electron (arbitrarily introduced). The first term in parentheses is the fine-structure constant, the second is the reduced electron Compton wavelength, and the third is a dimensionless ratio of energies. Therefore,

$$r_{min} = \frac{2Z\alpha\lambda_C mc^2}{E}$$

$$= \frac{2(79/137)(386 \text{ fm})(0.511 \text{ MeV})}{9 \text{ MeV}}$$

$$= 25.3 \text{ fm}.$$

For comparison, the nuclear radius is $R = 1.2(197)^{1/3}$ fm $= 7.0$ fm; the outermost "edge" of the nucleus is about $1.4(197)^{1/3}$ fm $= 8.1$ fm. The 9-MeV alpha particle cannot reach the nucleus. ■

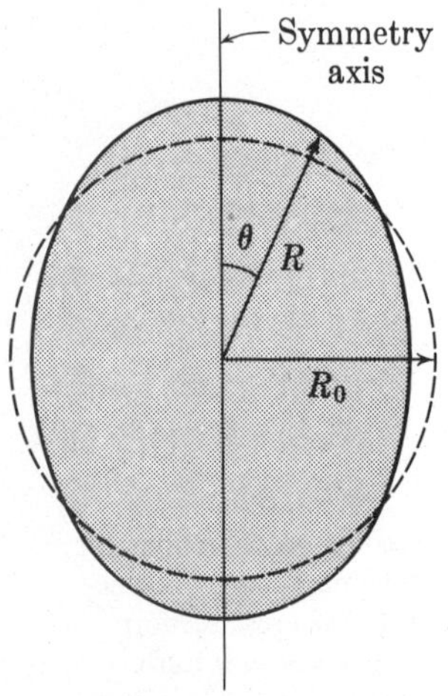

FIGURE 25.9   A spheroidal nucleus may be described by an angle-dependent radius (Equation 25.10).

NUCLEAR DEFORMATION

From a variety of sources—atomic hyperfine structure, electron scattering, muonic atoms, and others—we know that many nuclei are not spherical. A nonspherical nucleus is conveniently characterized by a deformation parameter α defined by the following formula (see Figure 25.9):

Radius of spheroid depends on angle and parameter α

$$R = R_0[1 + \alpha(\tfrac{3}{2} \cos^2 \theta - \tfrac{1}{2})]. \tag{25.10}$$

Here R is the radius of the nucleus, expressed as a function of the angle θ defined in the figure, and R_0 is the radius of a reference sphere. At its poles, the nucleus is stretched to $R = R_0(1 + \alpha)$; at its equator, it is shrunk to

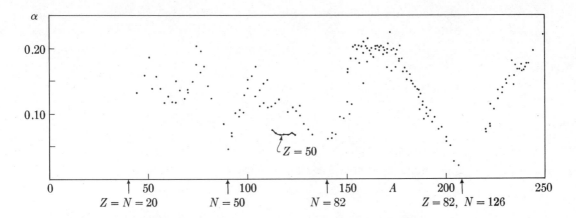

FIGURE 25.10 Nuclear deformation as a function of mass number. The parameter α is defined by Equation 25.10.

$R = R_0(1 - \frac{1}{2}\alpha)$. The particular form of the angular function is chosen so that for small α, the volumes of the deformed nucleus and the reference sphere are the same.*

Figure 25.10 presents the trend of nuclear deformations as a function of mass number. For $\alpha = 0$, a nucleus is spherical. For $\alpha > 0$, it is a prolate spheroid. For $\alpha < 0$, it would be an oblate spheroid. The reason for the regularity and periodicity of nuclear deformations will be mentioned in Section 25.8.

Deformation parameter α shows periodic variation

25.4 Energy levels and transitions

NUCLEAR ENERGY SCALE

Like other quantum systems, a nucleus has a set of stationary states of motion at discrete energy levels, between which quantum jumps can occur. On the average, nuclear binding energies are about one million times greater than atomic binding energies, and energy changes in nuclear quantum transitions are also typically about one million times greater than the energy changes of the atomic transitions responsible for the emission of visible photons. This million-fold difference in nuclear and atomic energy scales arises from the difference in *mass* of nucleons and electrons and the difference in *size* of the two systems. Application of the uncertainty principle is instructive.

$\dfrac{E_{\text{nucleus}}}{E_{\text{atom}}} \cong 10^6$

Choose any line through the center of the atom or the nucleus and call it the x axis. With respect to this line, the uncertainty principle for one particle in the system reads

$$\Delta x\, \Delta p_x \cong \hbar. \tag{25.11}$$

* The angular function, $\frac{3}{2}\cos^2\theta - \frac{1}{2}$, is called a Legendre polynomial. A standard notation for this function is $P_2(\cos\theta)$.

A suitable approximate value for Δx is R, the radius of the system, so we may write

$$(\Delta p_x)^2 \cong \frac{\hbar^2}{R^2}. \tag{25.12}$$

The uncertainty Δp_x is defined by

$$(\Delta p_x) = \sqrt{[(p_x - \overline{p_x})^2]_{av}}. \tag{25.13}$$

For a bound particle,
$\overline{p_x} = 0$

Since any particle bound in the system is confined in space, its mean component of momentum in any direction is zero: $\overline{p_x} = 0$. Therefore the uncertainty of momentum is simply related to the mean-square momentum:

$$(\Delta p_x)^2 = (p_x{}^2)_{av}.$$

For a particle moving in three dimensions, $(p_x{}^2)_{av} = \frac{1}{3}(p^2)_{av}$ (a result we made use of in Section 13.7). Equation 25.12 therefore takes the form

$$\frac{1}{3}(p^2)_{av} \cong \frac{\hbar^2}{R^2}.$$

Finally, in terms of the average kinetic energy, $K = (p^2)_{av}/2m$, the uncertainty principle for a bound particle gives

Approximate kinetic energy, according to the uncertainty principle

$$K \cong \frac{3\hbar^2}{2mR^2}. \tag{25.14}$$

The combination $\hbar^2/mR^2$, with the dimension of energy, is familiar from our treatment of a particle in a box (see Equation 23.59). To find the energy scale of an atom, we may let m be the mass of an electron and set $R = 1$ Å in Equation 25.14. The result is $K \cong 11$ eV, the correct order of magnitude. Here our special interest is the *ratio* of nuclear and atomic energy scales, which, from Equation 25.14, is

Uncertainty principle accounts for scale of atomic and nuclear energies

$$\frac{K_{\text{nuclear}}}{K_{\text{atomic}}} = \left(\frac{m_e}{m_p}\right)\left(\frac{R_{\text{atom}}}{R_{\text{nucleus}}}\right)^2, \tag{25.15}$$

in which the subscripts e and p designate electron and proton. If, as typical radii, we choose $R_{\text{atom}} = 1$ Å $= 10^5$ fm and $R_{\text{nucleus}} = 3$ fm, we get, for the energy ratio,

$$\frac{K_{\text{nuclear}}}{K_{\text{atomic}}} = \left(\frac{1}{1,836}\right)\left(\frac{10^5 \text{ fm}}{3 \text{ fm}}\right)^2 = 0.6 \times 10^6,$$

in agreement with the million-fold difference found experimentally. It is easy to remember that energies associated with outer electrons are measured in eV, whereas energies associated with nucleons in the nucleus are measured in MeV.

NUCLEAR TRANSITIONS (QUANTUM JUMPS)

Energy-level diagrams can be drawn for nuclear states just as for atomic states (Figure 25.11). Transitions between these states of motion occur in much richer variety for nuclei than for atoms. An isolated atom loses energy spontaneously

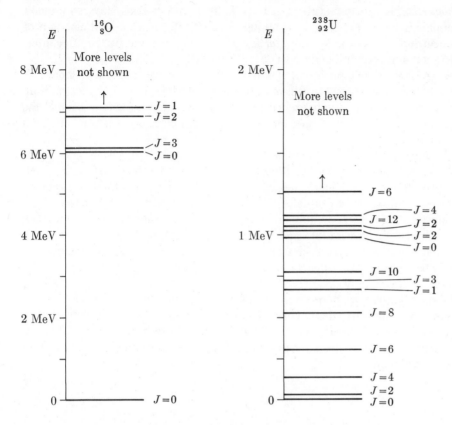

FIGURE 25.11   Partial energy-level diagrams for the same two nuclei pictured in Figure 25.1. Note that the two energy scales are not the same. The symbol *J* is the total-angular-momentum quantum number.

in only one way, by photon emission. For an isolated nucleus, four quite different modes of energy loss are possible: (1) It may, like an atom, emit a photon. This is called *gamma decay*. (2) It may emit an electron or a positron, along with an antineutrino or neutrino. In this process, called *beta decay*, the nucleus increases or decreases its charge by one unit—in short, it becomes a different nucleus, belonging to a different element. The emitted electron or positron is called a beta particle. (3) It may emit an alpha particle, the same as the nucleus of $^4_2$He, two neutrons and two protons bound together. In *alpha decay*, the nucleus literally emits a chunk of itself, losing four units of mass and two units of charge in the process. (4) It may split apart more drastically, breaking into two nearly equal fragments. This is nuclear *fission*, a process that occurs spontaneously only for the heaviest elements.

Normally, nuclei are not completely isolated; they are surrounded by orbital electrons. Two other modes of nuclear energy loss involve these electrons: (5) A nucleus may transfer its excess energy to an atomic electron causing the electron to shoot from the atom. This process, called *internal*

Six modes of spontaneous energy loss

conversion, is closely related to gamma decay. (6) A nucleus may capture and annihilate an orbital electron, simultaneous with the creation and emission of a neutrino. This process of *orbital capture* is brought about by the same interaction that is responsible for beta decay.

A few excited nuclear states have three or more alternative modes of energy loss available. Most have only one or two. Figure 25.12 illustrates an example in which a single excited nuclear state can choose among beta decay, gamma decay, and electron capture, a choice it makes according to quantum laws of probability.

Radioactivity is name for spontaneous nuclear change

Radioactivity is the spontaneous emission of energy in nuclear transitions —quantum jumps between stationary states. It includes the six processes listed above. Besides being more energetic and more diverse than atomic transitions, nuclear transitions are usually "slower"—that is, they are characterized by longer half lives. They also differ from atomic transitions in that they can transmute one element into another. Whereas the ground state of an atom is stable, enduring forever if the atom is undisturbed, the ground state of a nucleus may be unstable. Although it is the lowest energy state of that particular nucleus, alpha decay, beta decay, orbital capture, or spontaneous fission may enable it

It may involve successive transmutation

to make a quantum jump to a still lower energy state in another nucleus. In this way, radioactive decay chains can occur through a series of many nuclei. A nucleus of $^{238}_{92}$U, for instance, decays eventually to a nucleus of $^{206}_{82}$Pb, an isotope of lead with 10 fewer protons and 22 fewer neutrons than its uranium isotope parent.

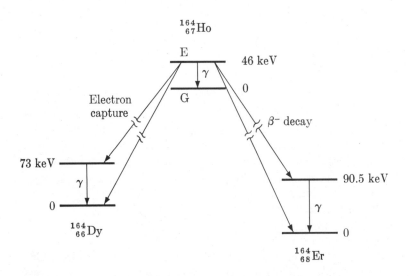

FIGURE 25.12   Excited nuclear state with three available modes of decay. The nucleus $^{164}_{67}$Ho in its excited energy state E can (a) capture an electron and emit a neutrino, transforming itself into $^{164}_{66}$Dy; (b) emit an electron and an antineutrino, transforming itself into $^{164}_{68}$Er; or (c) emit a photon, dropping down to its ground state G.

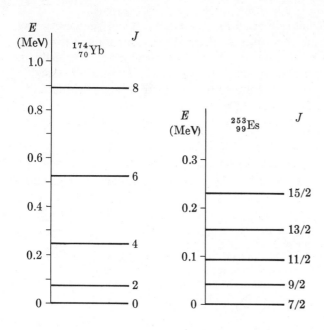

FIGURE 25.13   Two examples of rotational energy spectra. Both ^{174}Yb and ^{253}Es are strongly deformed nuclei. (See also the ^{238}U spectrum in Figure 25.11.)

ROTATIONAL STATES

A nucleus, like a molecule, cannot rotate about a symmetry axis—more exactly stated, it cannot acquire any energy in such a mode of motion. A spherical nucleus can be likened to a spherically symmetric atom. Every axis is a symmetry axis, so it has no rotational states. A deformed nucleus is more like a diatomic molecule. It has one symmetry axis and can rotate about an axis perpendicular to its symmetry axis. Most nuclei of substantial deformation exhibit rotational energy spectra with energies given by (compare Equation 24.58)

Deformed nuclei can rotate

$$E_{\text{rot}} = \frac{\hbar^2}{2I} \left[J(J + 1) - J_0(J_0 + 1) \right], \qquad (25.16)$$

where J is the angular-momentum quantum number of the excited rotational state, J_0 is the angular-momentum quantum number of the ground state, and I is the moment of inertia. The moment of inertia of a deformed nucleus is not a simple concept because it depends on details of the motion of nucleons within the nucleus. We mention only that I increases as the deformation parameter α (Equation 25.10) increases so that rotational energy states have the least energy for the most deformed nuclei. Two examples of nuclear rotational energy spectra appear in Figure 25.13. Note that the excitation energies are relatively small.

Greater α means greater I and lower energy

25.5   Charting nuclei

Except for very subtle isotopic differences, atomic properties depend on only a single number, the atomic number. Nuclear properties, by contrast, depend in an important way on two different numbers, the proton number and the neutron number. Nuclei of different isotopes of the same element can be in every way as distinct as nuclei of different elements. Because nuclei are built of two basic particles, a chart of the nuclei requires a two-dimensional array. Typically, in such a chart, proton number is plotted vertically, neutron number horizontally. A modern nuclear chart contains entries for more than 1,500 known nuclei.

LIGHT NUCLEI

Figure 25.14 shows the lower left corner of a chart of the nuclei, beginning with the single proton ($Z = 1$, $N = 0$) and the single neutron ($Z = 0$, $N = 1$). The shaded boxes indicate stable nuclei. The others are radioactive. The numbers

FIGURE 25.14   Small portion of a chart of the nuclei. Proton number (or atomic number) is plotted vertically, neutron number horizontally. The shaded boxes represent stable nuclei. The unshaded boxes represent unstable nuclei. Alpha decay, beta decay, and orbital capture are indicated by the letters α, β, and c. Other features of the chart are discussed in the text.

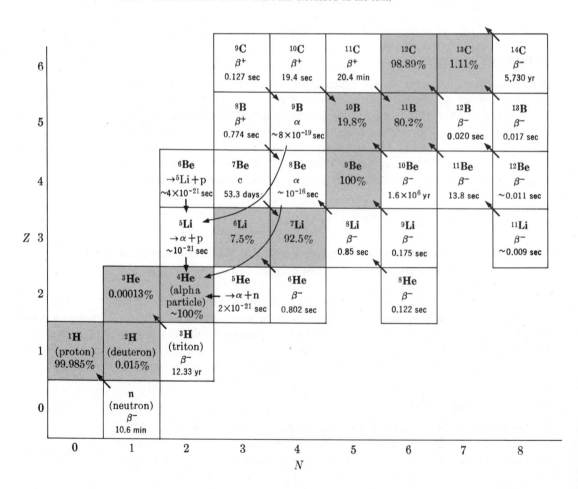

in the shaded boxes show the percentage abundance of that isotope in nature. In the unshaded boxes are shown the half life of the nucleus and the mode of its decay. Many other nuclear properties are known, of course, but no attempt is made to summarize them in this chart.

Beginning with hydrogen, we see three isotopes, ^{1}H, ^{2}H, and ^{3}H, containing 0, 1, and 2 neutrons respectively. The nucleus of ^{1}H is of course the proton. The nucleus of ^{2}H is the deuteron; the nucleus of ^{3}H is called a triton. Deuterons, making up 0.015 percent of hydrogen nuclei, are stable. The triton, with a half life of 12.26 years, undergoes beta decay, transforming itself into ^{3}He, a nucleus with two protons and one neutron. For this and other examples of beta decay with emission of an electron, short arrows pointing to the left and upward show the direction of the transformation. Beta decay with emission of a positron is indicated by a short arrow to the right and downward, as from ^{10}C to ^{10}B. Also indicated by an arrow to the right and downward is the closely related process of orbital electron capture. For instance, ^{7}Be transforms itself into ^{7}Li by means of orbital capture, with a half life of 53 days. Also shown in this small part of the chart of nuclei are two examples of alpha decay. One of them, the decay mode of ^{8}Be, is a very special example; when ^{8}Be emits an alpha particle, what is left behind is also an alpha particle. Actually, the alpha decay of ^{8}Be is equivalent to spontaneous fission because the nucleus breaks into equal fragments that fly apart with equal speed. The transformation can be written as

Rich variety, even among the lightest nuclei

$$^8_4\text{Be} \rightarrow {}^4_2\text{He} + {}^4_2\text{He}.$$

As shown in Figure 25.14, the half life of this decay is only about 3×10^{-16} sec. By contrast, a nucleus containing two more neutrons, ^{10}Be, has a half life of 2.7 million years. In between is ^{9}Be, a stable nucleus.

All of the unstable nuclei in Figure 25.14 are said to be artificially radioactive. This means that they have been created and studied in the laboratory but that they are not found in nature, at least not to an appreciable extent.* Naturally radioactive nuclei are those found in nature. The distinction between natural and artificial radioactivity is itself somewhat artificial, especially since man has learned how to cause large-scale nuclear reactions. Many isotopes not found in nature before 1952 are now found in nature.

Artificial and natural radioactivity

THE LINE OF STABILITY

It is clear in Figure 25.14 that the stable nuclei of low mass cluster approximately along the line of equal proton and neutron number. As is shown in Figure 25.15, the path traced through the nuclear chart by the stable nuclei starts out in this way, then bends over increasingly in the direction of a neutron excess. For the heaviest nuclei, the line of stability, as this path is called, has a slope corresponding to the addition of about two neutrons for every added proton and not the one-to-one ratio that characterizes the light nuclei. Also, as Figure 25.15 makes

---

* Carbon 14, although very rare in nature, is valuable because of its role in archaeological dating.

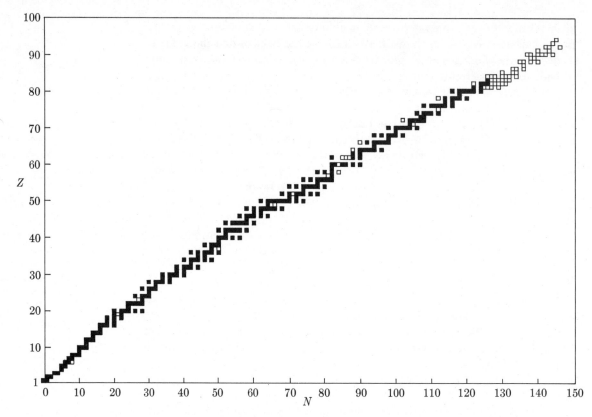

FIGURE 25.15   Nuclear chart.   Dark squares indicate stable nuclei; open squares indicate unstable or radioactive nuclei found in nature.   Artificially radioactive nuclei are not included in this chart.

Why does the line of stability bend and end?

clear, the line of stability ends.   Beyond a certain point, there are no stable nuclei, nor even any long-lived nuclei.   Both aspects of the line of stability, its shape and its termination, can be explained rather simply in terms of two effects: the action of the Pauli exclusion principle, and the action of the electrical repulsive force between protons.

Exclusion principle

The exclusion principle favors $N = Z$

Protons and neutrons, like electrons, obey the exclusion principle.   Because of this, there is a strong tendency for the neutron and proton number to be equal.   If a proton occupies a given state of motion within the nucleus, an added proton must go into a different state of motion, often with greater energy.   An added neutron, on the other hand, can drop into the same state of motion as the proton, since no exclusion acts between neutrons and protons.   Moreover, once in identical states of motion, a neutron and a proton are in the most favorable position to experience maximum attractive force and to contribute as much as possible to the binding energy.

Coulomb energy

Were it not for electrical forces in the nucleus, the line of stability would follow equal neutron and proton number indefinitely. Rather than some 100 elements, we might have thousands. The mutual electrical repulsion of protons both bends and ends the line of stability. Only because of the great strength of the nuclear forces can protons be held together in a nucleus at all. The greater the number of protons, the greater is their tendency to blow the nucleus apart. Associated with each pair of protons in the nucleus is a potential energy $e^2/4\pi\epsilon_0 r$. Since the total number of pairs is $\frac{1}{2}Z(Z-1)$, the total electric potential energy of the nucleus is

$$U_{\text{Coul}} = \frac{1}{2} Z(Z-1) \frac{e^2}{4\pi\epsilon_0} \left(\frac{1}{r}\right)_{\text{av}}, \tag{25.17}$$

where $(1/r)_{\text{av}}$ is the average inverse distance between all pairs of protons. For protons spread uniformly throughout a sphere of radius R, $(1/r)_{\text{av}} = 6/(5R)$, so

Positive energy associated with proton repulsion

$$U_{\text{Coul}} = \frac{3}{5} \frac{1}{4\pi\epsilon_0} \frac{Z(Z-1)e^2}{R}. \tag{25.18}$$

For the present discussion, the important fact about U_{Coul} is its proportionality to $Z(Z-1)$. This positive potential energy, working against the negative potential energy of the nuclear forces, increases rapidly in magnitude as Z increases. Therefore, despite the action of the exclusion principle, it becomes energetically favorable for heavy nuclei to contain more neutral particles than charged particles. Eventually, beyond 83 protons, there are no stable nuclei at all. Beyond 101 protons, no nuclei with half lives greater than an hour have been discovered. Figure 25.16 shows in detail the present limits of exploration in the upper right end of the chart of nuclei. According to present theory, as Z increases beyond 100, half lives should drop sharply at first and then rise to a peak possibly as great as 10^8 years in an "island" of semistable nuclei around $Z = 110$ to 114, and $N = 184$.* Intensive searches for such nuclei are now underway. Their predicted existence is related to the nuclear shell model (Section 25.8).

Extension of knowledge to $Z \cong 114$ is likely

■ EXAMPLE: Carbon 13, with 6 proton and 7 neutrons, and nitrogen 13, with 7 protons and 6 neutrons, are so-called "mirror nuclei." It is believed that they should have the same radius and that the contribution of nuclear forces to their binding energies should be equal. Their measured binding energies are

Mirror nuclei

$$B(^{13}_{6}\text{C}) = 93.2 \text{ MeV}, \qquad B(^{13}_{7}\text{N}) = 90.2 \text{ MeV}.$$

What do these numbers imply about the radius of the nuclei if the binding energy difference is attributable entirely to the Coulomb energy? From Equation 25.18,

$$U_{\text{Coul}}(Z+1) - U_{\text{Coul}}(Z) = \frac{3}{5} \frac{1}{4\pi\epsilon_0} \frac{e^2}{R} [(Z+1)Z - Z(Z-1)];$$

---

* See Glenn T. Seaborg and Justin L. Bloom, "The Synthetic Elements: IV," *Scientific American*, April, 1969; also James Rayford Nix, "Predictions for Superheavy Nuclei," *Physics Today*, April, 1972.

Z	N=150	151	152	153	154	155	156	157	158
105 Hahnium						^{260}Ha α 1.6 sec	^{261}Ha α, (f?) 1.8 sec	^{262}Ha α 40 sec	
104 Rutherfordium				^{257}Rf ? α 4.8 sec	^{258}Rf ? f 11 msec	^{259}Rf α, (f?) 3 sec	^{260}Rf ? f 0.1 sec	^{261}Rf α 65 sec	
103 Lawrencium			^{255}Lr α 2.2 sec	^{256}Lr α 31 sec	^{257}Lr α 0.6 sec	^{258}Lr α 4.2 sec	^{259}Lr α 5.4 sec	^{260}Lr α 180 sec	
102 Nobelium	^{252}No α, f 2.3 sec	^{253}No α 105 sec	^{254}No γ | α, f; 0.2 sec | 55 sec	^{255}No α 200 sec	^{256}No α, f 3.2 sec	^{257}No α 26 sec	^{258}No? f 1.2 msec	^{259}No α, f 57 min	
101 Mendelevium	^{251}Md c, α 4 min	^{252}Md c 8 min		^{254}Md c | c; 28 min | 10 min	^{255}Md c, α 27 min	^{256}Md c, α 77 min	^{257}Md c, α, f 5.0 hr	^{258}Md α 54 days	
100 Fermium	^{250}Fm γ | α; 1.8 sec | 30 min	^{251}Fm c, α 7 hr	^{252}Fm α, f 23 hr	^{253}Fm c, α 3.0 days	^{254}Fm α, f 3.24 hr	^{255}Fm α, f 20.1 hr	^{256}Fm f, α 2.6 hr	^{257}Fm α, f 82 days	^{258}Fm f 380 μsec

$N \longrightarrow$

FIGURE 25.16   Portion of a chart of the nuclei showing the heaviest known nuclei. Numbers in the boxes show half lives of the nuclei. Modes of decay are indicated by α (alpha), γ (gamma), c (electron capture), and f (fission). All nuclei can emit gamma rays. Gamma decay is shown as a mode of decay in this chart only for nuclei in which it is a relatively long-lived process—a so-called isomeric transition. (Data supplied by Albert Ghiorso, Lawrence Radiation Laboratory, University of California, Berkeley.)

the predicted binding-energy difference is

$$\Delta U = \frac{6Z}{5} \frac{1}{4\pi\epsilon_0} \frac{e^2}{R}. \tag{25.19}$$

In SI units, ΔU is (3.0 MeV)(1.60 $\times$ 10^{-13} J/MeV) = 4.8 $\times$ 10^{-13} J. For the radius, we therefore find

Another way to gain information on nuclear radii

$$R = \frac{6Z}{5} \frac{1}{4\pi\epsilon_0} \frac{e^2}{\Delta U}$$

$$= \frac{6 \times 6}{5} \frac{(9 \times 10^9)(1.60 \times 10^{-19})^2}{4.8 \times 10^{-13}}$$

$$= 3.5 \times 10^{-15} \text{ m} = 3.5 \text{ fm.}$$

(Note that this calculation could also have been carried out conveniently in the manner of Example 2 in Section 25.3.)   ■

TREND OF NUCLEAR BINDING ENERGY

Along the line of stability, as shown in Figure 25.17, the nuclear binding energy per nucleon rises quickly in the light elements, has a broad maximum, and declines slowly in the medium-weight and heavy elements. The most remarkable fact about this B/A curve is its near constancy. The binding energy of almost every nucleus lies between 7 MeV/nucleon and 9 MeV/nucleon. Nevertheless, the differences, small though they appear, are important. A uranium nucleus, when it divides by fission into two lighter nuclei, gains almost 1 MeV of extra binding per nucleon, or about 200 MeV altogether, which is released as kinetic energy and accounts for the explosive energy of fission bombs. For every light nucleus, binding energy is gained by fusion rather than fission.

The rise of the binding-energy curve for light nuclei comes about from the increase in the number of nucleons able to exert attractive forces on one another. Were it not for electrical forces, the curve would tend to flatten out, but it would not fall. It is the mutual repulsion of protons that drags the binding energy curve downward for heavy nuclei and makes it energetically attractive for heavy nuclei to split into lighter nuclei.

Coulomb energy pulls down B/A curve at large A

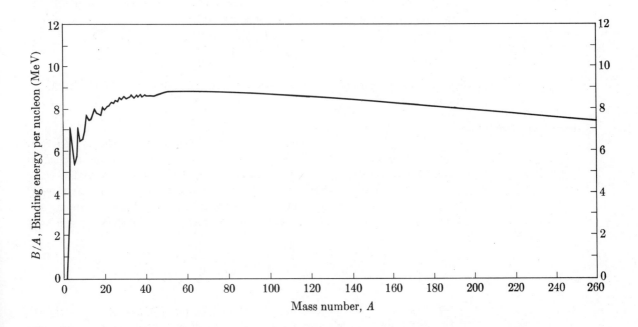

FIGURE 25.17   Binding energy per nucleon along the line of stability.

25.6   Pions and the nuclear force

Nuclear force: strong and of short range

The discovery of the nuclear force can be said to have coincided with the discovery of the neutron because as soon as the view of nuclei as aggregates of nucleons emerged, it was clear that there must exist a new kind of force—the nuclear force—with two important properties: It must be considerably stronger than the electrical force, because it holds protons together within the nucleus in spite of their electrical repulsion; and it also must act only over very short distances, not more than 10^{-14} m (10 fm) because nuclei are no larger than this, and their effect upon passing particles extends no farther than this. It was mainly to explain the second fact, the short range of the strong interactions, that Hideki Yukawa in 1935 postulated the existence of the pion, a particle whose exchange among the nucleons was supposed to generate the nuclear force.

To understand the pion's role, we must deal with a very important idea in contemporary thinking about the submicroscopic world, the idea of a "virtual particle." This idea provides a beautiful example of the workings of the Heisenberg uncertainty principle, and it helps to explain not only the strong interactions but all forces and all interactions.

The forms of the uncertainty principle that we have considered so far are

$$\Delta x \, \Delta p_x \cong \hbar,$$

$$\Delta y \, \Delta p_y \cong \hbar,$$

$$\Delta z \, \Delta p_z \cong \hbar.$$

These involve components of the position vector **r** and the momentum vector **p**. It is natural to suppose that the *fourth* components (the time components) of these vectors should also satisfy an uncertainty relation:

$$\Delta(ct) \, \Delta \left(\frac{E}{c}\right) \cong \hbar.$$

This is indeed a correct formula, which we may write more conveniently without factors of c:

Time-energy form of uncertainty principle

$$\Delta t \, \Delta E \cong \hbar; \tag{25.20}$$

the uncertainty of time (Δt) multiplied by the uncertainty of energy (ΔE) is approximately equal to $\hbar$.* This means that a precise measurement of energy (small ΔE) requires a long time (large Δt). Or if an event occurs at a very precisely known time (small Δt), its energy cannot be accurately determined (large ΔE). Never can time and energy both be precisely known at once. In particular, tests of the law of energy conservation require processes extending over some time.

Both the position-momentum and time-energy versions of the uncertainty principle can be understood in terms of the wave nature of matter. Just as a

---

* The uncertainty principle applies to many other measurable quantities as well. Any two quantities satisfying an uncertainty relation are called *conjugate variables*. Angular momentum about some axis and angle measured about the axis, for example, are conjugate variables, and $\Delta L_z \, \Delta \varphi \cong \hbar$.

wave cannot be confined in a region of space significantly smaller than its own wavelength, so it cannot be pinpointed in a time interval much shorter than one period of its vibration. The only way to further squeeze a wave in space is to shorten its wavelength; the only way to squeeze it more in time is to shorten its period (increase its frequency). However, the higher the frequency, the higher the energy. To confine a wave in space means mixing different wavelengths and, therefore, different momenta. To confine it in time means mixing different frequencies and, therefore, different energies. The wave nature of matter leads in a simple way to the time-energy uncertainty just as it led to the position-momentum uncertainty.

It is related to properties of waves confined in time

When nucleons collide at high energy, pion production is quite probable. A typical process of pion creation can be written symbolically,

$$p + p \rightarrow p + n + \pi^+.$$

A high-energy proton strikes a proton at rest in a target and from the collision emerge a proton, a neutron, and a positive pion. The simplest interpretation of this event is to say that one of the protons breaks up into a neutron and a pion:

$$p \rightarrow n + \pi^+.$$

This process obeys all the conservation laws but one—energy. The masses of neutron and pion add up to considerably more than the proton mass, so a single free proton left to itself would never decay in this way; to do so, it would need to violate energy conservation. But when it is struck by another energetic proton, some of the energy of motion in the collision can be converted to mass energy and the process becomes allowed.

Neither pions, nor accelerators energetic enough to make them, were known to Yukawa. However, he postulated the particle and initiated the theory of its strong interaction with nucleons that now accounts for its production. An essential idea in this theory is that processes such as

$$p \rightarrow n + \pi^+$$
$$n \rightarrow p + \pi^-$$

Energy is needed for these strong-interaction processes

are processes of high probability. Real pions are created in this way when energy is supplied in a collision. Even without extra energy, virtual pions can be created in this way. A virtual particle is one with a transitory existence, permitted by the uncertainty principle to endure briefly but prohibited by the conservation of energy from flying away as an independent free particle.

A virtual particle momentarily violates energy conservation

The spontaneous transformation of a proton, with a rest energy of about 940 MeV, into a neutron and a pion, with a combined rest energy of 1,080 MeV, requires an energy uncertainty ΔE of at least 140 MeV. The uncertainty principle sets the time limit for this "violation" of energy conservation:

$$\Delta t \cong \frac{\hbar}{\Delta E}. \tag{25.21}$$

Dividing $\hbar$ (6.6×10^{-22} MeV sec) by ΔE (140 MeV) gives the time uncertainty, $\Delta t = 4.7 \times 10^{-24}$ sec, a very short time indeed. In this time, a pion can move no farther than $c \, \Delta t$, or 1.4×10^{-15} m (1.4 fm).

According to this new view, nucleons are far from quiescent. A proton, even when all alone, is in a constant state of activity. It may eject and then immediately (after less than 10^{-23} sec) recall a positive pion,

$$p \leftrightarrow n + \pi^+.$$

The double arrows indicate the two-way nature of the process. Or it may eject and recall a neutral pion,

$$p \leftrightarrow p + \pi^0.$$

Explanation of the size of the proton

Because the interaction responsible for this activity is strong, these processes occur repeatedly and the proton must be regarded as a center of continual activity. The virtual pions, held within little more than 1 fm of their parent nucleon, can never leave a track in a bubble chamber or trigger a counter. Nevertheless, extensive indirect evidence, such as that provided by the scattering of high-energy electrons by nucleons (Figure 25.5), makes their existence almost certain. According to general quantum-mechanical principles, the cloud of virtual particles surrounding a proton must be regarded as a superposition of different states, some with one pion, some with two pions, some with one pion and one eta particle, etc. Because these states coexist simultaneously, it is somewhat of an oversimplification to think only in terms of sequential processes of emission and absorption of virtual particles. Nevertheless, the uncertainty principle gives the essential explanation of the limited range of the virtual particles.

The final step in this line of reasoning has to do with the force between two nucleons. All that the uncertainty principle requires is that each virtual pion in the cloud surrounding the proton must vanish almost immediately after it is created, to clear the books of this excess mass energy. If a nucleon stands alone, the pion must be reabsorbed by the same nucleon from which it emerged. But if two are close together, a pion could be emitted by one and absorbed by the other. Suppose, for instance, that a neutron approaches close to a proton. At a particular instant, the proton may have transformed itself momentarily into a neutron and a positive pion. The other neutron can absorb the pion to become, itself, a proton. The net result is that a pion has jumped across from proton to neutron and, in the process, proton and neutron have changed roles. Yukawa

Pion exchange force

realized that this kind of pion exchange could produce a strong attractive force between the two nucleons, a force now called an exchange force (Figure 25.18).

Further explanation of the exchange force is beyond the scope of this book. One aspect of the force, however, is easily understood. The energy uncertainty associated with the creation of a virtual particle of mass m is $\Delta E = mc^2$. From Equation 25.21, the time uncertainty is $\Delta t = \hbar/mc^2$. The range of the exchange force is $d = c \, \Delta t$, the distance the particle can move in this time if its speed is near the speed of light. This range is

Range of an exchange force

$$d = \frac{\hbar}{mc}, \tag{25.22}$$

which is the reduced Compton wavelength of the exchange particle. For a pion, $d = 1.4$ fm. Since he knew roughly the range of the nuclear force,

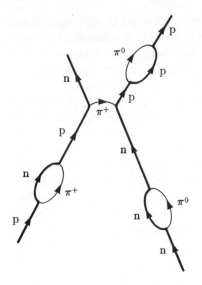

FIGURE 25.18   The mechanism of an exchange force. Well-separated nucleons may emit and reabsorb virtual pions. Close together, the nucleons may exchange virtual pions (or other mesons), a process that creates a force between them. Although this diagram contains the essence of what goes on, it is very highly oversimplified.

Yukawa was able to predict approximately the mass of the pion. Mass and range are inversely proportional. The pion, being the lightest strongly interacting particle, is responsible for the longest-range part of the nuclear force. Two nucleons, separated by about 1 fm or more, experience an interaction energy given by

$$U = -A\,\frac{e^{-r/d}}{r},$$
(25.23)

Potential energy produced by particle exchange

where A is a constant. Note that, for $r > d$, the exponential factor causes the interaction energy to fall rapidly to zero. For r less than about 1 fm, Equation 25.23 is not valid. Two nucleons, when sufficiently close together, experience a strong repulsion (Figure 25.19).

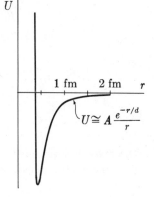

FIGURE 25.19   Approximate form of the inter-nucleon potential energy. The vertical scale extends over several hundred MeV. Actually, the interaction energy depends not only on the separation of the particles, but on their relative spin and their relative orbital angular momentum.

Yukawa was not the first to propose particle exchange as a mechanism of force. In fact, he built on an exchange theory of electromagnetic force that had been developed about five years earlier. Fermi and Dirac had shown that the

Electric and magnetic forces are photon-exchange forces

ordinary electric force between two charged particles could be attributed to the incessant exchange of photons between the particles. In this beautiful application of the new quantum mechanics to the centuries-old problem of electric force, they unified the description of photon emission, photon absorption, and electromagnetic interaction. To put it another way, exactly the same theory that explains how atoms gain and lose energy also explains how they are held together. Since photons are massless, the "range" of the electric force is infinite (Equation 25.22). Note that the substitution $d = \infty$ in Equation 25.23 gives $U = -A/r$, a Coulomb potential energy. The fact that this energy diminishes inversely with distance is a manifestation of the geometry of three-dimensional space, not a reflection of any inhibition on how far out the exchange photons can reach. It is a familiar fact that electric forces act over macroscopic distances. The truly short-range nuclear force, on the other hand, has no significant effect over a distance greater than a few fermis.

25.7   Stabilization of the neutron

Another fact about nuclear force needs to be discussed, not because it illustrates any new ideas or points to areas of ignorance but because of its enormous practical significance. This is the stabilization of the neutron. If a neutron were not stabilized in the presence of one or more protons, the world would have not 92 elements occurring naturally but only one: hydrogen. A neutron alone undergoes the beta decay process, transforming to proton, electron, and antineutrino after an average time of 16 min. Within a nucleus, it can acquire an infinite lifetime, making possible the building of all the elements heavier than hydrogen.

Let us calculate first how much energy is released when a free neutron decays. As the following numbers make clear, a single neutron is "barely" unstable.

Before	*After*
$m_n = 1.008665$ amu	$m_p = 1.007277$ amu
	$m_e = 0.000549$ amu
	$m_{\bar{\nu}} = 0$
	——————————
	$m_{total} = 1.007826$ amu

Decay of free neutron

————Allowed Decay———→

The mass difference is 0.000839 amu. Multiplication by $c^2 = 931.5$ MeV/amu gives the energy release, 0.782 MeV, about 0.08 percent of the rest energy of the neutron.

For allowed nuclear decay, mass of system must decrease

If a neutron in a nucleus decays, what is important is not the mass difference between the neutron and its products but the mass change of the whole system. Only if the mass of the system decreases is the decay possible. Consider the stable nucleus $^{20}_{10}\text{Ne}$, for example. If one of its 10 neutrons followed its normal inclination for beta decay, an electron and antineutrino would shoot out, leaving behind the nucleus $^{20}_{11}\text{Na}$. This nucleus of sodium is less tightly bound than the neon 20 nucleus, less by about 16 MeV. The difference in binding energy much more than offsets the mass decrease associated with changing one neutron to a proton. The mass of the supposed products ($^{20}_{11}$Na nucleus + electron + antineutrino) is greater than the mass of the parent ($^{20}_{10}$Ne nucleus), and the decay does not occur.

The stabilization of the neutron can be attributed primarily to the exclusion principle. In the example just discussed, the 10 protons in $^{20}_{10}$Ne can be thought of as occupying 10 distinct quantum states, with the 10 neutrons occupying the *same* set of states as the protons. If one neutron is changed to a proton, the new proton must occupy an eleventh state at greater energy than the first ten. For heavier nuclei, with $N > Z$, the Coulomb energy of the protons is also important, but the exclusion principle still plays an essential role. For neutron stabilization, it is also necessary, of course, that the nuclear force be strong enough to produce binding energies per particle that are greater than the energy of the neutron-proton mass difference. Were neutron and proton not so close together in mass, it would perhaps be a very different world.

Role of the exclusion principle

Role of strong nuclear force

The deuteron, the simplest nucleus that contains a neutron, is an interesting special case. It is more stable than a pair of protons because of a rather peculiar "chance," that the pion exchange force between two nucleons is somewhat stronger if the spins of the particles are parallel than if they are antiparallel. In the deuteron, the neutron and the proton share a common quantum state, with all quantum numbers, including their spin-orientation quantum number, the same. If the neutron were to undergo beta decay, the deuteron would suddenly become a pair of protons. Because of the exclusion principle, these two particles cannot occupy exactly the same state of motion. One of the protons must flip its spin. Then, however, their attractive force is slightly diminished. Although the change of interaction strength is not great, it is enough to make the difference between binding and no binding. The protons release their hold on each other and come apart. In this hypothetical decay process, the masses before and after compare as follows:

Spin-dependence of nuclear force accounts for deuteron stability

Before	After
m_d = 2.01355 amu	m_p = 1.00728 amu
	m_p = 1.00728 amu
	m_e = 0.00055 amu
	$m_{\bar{\nu}}$ = 0
	m_{total} = 2.01511 amu

——Forbidden Decay——→

The gain in going from heavier neutron to lighter proton plus electron is more than offset by the loss of binding energy. The deuteron is stable—no doubt a fortunate fact for man. This particle is an essential link in the nuclear cycle that lights the sun. And, if we are to meet our long-range energy needs in the future, it will probably have to be with the help of the plentiful deuterium in the ocean, used as thermonuclear fuel.

So thanks to the exclusion principle, to the smallness of the neutron-proton mass difference, and to slight spin-dependence of nuclear forces, the world has

The "miracle" of neutron stabilization

some 90 atomic building blocks rather than just one, and we are warmed to an agreeable temperature by a friendly sun. In terms of our present knowledge of elementary-particle interactions, we must regard this state of affairs as miraculous.

25.8   Nuclear shell structure

Probably the most striking fact about the modern description of nuclei is the success of the independent-particle approximation (analogous to the central-field approximation in atoms). Each nucleon in the nucleus moves throughout the nuclear volume in an average field of force created by the other nucleons. At least to a fairly good approximation, each nucleon occupies its own quantum state of motion independent of the details of the motion of other nucleons. This means that nuclear structure bears many points of similarity to atomic structure, a quite remarkable fact—a fact that physicists recognized and accepted only after the weight of experimental evidence forced them to do so.

Marked differences between atoms and nuclei

A nucleus has no massive center of force, as an atom does. In the nucleus, nucleons all share the same volume, in contrast to the partial separation in space of different electron shells in atoms. Nuclear forces are strong, and each nucleon in the nucleus is always within range of several other nucleons. These are some of the reasons that the approximately independent motion of nucleons within the nucleus seems surprising. In the 1930s, a heavy nucleus was looked upon as a system physically more like a liquid than like a gas. The fact that nuclear volume increases in proportion to the number of nucleons is consistent *The liquid-droplet model* with this "liquid-droplet model" of the nucleus. The fact that a high-energy proton or neutron striking the nucleus is almost sure to disrupt the nucleus rather than pass through it undisturbed is also consistent with the liquid-droplet model. The most stunning success of the liquid-droplet model came *It accounted for fission* in 1939 when Niels Bohr and John Wheeler used it as the basis of the theory of nuclear fission. An important ingredient of their theory (see Section 26.6) was the concept of nuclear surface tension. An ordinary liquid derives its surface tension from the fact that molecules at the surface, being only half surrounded by other molecules, are less tightly bound than molecules in the interior. As a result, a drop of liquid tends to minimize its surface area by assuming a spherical shape. If nucleons in the nucleus behave like molecules in a liquid, the nucleus too should form a spherical droplet. Also, like a liquid droplet, the nucleus should be capable of deformation and fission. According to the theory of Bohr and Wheeler, the Coulomb repulsion between the protons could, under certain circumstances, overcome the force of surface tension and cause the nucleus to split.

Despite the successes of the liquid-droplet model of the nucleus, certain bits of evidence began to accumulate in the late 1940s that pointed to a very different view of nuclear structure. *Periodicity* of nuclear properties began to show up, not unlike some of the periodicities of atomic properties and quite unlike the smooth regularity of properties to be expected of nuclei that behave like liquid droplets. Nuclear spins and nuclear binding energies showed a pattern consistent with independent motion of nucleons in a set of individual quantum states of motion within the nucleus. For certain particular numbers

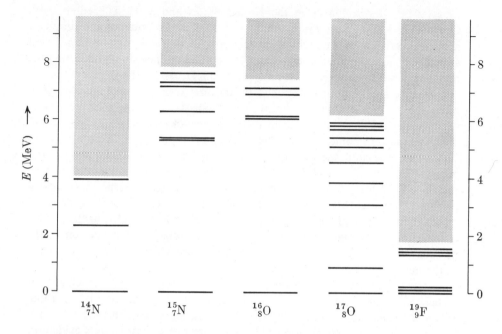

FIGURE 25.20   The first few energy levels in each of several light nuclei. The unusual stability associated with eight neutrons or eight protons is reflected in higher-than-normal excitation energies. In ^{16}O, with 8 neutrons and 8 protons, the energy of the first excited state is particularly high. (The shaded regions contain many additional energy levels whose number and position are unknown.)

of neutrons and/or protons, nuclei showed unusual stability, much as the rare-gas atoms show unusual stability. These numbers, known at first as the "magic numbers," are

$$2, 8, 20, 28, 50, 82, 126.$$

The "magic numbers"
(for Z and N)

One striking effect of the magic numbers is shown in Figure 25.20, which compares the set of energy levels up to a few MeV of excitation for several light nuclei. In the "doubly magic" nucleus of $^{16}_{8}O$ (8 neutrons and 8 protons), considerable energy is required to excite the nucleus. In "singly-magic" $^{17}_{8}O$ (9 neutrons and 8 protons), less energy separates the ground state and the first excited state. In $^{19}_{9}F$, containing neither 8 protons nor 8 neutrons, the low-energy levels are clustered even closer together.

Apart from the evidence on periodicity associated with certain special numbers, new experiments on the scattering of neutrons by nuclei began to indicate that at low energy the neutron had in fact a good chance to pass right through the nucleus, deflected by the average action of all the nucleons but not stopped or impeded by single encounters. Finally, the evidence was too strong to ignore. Surely nucleons in the nucleus, like electrons in the atom, move approximately independently in an average field of force, successively filling allowed states of motion. In independent papers published at about the same

New evidence favored the
independent-particle model

time (1949), Maria Mayer in the United States and J. H. D. Jensen (with O. Haxel and H. E. Suess) in Germany summarized the evidence and proposed a nuclear version of the central-field approximation with its resultant shell structure.* The magic numbers ceased to be magic. They simply indicated the numbers of protons or neutrons required to fill successive shells.

Its justification: 1. Again the exclusion principle

Despite the surprise occasioned by the first discovery that nucleons can move relatively freely within the nucleus, theorists (who are good at finding reasons after the fact) have since justified this view of the nucleus. The independence of nucleons comes in part from the exclusion principle. A proton in one state of motion cannot collide with another nucleon and be "scattered" into a different state of motion if that other state of motion is already occupied by a proton. Therefore, the nuclear particles tend to remain in specific states of motion. These theorists also emphasize that the nuclear force, although a "strong" interaction, is only barely strong enough to hold nuclei together. This is indicated by the fact that the average binding energy of a nucleon in the nucleus (about 8 MeV) is much less than the average kinetic energy of a nucleon in the nucleus (about 40 MeV).

2. Nuclear force is not "too" strong

Nuclear deformations confirm shell structure

One of the strong supports for the independent-particle model and its associated shell structure results from observations of nuclear deformation. When neutrons and protons occupy closed shells, nuclei are spherical. Partially filled shells lead to deformation.† The periodicity of deformation is evident in Figure 25.10.

★NUCLEON QUANTUM NUMBERS

1s state holds 2 protons and 2 neutrons

In nuclei, as in atoms, the lowest state of particle motion has principal quantum number 1, and orbital angular momentum zero. Because of the two possible spin orientations, this energy level holds two identical particles. Since the exclusion principle, which governs neutrons and protons separately, does not act between neutrons and protons, two overlapping and interpenetrating sets of particle states must be visualized, one set for protons and one for neutrons. The alpha particle, or helium 4 nucleus, with two protons and two neutrons, is the simplest doubly-closed-shell nucleus (previously called a doubly magic nucleus). The nucleus of helium 3 has a closed shell of two protons but an unclosed shell of one neutron.

Shape of potential dictates order of states

As shown in Figure 25.21, particle states of motion fill in a somewhat different order in nuclei than in atoms. The difference has two sources. One is the quite different shapes of the potential energy curves for the two structures (Figure 25.22). Because of this difference, the second proton shell is completed at $Z = 8$ (oxygen) and not at $Z = 10$ (neon). The quantum numbers of the second shell are

$$n = 2, \quad \ell = 1.$$

---

* In 1963, Mayer and Jensen shared the Nobel Prize with Eugene Wigner, another pioneer in modern nuclear theory.

† Partially filled electron shells do not deform atoms, because the nucleus remains as a center of force in the atom. Inside the nucleus there is no such fixed center of force.

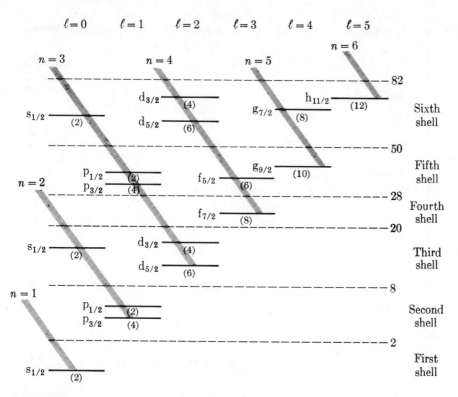

FIGURE 25.21   Approximate arrangement of first 82 states of motion of
nucleons in the nucleus. Numbers in parentheses show the number of nucleons
of a given kind that can be accommodated at a particular energy level.
Numbers at the right are the closed-shell numbers. The narrow shaded bands
join states of a given principal quantum number. Compare this diagram with
the diagram of Figure 24.12.

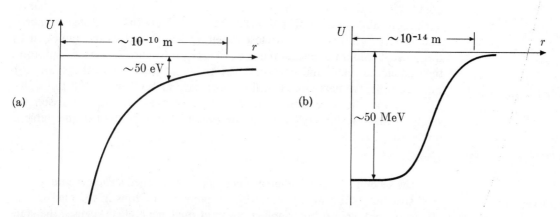

FIGURE 25.22   Comparison of average shapes of potential energy curves for
(a) the motion of electrons in a heavy atom and (b) the motion of nucleons in
a heavy nucleus. Note the difference in length scales and energy scales as well
as the differences in shape.

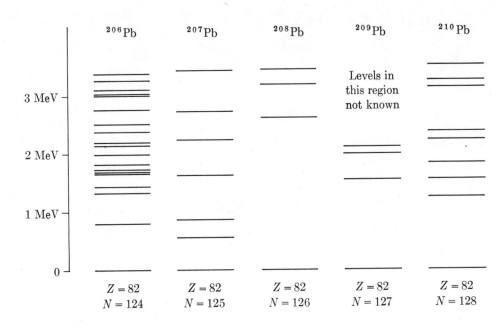

FIGURE 25.23   Partial energy-level diagrams of nuclei of several lead isotopes. The relatively large energy required to excite the nucleus of ^{208}Pb is one of the pieces of evidence that nucleon shells close at both 82 and 126 nucleons.

This shell contains the $2p_{3/2}$ and the $2p_{1/2}$ states. The $n = 2$ level with $\ell = 0$ (the $2s_{1/2}$ state) is at higher energy and is found in the third shell. After oxygen 16 ($Z = N = 8$), the next doubly-closed-shell nucleus is calcium 40 ($Z = N = 20$), with the third shell filled for both kinds of nucleons. Beyond calcium, the trend toward a neutron excess in nuclei precludes the appearance of another doubly-closed-shell nucleus until near the end of the periodic table. By chance, the line of stability passes near $Z = 82$ and $N = 126$, both closed-shell numbers. The nucleus $^{208}_{82}$Pb is a doubly-closed-shell nucleus, a fact clearly indicated by the unusual amount of energy required to excite it (Figure 25.23). For protons, the next closed-shell number beyond 82 is predicted to be 114 (rather than 126). For neutrons, the next closed-shell number beyond 126 is predicted to be 184. These numbers lie close to the extrapolated line of stabliity. For this reason, the small "island of stability" beyond the present limits of the periodic table is predicted to lie near

A predicted doubly-closed-shell nucleus

$$Z = 114, \qquad N = 184, \qquad A = 298.$$

Strong spin-orbit coupling alters the shells

The second source of difference between nuclear shell structure and atomic shell structure is the strong spin-orbit coupling of nucleons in the nucleus. In atoms, a weak spin-orbit coupling, an electromagnetic effect, causes the state with **L** and **S** antiparallel ($j = \ell - \frac{1}{2}$) to lie slightly below the state with **L** and **S** parallel ($j = \ell + \frac{1}{2}$). This gives rise to fine structure (Section 24.9). In nuclei, the spin-orbit coupling is a feature of the nuclear force. It is stronger and of the opposite sign. The $2p_{3/2}$ state, for example, lies significantly below the $2p_{1/2}$ state. The effect is larger for larger ℓ, becoming a coarse structure rather than a fine structure. As shown in Figure 25.21, the separation of the $4f_{7/2}$ and $4f_{5/2}$ states is so great that they occupy different shells. The same figure shows the $5g_{9/2}$ state in the fifth shell. Its partner, the $5g_{7/2}$ state, is in the sixth shell.

The use of the phrase "shell model" to describe the independent-particle approximation and its implications is common although somewhat misleading. It suggests a spatial separation of particles into layers. In atoms, this picture of separate layers is roughly correct but far from perfect, since the different shells overlap considerably. In a nucleus, the layer description has almost no validity whatever. The nuclear shells must be thought of as energy-level shells, not spatial shells. Each nuclear shell strongly overlaps all other nuclear shells.

The once-mysterious interior of the nucleus has shown itself to be a quantum gas of approximately independent particles. Perhaps someday, the unknown interior of a single elementary particle will reveal a comparably simple structure.

Summary of ideas and definitions

The nucleus of an atom, which is largely decoupled from the atomic electrons, accounts for the mass of the atom, its position in the periodic table, and its radioactivity, if any.

Nuclei are composed of protons and neutrons, collectively known as nucleons. These particles have

1. exactly the same spin ($s = \frac{1}{2}$) and strong interaction properties,

2. approximately the same mass,

3. very different electric (and magnetic) properties.

The older idea that nuclei contain electrons is unacceptable for two reasons:

1. The potential energy required of the confined electrons is too great.

2. The predicted number of spin-one-half particles in the nucleus is inconsistent with the observed spins of some nuclei.

A nucleus is characterized by its atomic number (or proton number) Z, its neutron number N, and its mass number, $A = Z + N$. A specific Z defines an *element*. *Isotopes* of an element have the same Z and different N.

The masses of most nuclei are given, to good approximation, by $M \cong A$ amu. The amu is defined as $\frac{1}{12}$ of the mass of an *atom* of $^{12}_{6}C$.

Sources of information about nuclear size and shape include electron scattering, alpha-particle scattering, and Coulomb energies of mirror nuclei, among many others.

Solid angle, measured in steradians, is defined by

$$\Omega = \frac{A}{R^2}. \qquad (25.5)$$

Differential cross section is defined by

$$\frac{d\sigma}{d\Omega} = \frac{\text{outgoing particles per steradian per sec}}{\text{incoming particles per m}^2 \text{ per sec}}. \qquad (25.6)$$

A distributed charge is a "soft" target, producing less large-angle scattering than would be produced by a point charge.

The density of nuclear matter is roughly constant near the center of the nucleus and falls to a small value over a distance of about 2 fm at the edge of the nucleus.

The nuclear radius (distance to half-density point) is, approximately,

$$R = 1.2A^{1/3} \text{ fm}. \qquad (25.8)$$

Strong-interaction effects remain significant out to about $1.4A^{1/3}$ fm.

Nuclear deformation is measured by a parameter α (Equation 25.10), which shows a regular and periodic variation with mass number.

Contributing to nuclear energy are
  a negative potential energy contributed by nuclear forces,

a positive potential energy contributed by electric forces,

a positive kinetic energy, required by the confinement of the nucleons.

Nuclear binding energy is near 8 MeV/nucleon for most nuclei.

A particle of mass m confined in a region of radius R has, according to the uncertainty principle, a kinetic energy

$$K \cong \frac{3\hbar^2}{2mR^2}. \qquad (25.14)$$

This formula correctly predicts the atomic energy scale of a few eV, the nuclear energy scale of a few MeV, and their ratio, about 10^6.

Modes of spontaneous energy loss by nuclei are

1. gamma decay,
2. beta decay,
3. alpha decay,
4. fission,
5. internal conversion,
6. orbital capture.

All but gamma decay and internal conversion result in transmutation of elements.

Deformed nuclei exhibit rotational energy spectra. The moment of inertia is greater for greater deformation.

A "periodic table" of nuclei requires a two-dimensional chart; both Z and N are important.

Neutrons and protons separately obey the exclusion principle, but a neutron and a proton may occupy the same state.

The exclusion principle in nuclei helps to explain

the fact that $Z = N$ for light nuclei,

the stabilization of the neutron in the nucleus,

the approximate validity of the independent-particle model.

Coulomb energy accounts for

the decrease of binding energy per nucleon at large A,

the neutron excess in heavy nuclei,

the termination of the periodic table.

The virtual creation of pions (and other particles) by nucleons explains the finite size of the proton and provides a mechanism for the strong interaction of nucleons. The range of an exchange force, calculable from the uncertainty principle, is

$$d = \frac{\hbar}{mc}. \qquad (25.22)$$

The independent-particle model assigns approximately free motion to nucleons within an average "potential well." The model is supported by periodicity of many nuclear properties and by the existence of well-defined closed-shell numbers,

$$2, \quad 8, \quad 20, \quad 28, \quad 50, \quad 82, \quad 126.$$

The ordering of states available to nucleons differs considerably from the ordering of states available to electrons in an atom because (a) the potential energy functions are of different shape, and (b) the nuclear spin-orbit coupling is much stronger than the atomic spin-orbit coupling.

QUESTIONS

Section 25.1

Q25.1 Nuclear binding energies are determined from nuclear masses. (1) Is it practical to determine atomic binding energies (energies binding electrons to atoms) in the same way? Why or why not? (2) Suggest a method other than mass measurement that could be used to determine either nuclear or atomic binding energies.

Q25.2 If the atomic mass unit were to be established as the mass of a ^{1}H atom instead of $\frac{1}{12}$ of the mass of a ^{12}C atom, atomic masses would not fall as close to integers as they now do. Give a physical reason for this fact.

Q25.3 The binding energy of a triton (the nucleus of $^3_1$H) is greater than the binding energy of a nucleus of $^3_2$He (see Exercise 25.3). The ^{3}H nucleus might therefore be said to be "more stable" than the ^{3}He nucleus. Yet the ^{3}H nucleus is in fact *unstable*; it decays radioactively into a nucleus of ^{3}He. Explain the apparent paradox. (HINT: The calculation of the nuclear masses called for in Exercise 25.3 may be helpful.)

Q25.4   Enrico Fermi was one of those who helped to "banish" electrons from the nucleus. In 1934 he wrote: "Another difficulty for the theory of nuclear electrons is the fact that the current relativistic theory of light-weight particles is unable to explain in a satisfactory way how such particles can be bound in orbits of nuclear dimensions." Explain what Fermi had in mind.

Q25.5   Which of the following properties of a cadmium atom are attributable primarily to its nucleus alone, and which depend also on its electronic structure: (a) its mass; (b) its ionization energy; (c) its valence; (d) its spectrum of visible light; (e) its spectrum of X rays; (f) its spectrum of gamma rays; (g) its ability to absorb neutrons?

Q25.6   (1) Explain in simple terms why there is no nuclear analog of molecule formation—that is, why two or more nuclei do not associate to form multinucleus systems without loss of their individual identities. (2) What is the nuclear analog of ionization? What is its consequence?

Q25.7   (1) What is a typical solid angle subtended by a television screen at the eye of a viewer? (2) A man looking at television moves his chair forward until the *angle* subtended by the horizontal dimension of the screen is doubled. By what factor does the *solid angle* subtended by the whole screen change?

Section 25.2

Q25.8   When high-energy electrons strike a hydrogen target, many more are scattered through small angles than through larger angles [see Figure 25.5(a)]. Explain this fact qualitatively in terms of electron trajectories passing protons at various distances.

Q25.9   Although the neutron's total charge is zero, the *density* of charge within the neutron is not zero. What general statement can you make about the neutron's internal charge density ρ_n? How would you expect a graph of ρ_n vs r to differ from Figure 25.5(b)?

Q25.10   Figure 25.7 shows that the nuclear "surface" is a region about 2 fm thick. (1) Why is it impossible for a nucleus to have a sharply defined edge? (2) Why is the surface of an atom even less well defined than the surface of a nucleus?

Section 25.3

Q25.11   Figure 25.7 shows that the density of nucleons near the center of the nucleus is about the same for the nuclei of all medium-weight and heavy elements. Does the density of electrons in the central portion of the atom exhibit a similar property?

Q25.12   The rather large horizontal error bars in Figure 25.8(a) could mean that the angles of measurement were not accurately determined or that particles scattered into a broad range of angles were measured together. Which is the more likely explanation? Why? Suggest an experimental reason why such horizontal error bars do not appear in Figure 25.8(b), which presents results of a more recent cyclotron experiment.

Q25.13   A careful examination of Figure 25.8(b) shows that the data exhibit a weak oscillatory pattern of maxima and minima superimposed on an overall pattern of rapid decrease as the scattering angle increases. (1) The overall decrease provides evidence for the finite size of the nucleus. Why? (2) The superimposed oscillation provides evidence for the wave nature of alpha particles. Why?

Q25.14 (1) With the help of Figure 25.10, name two elements whose nuclei are nearly spherical. (2) Name two elements (other than uranium) whose nuclei are strongly deformed.

Section 25.4   **Q25.15** Compare and contrast Equations 25.14 and 23.59. (1) For $n = 1$ and $d = 2R$, why are these equations similar but not identical? (2) Why is there no quantum number n in Equation 25.14?

Q25.16 (1) Radioactive isotopes that decay by orbital capture can be used as sources of X rays. Why? (2) Which is likely to be the more hazardous form of radioactivity, orbital capture or beta decay? Give a reason for your answer.

Q25.17 How does the phenomenon of orbital capture support the wave nature of electrons? (HINT: The weak interaction that is responsible for orbital capture is of very short range; it acts only when an electron and a nucleon are nearly coincident.)

Q25.18 Of two nuclei with the same deformation (the same value of α), the more massive one has the more closely spaced rotational energy levels. Explain this fact.

Section 25.5   **Q25.19** (1) Explain carefully why the beta decay of a nucleus is represented in Figure 25.14 by a diagonally pointing arrow—directed either to the left and upward or to the right and downward. (2) What sort of arrow would be appropriate to indicate gamma decay in such a nuclear chart?

Q25.20 (1) By reference to Figure 25.14, describe the sequence of "daughter" nuclei that result from the decay of a ^9C "parent" nucleus. (2) If a pellet of the pure isotope ^9C were placed in an evacuated chamber (this is not actually practical), what would the chamber contain a few seconds later?

Q25.21 What nucleus results from the beta decay of a ^{14}C nucleus?

Q25.22 The chart in Figure 25.14 stops short of ^{15}C. Would you expect ^{15}C to be a stable isotope? If so, why? If not, what would you expect to be the nature of its radioactive decay?

Q25.23 (1) The nuclei of ^{13}C and ^{13}N are "mirror nuclei." Name another pair of mirror nuclei. (2) Why are mirror nuclei known only among the light elements, not among the heavy elements?

Q25.24 Answer the following questions after consulting a wall chart of the nuclei. (1) Which element has the greatest number of known isotopes? (2) Which element has the greatest number of stable isotopes? (3) Which elements with $Z < 83$ have no stable isotopes? [An alternative source of information, in less convenient form than a wall chart, is the Table of Isotopes in the *Handbook of Chemistry and Physics* (Cleveland, Ohio: The Chemical Rubber Company).]

Q25.25 Very roughly, the contribution of the nuclear forces to the nuclear binding energy is proportional to the number of nucleons in the nucleus ($U_{nucl} \sim A$). The nuclear Coulomb energy, on the other hand, is roughly proportional to the square of the number of protons [actually $U_{Coul} \sim Z(Z - 1)$]. (1) Why is one of these energies determined by the number of *nucleons*, the other by the number of *protons*? (2) Why does one of these energies depend *linearly* on A, whereas the other depends *quadratically* on Z? (HINT: This difference has to do with the difference in the range of the forces.)

Q25.26 The only stable isotope of yttrium is $^{89}_{39}Y$. An unstable nucleus with the same number of nucleons is $^{89}_{36}Kr$. Give at least one reason why the mass of ^{89}Kr is greater than the mass of ^{89}Y.

Q25.27 The outer part of the cloud of virtual particles near a nucleus consists mostly of pions. Why pions in preference to other particles?

Section 25.6

Q25.28 In what sense is the Coulomb potential a special case of the Yukawa potential (Equation 25.23)?

Q25.29 When a nucleus undergoes positron decay, a proton in the nucleus is transformed into a neutron. Why can this happen as a spontaneous process despite the fact that the neutron mass is greater than the proton mass?

Section 25.7

Q25.30 Discuss features of any two of the following three hypothetical worlds: (a) a world in which the neutron mass (m_n) and proton mass (m_p) are identical; (b) a world in which m_p slightly exceeds $m_n + m_e$ (so that a free proton is unstable); (c) a world in which $m_n = 2m_p$.

Q25.31 The graph of binding energy per nucleon in Figure 25.17 shows a jagged structure for light nuclei. (1) Suggest a reason why it is not smooth. (2) In particular, why is there a peak at $A = 4$ (the alpha particle)?

Section 25.8

Q25.32 Why do the isotopes of tin have nuclei that are less deformed than the nuclei of neighboring elements?

Q25.33 In light of the predicted "island of stability" near $A = 298$, how would you expect points in Figure 25.10 to behave between $A = 250$ and $A = 300$ (if nuclear deformations could be measured for these nuclei)?

EXERCISES

E25.1 Which of the following nuclei contain the same number of (1) protons? (2) neutrons? (3) nucleons? (4) Which are surrounded by the same number of electrons in a neutral atom? (5) Which are isotopes of the same element?

(a) ^{12}C (b) ^{13}C (c) ^{14}C (d) ^{14}N (e) ^{16}O (f) ^{17}O

Section 25.1

E25.2 Because of the *atomic* binding energy, the mass of a hydrogen atom in its ground state is very slightly less than the sum of the masses of a proton and an electron. How much less? Express the answer in amu. If the mass of the atom is expressed to 7 significant figures, does this atomic binding effect make a difference?

E25.3 The mass of an atom of ^3_1H (tritium) is 3.01605 amu; the mass of an atom of ^3_2He (helium 3) is 3.01603 amu. Calculate (a) the masses in amu and (b) the binding energies in MeV of the nuclei of these two atoms. (Work to sufficient accuracy so that you can be sure which nucleus has the greater mass and which one has the greater binding energy.)

E25.4 The binding energy of the nucleus of ^{208}Pb is approximately 8 MeV per nucleon. (1) What is the approximate total binding energy of this isotope of lead? (2) (a) This total binding energy is equivalent to the rest mass of how many nucleons? (b) how many electrons?

E25.5   At the center of a helium nucleus, the electric potential energy of an electron is

$$U_0 \cong -\frac{3}{2} \frac{1}{4\pi\epsilon_0} \frac{2e^2}{R},$$

where R is the radius of the nucleus. (1) Explain the origin of this formula, especially the factor $\frac{3}{2}$, assuming the nucleus to be a spherical ball of charge. (2) How does the magnitude of U_0 compare with the kinetic energy of 124 MeV calculated in Section 25.1 for an electron held within a sphere of radius 2.5 fm (2.5×10^{-15} m).

E25.6   (1) If electrons and not neutrons were contained within nuclei, how many electrons and how many protons would comprise the deuteron ($^2_1$H)? (2) Would the angular momentum quantum number j of the deuteron then be expected to be integral or half-odd-integral? (The actual value of j for the deuteron is 1.)

Section 25.2   E25.7   If you are drifting in a life raft on a quiet ocean, approximately what solid angles are subtended at your eye by (1) the sky, (2) the ocean, and (3) the sun?

E25.8   An abandoned section of pipe is lying on the ground. Its length is l, one of its ends has an opening of area A_1, and its other end has an opening of area A_2. A field mouse whose instinct for survival is coupled with an innate sense of calculus builds its nest at such a point in the pipe that the total solid angle subtended at the nest by the two openings is a minimum. Show that if $A_1 \ll l^2$ and $A_2 \ll l^2$, (1) the distance of the nest from the opening of area A_1 is

$$r_1 = \frac{l}{1 + (A_2/A_1)^{1/3}}$$

and (2) the total solid angle of the openings is

$$\Omega_{min} = \frac{1}{l^2} [A_1^{1/3} + A_2^{1/3}]^3.$$

E25.9   A television viewer is in the habit of sitting 8 ft from a 21-in. screen (the screen measures 21 in. diagonally). How far should this viewer sit from a 17-in. screen in order to have the picture subtend the familiar solid angle?

E25.10   Figure 25.6 shows, in classical approximation, the effect of a distributed positive charge on the scattering of electrons (an attractive force is at work). Make a similar sketch that shows the effect of a distributed positive charge on the scattering of positrons (then a repulsive force is at work). Is the actual scattering of positrons at large angles produced by the distributed charge greater or less than it would be for a point charge?

E25.11   Figure 25.5(b) shows that the charge density within a proton is roughly 1 quantum unit of charge per fm^3. (1) Express this magnitude of charge density in C/m^3. (2) What is the potential in volts at a distance of 1 fm from the center of a proton?

Section 25.3   E25.12   If a nucleon in a uranium nucleus ($A = 238$) moves at a speed of $0.1c$, about how much time does it need to cross the nucleus? (See also Exercise 25.24.)

E25.13   The radius of a lead nucleus is about 7 fm. (1) What is the radius outside of which half of the nucleons in this nucleus lie? (2) What is the approximate mean spacing of the 208 nucleons in this nucleus?

E25.14　(1) Translate the nuclear density of 2.3×10^{17} kg/m^3 calculated in Section 25.3 to a density expressed in nucleons/fm^3. (2) How does your answer compare with the central densities of nuclei shown in Figure 25.7? Suggest a reason why the two are not the same.

E25.15　Figure 25.7 shows that there are about 0.175 nucleons/fm^3 near the center of a $^{197}_{79}$Au nucleus. (1) What is the number of protons per fm^3 in this region? (2) What is the central charge density in quantum units per fm^3? Why is this number substantially less than the charge density within a single proton [see Figure 25.5(b)]?

E25.16　Make up and solve a simple numerical example designed to illustrate the enormity of either nuclear matter density or nuclear charge density.

E25.17　(1) What is the wavelength of a "slow" neutron, one whose energy is 0.04 eV? How does this compare with the diameter of a typical nucleus? (2) At what energy in eV is the wavelength of a neutron equal to 10^{-14} m, or 10 fm (a typical nuclear diameter)?

E25.18　Verify by calculation that a 48-MeV alpha particle can surmount the "Coulomb barrier" of a lead nucleus ($Z = 82$) and penetrate to the nuclear surface. (There it encounters strong nonelectric forces that inhibit its large-angle scattering—see Figure 25.8.)

E25.19　The major and minor radii of a uranium nucleus are given approximately in Figure 25.1. From these numbers and Equation 25.10, obtain approximate values for (1) the mean radius R_0 and (2) the deformation parameter α for this nucleus. Check the former value against Equation 25.8. Check the latter value against Figure 25.10.

E25.20　Use Equation 25.14 to answer the following questions. (1) What is the approximate kinetic energy of an electron in the K shell of a heavy atom, where $R \cong 0.01$ Å? (2) What is the approximate zero-point energy of a neutron in a heavy nucleus for which $R \cong 7$ fm?

Section 25.4

E25.21　Use Figure 25.13 and Equation 25.16 to find the moment of inertia I of the nucleus of $^{174}_{70}$Yb. Show that this empirical moment of inertia is a little more than half as great as the value $\frac{2}{5}MR^2$ that would be calculated on the assumption that the nucleus rotates like a solid sphere.

E25.22　The table in the margin gives the angular-momentum quantum numbers J and energies E of some of the low-lying states in $^{249}_{97}$Bk. How well do these energies conform to the theoretical formula for rotational energies, Equation 25.16? (NOTE: It is sufficient to work with energy *ratios* only.)

J	E (keV)
$\frac{7}{2}$	0
$\frac{9}{2}$	41.8
$\frac{11}{2}$	93.7
$\frac{13}{2}$	155.8
$\frac{15}{2}$	229.3

E25.23　The mass of a $^8_4$Be atom (including its electrons) is 8.005305 amu. The mass of a $^4_2$He atom is 4.002603 amu. What is (1) the kinetic energy in MeV and (2) the speed in m/sec of each ^{4}He nucleus that results from the decay of a ^{8}Be nucleus at rest?

Section 25.5

E25.24　There is a characteristic time associated with a nucleus, roughly the time required for a nucleon in the nucleus to move across the diameter of the nucleus. Calculate this time, using a nuclear diameter of 5 fm (a small nucleus) and a nucleon kinetic energy of 50 MeV. How does this characteristic nuclear time compare with the "short" lifetimes of nuclei such as ^{8}Be or ^{9}B (see Figure 25.14)?

E25.25   (1) What is the electrical potential energy (the so-called Coulomb energy) of the $^{13}_{6}$C nucleus? (Use $R = 3.5$ fm for the radius of this nucleus. Note the useful combination of constants given on page A10.) (2) The total binding energy of the ^{13}C nucleus is 97.1 MeV. What is the negative potential energy associated with the attractive nuclear forces? (Be careful about relative signs; a binding energy is the magnitude of a negative energy.)

E25.26   What is the Coulomb energy of the $^{238}_{92}$U nucleus, whose radius is about 8 fm? How does U_{Coul} compare in magnitude with the total binding energy of this nucleus? (The latter quantity can be calculated approximately with the help of Figure 25.17.)

Section 25.6   E25.27   The mean lifetime of the $2p_{3/2}$ state in the hydrogen atom is 1.6×10^{-9} sec. Using the time-energy form of the uncertainty principle (Equation 25.20), find the energy uncertainty of this state. How does this energy "broadening" compare in magnitude with the 2p fine-structure splitting, which is 4.5×10^{-5} eV.

E25.28   The lifetime of the extremely unstable nucleus of ^{5}Li is about 10^{-21} sec. (1) Use the uncertainty principle to estimate the uncertainty of the total energy of this nucleus. (2) Is this uncertainty large enough to have an influence on the result of an experiment designed to measure the mass of the nucleus to an accuracy of 10^{-30} kg?

E25.29   Equation 25.23 expresses the "Yukawa potential." (1) Is it a central potential? (2) Obtain an expression for the "Yukawa force." Show that in the limit $d \rightarrow \infty$, the Yukawa force becomes an inverse-square force.

E25.30   The mass of the photon is established experimentally to be no greater than about 10^{-50} kg. Suppose it were exactly 10^{-50} kg. (1) What would be the reduced Compton wavelength of the photon (see Equation 25.22)? (2) Would you expect deviations from Coulomb's law to be measurable over laboratory distances (see Equation 25.23)?

Section 25.7   E25.31   (1) Suggest two ways in which the energy required to break a deuteron into a neutron and a proton might be supplied. (2) If a neutron and a proton coalesce to form a deuteron, a gamma ray is radiated. What is its energy in eV?

E25.32   (1) The mass of the ^{6}He nucleus is 6.01779 amu. What is its binding energy B? What is B/A, its binding energy per nucleon? (2) Answer the same questions for the ^{6}Li nucleus, whose mass is 6.01348 amu. (3) In the decay $^6_2$He $\rightarrow$ $^6_3$Li + e$^-$ + $\overline{\nu}_e$, what is the total kinetic energy imparted to the electron and the antineutrino?

Section 25.8   E25.33   (1) Specify the proton and neutron states that are filled in (a) the $^{13}_{6}$C nucleus and (b) the $^{48}_{20}$Ca nucleus. (2) What should be the angular momentum quantum number J of the ground state of each of these nuclei?

E25.34   The seventh nuclear shell is closed at 126 neutrons. Working from the pattern of Figure 25.21, specify the states that are contained in the seventh shell.

P25.1 In order of magnitude, the atomic binding energy (the energy required to remove all electrons from the atom) is 10^1 eV for $_1$H, 10^2 eV for $_2$He, and 10^2 eV for $_3$Li. Estimate the atomic binding energy of $_{18}$Ar, only accurately enough to specify it to the nearest power of 10. If this energy is 10^α eV, is α closest to 3, 4, 5, or 6? (NOTE: The binding energy of an electron in an atom depends on the effective nuclear charge "seen" by the electron and on its principal quantum number n.)

Atomic binding energy

P25.2 The following data show the range of alpha particles of several energies in a certain photographic emulsion:

Energy loss of alpha particles in matter

Energy (MeV)	Range (μm)
5	20
10	57
15	110
20	180

(1) By a combination of graphical and numerical means, estimate the average rate of energy loss in MeV/μm at each of these energies. Sketch graphs of range vs energy and rate of energy loss (dE/dx) vs energy. (2) If an alpha particle loses 30 eV per ionization event, how many atoms or molecules does it ionize in the last 20 μm of its track? (3) By examining the track of an alpha particle in a photographic emulsion, how could you determine the direction in which the particle moved?

P25.3 The charge-density function shown in Figure 25.5(b) is expressed by

Properties of proton's distributed charge

$$\rho(r) = e\,\frac{12\sqrt{3}}{4\pi a^3}\,e^{-\sqrt{12}\,r/a},$$

where a is a constant with the dimension of length (for the proton, $a \cong 0.80$ fm). (1) The proton's total charge is given by

$$q = 4\pi \int_0^\infty \rho(r) r^2\,dr.$$

(a) Explain why this is the correct formula for q. (b) Show that $q = e$. (2) The proton's mean-square radius is given by

$$\langle r^2 \rangle = \frac{4\pi}{e} \int_0^\infty \rho(r) r^4\,dr.$$

(a) Explain why this is the correct formula for $\langle r^2 \rangle$. (b) Show that $\langle r^2 \rangle = a^2$.

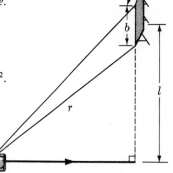

P25.4 As shown in the figure, a billboard of height a and width b is located at a distance l from a highway; the plane of the billboard is perpendicular to

Solid angle

the highway. Find the distance r of a driver from the billboard when the billboard subtends the maximum solid angle at his eye. (Assume $a \ll l$ and $b \ll l$.)

P25.5　(1) Show that the element of solid angle defined by the lightly shaded cone in the figure is $d\Omega = \sin\theta\,d\theta\,d\varphi$. (2) By integrating this expression over all directions, verify that $\Omega_{total} = 4\pi$. (CAUTION: Pay attention to the appropriate ranges of integration of θ and φ.) (3) Show that the element of volume defined by the darkly shaded region in the figure is $d\tau = r^2 \sin\theta\,dr\,d\theta\,d\varphi = r^2\,dr\,d\Omega$.

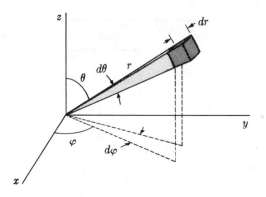

Classical differential
scattering cross section

P25.6　A beam of particles enters a target region and is scattered. As shown in the figure, particles that approach the target in the annular region between cylinders of radii b and $b + db$ are scattered into the annular region between cones of half-angle θ and $\theta + d\theta$. The scattering phenomenon is assumed to have cylindrical symmetry. (1) Show that the area dA in the figure is $dA = 2\pi b\,db$. (2) Show that the solid angle $d\Omega$ in the figure is $d\Omega = 2\pi \sin\theta\,d\theta$. (3) Using the definition given by Equation 25.6, show that the classical differential scattering cross section is given by

$$\frac{d\sigma}{d\Omega} = \left| \frac{b\,db}{\sin\theta\,d\theta} \right|.$$

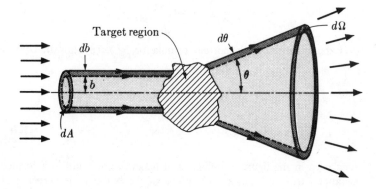

Optional: Equation 25.6 is valid quantum-mechanically as well as classically. Explain why the result derived in this problem cannot be valid quantum-mechanically.

P25.7   A beam of particles impinges on a perfectly reflecting sphere of radius R (see the figure). (1) Express the "impact parameter" b as a function of the scattering angle θ. (2) Using the result of the preceding problem, obtain an expression for the differential scattering cross section $d\sigma/d\Omega$. (NOTE: Usually $d\sigma/d\Omega$ is a function of θ. Its independence of θ in this example is not typical.)

Classical scattering by a reflecting sphere

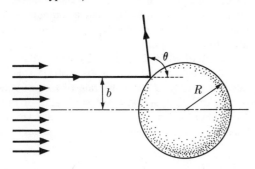

P25.8   Discuss carefully, with quantitative examples, the following two aspects of nuclear Coulomb energy as it is related to the fission of a $^{236}_{92}\mathrm{U}$ nucleus. (1) If a uranium nucleus splits into two nearly equal fragments, the total Coulomb energy of the fragments is not the same as the Coulomb energy of the original nucleus. [What is the approximate magnitude of this change of Coulomb energy in fission? What is its sign (does it represent energy that is released or absorbed in fission)?] (2) If a uranium nucleus splits into unequal fragments, the change of Coulomb energy is not the same as it is for equal fragments. [Does the change of Coulomb energy tend to favor equal or unequal fragments?]

Coulomb energy and fission

P25.9   Atomic masses are given to good approximation by a so-called semi-empirical mass formula. One version of the formula, expressed in amu, is

$$M(A, Z) = 1.008665(A - Z) + 1.007825Z$$

$$-a_1A + a_2A^{2/3} + a_3\frac{Z(Z - 1)}{A^{1/3}} + a_4\frac{(\frac{1}{2}A - Z)^2}{A} + \delta,$$

Semi-empirical mass formula

where a_1, a_2, a_3, and a_4 are positive constants. (1) Explain the meaning of (a) the term proportional to $A - Z$, (b) the term proportional to Z, and (c) the term proportional to $Z(Z - 1)/A^{1/3}$. (2) Before checking an outside reference, estimate the magnitude of a_1 and explain the basis of your estimate. (3) Which term is a surface-energy term? Why does it have the sign that it does have? (4) Ignoring the correction term δ, minimize M with respect to Z for fixed A. For $a_3 = 0.00075$ and $a_4 = 0.100$, what value of Z yields the minimum mass for $A = 208$? How does this accord with the experimental fact that the line of stability passes near $Z = 82$, $A = 208$? [REFERENCE: Alex E. S. Green and Nicholas A. Engler, *Physical Review* **91**, 40 (1953); or a nuclear physics textbook.]

Neutron stars   P25.10   Astrophysicists have predicted the existence of "neutron stars," stars in which gravitational attraction has so strongly compressed matter that electrons have been "squeezed" into nuclei; the stars then consist of closely packed neutrons. (1) What is the radius of a neutron star of 1.5 solar masses if the density of the star is the same as the density of nuclear matter? (2) Pulsars, which emit bursts of electromagnetic radiation at regular intervals, are thought to be rotating neutron stars. The pulsar NP0531 in the Crab nebula pulses about 30 times per sec. If it has the radius calculated in part 1 and a rotation period of $\frac{1}{30}$ sec, what is the rotation speed of its surface (at its equator)? (3) The duration of a single pulse of NP0531 is about 2 msec. Using the speed of light as a connecting link, calculate a characteristic length associated with this time and compare this length with the radius calculated in part 1. Can one part of the star "communicate" with every other part in a time of 2 msec? (4) The period of NP0531 increases by 38 nsec/day. Assume that this pulsar is a rotating neutron star with a mass of 1.5 solar masses and the radius calculated in part 1. What is its rate of loss of rotational kinetic energy? How does this compare with the sun's rate of radiation, which is 3.9×10^{26} J/sec? (For further information on pulsars, see Jeremiah P. Ostriker, "The Nature of Pulsars," *Scientific American*, January, 1971.)

26

Nuclear Transformations

In this chapter, our focus will shift from nuclear structure to nuclear *change*—transitions and reactions.

For the most part, every nucleus lives in splendid isolation, shielded from the rest of the world by its own encircling electrons. Even if an atom is stripped of all electrons by ionization, the force of electrical repulsion will normally keep its nucleus from coming into contact with other nuclei. Whereas atoms interact with one another incessantly, around us and within us, nuclei rarely interact. Nevertheless, it is not difficult to gain information about nuclei from processes of nuclear transformation, because these processes almost always involve energy changes that are large on an atomic scale. A nucleus may undergo spontaneous decay (radioactivity) through several mechanisms (see the longer list in Section 25.4).

Alpha decay: An alpha particle (nucleus of $^4_2$He) is emitted.

Beta decay: An electron and antineutrino or a positron and neutrino are emitted.

Gamma decay: A photon is emitted.

Fission: A nucleus breaks in two.

Or a nucleus may be caused to react in several ways.

Bombardment by high-energy charged particles (of order 1 MeV or more).

Bombardment by neutrons of any energy.

Thermal agitation at extreme temperature (10^7 K or more).

26.1 Probability and exponential decay

It is easy to "listen in" on quantum-mechanical probability. Anyone with a luminous-dial wrist watch and a Geiger counter can do so. The Geiger counter should be of the common type arranged to give an audible click when a high-speed particle triggers the device. The watch is held at such a distance from the counter that the individual clicks can be heard. It will be obvious to the listener that the clicks are not coming in a regular sequence like the ticks of the watch, but occur in an apparently random fashion. Indeed, a mathematical analysis would show that they are truly random. The time at which a given click occurs is completely unrelated to the time elapsed since the previous click or to the time at which any other click occurs.

Randomness in radioactive decay

In doing such an experiment, one is in unusually close touch with the sub-microscopic world. The action of a *single* nucleus is rendered audible, and one directly senses the fundamental law of probability that governs nuclear events. As we shall now show, such a law of probability, acting separately on every nucleus, leads to an exponential law of decay for many nuclei.

Each radioactive nucleus of a particular kind is responsive to a fixed decay probability per unit time,

Decay probability per unit time for parent nucleus

$$p_0 = \frac{1}{\tau}. \tag{26.1}$$

This constant is written $1/\tau$ because its dimension is $(\text{time})^{-1}$. If at time t a specific nucleus has not yet decayed, the probability that it *will* decay in the ensuing short time interval Δt is $p_0 \Delta t$, or

$$\frac{\Delta t}{\tau}.$$

Let $n(t)$ be the number of parent nuclei (those that have not yet decayed) present in a sample at time t. The number expected to decay in the next interval Δt is this number n multiplied by the probability $\Delta t/\tau$ that any one will decay. The expected change of n (a decrease) is, therefore,

$$\Delta n = -n \frac{\Delta t}{\tau}.$$

This equation can be written $\Delta n/\Delta t = -n/\tau$. In the limit of small Δt, it becomes a differential equation,

Number decaying per unit time is proportional to number present

$$\frac{dn}{dt} = -\frac{n}{\tau}. \tag{26.2}$$

This is an *approximate* equation, for two reasons: (1) The quantity n is an integer, not a continuous variable; and (2) because probability rules the process, the actual rate of decay may be somewhat greater or less than this expected rate. However, for large n, the actual decay closely follows Equation 26.2. This differential equation is asking the question, What function $n(t)$ has a derivative proportional to the negative of itself? The answer is a decreasing exponential function. As can be verified by substituting back into Equation 26.2, the required solution is

$$n(t) = n_0 e^{-t/\tau}. \tag{26.3}$$

A graph of such a function appears in Figure 5.30.

The quantity measured experimentally is not n, the number of parent nuclei remaining in the sample, but the number of distintegrations per second. This rate of decay we may call the intensity I. It is

$$I = -\frac{dn}{dt} = I_0 e^{-t/\tau}, \tag{26.4}$$

Exponential law of intensity

also a decreasing exponential. The initial intensity is $I_0 = n_0/\tau$. (In practice, of course, a detector measures only some fixed fraction of the total intensity I.) Figure 26.1 shows experimental intensity data obtained with a sample of ^{194}Ir.

The constant τ is called the mean life because it is the average lifetime of all the radioactive nuclei in the sample. Let us prove this statement. The probability per unit time for a nucleus to decay at (or near) time t is the product of two factors:

$$p(t) = P(t)\,p_0. \tag{26.5}$$

The first factor is the probability that a parent nucleus known to be present at $t = 0$ is still present at time t. The second factor is the probability *per unit time*

FIGURE 26.1   Exponential decay of a sample of ^{194}Ir, whose mean life is $\tau = 0.995 \times 10^5$ sec. In this semilog plot (vertical scale logarithmic, horizontal scale linear), an exponential function appears as a straight line. These experimental data of James S. Geiger, AECL, Chalk River, Canada, conform well to an exponential function. Over a time span of 9.3×10^5 sec (about 10.8 days), which is 9.3 mean lives or 13.5 half lives, the intensity falls by a factor of approximately 10,000.

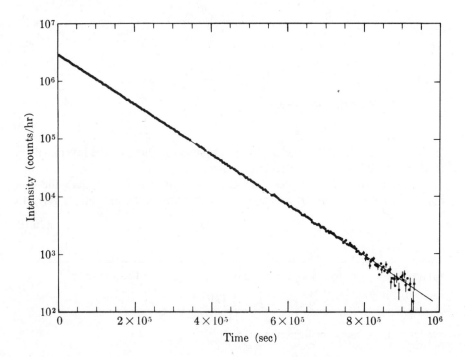

that the nucleus, having survived this long, then decays. The first factor may be deduced from Equation 26.3. It is

$$P(t) = \frac{n(t)}{n_0} = e^{-t/\tau}.$$ (26.6)

The second factor is a constant, given by Equation 26.1. The net decay probability per unit time for a nucleus in the original sample is, therefore,

$$p(t) = \frac{1}{\tau} e^{-t/\tau}.$$ (26.7)

The meaning of $p(t)$ is made clear with these formulas:

Probability for a nucleus to decay in the infinitesimal interval from t to $t + \Delta t$ $\Big\}$ $= p(t) \, \Delta t;$

Probability for a nucleus to decay in the finite interval from t_1 to t_2 $\Big\}$ $= \int_{t_1}^{t_2} p(t) \, dt;$

Probability for a nucleus to decay at any time $\Big\}$ $= \int_0^\infty p(t) \, dt.$

It is easy to verify that the third integral is equal to 1. The average lifetime that we seek is a weighted average, defined by*

Average lifetime is a weighted mean

$$\bar{t} = \int_0^\infty t \, p(t) \, dt.$$ (26.8)

Substituting for $p(t)$ from Equation 26.7 gives

$$\bar{t} = \frac{1}{\tau} \int_0^\infty t e^{-t/\tau} \, dt.$$

The substitution $u = t/\tau$ casts this in the form

$$\bar{t} = \tau \int_0^\infty u e^{-u} \, du.$$

Integration by parts then gives

Average lifetime is τ, or 1/p₀

$$\bar{t} = \tau.$$ (26.9)

The mean lifetime of the nuclei in the sample is the same as the inverse of the fundamental decay probability per unit time.

We have previously noted that the mean life τ is longer than the time required for half the nuclei to decay. This latter time, the half life, is given by

$$t_{1/2} = 0.693\tau.$$ (26.10)

---

* If one were working with *relative* probabilities, the average would be defined by

$$\bar{t} = \frac{\int_0^\infty t \, p(t) \, dt}{\int_0^\infty p(t) \, dt}.$$

In this instance, the denominator is equal to 1.

Including elementary particles as well as nuclei, the span of known half lives from the shortest to the longest is unimaginably great. At one extreme are the super-short-lived particles, or resonances, with half lives of 10^{-20} sec or less. Other particles live from 10^{-10} sec up to several minutes—except, of course, for the stable particles, which, as far as we know, live forever. Radioactive nuclei are known with half lives ranging from 10^{-3} sec up to more than 10^{15} years.

It was through the exponential pattern of decay that Ernest Rutherford first identified the action of probability in radioactive decay (1899). At the time, he had no reason to suspect that he was face to face with a new kind of probability. He must have supposed that a complex inner structure in the atom caused the timing of its decay to be uncertain, a reflection of thermodynamic probability. Not until 1926 was probability accepted as a fundamental attribute of nature's most basic laws.

Exponential decay reveals role of probability

26.2   Alpha decay

The characteristic spectra of atoms were identified and classified long before the atomic structure responsible for the radiation was understood. Similarly, nuclei made themselves known first by their radiation—alpha, beta, and gamma rays—before scientists had any inkling of the size and structure of nuclei, or indeed of the existence of nuclei.

In very early studies (1897) of the radioactivity of uranium, Ernest Rutherford found the radiation to be of at least two kinds. To the radiation of greater ionizing power and less range he gave the name "alpha rays." Another radiation, of less ionizing power and greater range, he called "beta rays." A modern picture of alpha and beta ray tracks in special photographic emulsion (Figure 26.2) shows this characteristic difference. Gamma rays were identified as electromagnetic radiation several years later.

The early names: α, β, γ

In the history of alpha particles, from their discovery to the present day, three landmarks stand out. First was their identification as helium nuclei. Second was the use of alpha particles as projectiles to study the interior of the atom. Third was the quantum-mechanical explanation of alpha decay. The first two advances were made by Rutherford and his associates. The third was the work of George Gamow and (independently) Edward Condon and Ronald Gurney.

THE NATURE OF ALPHA PARTICLES

In 1902 Rutherford succeeded in deflecting alpha particles with a magnetic field and showed them to be positively charged particles much heavier than electrons. The conclusive evidence on their nature came from spectra. In 1908 Rutherford was able to bring to rest, and collect in an evacuated space, enough alpha particles to allow a study of their spectra. Once stopped, of course, alpha particles collect electrons and become helium atoms. These atoms, if excited, emit the characteristic line spectrum of helium. Here was clear evidence that radioactivity was indeed a catastrophic event on the atomic scale, bringing into being entirely new atoms. The discovery also explains why

Stopped alpha particles become helium atoms

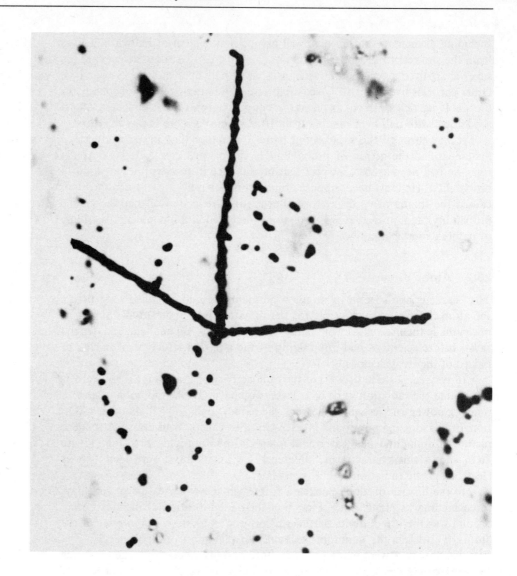

helium is found in radioactive mineral deposits. It is a fascinating thought that in the thousands of cubic feet of helium pumped from the earth every day, practically every atom had its origin in the tiny violence of a radioactive disintegration some time within the past few billion years.

SCATTERING OF ALPHA PARTICLES

In Rutherford's Manchester laboratory in 1908 began the historic series of experiments on the deflection of alpha particles by matter that was to culminate five years later in Bohr's theory of the hydrogen atom. Carried out by Hans Geiger and Ernest Marsden, the experiments seemed at first routine. But before long they took on central interest in the laboratory because the results were

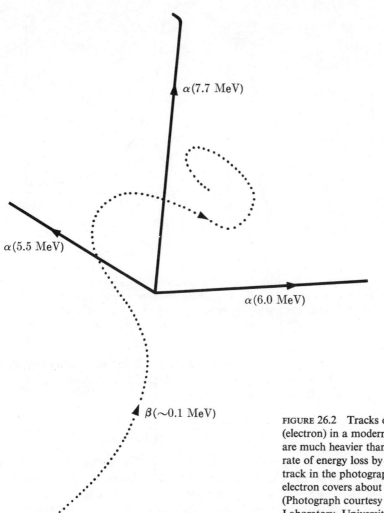

α(7.7 MeV)

α(5.5 MeV)

α(6.0 MeV)

β(∼0.1 MeV)

FIGURE 26.2   Tracks of alpha particles and a beta particle
(electron) in a modern photographic emulsion. The alpha tracks
are much heavier than the electron track, indicating a greater
rate of energy loss by the alpha particles. The longest alpha
track in the photograph covers about 3.9 μm. The wandering
electron covers about 8 μm. Magnification is by a factor of 2,000.
(Photograph courtesy of Harry H. Heckman, Lawrence Radiation
Laboratory, University of California, Berkeley.)

unexpected. A small fraction of alpha particles directed at a metal foil were
deflected through large angles. Even this small fraction was too much to be
consistent with the then-current view that the positive charge in the atom is
spread over the whole atomic volume. In such an atom, the electric field is
nowhere strong enough to significantly deflect a high-speed alpha particle.
The electrons, because of their small mass, are also unable to account for large
deflections. Rutherford seized on the results of Geiger and Marsden and
interpreted them correctly. In the heart of the atom, he said, must reside an
object that is massive enough and forceful enough to turn back an alpha
particle that comes close to it. He postulated that since electrons, known to be
atomic constituents, are light and negative, the central nucleus should be
heavy and positive.

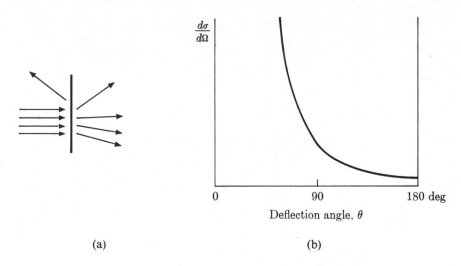

FIGURE 26.3   Scattering of alpha particles. (a) Experimental finding. Of many
alpha particles striking a metal foil a few are deflected through a large angle.
(b) The theoretical differential cross section for scattering by a heavy point charge.

In 1911, Rutherford went on to calculate the differential scattering cross
section of alpha particles impinging on a small positive nucleus. His result,
which we state without proof, is

*Differential cross section for
Coulomb scattering*

$$\frac{d\sigma}{d\Omega} = \left(\frac{1}{4\pi\epsilon_0}\frac{ZZ'e^2}{4K}\right)^2 \frac{1}{\sin^4(\theta/2)}. \tag{26.11}$$

Here Z is the atomic number of the target, Z' is the atomic number of the
projectile (2 for an alpha particle), K is the initial kinetic energy of the projectile,
and θ is the angle of deflection. As illustrated in Figure 26.3, the probability of
*It predicts significant
scattering at large angles* scattering is much greater at small angles than at large angles. However, it is
not negligible at large angles. Experiments soon confirmed the correctness of
Equation 26.11, in the dependence of $d\sigma/d\Omega$ on Z, K, and θ. Later (see Figure
25.8), deviations from Equation 26.11 were discovered, caused by the finite size
of the nucleus.

By what may be called nature's kindness, Rutherford's classical calculation
agrees with a quantum calculation carried out many years later. His hyperbolic
trajectories must be replaced by propagating waves; yet, remarkably, the results
based on Newtonian mechanics agree with the quantum results. This is a
special feature of a Coulomb potential ($U \sim 1/r$), which does not carry over
to other potential-energy functions.

BARRIER PENETRATION AND ALPHA DECAY

Alpha decay, unlike alpha-particle deflection, is a uniquely quantum phenomenon completely at variance with classically expected behavior. Inside a
nucleus, an alpha particle feels an attractive nuclear force. This is a region of

negative potential energy [see Figure 25.22(b)]. Outside the nucleus, an alpha particle feels an electrical force of repulsion. This is a region of positive potential energy. As shown in Figure 26.4, the potential-energy diagram for the alpha particle-nucleus system contains a barrier near the nuclear surface. According to classical mechanics, an alpha particle with insufficient energy to surmount the barrrier, if fired at the nucleus from outside, is turned back by the barrier (the electric repulsion) and cannot penetrate the nucleus. Classically, an alpha particle of the same energy, if inside the nucleus, is constrained by the same barrier to remain there forever. In short, if classical mechanics were valid in the nuclear domain, the potential-energy barrier would be impenetrable from both sides for any alpha particle with energy less than the peak of the barrier. However, alpha particles of less than this energy do shoot out of nuclei; quantum mechanics permits barrier penetration. The wave function of an alpha particle within the nucleus [Figure 26.4(b)] penetrates into the classically

Classically, a potential-energy barrier is impenetrable

Quantum-mechanically, it can be breached

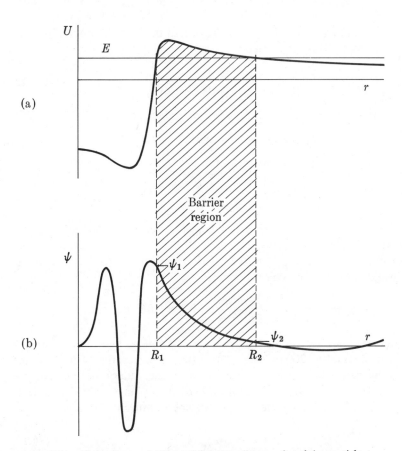

FIGURE 26.4 Alpha decay. (a) Potential-energy diagram for alpha particle–nucleus system, the sum of a negative potential well arising from the attraction of nuclear forces and a positive potential hill resulting from electric repulsion. (b) Wave function of alpha particle (approximate), showing large probability to be within nucleus and small probability to appear outside.

forbidden region, where it falls rapidly toward zero. A small part of the wave reaches through the barrier, emerging on the other side as an oscillatory wave of small amplitude. This means that the alpha particle has a certain probability to materialize outside the nucleus, where the electrical force accelerates it to a high kinetic energy, typically 5 to 10 MeV. This is alpha decay. The inverse process—barrier penetration from outside to inside—can also be important when the energy of the incident particle is not much less than the peak height of the barrier.

★ESTIMATE OF ALPHA-DECAY LIFETIMES

An estimate of alpha-decay lifetimes may be obtained with the help of a crude theory that mixes classical and quantum reasoning. Picture the alpha particle moving back and forth within the nucleus. It strikes the barrier (knocks at the gate to be let out) v_α times per second. Each time, there is a certain probability P that it penetrates the barrier. This probability is related to the quantum wave amplitude in the barrier region. From inside to outside the barrier, the wave function falls from ψ_1 to ψ_2 [Figure 26.4(b)], and the particle probability falls from $|\psi_1|^2$ to $|\psi_2|^2$. The barrier penetration probability is therefore

Barrier penetration probability

$$P = \frac{|\psi_2|^2}{|\psi_1|^2}. \qquad (26.12)$$

The net decay probability per unit time is the product of v_α and P:

$$p_0 \text{ (decay probability/sec)} = v_\alpha P. \qquad (26.13)$$

The inverse of this quantity is the mean life τ:

$$\tau = \frac{1}{p_0} = \frac{1}{v_\alpha P}. \qquad (26.14)$$

To obtain a value for v_α, we may take, as a typical kinetic energy of the alpha particle within the nucleus, $K_{\text{inside}} = 50$ MeV. This corresponds to an alpha-particle speed of 5×10^7 m/sec. The frequency of striking the barrier is this speed divided by the nuclear diameter:

$$v_\alpha = \frac{v}{d} = \frac{5 \times 10^7 \text{ m/sec}}{18 \times 10^{-15} \text{ m}} = 2.8 \times 10^{21} \text{ sec}^{-1}.$$

For the nuclear diameter we have used 18 fm. The usual figure for the radius of a heavy nucleus ($A = 200$ to 250) is 7 to 8 fm. However, the radius at which the alpha particle encounters the barrier, near the outermost edge of the nucleus [see Figure 26.4(a)], is more nearly equal to 9 fm. Since the value of v_α is at best a rough estimate, no more than one significant figure is justified. We shall use

Rate of collision of alpha particle with barrier

$$v_\alpha = 3 \times 10^{21} \text{ sec}^{-1}. \qquad (26.15)$$

This number is roughly the same for all alpha-unstable nuclei. Yet, observed lifetimes vary from microseconds to billions of years. Clearly the other factor P in Equation 26.14 must vary tremendously from one nucleus to another. Also, P must be exceedingly small. A one-second mean life, for instance, requires the barrier-penetration probability P to be less than 10^{-21}.

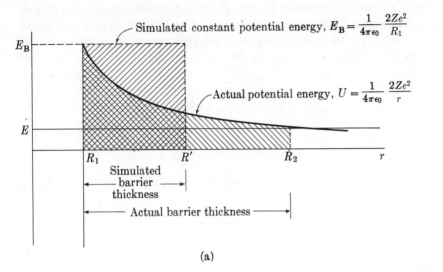

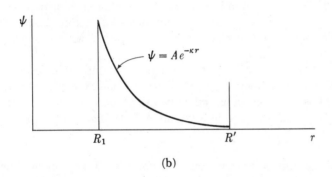

FIGURE 26.5 (a) Crude model for calculating the probability of barrier penetration by alpha particles. The actual barrier is replaced by a barrier of constant potential energy, half as thick as the actual barrier. (b) Within the simulated barrier, the wave function is a decreasing exponential.

To estimate P, we adopt the approximate model illustrated in Figure 26.5. The actual potential-energy barrier is replaced by a "rectangular" barrier of height E_B extending from an inner radius R_1 to an outer radius R'. We choose

$$R_1 = 9 \text{ fm},$$

$$R' = \tfrac{1}{2}(R_1 + R_2).$$

This makes the simulated barrier half the thickness of the actual barrier. The outer radius R_2 of the actual barrier is determined by the condition $E = U$. It is

$$R_2 = \frac{1}{4\pi\epsilon_0} \frac{2Ze^2}{E}. \tag{26.16}$$

The height of the simulated barrier is set equal to the height of the actual barrier at R_1:

$$E_B = \frac{1}{4\pi\epsilon_0} \frac{2Ze^2}{R_1}. \tag{26.17}$$

In these two equations, the factor 2 in the numerator is the atomic number of the alpha particle.

Next, we must learn about the wave function within the rectangular barrier. It must satisfy the Schrödinger equation. Since we are dealing with an approximate theory of the alpha-decay process, it will suffice to use the one-dimensional form of the Schrödinger equation (Equation 23.75). For this application (with $U = E_B$ and x replaced by r), it is

Schrödinger equation in barrier region

$$\frac{d^2\psi}{dr^2} = \frac{2m}{\hbar^2}(E_B - E)\psi.$$

The combination on the right, $2m(E_B - E)/\hbar^2$, is a positive constant within the barrier region. For notational convenience, we may define

$$\kappa_1 = \sqrt{\frac{2m}{\hbar^2}(E_B - E)} \qquad (26.18)$$

and write the Schrödinger equation in the form

$$\frac{d^2\psi}{dr^2} = \kappa_1^2\psi. \qquad (26.19)$$

Note that κ_1, like the wave number k, has the dimension of inverse length. These two quantities are closely related but not identical. Within the classically forbidden barrier region, where kinetic energy is negative, wave number is an imaginary quantity.

Equation 26.19 is a simple differential equation. As implied in Section 5.11, exponential functions, both increasing and decreasing, have the property needed for a solution of this equation—a second derivative proportional to the function. It is easy to verify by substitution into Equation 26.19 that a solution is

General solution

$$\psi = Ae^{-\kappa_1 r} + Be^{\kappa_1 r},$$

where A and B are arbitrary constants. The constant B may, in fact, be set equal to zero. The full argument for this contains some subtleties but in essence it is the following. The decreasing-exponential term describes a physical situation in which the alpha particle has a large probability to be inside the nucleus, a small probability to be outside. This is the alpha-decay problem, in which we are interested. The increasing-exponential term describes an opposite physical situation, in which the alpha particle has a large probability to be outside the nucleus, a small probability to be inside. This is the problem of alpha-particle scattering, in which we are not interested here. For alpha decay, therefore, we take the wave function in the barrier region to be

Solution appropriate to alpha-decay problem

$$\psi = Ae^{-\kappa_1 r}. \qquad (26.20)$$

At the inner and outer edges of the simulated barrier, it is $\psi_1 = Ae^{-\kappa_1 R_1}$ and $\psi_2 = Ae^{-\kappa_1 R'}$. From Equation 26.12, the barrier penetration probability is

$$P = \frac{e^{-2\kappa_1 R'}}{e^{-2\kappa_1 R_1}} = e^{-2\kappa_1 \cdot (R' - R_1)}.$$

Since we make the approximation $R' - R_1 = \frac{1}{2}(R_2 - R_1)$, this can also be

Estimated barrier-penetration probability

written

$$P = e^{-\kappa_1 \cdot (R_2 - R_1)}. \qquad (26.21)$$

Finally, substituting from Equations 26.15 and 26.21 into 26.14, we have, for the estimated alpha-decay lifetime,

$$\tau = \tfrac{1}{3} \times 10^{-21} e^{\kappa_1 \cdot (R_2 - R_1)} \text{ sec.}^*$$ (26.22)

Lifetime, according to crude theory

Polonium isotopes

Probably the most interesting thing about Equation 26.22 is the extreme sensitivity of lifetime to alpha-particle energy that it implies. This feature can best be illustrated by example. Let us consider isotopes of polonium ($Z = 84$). For use in Equations 26.16 and 26.17, the combination $2Ze^2/4\pi\epsilon_0$ is needed. In convenient units, it is

$$\frac{2Ze^2}{4\pi\epsilon_0} = 2.88Z = 242 \text{ MeV fm.}$$ (26.23)

Another handy combination (m is the mass of the alpha particle) is

$$\frac{2m}{\hbar^2} = 0.191 \frac{1}{\text{MeV fm}^2}.$$ (26.24)

With the help of these numbers, Equations 26.16–26.18 give

$$R_2 \text{ (fm)} = \frac{242}{E \text{ (MeV)}},$$ (26.25)

$$E_B = \frac{242 \text{ MeV fm}}{9 \text{ fm}} = 26.9 \text{ MeV},$$ (26.26)

$$\kappa_1 \text{ (fm}^{-1}) = \sqrt{0.191[26.9 - E \text{ (MeV)}]}.$$ (26.27)

Since typical values of alpha-particle energies are 5 to 10 MeV, κ_1 is in the neighborhood of 2 fm^{-1}. This means that a change in R_2 of only 1 fm (see Equation 26.22) is sufficient to change the lifetime by a factor of e^2, or about 7. We shall calculate the approximate lifetime of two isotopes.

1. ^{212}Po: $E = 8.78$ MeV, $t_{1/2} \cong 0.3$ μsec, $\tau \cong 0.4$ μsec. For this energy, Equations 26.25 and 26.27 give $R_2 = 27.6$ fm and $\kappa_1 = 1.86$ fm^{-1}. The exponent needed in Equation 26.22 is

$$\kappa_1 \cdot (R_2 - R_1) = 1.86 \, (27.6 - 9.0) = 34.6,$$

and the exponential factor is $e^{34.6}$, which is $10^{15.0}$ (the conversion to a power

---

* In a more accurate theory, the exponent $\kappa_1(R_2 - R_1)$ is replaced by the integral

$$\mathscr{I} = 2 \int_{R_1}^{R_2} \kappa(r) \, dr = 2 \int_{R_1}^{R_2} \sqrt{\frac{2m}{\hbar^2} [U(r) - E]} \, dr.$$

For $U(r) = 2Ze^2/(4\pi\epsilon_0 r)$, this integral can be evaluated in terms of familiar functions. It is

$$\mathscr{I} = 2\kappa_1 R_2 \left[\frac{\arctan \sqrt{(R_2/R_1) - 1}}{\sqrt{(R_2/R_1) - 1}} - \frac{R_1}{R_2} \right].$$

^{212}Po: $P \cong 10^{-15}$

of 10 uses the fact that $e^{2.303} = 10$). The barrier penetration probability is 10^{-15}, and the theoretical lifetime is

$$\tau = (\tfrac{1}{3} \times 10^{-21} \text{ sec})(10^{15})$$

$$= 0.3 \times 10^{-6} \text{ sec} = 0.3 \ \mu\text{sec}.$$

This calculated value is fortuitously close to the observed value. The approximations we have used happen to be nearly correct for lifetimes this short. They are less satisfactory for longer lifetimes.

2. ^{213}Po: $E = 8.38$ MeV, $t_{1/2} \cong 4 \ \mu\text{sec}$, $\tau \cong 6 \ \mu\text{sec}$. For this slightly lower energy, the outer edge of the barrier is at

$$R_2 = \frac{242}{8.38} = 28.9 \text{ fm},$$

and the quantity κ_1 is 1.88 fm^{-1}. The exponent for Equation 26.22 is

$$\kappa_1 \cdot (R_2 - R_1) = 1.88 \ (28.9 - 9.0) = 37.4,$$

^{213}Po: $P \cong 6 \times 10^{-17}$

and the exponential factor is $e^{37.4} = 10^{16.2} = 1.7 \times 10^{16}$. This leads to a theoretical lifetime

$$\tau = (\tfrac{1}{3} \times 10^{-21} \text{ sec})(1.7 \times 10^{16})$$

$$= 6 \times 10^{-6} \text{ sec} = 6 \ \mu\text{sec}.$$

Lifetime extremely sensitive to energy of alpha particle

Comparison of the two calculations is instructive. A 5 percent change in alpha-particle energy is sufficient to change the lifetime—both theoretically and actually—by a factor of more than 10. This great sensitivity results from the wave function falling exponentially by many orders of magnitude through the barrier region. The sensitivity of lifetime to energy is further emphasized by the experimental data of Table 26.1.

26.3   Beta decay

The nature of beta particles was established by Henri Becquerel in 1900. Using both electric and magnetic fields, he deflected beta rays, just as Thomson had deflected cathode rays a few years earlier. He found that beta rays were negatively charged, and that their charge-to-mass ratio agreed with the charge-

Beta particles are electrons

to-mass ratio of cathode rays. In short, he showed that beta particles were electrons. When Rutherford later established the nuclear atom, it became clear that the nucleus must be the seat of radioactivity—for the vast energy of radioactivity was not to be found in the orbital electrons, and alpha particles, at least, could come from nowhere else than the nucleus. So the existence of beta decay implied—or so it seemed—that the nucleus must contain electrons: in the violence of a radioactive transformation, one of these could be ejected at high speed.

The puzzle of beta decay: apparent nonconservation of energy

Over the years, more extensive and more accurate measurements on beta decay gradually built up a real puzzle for physics. Apart from the fact that quantum mechanics cast doubt on the presence of electrons in the nucleus, a more serious problem loomed: the apparent nonconservation of energy. In

TABLE 26.1   ALPHA-DECAY PROPERTIES OF SEVERAL NUCLEI

Nucleus	Energy of Alpha Particle (MeV)	Half Life
$^{212}_{84}Po$	8.78	0.30 μsec
$^{217}_{86}Rn$	7.74	0.54 msec
$^{216}_{84}Po$	6.78	0.15 sec
$^{209}_{85}At$	5.65	5.4 hr
$^{228}_{90}Th$	5.42	1.9 year
$^{226}_{88}Ra$	4.78	1,600 years
$^{235}_{92}U$	4.40	7.0×10^8 years
$^{232}_{90}Th$	4.01	1.4×10^{10} years

alpha decay and in gamma decay, as in photon emission by atoms, the energy carried away by the ejected particle (its mass energy, if any, plus its kinetic energy) is exactly equal to the difference in energy between the initial and final states of motion. To borrow an expression from optical spectra, we can say that alpha and gamma radioactivity exhibit *line spectra*. Beta decay, by contrast, exhibits a *continuous spectrum* (Figure 26.6). A group of identical radioactive atoms undergoing beta decay emit electrons of all energies from zero to some maximum. Apparently (and we now know this indeed to be the case), any given atom undergoing a particular transition transfers to the emitted electron an unpredictable amount of energy.

By this point in history (the late 1920s), physicists had been conditioned by the successes of relativity and quantum mechanics to expect the unexpected. Some were willing to abandon the law of energy conservation in the nuclear domain. Wolfgang Pauli in 1930 made a suggestion that was at once conservative and bold. In order to "save" the law of energy conservation, he postulated an entirely new particle, uncharged and so far unseen, that could exist within nuclei and be emitted, along with an electron, in beta decay. This light-weight "neutron," as he called it, could carry away the energy not given to the electron. It could also do a job within the nucleus, accounting for some problems in understanding nuclear spin (see page 1269). Eventually, two different neutral particles were needed to solve all the puzzles. The neutron resides in the nucleus. The neutrino (or antineutrino) is emitted in beta decay.

Pauli's postulate: a new neutral particle

Enrico Fermi's successful theory of beta decay in 1934 showed this phenomenon to be quite different from alpha decay. Borrowing the general ideas of the quantum theory of photon emission, he constructed a theory based on particle creation. He proposed that an electron and an antineutrino are created at the instant of the radioactive transformation, just as a photon is created at the instant of an atomic quantum transition. Simultaneous with the creation of the pair of particles (both of which at once escape from the nucleus), the nucleus is transmuted into the nucleus of a different element ($\Delta Z = +1$). Beta decay seems to be a process very different from photon emission. Yet, in what we now regard as the essentials, both are quite similar. One happens to involve the creation of a particle with mass; the other involves only the creation of a particle without mass. In one, the emitting particle (a nucleon) happens

Particle creation in beta decay

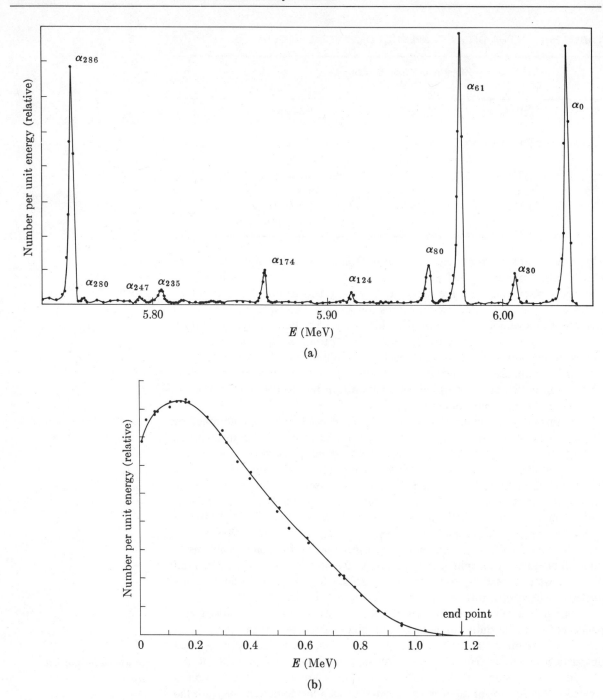

FIGURE 26.6 (a)   A line spectrum observed in the alpha decay of $^{227}_{90}$Th. The daughter nucleus is left in various excited states, whose energies in keV are designated by subscripts in the figure. [Data of R. C. Pilger, F. Asaro, J. P. Hummel, and I. Perlman, published in F. Ajzenberg-Selove, ed., *Nuclear Spectroscopy, Part A* (New York: Academic Press, 1960), p. 176.] (b) Continuous spectrum observed in the beta decay of ^{210}Bi. [Data of G. J. Neary, *Proceedings of the Royal Society, London,* **A175,** 71 (1940).]

to change its charge; in the other, the emitting particle (an electron) does not. One thing that *is* very different is the strength of the interaction responsible for the transition. The electromagnetic interaction that creates photons is many orders of magnitude stronger than the weak interaction that creates electrons and neutrinos.

The Fermi theory of beta decay has stood very well the test of time. Only slightly modified, it successfully accounts for all nuclear beta decay, with both electron and positron emission; for the process of orbital capture, in which the nucleus annihilates an atomic electron instead of emitting a positron; for the beta decay of the free neutron; and for a variety of other weak interactions involving elementary particles, such as the beta decay of a muon, in which a muon transforms itself into an electron, a neutrino, and an antineutrino. So apparent were the successes of the Fermi theory that the neutrino was generally counted as a reliably classified member of the elementary-particle family many years before it was actually observed. Its eventual identification in 1956 will be described in the next chapter.

Beta decay is one of many weak interaction processes

26.4   Radioactive decay chains

Luckily for the progress of atomic science, radioactivity occurs naturally in the heavy elements. Although natural radioactivity contains a store of valuable information, one basic fact about it made particularly difficult the task of decoding its message about submicroscopic nature: it occurs in long chains of successive transformation and transmutation. In a natural sample of uranium are juxtaposed 18 different radioactive isotopes of 10 elements with half lives ranging from 164 μsec to 4 billion years, all undergoing their individual processes of decay simultaneously. It was a triumph of human intellect, and also international cooperation and communication, that only fifteen years elapsed from Becquerel's discovery of radioactivity to Rutherford's discovery of the nucleus.*

Among the new insights gained from the study of radioactive decay chains, two stand out as dramatic revolutions in thinking about the structure of matter: (1) Transmutation accompanies radioactivity; one element can transform itself into another. (2) There exist different versions of the same element; isotopes are identical chemically but differ in atomic weight and in radioactive properties. This pair of discoveries toppled two nineteenth-century axioms of chemistry—that each element is composed of identical atoms of a single kind and that atoms are immutable. It is ironic that after alchemists had expended so much fruitless effort in trying to transmute elements, transmutation was finally discovered to be a spontaneous process in nature.

New insights: atoms of an element neither immutable nor identical

The large number of radioactive isotopes among the heavy elements fit into three series, each based on a very long-lived parent isotope. The uranium series springs from $^{238}_{92}\text{U}$, whose half life is 4.5 billion years. The thorium series springs from $^{232}_{90}\text{Th}$, whose half life is 14 billion years. The actinium series

Three decay series

---

* See Lawrence Badash, "How the 'Newer Alchemy' Was Received," *Scientific American*, August, 1966.

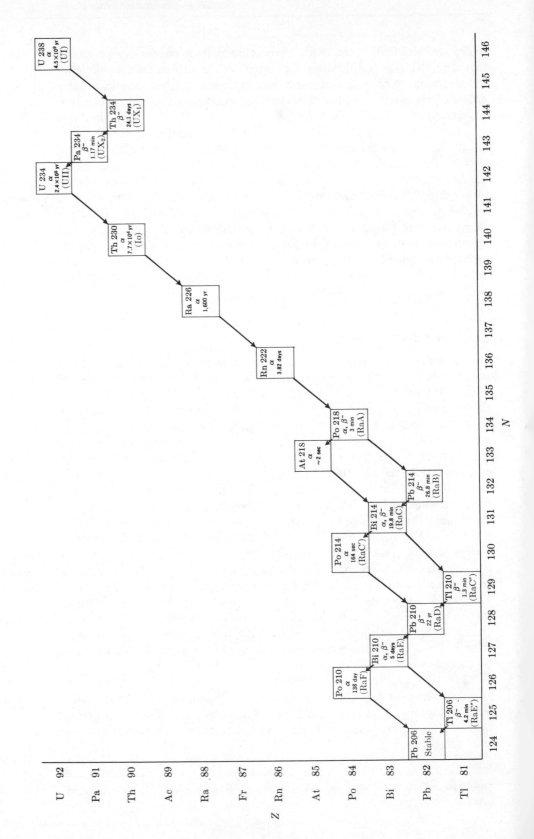

FIGURE 26.7 The uranium series of natural radioactive transformations, beginning with ^{238}U and terminating in ^{206}Pb, a stable isotope of Pb. Some squares in the chart show the names assigned to particular members of the series before their true isotopic identities were established. Half lives are also shown.

(named for one of its members, not for its parent) springs from $^{235}_{92}$U, whose half life is 704 million years. Because of its shorter half life, most of the uranium 235 that was present when the earth was formed has since decayed away, but enough remains—one atom of ^{235}U for every 138 atoms of ^{238}U—to give rise to a significant chain of decay. Figure 26.7 illustrates the uranium series. This diagram is a selected part of the upper right end of a chart of the nuclei.

UNRAVELING ELEMENTS AND ISOTOPES: SOME EARLY HISTORY

When radioactivity was discovered, only two elements heavier than bismuth were known, thorium and uranium. Since the atomic numbers of these elements were unknown, the number of missing elements between bismuth and uranium was also unknown. After radioactivity became available as a new tool of analysis, the missing pieces began to fill in rapidly. In 1898, Marie and Pierre Curie isolated, identified, and named two new elements, polonium and radium. Although they did not know it at the time, they had actually isolated particular isotopes of these elements, those produced by the uranium decay chain: $^{210}_{84}$Po, whose half life is 138 days, and $^{226}_{88}$Ra, whose half life is 1,600 years. (This isotope of radium is now commonly used in the luminous paint of watch dials.) In the following year, André Debierne identified another new element, actinium (now known to have atomic number 89). At about the same time, Rutherford in Canada and Ernst Dorn in Germany were finding evidence for new radioactive gases. Rutherford named his new substance *emanation*. It came from thorium, had a half life of 1 min, and, as he and Frederick Soddy later learned, was chemically inert. Dorn's gas, also chemically inert, came from radium and had a half life of 3.8 days. He called it radon. Both are now recognized as isotopes of radon ($Z = 86$), the heaviest of the rare gases. Rutherford's emanation (also known for a time as thoron) is $^{220}_{86}$Rn. Dorn's "radon" is $^{222}_{86}$Rn. With the discovery of these isotopes began a decade of confusing multiplicity in the apparent number of elements.

New elements between bismuth and thorium

A century of progress in chemistry had seemingly made clear that all atoms of a given element are identical. Therefore, scientists engaged in the study of radioactivity quite naturally assumed that if two substances, both identifiable as elements, differed in any way at all—for instance, in half life—they must be different elements. As radioactive decay chains were gradually untangled, new "elements" proliferated remarkably. Some of the names assigned to isotopes in the uranium series are shown in Figure 26.7. At one time, six isotopes of thorium bore six different names, as shown in Table 26.2. Before long, this element proliferation began to frustrate the chemists. In 1907, Herbert McCoy and William Ross in Chicago found thorium and radiothorium to be chemically inseparable. In 1908, Otto Hahn in Berlin found it impossible to separate ionium and thorium by chemical means. Finally, in 1910, totally frustrated in his efforts to separate these substances, Soddy took the courageous step. He suggested that a single element might exist in two or more forms, different in mass and in radioactive properties, but chemically identical. Later he named these separate forms *isotopes*. The decisive evidence for isotopes came from two quite different experiments in 1913. In that year, Soddy showed the spectra of ionium and thorium to be identical. At about the same time, J. J. Thomson

Too many "elements"

The discovery of isotopes

TABLE 26.2   EARLY NOMENCLATURE FOR THORIUM ISOTOPES

Original Name	Modern Designation	Comments
Radioactinium	^{227}Th	Member of actinium series
Radiothorium	^{228}Th	Member of thorium series
Ionium	^{230}Th	Member of uranium series
Uranium Y	^{231}Th	Member of actinium series
Thorium	^{232}Th	Member of thorium series
Uranium X$_1$	^{234}Th	Member of uranium series

magnetically deflected a beam of neon ions moving in an evacuated space and discovered that some of the ions were of atomic mass about 20, others of atomic mass 22. He thereby demonstrated that multiple iostopes are not exclusively an attribute of radioactive elements.

Working with Rutherford, Soddy had also figured in another courageous conclusion in 1902. Stimulated by a suggestion of Becquerel, Rutherford and Soddy studied a radioactive "impurity" in thorium, which they named thorium X.* Finding that thorium and thorium X were undeniably distinct chemically and that thorium X was a product created by thorium, they concluded that *transmutation* accompanies radioactivity. The Curies, less willing than Ruther-

Transmutation

ford to abandon the solid rock of immutability of atoms, were at first reluctant to accept this revolutionary proposal. But in 1903 (the year Marie Curie received her doctorate and a Nobel Prize), they too accepted the idea of transmutation. Before long transmutation was established beyond question by the combined evidence of chemistry and radioactivity.

Following up their proposal of transmutation, Rutherford and Soddy drew two other related conclusions about the nature of radioactivity that stand as landmarks of discovery in this period. First, they proposed the "one-step"

Radioactivity as an atomic "explosion"

theory of transmutation; an atom does not gradually evolve into another as it releases radioactive energy but rather instantaneously transforms itself at the moment of radioactive decay. In this proposal, they were coming very close to the idea of probability working at a fundamental level, since radioactive decay was known to follow rules of probability. But in the absence of forcing evidence, to abandon certainty in science was inconceivable. The hint provided by radioactive decay was ignored for many years. Second, Rutherford and Soddy, analyzing the energy released by radioactivity, concluded that radio-active transmutation must involve at least 100,000 times as much energy per atom as does chemical change. From their work emerged the picture of radioactive decay that is still valid—a violently disruptive explosion of a single atom.

INTENSITY OF RADIATION

Apart from half life and mode of decay, a matter of practical concern in dealing with radioactivity is its intensity. Two units are used to measure different

---

* Thorium X is now recognized as an isotope of radium, $^{224}_{88}$Ra.

aspects of the strength of a sample of radioactive material. First is the curie, a measure of the number of radioactive disintegrations per second in the sample:

$$1 \text{ curie} = 3.7 \times 10^{10} \text{ disintegrations/sec.} \qquad (26.28)$$

The curie measures the intensity

■ EXAMPLE: What is the radioactivity in curies of 1 gm of radium 226? It is necessary to find out how many atoms of radium are in 1 gm, then to multiply this number by the probability that any one of the atoms will decay in a second. The mass of an atom of ^{226}Ra is 226 amu, or $(226)(1.66 \times 10^{-27}) = 3.75 \times 10^{-25}$ kg. In 1 gm, the number of atoms is

$$N = \frac{10^{-3} \text{ kg}}{3.75 \times 10^{-25} \text{ kg}} = 2.67 \times 10^{21}.$$

(Note that this number is 1/226 mole.) The mean life τ of radium 226 is

$$\tau = \frac{t_{1/2}}{0.693} = \frac{1,600 \text{ years}}{0.693} = 2,310 \text{ years}$$

$$= 7.3 \times 10^{10} \text{ sec.}$$

Its decay probability per second is the inverse of this time,

$$p_0 = \frac{1}{\tau} = 1.37 \times 10^{-11} \text{ sec}^{-1}.$$

This probability multiplied by the number of radioactive atoms in the sample gives the probable number of disintegrations in one second:

$$N p_0 = (2.67 \times 10^{21})(1.37 \times 10^{-11} \text{ sec}^{-1})$$

$$= 3.7 \times 10^{10} \text{ disintegrations/sec.}$$

It is no coincidence that this turns out to be 1 curie. The curie is defined to be (very nearly) the number of radioactive decay events in 1 gm of radium 226 in 1 sec.   ■

In assessing the effect of radioactivity on living matter, as well as for some other purposes, knowing the total ionizing power of the emitted radiation over some period of time is more important than knowing the nuclear decay rate. Therefore, a second unit of measurement of the strength of radioactivity has come into use. This unit is the rad,* a measure of the energy deposited per unit mass of matter by alpha, beta, or gamma rays traversing the matter:

$$1 \text{ rad} = 100 \text{ erg/gm} = 0.01 \text{ J/kg.} \qquad (26.29)$$

The rad measures the effect on matter

---

* A unit closely related to the rad is the roentgen, defined as the amount of electromagnetic energy that dislodges 1 esu of electrons from the molecules contained in 1 cm^3 of dry air at standard conditions of temperature and pressure. The rep (roentgen physical) is the amount of ionizing radiation that deposits 93 ergs in 1 gm of living tissue. Still another unit is the rem (roentgen equivalent man). The rad, the rem, the rep, and the roentgen do not differ greatly from one another.

To raise the temperature of water by 1 K requires energy of about 4,000 J/kg. Therefore, a radiation dose of 100 rad, or 1 J/kg, even if delivered almost instantaneously, would produce no perceptible sensation of warmth. Nevertheless, because of the disruptive effect of high-energy particles on molecules, one hundred rad delivered to all parts of the body is a highly dangerous dose. It is very likely to produce sickness. Several hundred rad delivered to major parts of the body within a few weeks or less could be fatal. Typically, in the United States, a person is exposed to about 0.15 rad per year from cosmic rays and natural radioactivity, or about 10 rad in a lifetime. Workers at nuclear installations are not supposed to receive more than 5 rad per year.*

26.5   Nuclear reactions

When a particle strikes a nucleus, many outcomes of the collision are possible. The incident particle may be scattered; it may be captured, followed by the emission of a gamma ray; one or more other particles may be emitted; with enough energy available, new particles may be created. Any process other than elastic scattering is classed as a *nuclear reaction*. From among the nearly limitless range of possible reactions, we select a few for discussion in this section.

REACTIONS INDUCED BY ALPHA PARTICLES

Since alpha particles were the first nuclear projectiles, it is not surprising that they figured in the first reported nuclear reaction. In 1919, Rutherford reported that alpha particles striking nitrogen produced a "radiation" that he tentatively identified as protons. The particles produced were electrically charged and had a range in air greater than the range of alpha particles. In modern notation, the reaction observed by Rutherford is written

The first observed nuclear reaction (1919)

$$\ce{^4_2He} + \ce{^{14}_7N} \rightarrow \ce{^1_1H} + \ce{^{17}_8O},$$

or

$$\alpha + \ce{^{14}_7N} \rightarrow p + \ce{^{17}_8O}.$$

This is an example of what is now called an (α, p) reaction. An early cloud-chamber picture of this reaction is shown in Figure 26.8.

The reaction that led to the discovery of the neutron is

Discovery of the neutron (1932) was based on this reaction

$$\alpha + \ce{^9_4Be} \rightarrow n + \ce{^{12}_6C},$$

a so-called (α, n) reaction. Beginning in 1930, several investigators noticed that alpha particles striking beryllium produced an uncharged highly penetrating radiation. Irene Joliot-Curie and her husband, Frederic Joliot, suggested that the radiation consisted of very energetic photons. James Chadwick, studying the same phenomenon in England, reached a different conclusion. Noting (1) that the apparent energy of such photons, about 50 MeV, seemed inconsistent

---

* Exposures up to 12 rad in a year are permitted provided the worker's total dose since age 18 does not average more than 5 rad/year. For the general public living near a reactor, the limit of exposure is 0.5 rad/year.

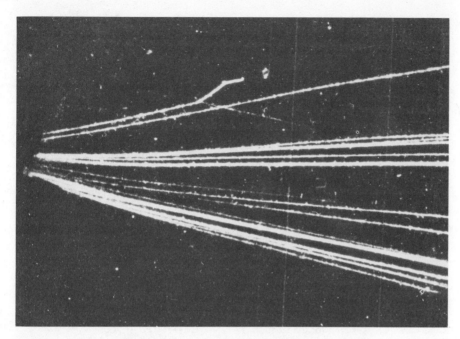

FIGURE 26.8   Early cloud-chamber photograph of a nuclear reaction. Alpha
particles emanate from a source to the left of the region photographed. The
uppermost alpha particle struck a nucleus of ^{14}N, ejecting a proton, whose light
track slopes downward to the right. The recoiling nucleus of ^{17}O left a short
heavy track sloping upward. (Photograph courtesy of P. M. S. Blackett.)

with energy conservation and (2) that the cross section for interaction of the
new radiation in a hydrogen target was greater than the cross section calculated
for photons, he suggested instead a neutral particle of mass comparable to the
proton mass—a neutron. As noted earlier, this idea found immediate acceptance,
and provided the basis for Heisenberg's theory of nuclear composition. The
(α, n) reaction still provides a convenient laboratory source of neutrons. In a
mixture of polonium and beryllium, the alpha particles from the spontaneous
decay of polonium react with beryllium nuclei to produce neutrons.

   An interesting reaction that is related to nuclear shell structure is the (α, t)
reaction. In this so-called *stripping reaction*, a proton is "stripped" from the
alpha particle, converting it to a triton. The cross section for the process and
the angular distribution of the outgoing tritons provide information on the
states of motion available to the proton that is left behind in the target nucleus.
The dependence of an (α, t) reaction cross section on energy is shown in Figure
26.9.

*Stripping reactions give
information on shell structure*

REACTIONS INDUCED BY PROTONS

Protons are the most common projectile particles in modern accelerators.
Consequently, their reactions are among the most widely studied. In (p, n)
reactions, the incident proton ejects a neutron from the nucleus. This reaction,
when carried out at high energy, reveals the distribution of momentum of

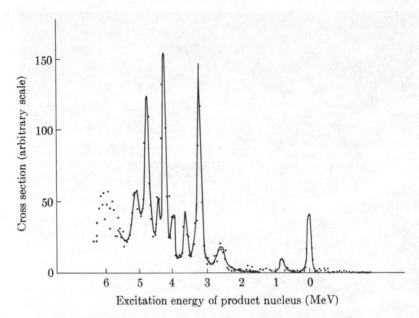

FIGURE 26.9   Cross section for the reaction $^{205}_{81}\text{Tl} + ^{4}_{2}\text{He} \rightarrow ^{206}_{82}\text{Pb} + ^{3}_{1}\text{H}$, denoted more simply $^{205}\text{Tl}(\alpha, \text{t})^{206}\text{Pb}$. In this stripping reaction, the target nucleus gains a proton, thereby increasing its atomic number and atomic mass by 1. The horizontal scale, running from right to left, is the excitation energy of the ^{206}Pb nucleus. The peaks indicate various quantum states in the ^{206}Pb nucleus, the farthest peak to the right corresponding to its ground state. [Data of O. Nathan *et al.*, *Nuclear Physics* **A109**, 481 (1968).]

neutrons in the nucleus. A (p, n) event can be considered to result from the elastic scattering of the proton and a single neutron in the nucleus (Figure 26.10).

Pickup reactions are also related to shell structure

The inverse of a stripping reaction is a *pickup reaction*. In a (p, d) reaction, for example, the proton "picks up" a neutron from the nucleus and the two emerge as a deuteron. Details of the reaction are sensitive to the shell-model state of the neutron before its pickup.

One proton-induced reaction has an important place in history, because it provided the first experimental verification of Einstein's mass-energy equivalence. In 1932, John Cockcroft and Ernest Walton, using a recently constructed accelerator of their own design, studied the following (p, α) reaction:

The reaction that first verified $E = mc^2$

$$\text{p} + ^{7}_{3}\text{Li} \rightarrow 2\alpha.$$

The two alpha particles that are products of the reaction gain kinetic energies much greater than the kinetic energy of the incident proton. Cockcroft and Walton found that the net increase of kinetic energy matched the loss of rest energy in the reaction.

■ EXAMPLE 1: If the kinetic energy of the incident proton is 600 keV (0.6 MeV), what should be the observed total kinetic energy of the two alpha particles? We may determine the mass change in tabular form (it is convenient to use *atomic* instead of nuclear masses; the extra electron masses cancel):

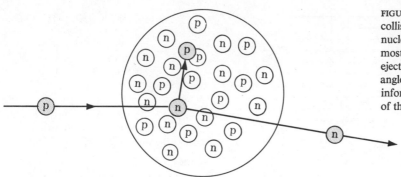

FIGURE 26.10   Model of a very high energy collision. The incoming proton "sees" the nucleus as a gas of nucleons. It may give up most of its energy to a single neutron and eject it from the nucleus. The energies and angles of neutrons ejected in this way give information on the momentum distribution of the nucleons in the nuclear "gas."

	Before		*After*
	$m(^1\mathrm{H}) = 1.00783$ amu		$m(^4\mathrm{He}) = 4.00260$ amu
	$m(^7\mathrm{Li}) = 7.01601$ amu		$m(^4\mathrm{He}) = 4.00260$ amu
	Initial mass $= 8.02384$ amu		Final mass $= 8.00520$ amu

The decrease of mass is 0.01864 amu, whose equivalent energy is $\Delta M\,c^2 =$ (0.01864 amu)(931.5 MeV/amu) = 17.36 MeV.* The process is strongly exothermic (energy-producing). This energy, added to the initial kinetic energy (0.6 MeV), gives the predicted total kinetic energy of the alpha particles, 17.96 MeV.   ∎

REACTION CROSS SECTIONS

Classically, a nucleus presents to a beam of incident particles a cross section πR^2 (Figure 26.11).   For a typical nuclear radius of 6 fm, this classical cross section is

$$\sigma = \pi R^2 = \pi(6 \times 10^{-15}\ \mathrm{m})^2$$

$$\cong 1.1 \times 10^{-28}\ \mathrm{m}^2 = 1.1\ \mathrm{barn}.$$

The barn, originally a tongue-in-cheek name for the "large" area, 10^{-28} m², has become a standard unit for expressing nuclear cross sections. It typifies the size of a nucleus.

Nuclei are about as large as a "barn"

   Cross sections are measured in two ways.   Easiest to determine is the *total* cross section, the effective area of the target for removing a particle from the

$\sigma = \pi R^2$

$L = pb$

b

p

Undeflected

trajectory

R

Target nucleus

FIGURE 26.11   Classical view of projectiles approaching a target nucleus. A particle of momentum p and impact parameter b has angular momentum $L = pb$ relative to the center of the nucleus.

---

* Using mass data available at the time, Cockcroft and Walton calculated this quantity to be 14.3 ± 2.7 MeV. For the gain in kinetic energy they measured the remarkably accurate value 17.2 MeV. [*Proceedings of the Royal Society, London,* **137,** 229 (1932).]

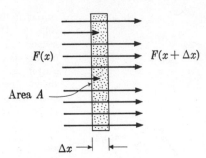

FIGURE 26.12   The decrease of flux of a beam passing through a piece of target material measures the total cross section.

incident parallel beam in any way (including scattering and reactions). Consider flux $F(x)$ incident on a thin sheet of target material containing n nuclei/m^3 (Figure 26.12). The total number of nuclei in the target of area A and thickness Δx is $N = nA\,\Delta x$. If each nucleus presents a total cross section σ_T to the beam, the total area that will intercept the beam is $N\sigma_T$. The fraction of incident particles that do *not* get through undeflected is the fraction of the total area A occupied by the intercepting area $N\sigma_T$. (We assume Δx to be sufficiently small that $N\sigma_T$ is much less than A; the target is mostly transparent.) The fractional change of flux is

$$\frac{\Delta F}{F} = -\frac{N\sigma_T}{A} = -n\sigma_T\,\Delta x.$$

This can be rewritten as $\Delta F/\Delta x = -n\sigma_T F$. In the limit of small Δx, it is a differential equation,

$$\frac{dF}{dx} = -n\sigma_T F, \tag{26.30}$$

Attenuation of undeflected flux measures total cross section

whose solution is a decreasing exponential,

$$F = F_0 e^{-n\sigma_T x}. \tag{26.31}$$

For a target of any thickness, the undeflected flux diminishes exponentially with thickness. A measurement of F/F_0 for any known thickness provides a measure of the total cross section σ_T.*

■ EXAMPLE 2:   For a typical density of atoms in solid matter, $n = 6 \times 10^{28}$ atoms/m^3, and for a total cross section of 3 barns, what thickness of target is required to decrease the intensity of the undeflected beam by a factor of e? The required thickness is determined by the condition $n\sigma_T x = 1$, which implies

$$x = \frac{1}{n\sigma_T} = \frac{1}{(6 \times 10^{28})(3 \times 10^{-28})}$$

$$= 0.056 \text{ m} = 5.6 \text{ cm}.$$

This substantial macroscopic thickness reinforces the idea that the atom is mostly empty space.   ■

---

* For a beam of charged particles, the *total* cross section is always infinite, because of the long range of the electric force. However, if particles deflected by less than some specified small angle are counted as part of the undeflected beam, a finite cross section will be measured.

To measure particular kinds of cross sections, more elaborate experiments are needed. The flux of outgoing particles must be measured as a function of angle (perhaps at each of several energies), to obtain a differential cross section. The differential cross section must then be integrated over solid angle to obtain the net cross section for the process.

The quantum description of scattering and reactions must take into account the wave aspect of the incident beam. To discuss this wave aspect, it is useful to invoke a form of the correspondence principle: If the part of the beam intercepted by the target includes many angular momenta, a semiclassical description is possible; if it includes only one or a few angular momenta, a quantum description is essential. As shown in Figure 26.11, the classical angular momentum of an incident particle, relative to the center of the nucleus, is

A correspondence principle for scattering

$$L = pb,$$

where p is the momentum of the particle and b is the "impact parameter," the distance by which the extrapolated trajectory would miss the center of the nucleus. Setting $L = \sqrt{\ell(\ell + 1)}\,\hbar$, we obtain

$$\sqrt{\ell(\ell + 1)} = \frac{pb}{\hbar} = \frac{b}{\lambdabar}, \qquad (26.32)$$

where $\lambdabar\ (= \hbar/p)$ is the reduced de Broglie wavelength of the incident particles. For the part of the beam directed at the edge of the nucleus, $b = R$, and

$$\sqrt{\ell_{max}(\ell_{max} + 1)} = \frac{R}{\lambdabar}. \qquad (26.33)$$

If the reduced de Broglie wavelength is much less than the nuclear radius, $\ell_{max} \gg 1$. Then many angular momenta strike the nucleus, and a semiclassical description is possible. Interestingly, however, diffraction effects remain important even in this limit. The wave is influenced at distances greater than R, and the total cross section proves to be twice the classical value,

$$\sigma_T = 2\pi R^2 \qquad (\ell_{max} \gg 1). \qquad (26.34)$$

Many angular momenta strike the nucleus

If $\lambdabar$ is greater than R, a single wavelength encompasses the nucleus. The part of the wave striking the nucleus has orbital quantum number $\ell = 0$. The most interesting implication of this situation is that the cross section may be much larger than πR^2. The wave can be influenced at distances comparable to $\lambdabar$. A theorem of quantum mechanics specifies a maximum cross section in this limit:

$$\sigma_T \leq \pi \lambdabar^2 \qquad (\lambdabar \gg R). \qquad (26.35)$$

Only $\ell = 0$ strikes the nucleus

The nearest we can come to a classical view of a wave impinging on a target nucleus is to think of a set of annular regions of radii $\lambdabar$, $2\lambdabar$, $3\lambdabar$, and so on (Figure 26.13). Between $b = \ell\lambdabar$ and $b = (\ell + 1)\lambdabar$ is an area $(2\ell + 1)\pi\lambdabar^2$, which corresponds to classical trajectories with $L \cong \ell\hbar$. Roughly, each region represents the part of the incident beam with a particular orbital quantum number ℓ. The correspondence-principle condition is that the nucleus intercept many of these regions.

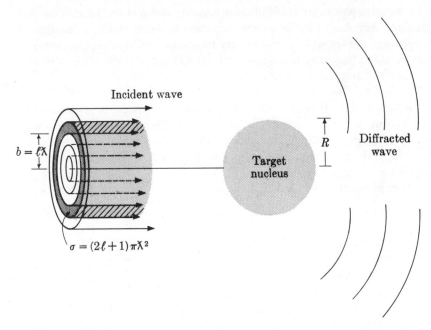

FIGURE 26.13   Quantum view of projectiles approaching a target nucleus. The annular part of the wave of impact parameter $\ell\lambdabar$ to $(\ell + 1)\lambdabar$ corresponds to classical trajectories of angular momentum $L \cong \ell\hbar$ relative to the center of the nucleus.

■ EXAMPLE 3:   A beam of 100-MeV neutrons strikes a lead target. The radius of the lead nucleus is 7 fm. What is the expected total cross section? In a non-relativistic approximation (only fair in this case), the neutron momentum is $p = \sqrt{2mE}$, and its reduced de Broglie wavelength is

$$\lambdabar = \frac{\hbar}{p} = \frac{\hbar}{\sqrt{2mE}}.$$

For ease of evaluation, multiply numerator and denominator by c, to obtain

$$\lambdabar = \frac{\hbar c}{\sqrt{2mc^2E}} = \frac{197 \text{ MeV fm}}{\sqrt{2(940 \text{ MeV})(100 \text{ MeV})}} = 0.45 \text{ fm.}$$

Since this is much smaller than the radius, many angular momenta participate ($\ell_{\max} \cong R/\lambdabar \cong 15$), and Equation 26.34 can be used:

$$\sigma_{\mathrm{T}} = 2\pi R^2 = 2\pi(7 \times 10^{-15} \text{ m})^2 = 3.1 \text{ barns.}\qquad ■$$

REACTIONS INDUCED BY SLOW NEUTRONS

Since a neutron has no appreciable electromagnetic interaction with nuclei or with electrons, it can reach a nucleus even if it is of very low energy. A neutron brought into thermal equilibrium with matter at room temperature has a reduced de Broglie wavelength

For thermal neutron, $\lambda \gg R$

$$\lambdabar = 2.3 \times 10^{-11} \text{ m} = 23{,}000 \text{ fm.}$$

Since this is much greater than the nuclear radius, it opens up the possibility of very large cross sections. In practice, the limiting cross section permitted by Equation 26.35 is reached only at certain resonance energies. On the average, at low energies, the cross section for neutron-induced reactions is, in order of magnitude,

$$\sigma_T \approx \pi \lambdabar R. \qquad (26.36)$$

Although much less than $\pi \lambdabar$, this is much greater than πR^2. Thermal neutron cross sections of several thousand barns are not unusual.

The most common reaction induced by a slow neutron is capture followed by the emission of one or more gamma rays. The cross section for a reaction of this kind,

$$n + {}^{113}_{48}\text{Cd} \rightarrow {}^{114}_{48}\text{Cd} + \gamma\text{'s},$$

Neutron capture reaction

is shown in Figure 26.14. Cadmium happens to have an especially large neutron capture cross section and is, therefore, one of the elements used in reactor control rods. For a few of the heavy elements, fission can also be induced by slow neutrons. Figure 26.15 shows the fission cross section as a function of neutron energy for ${}^{235}_{92}\text{U}$.

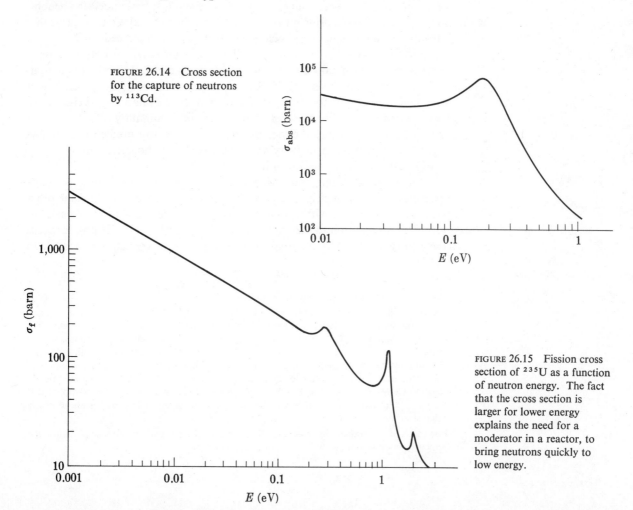

FIGURE 26.14   Cross section for the capture of neutrons by ^{113}Cd.

FIGURE 26.15   Fission cross section of ^{235}U as a function of neutron energy. The fact that the cross section is larger for lower energy explains the need for a moderator in a reactor, to bring neutrons quickly to low energy.

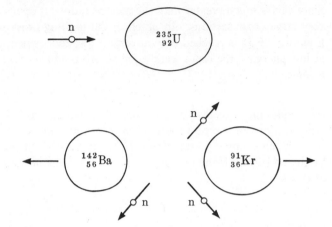

FIGURE 26.16 One of many possible modes of fission. A nucleus of ^{235}U, after absorbing a neutron to become an excited nucleus of ^{236}U, might break apart into fragments that are isotopes of barium and krypton and at the same time emit several neutrons.

26.6   Fission

Fission and fusion, the sources of large-scale nuclear energy, deserve more than passing notice in a modern survey of physics. Each is a basic nuclear phenomenon depending on the principles of quantum mechanics and relativity; together their impact on contemporary society is enormous and unprecedented.

In its essentials, fission is quite similar to alpha decay. In both processes, a piece of a nucleus breaks off, and the two parts fly apart. In both, a potential-energy barrier prevents very rapid decay. Although the energetic possibility of fission had been known for years, its discovery in 1939 came as a surprise—both to its discoverers* and to the rest of the scientific community. This is not to say that fission upset any theories or disagreed with any predictions. It was simply unexpected since in forty years of work in radioactivity and nuclear transformations, no one had seen it.

Among the naturally occurring elements, spontaneous fission is rare.† However, if a heavy nucleus is excited, by neutron absorption or in some other way, fission may occur swiftly. In a typical fission process, one or more neutrons are emitted, in addition to the major nuclear fragments (Figure 26.16). Because these neutrons can serve as triggers of further fission events, a fission chain reaction is possible.

---

* Fission products were probably first observed (through their radioactivity) by Enrico Fermi and coworkers in 1934, but they were not recognized as such at the time. In December, 1938, Otto Hahn and Fritz Strassmann in Berlin found definite chemical evidence for the production of barium ($Z = 56$) by uranium bombarded by neutrons. Although they probably suspected that fission was responsible, they did not at once commit themselves to this hypothesis in print. Credit for first correctly interpreting the Hahn-Strassmann results goes to Lise Meitner and Otto Frisch in Stockholm. In January, 1939, they proposed that uranium, activated by neutron bombardment, could break apart into fragments of nearly equal size.

† For some of the transuranic elements discovered in recent years, spontaneous fission is a principal mode of radioactive decay (see Figure 25.16).

THEORY OF FISSION

The discovery of fission was a seed dropped on fertile ground. With remarkable speed, Niels Bohr and John Wheeler published a theory of the dynamic process of fission. With equal speed, physicists grasped its practical potentialities. In assessing the prospects of large-scale energy release by means of fission, three basic questions needed to be answered. The first, the easiest, and the least important was: How much energy is released in a fission event? From a binding-energy curve like that in Figure 25.17, the answer could be predicted to be about 1 MeV per nucleon, or about 200 MeV per fission event. This prediction was soon verified by experiment. The reason the precise magnitude of the energy release is not very important is that this energy, quickly transformed to heat, is irrelevant to the nuclear course of events. Although it is obviously of great practical significance, fission energy contributes nothing to the chain-reaction process.

Energy release in fission event about 200 *MeV*

The second question was: Which nuclei are most fissionable? The third was: How many neutrons are emitted in a fission event? Once these questions were answered, it could be decided whether a fission chain reaction could be self-sustaining and if so, with what isotopes.

Nuclear fission would have been a dramatic discovery at any time. Coming as it did on the eve of a major war and in the midst of a period of persecution of Jews in Germany, its drama was heightened. The persecution drove many of Europe's leading scientists to the United States, and the war drove fission work into secrecy. Half a dozen years after the discovery of fission, the United States emerged as the scientific leader of the world, atomic energy was a household word, and ties forged between science and government set a pattern for the support of large-scale research that has lasted to the present day.

In essence, the Bohr-Wheeler theory of fission is simple. Two forces are at work in a heavy nucleus—the nuclear force, holding the nucleus together, and the Coulomb force, tending to blow the nucleus apart (see Figure 26.17). For all the nuclei we know the nuclear force is in control, but for the heaviest known nuclei it is only barely in control. The problem of the fissionability of a nucleus can be posed this way: If a nucleus is stretched into an elongated shape, which is greater—the repulsive electric force tending to push it into an even more elongated shape or the attractive nuclear force tending to restore it to a

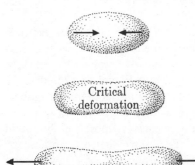

FIGURE 26.17 The mechanism of fission. Attractive nuclear forces create an effective surface tension tending to keep the nucleus in near-spherical form. Electrical repulsion between protons tends to blow the nucleus apart. Below a critical deformation, the surface tension wins. Beyond the critical deformation, the electrical repulsion wins.

The fission barrier

spherical or near spherical shape? If a nucleus like uranium is slightly distorted from its normal shape, the nuclear force wins out, tending to restore it to its original shape. If it is distorted much further, the electric force wins out and it splits in two (or occasionally three). Between these two degrees of distortion is an energy barrier. In slow spontaneous fission, this barrier can be penetrated, just as a barrier is penetrated in alpha decay. For the rapid fission that occurs in reactors or bombs, the barrier must be surmounted. The magnitude of the energy barrier to be overcome depends sensitively on the relative magnitude of two energies of opposite sign: the Coulomb energy, arising from the mutual repulsion of the protons, and the surface-tension energy, arising from the nuclear forces. From approximate considerations of these energies, we can extract a significant parameter, which measures nuclear fissionability.

Consider first the electric energy. According to Equation 25.18, this energy is approximately proportional to Z^2/R:

$$U_{\text{coulomb}} \sim \frac{Z^2}{R}.$$

The other relevant energy is the nuclear surface-tension energy. It is proportional to the surface area of the nucleus, or to the square of the nuclear radius

$$U_{\text{surface}} \sim R^2.$$

The ratio $U_{\text{coulomb}}/U_{\text{surface}}$ is then proportional to Z^2/R^3. Since R^3 is proportional to the mass number A (see Equation 25.8), we can write

Barrier height depends on
Z^2/A

$$\frac{U_{\text{coulomb}}}{U_{\text{surface}}} \sim \frac{Z^2}{A}. \tag{26.37}$$

Bohr and Wheeler recognized that this ratio, Z^2/A, is an important parameter of fission. The greater its magnitude, the more nearly does the repulsive electric force win out over the attractive nuclear force, and the more easily fissionable is the nucleus. Consider nuclei of the two principal isotopes of uranium, to each of which a neutron is added:

$$^{235}\text{U} + \text{n} = {}^{236}\text{U}: \qquad Z^2/A = 35.9,$$
$$^{238}\text{U} + \text{n} = {}^{239}\text{U}: \qquad Z^2/A = 35.4.$$

Because of this small difference, the fission energy barrier is slightly lower for ^{236}U than for ^{239}U.

Another and even more important contributor to the distinction between the fissionability of these two uranium isotopes is the somewhat greater excitation energy provided when ^{235}U absorbs a neutron than when ^{238}U absorbs a neutron. A subtle effect not evident in the graph of Figure 25.17 is that the binding energy per nucleon is slightly greater in even-A nuclei than in neighboring odd-A nuclei (an effect related to the exclusion principle). Thus a slow

Neutron capture by odd-A
nucleus releases more energy

neutron captured by ^{235}U, forming an even-A nucleus, is more tightly bound and provides more excitation energy than does a slow neutron captured by ^{238}U. The difference is all-important. In ^{235}U, the absorption of a slow neutron provides enough energy to surmount the fission barrier. In ^{238}U, it does not.

Considerations of this kind led to a prediction and a gamble. The transuranic elements, with Z greater than 92, should be even more easily fissionable than uranium. Once a self-sustaining reactor had been achieved, a new prospect appeared: transuranic isotopes could be "manufactured" in quantity, then used in new reactors or in bombs. The practical isotope to consider was plutonium 239 ($Z = 94$). It can be created from the abundant isotope, uranium 238, by the following sequence:

$$n + {}^{238}_{92}U \rightarrow {}^{239}_{92}U + \gamma\text{'s},$$

$$^{239}_{92}U \rightarrow {}^{239}_{93}Np + e^- + \overline{\nu}_e \quad \text{(half life 24 min)},$$

$$^{239}_{93}Np \rightarrow {}^{239}_{94}Pu + e^- + \overline{\nu}_e \quad \text{(half life 2.35 days)}.$$

The manufacture of ^{239}Pu

A nucleus of ^{238}U absorbs a neutron to become ^{239}U. In a few days, the ^{239}U nucleus spontaneously transforms itself via two beta decays into $^{239}_{94}Pu$, a highly fissionable isotope:

$$^{239}Pu + n = {}^{240}Pu: \quad \frac{Z^2}{A} = 36.8.$$

Because of its greater Z^2/A value, plutonium 240 has a lower fission barrier than either isotope of uranium. It also shares with uranium 236 an even value of A, giving it the advantage of a large neutron binding energy.

In 1939, plutonium was unknown and unnamed. By the summer of 1945, only two and a half years after the first reactor went critical, an enormous and uncertain investment in plutonium-producing reactors had paid off. Transmutation on a large scale was successful. Enough ^{239}Pu had been created for the bomb tested in New Mexico and for the bomb that devastated Nagasaki. (The Hiroshima bomb was an untested model with a core of ^{235}U.)

REACTORS

The third question posed above was: How many neutrons are emitted in a fission event? This was a question that had to be settled by experiment. Nuclear theory was not refined enough to deal with it. For ^{235}U, the number is approximately 2.5. As with most other submicroscopic events, laws of probability govern the fission event. One nucleus of ^{235}U might split without emitting any neutrons; another might emit six. The average number is 2.5. The absorption of even a single neutron can induce fission. Consequently, the average production of 2.5 neutrons for each one absorbed by a fissioning nucleus appears to be quite favorable for a chain reaction. Indeed it is, in a solid chunk of ^{235}U or ^{239}Pu. These are what lie in the core of an atomic bomb. In them, the chain reaction is not only self-sustaining but is explosively multiplying. The neutron multiplication in each "generation" produces an exponential increase of energy release until the reaction is slowed by a combination of depletion of the fissionable material and expansion of the core.

Neutron multiplication, the key to a chain reaction

In the early 1940s, purified ^{235}U and ^{239}Pu were unavailable. Fermi and his coworkers had to work with ordinary uranium, less than one percent of which is the easily fissionable isotope, ^{235}U. In this material, a neutron has available several possible fates other than to cause fission. Chief among these are escape from the material into nonfissionable surroundings and absorption by ^{238}U without inducing fission. To counter escape, the designers of the first reactor—or atomic pile, as it was then called—made it large, about 20 feet across, with its pieces of uranium buried in 400 tons of graphite. The carbon nuclei in graphite happen to have a very low capture cross section for neutrons,* and they are light enough so that their recoil drains energy from neutrons in collisions between neutrons and nucleus. This degrading of the neutron energy serves to enhance the probability that a neutron finds its way into a ^{235}U nucleus rather than a ^{238}U nucleus. The lower the energy of the neutron, the greater is the fission cross section of ^{235}U (Figure 26.15). To avoid a runaway reaction, the reactor includes control rods made of a material whose nuclei have a high cross section for neutron absorption. Fully inserted into the reactor, the control rods halt the chain reaction; fully removed, they could permit the reaction to build up to explosive level or at least to a level sufficient to melt the uranium.

The importance of slowing the neutrons

Under the leadership of Enrico Fermi, the first reactor, a latticework of uranium and graphite with cadmium control rods, achieved a self-sustaining chain reaction on December 2, 1942. On that day, Arthur Compton, who had witnessed the event, telephoned James Conant, then president of Harvard University, and said, "Jim, you'll be interested to know that the Italian navigator has just landed in the new world."†

Reactor fuel now enriched in ^{235}U

The earliest production reactors—those at Hanford, Washington, built to produce plutonium—necessarily used normal uranium as fuel. Contemporary reactors, both for research and for power production, use uranium partially enriched in the isotope ^{235}U. One design of a power reactor is shown schematically in Figure 26.18.

FISSION BOMBS

The idea of critical mass

Among other things, nuclear fission has contributed to our society some new phrases—"critical mass" and "critical size." For any chosen composition and design, a reactor must be greater than some minimum size and minimum mass in order to function. Otherwise, neutron loss makes it impossible for one fission event to trigger one or more others and propagate the chain reaction. A reactor is subcritical if its rate of energy generation is decaying, supercritical if its rate of energy generation is increasing, and just critical if its rate of energy generation is steady. The same ideas of critical size and critical mass apply to bombs. For a sphere of pure ^{239}Pu, the critical size is a few inches in diameter.

Two bomb designs

The aim of bomb design is to create a supercritical mass and to keep it that way for as long as possible, perhaps as long as a microsecond. A supercritical mass can be created by bringing together two subcritical pieces or

* The German atomic bomb project was seriously set back by an error of measurement that led scientists there to believe that carbon could not be used in a reactor because they thought it had a high capture cross section for neutrons. As a result, they worked instead toward a reactor using heavy water. Even as late as 1945, not enough heavy water had been accumulated in Germany to make a self-sustaining reactor. See David Irving, *The German Atomic Bomb* (New York: Simon and Schuster, 1967).

† Arthur Compton, *Atomic Quest* (New York: Oxford University Press, 1956).

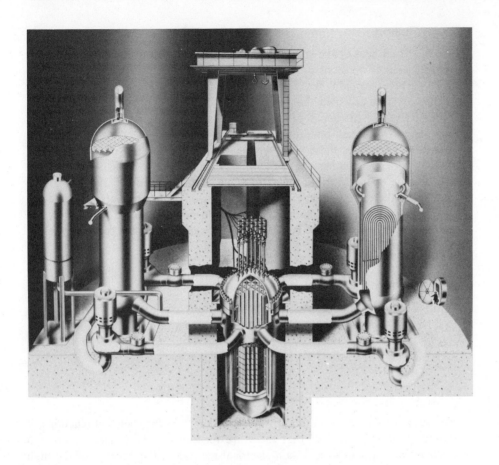

FIGURE 26.18   Schematic diagram of a pressurized-water reactor. Water at a
pressure of about 150 atm and a temperature of about 285 °C enters the
bottom of the reactor vessel (center of diagram). At a temperature of about
315 °C, still liquid because of its high pressure, it leaves the reactor and cir-
culates through pipes in the large heat-exchanger vessels (left and right of
diagram). There, lower-pressure water in a separate system is converted to
steam. The steam drives turbines (not shown), which turn generators to supply
electricity. Control rods, which move vertically, are controlled from above the
reactor vessel. (Illustration courtesy of the U.S. Atomic Energy Commission.)

by compressing a single subcritical piece. In either case, speed is important.
In the uranium bomb dropped on Hiroshima, an explosive charge drove one
piece of uranium against another. In the plutonium bomb dropped on Nagasaki,
a small sphere of plutonium at the center was compressed by the implosion of
a surrounding mass of high explosive. Sitting now in the arsenals of the world's
great powers are thousands of bombs, each containing a not quite critical mass
of fissionable material and a charge of chemical explosive capable of making it
go supercritical. A good many of these atomic bombs in turn stand ready to
trigger even more devastating thermonuclear explosions.

26.7   Fusion

The light and heat of the sun are derived principally from the energy released by the fusion of nucleons to form alpha particles. In stars older than our sun, alpha particles probably fuse to form the nuclei of heavier elements. According to the currently accepted theories of stellar evolution, all of the elements (or, more accurately, the nuclei of all of the elements) up to and beyond uranium are created by nucleus-building reactions in the late stages of the life of a star. In a nova explosion, these newly created nuclei are sprayed into the cosmos. As they cool, they gather about themselves their protective shells of electrons, and become docile neutral atoms. It is an interesting thought that the atoms making up the elaborate order of living matter on earth probably originated in the nuclear chaos at the centers of remote and now long-dead stars. Only the residual radioactivity of the heavy elements reminds us of the turbulent beginnings of terrestrial matter.

Man is made of stardust

SOLAR ENERGY

In the sun, which still consists mostly of protons and electrons, protons unite to form alpha particles according to the following sequence of reactions:

Principal solar energy cycle

$$1. \qquad {}_1^1\mathrm{H} + {}_1^1\mathrm{H} \to {}_1^2\mathrm{H} + \mathrm{e}^+ + \nu_e,$$

$$2. \qquad {}_1^1\mathrm{H} + {}_1^2\mathrm{H} \to {}_2^3\mathrm{He},$$

$$3. \qquad {}_2^3\mathrm{He} + {}_2^3\mathrm{He} \to {}_2^4\mathrm{He} + 2{}_1^1\mathrm{H}.$$

Although we use here a notation similar to that used for chemical reactions, it is important to remember that these are reactions of bare nuclei. Enough electrons are present to maintain electrical neutrality, but because of the high temperature, they are not bound to nuclei, nor do they participate in the reaction. The first of these three solar reactions is especially interesting because it involves strong and weak interactions simultaneously. Normally, a neutron undergoes beta decay to become a proton. According to the theory of weak interactions, a proton is equally favorably disposed to undergo beta decay (transforming itself into a neutron by emitting a positron and a neutrino). Energy conservation prevents a free proton from doing so. In many radioactive nuclei, however, the inhibition is overcome by a release of nuclear binding energy. That is what happens in this solar fusion reaction. The binding energy of the deuteron (2.2 MeV) is more than sufficient to provide the neutron-proton mass difference plus the mass of the emitted positron. Once two protons create a deuteron in this way, the deuteron can fuse with another proton to make a helium 3 nucleus. Finally, two helium 3 nuclei react to form an alpha particle and two protons. The net result of two reactions of type 1, two of type 2, and one of type 3 can be summarized by a single reaction equation,

$$4{}_1^1\mathrm{H} \to {}_2^4\mathrm{He} + 2\mathrm{e}^+ + 2\nu_e,$$

or, in somewhat simpler notation,

$$4\mathrm{p} \to \alpha + 2\mathrm{e}^+ + 2\nu_e. \tag{26.38}$$

Note, in this net reaction, the conservation of charge, of baryon number, and of electron family number.

In this so-called proton-proton cycle in the sun, 6.2 MeV of energy per proton is released. A few percent of this energy is given to neutrinos, which escape at once from the center of the sun without impediment. Nearly 10^{11} of these solar neutrinos strike each square centimeter of the earth each second. The rest of the energy goes at first into kinetic energy of charged particles, eventually into electromagnetic energy—photons. In addition, by annihilating with electrons, the positrons add another increment of energy to the total. In each annihilation event,

$$e^+ + e^- \rightarrow 2\gamma,$$

the complete conversion of mass to energy yields about 1 MeV. Although positron annihilation involves neither nuclei nor nuclear force, it is another exothermic contributor to the proton-proton cycle, raising the total energy release from 6.2 to 6.7 MeV per nucleon. Including positron annihilation, the net reaction is

$$2e^- + 4p \rightarrow \alpha + 2\nu_e + k\gamma. \qquad (26.39)$$

Net reaction in the sun

The notation $k\gamma$ on the right designates an unknown number of photons. Eventually, for each proton burned in the solar furnace, millions of photons are radiated at the surface.

The net energy release in the sun's proton-proton cycle may be calculated readily from the masses of the participating particles:

Before

Mass of 4 protons $= 4(1.007277)$	$= 4.02911$ amu
Mass of 2 electrons $= 2(0.000549)$	$= 0.00110$ amu
Total mass of reacting particles	$= 4.03021$ amu

After

Mass of alpha particle	$= 4.00150$ amu
Net loss of mass	$= 0.02871$ amu
Net loss of energy $= (0.02871$ amu$)(931$ MeV/amu$) = 26.7$ MeV.	

Dividing 26.7 MeV by 4, we get 6.7 MeV, the energy release per nucleon quoted above. The fractional conversion of mass to energy in the sun's fusion reactions is 0.7 percent, or one part in 140. This is about eight times the fractional conversion in uranium fission and more than 100 million times the fractional conversion in a typical chemical explosion. Each day the sun burns 5.3×10^{16} kg of its hydrogen into alpha-particle ashes, thereby transforming about 3.7×10^{14} kg of its mass into energy, a rate of output equivalent to the explosions of billions of multimegaton weapons each second.

Energy production in solar fusion

Fusion reactions in the sun and other stars are examples of *thermonuclear reactions*—that is, nuclear reactions brought about by high temperature. Thermonuclear reactions are, quite literally, nuclear burning. They are completely analogous to ordinary chemical combustion. In chemical (or atomic) burning, high temperature initiates the reaction, and energy released by the reaction keeps the temperature high and spreads the fire. The chemical reaction

A close analogy: thermonuclear reactions and ordinary combustion

may proceed through several steps; its net result is a combination of atoms into more tightly bound molecules. All of these features characterize nuclear burning as well. More tightly bound nuclei are produced by a reaction or series of reactions initiated and propagated by high temperature. Apart from the nature of the reacting particles, the difference is one of scale. At a temperature of 10^7 K or more, the thermonuclear flame is at least 10^4 times hotter and at least 10^6 times more potent as an energy source than a typical chemical flame. For the design of thermonuclear weapons, one more common feature of nuclear and atomic combustion is important—the harmlessness of cold reactants. The concept of critical mass, important for fissionable material, is not applicable to thermonuclear fuel. Just as there is no limit to the size of a lumber yard or an oil storage depot, there is no theoretical limit to the size of a thermonuclear weapon. Any amount of nuclear fuel can be stored with safety—until it is ignited. Although a match is sufficient to set ablaze the lumber yard or the oil depot, nothing less than a fission bomb can ignite a thermonuclear reaction.*

FUSION POWER

The sun is forced, as it were, to make do with protons as its nuclear fuel. On earth, man has available a variety of other nuclei, some of which react with higher probability and at lower temperatures than do protons. Actually, the sun's proton-proton cycle proceeds at a very leisurely pace. It would be impractical to use the same reaction as an energy source on earth. More reactive are the heavier isotopes of hydrogen, deuterium and tritium. Especially favorable is the reaction between a deuteron and a triton, known as the DT reaction, which can proceed rapidly at a temperature of about 6×10^7 K:

$$\text{$_1^2$H} + \text{$_1^3$H} \rightarrow \text{$_2^4$He} + \text{n},$$

The DT reaction   or, in simpler notation,

$$\text{d} + \text{t} \rightarrow \alpha + \text{n}. \tag{26.40}$$

This reaction releases 17.6 MeV, or about 3.5 MeV per nucleon. Most of this energy—14 MeV—appears as kinetic energy of the neutron.

Except for trace amounts produced by cosmic rays, tritium does not occur in nature. It must be manufactured at great expense in nuclear reactors; once manufactured, it decays into ^{3}He with a half life of 12.33 years. If fusion is to be practical as a *controlled* power source in the future, it must rely on plentiful deuterium for fuel. The DD reaction proceeds with approximately equal probability in two ways:

DD reactions

1. $\text{d} + \text{d} \rightarrow \text{^{3}He} + \text{n}$ (energy release = 3.3 MeV),   (26.41)

2. $\text{d} + \text{d} \rightarrow \text{t} + \text{p}$ (energy release = 4.0 MeV).   (26.42)

In conditions that can be visualized on earth (even in a thermonuclear explosion), the helium 3 produced does not significantly react further. The tritium, however, is consumed by the DT reaction, adding a large increment of energy. The net

---

* There is speculation that a sufficiently powerful laser might also be able to ignite a thermonuclear reaction.

reaction in the burning of pure deuterium is, approximately,

$$5d \rightarrow {}^3He + {}^4He + 2n + p \quad \text{(energy release} = 25 \text{ MeV).} \quad (26.43)$$

The high temperature required for thermonuclear reactions can be understood quite simply in terms of the small size of nuclei and the electric repulsive force between them. In order for a pair of deuterons, or a deuteron and a triton, to "touch"—that is, to be close enough together for their wave amplitudes to overlap significantly—their centers must be separated by not more than about 10 fm. At this separation, the electric potential energy associated with their relative position can readily be calculated:

$$U = \frac{1}{4\pi\epsilon_0} \frac{e^2}{r} = \frac{(9.0 \times 10^9)(1.60 \times 10^{-19})^2}{10^{-14}}$$

$$= 2.30 \times 10^{-14} \text{ J}$$

$$= 1.44 \times 10^5 \text{ eV} = 144 \text{ keV}.$$

Although small compared with energies available in cyclotrons and other accelerators, this energy is enormous compared with ordinary thermal energy. Normally the electric repulsion between hydrogen nuclei, or between any other nuclei, very effectively keeps them apart, even if their atomic electrons are stripped away. Even at a temperature of 10,000 K, capable of vaporizing all matter, the mean kinetic energy of thermal motion is only 1.3 eV per particle, smaller by a factor of 10^5 than the potential barrier of 144 keV calculated above. What temperature would be required in order that an average pair of deuterons, in a head-on collision, could come within 10 fm of each other? Suppose that each deuteron has an energy $\frac{3}{2}kT$ equal to half the total required, or

Coulomb repulsion imposes the need for high temperature

$$\tfrac{3}{2}kT = 72 \text{ keV} = 1.15 \times 10^{-14} \text{ J}.$$

Using $k = 1.38 \times 10^{-23}$ J/K, we find that

$$T = 5.6 \times 10^8 \text{ K}.$$

In energy units, $kT = 48$ keV. The actual temperature requirement to ignite deuterium is not quite this extreme, for two reasons. First, some nuclei have considerably more kinetic energy than the average; they can more easily overcome the force of electric repulsion. Second, barrier penetration can be significant; the nuclei need not all surmount the potential-energy barrier in order to react. In practice, thermonuclear *explosions* proceed at temperatures of about 6×10^7 K ($kT = 5$ keV). A fission bomb can provide ignition at this temperature. The temperature envisioned for the controlled release of fusion energy is higher, about 2×10^8 K.

Since the early 1950s, considerable research in the United States and other countries has been directed toward the development of a controlled thermonuclear reactor. Most experts are optimistic about eventual success; time estimates vary from years to decades.* In the schemes that have received the

Prospects of fusion power

---

* See William C. Gough and Bernard J. Eastlund, "The Prospects of Fusion Power," *Scientific American*, February, 1971.

most attention, the extraordinarily hot reacting plasmas are confined by means of magnetic fields.* So far, plasmas have shown themselves to be very resourceful at avoiding lengthy confinement, although confinement times have gradually increased over the years. Because of our reserves of fossil fuels and fissionable materials, it is not crucial that the thermonuclear power project succeed in the next few decades or even in the next hundred years. However, an abundant supply of energy in the long term may hinge on its eventual success.

THERMONUCLEAR WEAPONS

As a major component of a bomb, deuterium has a serious disadvantage. In order to be stored compactly at high density, it must be cooled to its liquefaction temperature of 20 K (-253 °C). This requires elaborate refrigeration techniques. The fusion fuel actually used in the "H bomb" is a particular isotopic form of lithium hydride, called lithium 6 deuteride ($^6_3$Li $^2_1$H), which is a solid at normal temperature. The lithium plays two important roles as a constituent of the thermonuclear fuel. First, through its chemical combination with deuterium, it holds the deuterons close together, thereby helping to make possible the DD reaction (Formulas 26.41 and 26.42). Second, the lithium itself participates in a key reaction that "manufactures" tritium to stoke the DT reaction.

Lithium deuteride is the H bomb fuel

The significant nuclear reactions in lithium 6 deuteride are these:

1. $\quad ^2_1$H $+ \, ^2_1$H $\rightarrow \, ^3_2$He $+$ n $\qquad$ (energy release $= 3.3$ MeV),

2. $\quad ^2_1$H $+ \, ^2_1$H $\rightarrow \, ^3_1$H $+$ p $\qquad$ (energy release $= 4.0$ MeV),

3. $\quad ^2_1$H $+ \, ^3_1$H $\rightarrow \, ^4_2$He $+$ n $\qquad$ (energy release $= 17.6$ MeV),

4. $\qquad ^6_3$Li $+$ n $\rightarrow \, ^3_1$H $+ \, ^4_2$He $\qquad$ (energy release $= 4.9$ MeV).

Tritium is manufactured during the burning

The first two are the branches of the DD reaction. The third is the DT reaction. The fourth reaction, like the second branch of the DD reaction, is a supplier of tritium for the DT reaction. This neutron-induced reaction is not itself a thermonuclear reaction since the neutron has no energy barrrier to overcome to reach the ^{6}Li nucleus. It is in fact a fission reaction (although the word "fission" is usually reserved to describe the splitting of heavy nuclei). The ^{6}Li nucleus absorbs a neutron, temporarily becoming a ^{7}Li nucleus that splits into a triton and an alpha particle. Note that in these four interlocked reactions, both tritons and neutrons play important roles, although neither is initially present in the fuel. Reactions 1 and 3 produce neutrons to stimulate the ^{6}Li reaction; reactions 2 and 4 produce tritium to burn in the DT reaction.

Fission of ^{238}U in H bomb case

One way to increase both the rate of burning and the energy release of a thermonuclear weapon is to encase its lithium 6 deuteride fuel in ^{238}U. The 14-MeV neutrons produced by the DT reaction, many of which escape from the combustion zone, are energetic enough to induce fission in ^{238}U. From the fission event emerge several lower energy neutrons that can stimulate the

---

* See Bruno Coppi and Jan Rem, "The Tokamak Approach in Fusion Research," *Scientific American*, July, 1972. An alternative to magnetic confinement is discussed in an article by Moshe J. Lubin and Arthur P. Fraas, "Fusion by Laser," *Scientific American*, June, 1971.

tritium-producing reaction in ^{6}Li. Through this sequence of fission-fusion-fission-fusion, the energy of the atomic bomb trigger can be multiplied a thousandfold, using only cheap and readily available materials—lithium 6, deuterium, and uranium 238. In such a uranium-encased weapon, about half of the energy and almost all of the hazardous fallout result from uranium fission. Most of the energy of so-called "clean" bombs comes from fusion.

The size and nature of the weapons stockpiles in the United States and other countries are not, of course, public information. A rough figure for the world total is about 100,000 nuclear weapons capable of releasing about 50 million kilotons of energy.* This is an explosive energy equivalent to more than 10 tons of TNT for each person on earth. (For comparison, the energy per fatality in the Hiroshima explosion was about 0.2 ton; 50 times more is now available for all of humanity.) Apart from blast and fire, the explosion of any major portion of the world stockpile of nuclear weapons would produce enough radioactive fallout to wipe out most of human life. That is the insane situation in which civilized man finds himself in the 1970s.

The world's weapons

The fruits of science give man power—power for good and power for ill. In the form of the world's weapons, nuclear energy is a major threat to human life. At the same time, through a myriad of research applications and, most notably, through the prospect of controlled fusion power, it is of enormous potential benefit to man. In a sane world, the threat could wither and the promise could bloom.

The two faces of knowledge

---

* See Herbert York, *Race to Oblivion* (New York: Simon and Schuster, 1970), pp. 41–48.

Summary of ideas and definitions

In radioactive decay, a fixed decay probability per unit time ($p_0 = 1/\tau$) for each parent nucleus leads to an exponential decay of intensity for a large sample,
$$I = I_0 e^{-t/\tau}. \tag{26.4}$$
The average lifetime of the parent nuclei is τ.

Alpha particles are nuclei of ^{4}He. They can be ejected spontaneously by some heavy nuclei. They were the principal projectiles of nuclear research before the invention of accelerators.

Alpha decay is a barrier-penetration phenomenon. For the "thick" barrier surrounding a heavy nucleus, the barrier penetration probability is extremely small (10^{-15} to 10^{-38}) and extremely sensitive to alpha-particle energy.

Beta particles are electrons (or positrons) created by the weak interaction, together with antineutrinos (or neutrinos), at the moment of radioactive decay.

Alpha and beta decay involve transmutation (change of atomic number); gamma decay does not.

Unraveling of the radioactive decay chains of heavy elements (1898–1913) led to

1. the discovery of new elements between bismuth ($Z = 83$) and thorium ($Z = 90$),
2. the discovery of isotopes,
3. the identification of radioactivity as an explosive event of great energy in an atom.

The curie is a unit of radioactive intensity (Equation 26.28), approximately equal to the number of disintegrations/sec in 1 gm of ^{226}Ra.

The rad (which differs little from the rem, the rep, and the roentgen) measures the energy deposited in matter by radiation (Equation 26.29).

Rutherford, in 1919, reported the first nuclear reaction, an (α, p) reaction: $\alpha + {}^{14}\text{N} \rightarrow p + {}^{17}\text{O}$.

The neutron was discovered (1932) as the product of an (α, n) reaction: $\alpha + {}^9\text{Be} \rightarrow n + {}^{12}\text{C}$.

The properties of stripping reactions, such as (α, t), and pickup reactions, such as (p, d), are sensitive to the shell-model state of the particle that is gained or lost by the target nucleus.

The first definite proof of the mass-energy equivalence (1932) came through an exothermic (p, α) reaction: $p + {}^{7}Li \rightarrow 2\alpha$.

The number of angular-momentum values involved in a reaction process is roughly

$$\ell_{max} \cong \frac{R}{\lambda}.\qquad \text{(approximate form of 26.33)}$$

The total cross section for particles of moderate and high energy striking nuclei (when $\lambda < R$) is about $2\pi R^2$, or twice the classically expected value.

The total cross section for a neutron of low energy striking a nucleus (when $\lambda > R$) may, at certain resonance energies, be as large as $\pi \lambda$ and is typically of order $\pi \lambda R$.

The barn (10^{-28} m^2) is a common unit of area used to measure nuclear cross sections.

Total nuclear cross sections are measured by attenuation experiments. The undeflected flux passing through a target follows the law

$$F = F_0 e^{-n\sigma_T x}.\qquad (26.31)$$

An energy barrier prevents rapid spontaneous fission of heavy nuclei. The barrier height depends on Z^2/A, which measures the relative magnitude of Coulomb energy and surface-tension energy.

^{235}U and ^{239}Pu are fissionable by slow neutrons; ^{238}U is not.

The earliest reactors, using natural uranium as fuel, were necessarily large. Modern reactors use uranium partially enriched in ^{235}U. Fission bombs use highly enriched fuel. The greater the enrichment, the less the critical mass.

In a "gun-type" weapon (such as the Hiroshima bomb), two subcritical masses are fired together to make a supercritical mass; in an "implosion-type" weapon (such as the Nagasaki bomb), a subcritical sphere is made supercritical by compression.

The proton-proton cycle is the principal source of the sun's energy. It transforms protons to alpha particles, with deuterons and ^{3}He nuclei reacting in intermediate steps.

Fusion reactions are literally nuclear burning and share many properties with ordinary combustion.

The fuel expected to power controlled fusion reactors is deuterium, in which the **DD** and **DT** reactions are important.

The fuel of H bombs is lithium deuteride ($^{6}Li\,^{2}H$). It burns at a temperature of about 6×10^7 K ($kT = 5$ keV). About half the energy and most of the radioactive fallout of an H bomb come from its case of ^{238}U.

Nuclear energy starkly illustrates the two faces of all knowledge. It is of enormous potential benefit to man and an unprecedented hazard.

QUESTIONS

Section 26.1

Q26.1   A prospector hiking in the desert with a Geiger counter hears a *regular* succession of clicks from his counter, one every half second for 10 sec. (1) Is it likely that he is passing over a vein of radioactive material? Why or why not? (2) Should he next (a) hold the Geiger counter over the same place for a longer time? (b) keep walking? (c) start digging? (d) check the Geiger counter for malfunction?

Q26.2   Exponential *growth* as well as exponential decay can result from the action of a law of probability on individual events. Cite an example (not necessarily from the world of atoms or nuclei) in which an aggregate grows exponentially as the result of a law of probability acting on its parts.

Q26.3   Explain the principle of carbon dating.

Q26.4   The mean life of ^{14}C is given in Exercise 26.1. Could measurement of the intensity of radioactivity of this isotope be used to measure the age of materials (a) a few years old? (b) a few thousand years old? (c) a few million years old?

Q26.5   If the neutron were a complex structure built of a very large number of subunits, its exponential decay would not necessarily indicate that the basic laws governing the submicroscopic world are probabilistic. Explain this statement.

Q26.6   If half of the persons in a human population die before reaching a certain age and half surpass that age, that age is called the *half life* of the population. The *mean life* is the average life span of all persons in the population. Are these two quantities related by Equation 26.10? Why or why not?

Q26.7   Suggest a reason why the alpha decay (or fission) of $^8_4$Be proceeds far more rapidly ($t_{1/2} \cong 10^{-16}$ sec) than the alpha decay of heavy nuclei.   Section 26.2

Q26.8   Some nuclei emit alpha particles of more than a single energy. Explain why.

Q26.9   Why are the alpha-particle tracks in Figure 26.2 straighter than the electron track? (NOTE: In passing through matter, charged particles lose energy principally by interacting with atomic electrons, not nuclei.)

Q26.10   (1) Why do many heavy nuclei spontaneously emit alpha particles but not single neutrons or single protons? (2) If neutron emission is energetically possible from a nucleus, the process usually occurs with a half life very much shorter than typical half lives for alpha decay or beta decay. Why is this?

Q26.11   Why is helium largely a nonrenewable resource? Consider both its method of formation in the earth and its fate when it is released into the atmosphere.

Q26.12   An isotope of argon decays via electron capture as follows: Section 26.3

$$^{37}_{18}\text{Ar} + \text{e}^- \rightarrow {}^{37}_{17}\text{Cl} + \nu_\text{e}.$$

(1) Explain why this process is closely related to beta decay. (2) What happens to the atomic electrons following this radioactive decay event?

Q26.13   If a nucleus undergoes beta decay and the product nucleus then undergoes gamma decay, what can you conclude about the state of the product nucleus immediately following the beta decay? Would you expect all beta decay events to be followed by gamma decay?

Q26.14   Many radioactive nuclei spontaneously emit electrons or positrons (in beta decay). Why do no nuclei spontaneously emit muons (which, like electrons, would have to be created at the moment of decay)?

Q26.15   The isotope ^{226}Ra used on some luminous watch dials emits alpha particles. If a watch with such a dial is held near a Geiger counter, however, gamma rays, not alpha rays, trigger the Geiger counter. Explain the reason for this fact.   Section 26.4

Q26.16   With the help of a chart or table of isotopes, develop a presentation of the thorium series (springing from $^{232}_{90}$Th) analogous to the presentation of the uranium series in Figure 26.7. What is the stable end product of the thorium series?

Q26.17   Chemical analysis and spectral analysis are governed by the properties of the outer electrons in atoms. Why were these analyses so important in the early study of radioactivity, which is a *nuclear*, not an atomic, process?

Q26.18   Two samples of radioactive material have the same intensity as measured in curies. Do they necessarily have the same ionizing power as measured in rads or roentgens? Why or why not?

Section 26.5   Q26.19   A common "stripping reaction" is a (d,p) reaction in which a deuteron strikes a nucleus and a proton is emitted. (1) Why is this called a stripping reaction? (2) What is the product nucleus if a (d,p) reaction occurs in a target of $^{27}_{13}$Al? (3) A (d,p) reaction often produces beta radioactivity. Is the isotope produced in the reaction more likely to emit electrons or positrons?

Q26.20   A deuteron can initiate either a "stripping reaction" (see the preceding question) or a "pickup reaction." What particle or light nucleus would you expect to be produced in a deuteron-induced pickup reaction?

Q26.21   Name at least one reaction that could produce the radioactive isotope $^{60}_{27}$Co from the stable isotope $^{59}_{27}$Co.

Q26.22   Describe an experimental arrangement to measure the *total* cross section of some metallic element for incident protons. Would you expect this measurement to be easier or more difficult than the measurement of a cross section for a specific reaction such as a (p,n) reaction?

Q26.23   What is the significance of the length $1/n\sigma$, where n is the number of atoms per m^3 in a target and σ is the cross section of an atomic nucleus in the target for incident particles of a particular kind?

Section 26.6   Q26.24   (1) If a nucleus of $^{232}_{90}$Th absorbs a neutron, and the resulting nucleus undergoes two successive beta decays (emitting negative electrons), what nucleus results? (2) This nucleus is more easily fissionable than the $^{232}_{90}$Th that was its source. Explain why. (NOTE: This transformation is potentially useful in breeder reactors.)

Q26.25   If the energy released in a fission event were 100 MeV instead of 200 MeV (and all other aspects of the process were unchanged), would the critical mass for a self-sustaining chain reaction change (a) by about a factor of 2, (b) by much more than a factor of 2, or (c) by much less than a factor of 2? Give a reason for your answer.

Q26.26   In the 1920s and 1930s, before the discovery of fission, space explorers in science fiction were using nuclear energy. Were the authors just "lucky" or was their vision of the nucleus as a source of energy based realistically on scientific facts?

Q26.27   If a nucleus is stretched into an elongated shape, its surface area increases. Explain why this increase of surface area causes the binding energy to decrease. (Note that a *decrease* of binding energy is the same as an *increase* of total energy. This increase is called the surface energy or surface-tension energy.)

Q26.28   Explain why most of the product nuclei resulting from nuclear fission lie well off the line of stability (see Figure 25.15). (2) Being off the line of stability, fission products are radioactive. Are they more likely to emit electrons or positrons?

Q26.29   (1) Explain why water should be a good neutron moderator. (2) Can you think of a reason why heavy water (containing deuterium, $^2_1$H, instead of ordinary hydrogen, $^1_1$H) might be preferred to ordinary water as a moderator and neutron reflector in a reactor?

Q26.30 A neutron starting at one side of a sphere of plutonium has a certain chance to cross the diameter of the sphere and escape out the other side without being absorbed. (1) If the sphere is compressed (same mass, smaller radius), does the chance of crossing and escaping increase, decrease, or stay the same? Give a reason for your answer. (2) Explain the connection between your answer to part 1 and the fact that compression can make a subcritical mass go supercritical.

Q26.31 (1) List one or more important *similarities* between fission and fusion. (2) List two or more important *differences* between fission and fusion.

Section 26.7

Q26.32 A 400-keV Van de Graaf accelerator can be used to make 14-MeV neutrons—a 35-fold gain in energy. (1) What reaction can be used for this purpose? (2) In this context, is it a *thermonuclear* reaction?

Q26.33 When the nucleus $^6_3$Li absorbs a neutron, it becomes the nucleus $^7_3$Li and splits into a triton and an alpha particle ($^3_1$H + $^4_2$He). Yet $^7_3$Li is a *stable* isotope of lithium. Explain the apparent paradox.

Q26.34 How might a "clean" thermonuclear weapon differ from a "dirty" thermonuclear weapon? Which of the two would you expect to have the greater energy release if both had the same total mass?

Q26.35 Find out something about the life of Bohr, Pauli, Chadwick, Meitner, or Fermi. In a single paragraph, summarize what you learned that is of special interest—preferably including something about his or her human qualities and attitude toward science.

Biography

EXERCISES

Section 26.1

E26.1 (1) The mean life of the isotope ^{14}C is 8,270 years. What is its half life? (2) From measurements of the beta radioactivity of an ancient piece of charcoal, archaeologists conclude that the ^{14}C content of their sample is one-quarter as great as the ^{14}C content of a modern piece of charcoal of the same mass. What is the age of their find?

E26.2 (1) The half life of the isotope $^{232}_{90}$Th is 1.40×10^{10} years. What is its mean life? (2) In a sample containing 10^{22} atoms of ^{232}Th, what is the expected number of radioactive decay events per second?

E26.3 The number of radioactive atoms in a sample decreases by a factor of about 1 million in 20 half lives. (1) Verify the correctness of this statement. (2) A sample containing 10^{12} atoms with a half life of two hours is prepared on Monday morning. Which of the following phrases best characterizes the probability that one or more radioactive atoms remain in the sample on Saturday afternoon: (a) definitely, (b) probably, (c) possibly, (d) very unlikely, (e) impossible? State the reason for your answer.

E26.4 At present the earth contains 138 atoms of ^{238}U for every atom of ^{235}U. What was the approximate ratio 4.2 Gyr (4.2×10^9 years) ago? (The half life of ^{238}U is 4.5 Gyr; the half life of ^{235}U is 0.70 Gyr.)

E26.5 Derive the formula $t_{1/2} = 0.693\tau$ that relates the half life and the mean life of nuclei obeying an exponential law of decay.

E26.6   Let n' be the number of daughter nuclei produced by a given sample of radioactive parent nuclei. (1) Write a formula for $n'(t)$ (Note that $n'(0) = 0$.) (2) Verify that n' reaches half its final value in the time $t_{1/2} = 0.693\tau$, the same as the half life of the parent nuclei.

E26.7   The bacteria in a certain culture grow in such a way that the fractional increase in their number in a given time interval is proportional to that time interval ($\Delta N/N = \lambda\,\Delta t$). (1) How many bacteria are present at time t if N_0 were present at $t = 0$? (2) How is the doubling time t_2 related to the proportionality constant λ? (Growth of this kind can, of course, be sustained only for a limited time.)

E26.8   The mean-square time for radioactive decay is

$$\overline{t^2} = \frac{1}{\tau}\int_0^\infty t^2 e^{-t/\tau}\,dt$$

(Compare Equations 26.7 and 26.8). (1) Prove that $\overline{t^2} = 2\tau^2$. (2) For a nucleus whose *half life* is 1 sec, what is the rms time of decay, $t_{\rm rms} = \sqrt{\overline{t^2}}$?

Section 26.2   E26.9   Calculate the differential scattering cross section in fm^2/steradian for 6-MeV alpha particles being scattered through 90 deg by gold nuclei ($Z = 79$). (Note that the result is more suggestive of nuclear dimensions than of atomic dimensions.)

E26.10   Show that according to a classical calculation, a 7.7-MeV alpha particle headed straight for a $_{12}$Mg nucleus is turned back at a point outside the nucleus. (Since alpha particles of this energy are in fact influenced by the nuclear forces—see Figure 25.8(a)—barrier penetration must occur.)

E26.11   The isotope $^{215}_{85}$At is an alpha-emitter with a mean life of 10^{-4} sec. Because of the uncertainty principle, the most energetic group of alpha particles is not precisely monoenergetic. Calculate their approximate energy spread in eV. Is this spread of any significance in comparison with the alpha-particle energy of 8 MeV?

E26.12   Using the results of the simplified theory of alpha decay presented in Section 26.2, calculate the mean life for the alpha decay of ^{217}Rn. The alpha-particle energy is 7.74 MeV; for the nuclear radius, use $R = 9$ fm. How does the calculated value of τ compare with the observed value, which is about 0.5 msec?

E26.13   Some physicists speculate that the fundamental constants may change slowly in time. (1) Suppose that $\hbar$ was larger in the distant past than it is now. Would alpha-decay lifetimes have been longer or shorter then than now? (2) If $\hbar$ were changed by a few percent, would alpha-decay lifetimes change by (a) much less than a few percent, (b) a few percent, or (c) much more than a few percent? Justify both answers by reference to appropriate equations in the text.

Section 26.3   E26.14   Fill in the blanks on the right for these three examples of radioactive decay:

(a) $^{56}_{27}$Co $\rightarrow$ $^{56}_{26}$Fe $+$

(b) $^{60}_{27}$Co $\rightarrow$ e^- $+$ $\overline{\nu}_e$ $+$

(c) $^{212}_{84}$Po $\rightarrow$ $^{208}_{82}$Pb $+$

E26.15   (1) Write a transformation formula for the beta decay of the free neutron.

(2) What is (a) the minimum and (b) the maximum kinetic energy of the emitted electron?

E26.16 Figure 26.6(b) shows the relative number of electrons of different energy emitted by a sample of $^{210}_{83}$Bi. Sketch an analogous graph in which the vertical scale is the number of *antineutrinos* per unit energy emitted by this isotope and the horizontal scale is the antineutrino energy.

E26.17 According to Figure 26.7, the ^{226}Ra used in luminous watch dials gives rise to a dozen product nuclei through successive radioactive transformations. (1) For a watch dial a few years old, which of these isotopes will be the most populous, assuming that the original radium was chemically purified? (2) After 50 years which product isotope will be most populous? (3) After 1,000 years, how many elements would a chemical analysis of the original radium and its products reveal?   Section 26.4

E26.18 The half life of ^{60}Co is 5.27 years. What is the intensity of radioactivity in curies of 1 mg of this isotope?

E26.19 The half life of $^3_1$H (tritium) is 12.3 years. (1) Show that the radioactive intensity of 1 gm of tritium is about 14,000 curies. (2) A researcher purchases a 1-curie tritium source in 1975. What is the intensity of this source in 1980?

E26.20 The roentgen is defined in the footnote on page 1331. Assume that a gamma ray passing through air loses on the average 30 eV for each electron it dislodges from a molecule. If this is so, express the roentgen in the rad unit defined by Equation 26.29. (Use standard dry-air density of 1.29 kg/m^3.)

E26.21 Below are the atomic masses (including normal complements of electrons) of four isotopes that figured in Rutherford's landmark discovery of a nuclear reaction in 1919 (see Figure 26.8).   Section 26.5

^{1}H : 1.00783 ^{14}N : 14.00307
^{4}He : 4.00260 ^{17}O : 16.99913

Prove that the net change of *atomic* mass in the reaction $\alpha + {}^{14}\text{N} \rightarrow \text{p} + {}^{17}\text{O}$ is the same as the net change of *nuclear* mass (overlooking tiny effects of electron binding energies). (2) Is this reaction *exothermic* (one in which kinetic energy increases) or *endothermic* (one in which kinetic energy decreases)? (3) If the kinetic energy of the incident alpha particle is 6 MeV, what is the approximate kinetic energy of the proton that is produced? (For this calculation, ignore the kinetic energy of the recoiling oxygen nucleus.)

E26.22 (1) Which of the following are "stripping reactions"? (2) Which are "pickup reactions"? (3) Which are neither?

(a) $\text{d} + {}^{208}_{82}\text{Pb} \rightarrow \text{t} + {}^{207}_{82}\text{Pb}$
(b) $\alpha + {}^{12}_{6}\text{C} \rightarrow \text{t} + {}^{13}_{7}\text{N}$
(c) $\text{t} + {}^{12}_{6}\text{C} \rightarrow \text{d} + {}^{13}_{6}\text{C}$
(d) $\text{n} + {}^{64}_{30}\text{Zn} \rightarrow \text{p} + {}^{64}_{29}\text{Cu}$
(e) $\text{p} + {}^{197}_{79}\text{Au} \rightarrow \text{d} + {}^{196}_{79}\text{Au}$

E26.23 An experimenter finds that half of the neutrons in a certain beam penetrate undeflected through a sheet of iron 5 cm thick. If the number density of atoms in the iron is 8.4×10^{28} atoms/m^3, what is the total cross section of an iron nucleus for these neutrons? Express the answer in barns.

E26.24   If a neutron has kinetic energy of only 0.001 eV, roughly how far will it move on the average through a piece of ^{235}U before it induces a fission event? (The density of ^{235}U is 1.87×10^4 kg/m^3. For its fission cross section, see Figure 26.15.)

E26.25   (1) What is the wavelength λ of a neutron whose kinetic energy is 0.001 eV? How does this wavelength compare with a typical nuclear radius? (2) What is the upper limit $\pi\lambda^2$ of the nuclear cross section for such a neutron? Express the answer in barns and compare it with the fission cross section shown in Figure 26.15.

E26.26   A typical order of magnitude for the total cross section of a nucleus exposed to low-energy neutrons is $\sigma_T \cong \pi\lambda R$ (Equation 26.36). The maximum possible nuclear cross section for low-energy neutrons is $\sigma_{max} = \pi\lambda^2$ (see Equation 26.35). Express (1) σ_T and (2) σ_{max} as functions of the mass m and kinetic energy K of the neutrons. (3) Show that the ratio σ_T/σ_{max} can be written

$$\frac{\sigma_T}{\sigma_{max}} = \frac{R}{\lambda_C} \sqrt{\frac{2K}{mc^2}},$$

where λ_C is the neutron's reduced Compton wavelength.

E26.27   Show that for a beam of superrelativistic particles of energy E, the angular-momentum quantum number of a particle that just grazes the surface of a nucleus of radius R is given approximately by

$$\ell = \frac{ER}{\hbar c}.$$

(Note that in using this formula, the numerical expression $\hbar c = 197$ MeV fm would be useful.)

Section 26.6   E26.28   (1) In the first paragraph of Chapter 25, it is stated that 1 kg of uranium devastated Hiroshima. The estimated energy of that explosion was 15 to 20 kilotons. Verify that approximately 1 kg of uranium must undergo fission to release this much energy. (2) Would you estimate the total mass of uranium in the Hiroshima bomb to have been closest to 1 kg? 10 kg? 100 kg? 1,000 kg?

E26.29   A 20-kiloton nuclear explosion occurs under water. What mass of water can be heated through 50 K by the energy released in this explosion? (Note, according to the preceding exercise, that only about 1 kg of uranium need undergo fission to provide this energy.)

E26.30   The isotopes $^{91}_{36}$Kr and $^{142}_{56}$Ba shown in Figure 26.16 are two among many possible fission products. With the help of a table or chart of nuclei, trace the paths of radioactive decay of these two isotopes. What are their stable end products?

E26.31   The nuclear surface energy can be written $U_{surface} = CR^2$. (1) Show that if $C = 100$ MeV/fm^2, the surface energy of a uranium isotope is roughly 7 times its Coulomb energy. (Use $R = 1.3A^{1/3}$ fm.) (2) Show that if a fissionable nucleus breaks into two equal fragments, the ratio $U_{Coulomb}/U_{surface}$ is only about half as great for the fragments as for the original nucleus.

E26.32   In the explosive chain reaction in a certain nuclear "device" the average number of neutrons from a fission event that go on to stimulate further fission events is exactly 2. The average time between a neutron's emission and its capture is 10^{-8} sec. (1) What is the energy doubling time in the explosion? (2) Starting from a single fission event, how much time elapses until 10^{24} nuclei have undergone fission?

E26.33 How long could a 100-W light bulb be kept burning by the energy provided by the fission of 1 gm of uranium?

E26.34 In the solar fusion reaction $p + p \rightarrow d + e^+ + \nu_e$, what is the maximum neutrino energy? (The mass of a bare deuteron is $m_d = 2.01355$ amu.)

Section 26.7

E26.35 When Hans Bethe first proposed nuclear fusion as the source of the sun's energy (1939), he suggested the following "carbon cycle" as a possible mechanism:

1. $^{1}_{1}H + ^{12}_{6}C \rightarrow ^{13}_{7}N + \gamma$ 4. $^{1}_{1}H + ^{14}_{7}N \rightarrow ^{15}_{8}O + \gamma$
2. $^{13}_{7}N \rightarrow ^{13}_{6}C + e^+ + \nu_e$ 5. $^{15}_{8}O \rightarrow ^{15}_{7}N + e^+ + \nu_e$
3. $^{1}_{1}H + ^{13}_{6}C \rightarrow ^{14}_{7}N + \gamma$ 6. $^{1}_{1}H + ^{15}_{7}N \rightarrow ^{12}_{6}C + ^{4}_{2}He$

(1) Write a formula analogous to Formula 26.38 or 26.39 that expresses the *net* nuclear transformation that is taking place. (2) According to current theory, it is the proton-proton cycle, rather than the carbon cycle, that is primarily responsible for solar energy production. Would you expect the central temperature in a star in which the carbon cycle predominates to be greater or less than the sun's central temperature? Why?

E26.36 The total energy released in the DT reaction is 17.6 MeV. Show that the neutron that is produced acquires about 80 percent of this energy, or 14 MeV, if the initial energies of deuteron and triton are relatively small.

E26.37 In the reaction $d + d \rightarrow t + p$, the energy released (the energy transformed from mass energy to kinetic energy) is 4.0 MeV. What are the individual kinetic energies of the triton and the proton if the kinetic energies of the deuterons are small enough to neglect?

E26.38 In 1973, nuclear power stations in the United States generated about 5×10^{10} kW hr. At the same time, the U.S. weapons stockpile amounted to about 20,000 megatons (this is only a crude guess). If the entire weapons stockpile were exploded in 1 year, how would its energy release compare with the annual energy production of the power stations?

PROBLEMS

P26.1 A Geiger counter near a sample of ^{212}Bi (a radioactive isotope of bismuth, also known as thorium C) recorded the following number of counts.

Analysis of radioactive decay

Time (min)	Counts/min	Time (min)	Counts/min
0	2,500	41	1,634
2	2,517	50	1,339
4	2,433	51	1,325
7	2,438	63	1,246
24	1,966	64	1,212
25	1,983	69	1,165
40	1,609	72	1,197

(1) Draw a graph of intensity (counts/min) vs time. From your graph deduce the half life of ^{212}B. (2) Estimate approximately how accurately you have determined the half life. (3) State *two* ways in which these actual experimental data tend to support the idea that fundamental processes in nature are governed by laws of probability.

Uncertainty of time for unstable nucleus **P26.2**   For an unstable nucleus (or elementary particle), the uncertainty of time associated with the finite lifetime of the entity is defined by

$$(\Delta t)^2 = [(t -)\bar{t}^2]_{average}.$$

Here $\bar{t}$ is the weighted average time (Equation 26.8), which is the same as the mean life of the system; the subscript "average" also designates a weighted average. The weighting function is the probability $p(t)$ (Equation 26.7). (1) Show that

$$\Delta t = \sqrt{\overline{t^2} - \bar{t}^2}.$$

Explain why this result does not depend on the particular form of the function $p(t)$. (2) For exponential decay, obtain the simple result $\Delta t = \tau$.

Exponential law of absorption **P26.3**   A searchlight beam is directed into a cloud. Within the cloud, the fractional change of intensity per unit distance is a constant μ. (1) Derive a formula for the intensity I of the beam as a function of its penetration distance into the cloud. (2) If $\mu = 0.05$ m^{-1}, what thickness of cloud will produce a thousand-fold decrease of intensity?

Linear law of decay **P26.4**   A plant manager finds that if he installs n_0 new belts on his machinery, the number of these belts still in service after time t ($0 \leq t \leq T$) is given approximately by $n = n_0[1 - (t/T)]$; the belts follow a linear law of "decay." (1) What is the "rate of decay" (the number of belts that fail per unit time)? (2) Show that for $0 \leq t \leq T$, the three probabilities defined near Equation 26.5 are given by

$$\text{(a)} \ p(t) = \frac{1}{T},$$

$$\text{(b)} \ P(t) = 1 - \frac{t}{T},$$

$$\text{(c)} \ p_0(t) = \frac{1}{T - t}.$$

(3) Sketch a graph of p_0 vs t. Comment on the way in which this p_0 differs from the intrinsic decay probability per unit time for a radioactive nucleus (Equation 26.1). (4) Show that the half life and mean life of the belts are the same and given by $t_{1/2} = \bar{t} = \frac{1}{2}T$.

For probability, the exponential law is exact **P26.5**   Let $P(t)$ be the probability that a single nucleus known to be present at $t = 0$ is still present at the later time t (see Equation 26.6). (1) Prove that the differential equation

$$\frac{dP}{dt} = -\frac{P}{\tau}$$

is an *exact* equation for P (even though, for reasons stated below Equation 26.2, the equation $dn/dt = -n/\tau$ is *not* exact). (2) The solution to this equation is $P(t) = Ae^{-t/\tau}$. Explain why $A = 1$.

P26.6   At $t = 0$, n_0 atoms of radioactive isotope 1 are present. This isotope decays with a mean life τ_1 to an isotope 2, which is also radioactive and decays in turn with a different mean life τ_2 to the stable isotope 3. (This short decay chain is indicated schematically in the figure.) (1) Derive the simple differential equation that governs n_2, the number of atoms of isotope 2 that are present, and show that the solution to this equation that satisfies the boundary condition $n_2(0) = 0$ is

Successive radioactive decays

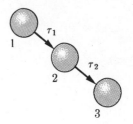

$$n_2(t) = \frac{\lambda_1 n_0}{\lambda_2 - \lambda_1} (e^{-\lambda_1 t} - e^{-\lambda_2 t}),$$

where $\lambda_1 = 1/\tau_1$ and $\lambda_2 = 1/\tau_2$. (2) Sketch a graph of n_2 vs t. *Optional:* If you have studied differential equations, you should also be able to find $n_2(t)$ for the special case $\tau_1 = \tau_2$.

P26.7   Suppose that the positive charge in a gold atom were spread uniformly over a sphere of radius 1 Å. (J. J. Thomson proposed such an atomic model in the early 1900s. He visualized the electrons being distributed in the atom like raisins in a pudding. In this problem, ignore the effects of the electrons.) (1) Where is the electric field of this charged ball greatest? What is its maximum magnitude? (2) Where is the electric potential (relative to the potential at infinity) greatest? What is its maximum value? (3) What kinetic energy would an alpha particle need in order to pass undeflected through the center of the atom?

Thomson model of the atom

P26.8   A projectile particle of kinetic energy K and charge $Z'e$ passes near a nucleus of charge Ze and is deflected through an angle θ (see the figure). If the deflection angle is small, the momentum $\Delta \mathbf{p}$ transferred to the particle can be accurately calculated by approximating the particle's trajectory as a straight line (the dashed line in the figure) executed at constant velocity. Then Δp can be calculated as the impulse integral $\int F_\perp \, dt$ and the deflection angle can be written $\theta \cong \Delta p / p_0$. (1) Show that this approach leads to

Rutherford scattering at small angles

$$\theta = \frac{ZZ'e^2}{4\pi\epsilon_0 K} \frac{1}{b} \qquad (\theta \ll 1),$$

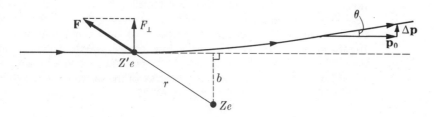

where b is the "impact parameter" defined in the figure. (2) For 6-MeV alpha particles incident on gold ($Z = 79$), what range of values of b makes $\theta \le 0.01$ radian? (3) According to Problem 25.6, the classical differential cross section is given by

$$\frac{d\sigma}{d\Omega} = \left| \frac{b \, db}{\sin \theta \, d\theta} \right|.$$

Show that for small θ, this formula coupled with the result of part 1 leads to an expression for $d\sigma/d\Omega$ that agrees with Equation 26.11.

Barrier penetration   **P26.9**   In the approximate theory developed in the text, the barrier-penetration probability for alpha particles is $P = e^{-\kappa_1(R_2 - R_1)}$ (Equation 26.21). In a more accurate theory, it is

$$P = e^{-2\kappa \int(r)\, dr},$$

in which $\kappa = \sqrt{2m(U - E)/\hbar^2}$ and the limits of integration are R_1 and R_2 (see Figure 26.5). (1) With the help of a table of integrals, evaluate the integral in the exponent for a Coulomb potential and show that it has the form given in the footnote on page 1323. (2) For ^{212}Po, the simplified theory gives $P = e^{-34.6}$ (see the equation below Equation 26.27). What does the more accurate theory give for P for this isotope?

P26.10   For a potential-energy barrier of fixed magnitude $U - E$ extending over a distance Δx, the barrier penetration probability is

$$P = e^{-2\kappa \Delta x},$$

where $\kappa = \sqrt{2m(U - E)/\hbar^2}$. (1) Explain how this formula conforms to Equation 26.12. (2) The figure shows a cart rolling toward a gravitational potential barrier. Show that the penetration probability of the cart through the barrier is roughly $10^{-10^{32}}$. Try to think of a dramatic way to explain how *small* (!) this probability is.

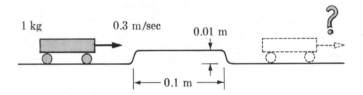

P26.11   (1) Replace the cart in the preceding problem by an electron and the gravitational barrier by an electrostatic barrier of height $U - E = 1$ eV and thickness $\Delta x = 1$ Å. What is the barrier penetration probability? (2) Because of the work function W, electrons do not leak away from a cold metallic surface. But if two metal surfaces are brought close together (see the figure), electrons may "tunnel" through the potential barrier that separates them. For $W = 2$ eV, what must be the separation Δx of the surfaces in order to have (a) $P = 0.1$? (b) $P = 10^{-3}$? (c) $P = 10^{-6}$?

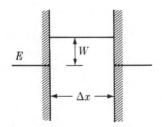

P26.12   As shown in the figure, a neutron with initial momentum p_0 strikes a carbon nucleus, is deflected through angle θ, and rebounds with momentum p. The nucleus recoils with momentum p'. (1) Write three conservation equations (two of momentum, one of energy) and show that these equations can be expressed in such a way that the momenta appear only in the ratios p/p_0 and p'/p_0. (This means that for a given angle θ, the neutron's fractional loss of momentum is the same regardless of its initial momentum.) (2) For $\theta = 90$ deg, show that the fractional changes of momentum and energy for the neutron are

Thermalizing neutrons

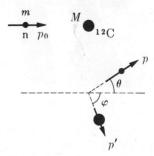

$$\frac{p}{p_0} = \sqrt{\frac{M-m}{M+m}} = 0.919, \qquad \frac{K}{K_0} = \frac{M-m}{M+m} = 0.845.$$

About how many 90-deg collisions must a neutron make with carbon nuclei before the neutron's energy is reduced from 1 MeV to 0.1 eV? (4) Answer part 3 if the neutrons are colliding with deuterons in heavy water instead of carbon nuclei in graphite.

27 Particles

The submicroscopic frontier of physics is the domain of elementary particles. This is where the known and the unknown meet. Most physicists believe that a radical new theory is needed to fully account for the properties and behavior of the particles and that such a theory may not be long in coming. Yet, despite the deep puzzles of the elementary-particle world, we understand a great deal about this subnuclear realm. Quantum mechanics, a theory developed nearly fifty years ago to explain atomic structure, has held up surprisingly well as new experiments have probed spacetime regions many orders of magnitude beneath the scale of atoms. In fact, many of the key ideas of quantum mechanics are most clearly illustrated by particle phenomena.

This chapter contains a selection of topics from elementary-particle physics,* with emphasis on the interactions among the particles and on invariance principles. (A note on nomenclature: we shall often omit the adjective "elementary." As applied to particles, it is indicative only of the interim state of our knowledge. It does not reflect any conviction on the part of scientists that the presently known particles are the ultimate building blocks of matter.)

27.1 The classes of interactions

By far the most striking fact about the particle interactions known so far is that they all belong to one or another of just four distinct and markedly different classes:

The four kinds of interaction

1. the strong interactions,
2. the electromagnetic interactions,
3. the weak interactions,
4. the gravitational interactions.

---

* Because of the need for high-energy projectiles to study particles, elementary-particle physics is often called high-energy physics.

The photon is associated with the electromagnetic interactions, the neutrinos with the weak interactions, and the graviton with the (still weaker) gravitational interactions. The pion is a principal carrier of the strong interactions. Since for the 36 different particles in Table 27.1, taken two at a time, there are 630 different pairs to interact, it is a giant step toward simplicity to discover that only four different kinds of interactions govern what goes on between all of these pairs.

Though the strong and the weak interactions are imperfectly understood (as their uninspired names suggest) and though the connections, if any, among the different kinds of interaction are entirely unknown, there are some intriguing facts in hand about the four types of interaction—facts that nature dangles tantalizingly before the theoretical physicist.

First is the quite remarkable disparity of strength among the different interactions. The strong interactions exceed the strength of electromagnetic interactions by a factor of about 100. The electromagnetic interactions are stronger than the weak interactions by a factor of 10^{11}. The weak interactions in turn are about 10^{28} times stronger than the gravitational interactions. Between the strong and the gravitational interactions, then, is the enormous factor of 10^{41}. In fact, these numbers have no very precise meaning, but they indicate clearly that there exist vast gulfs between the strength of one interaction and another.

Vastly different strengths

The second intriguing fact about the four types of interaction is a rule that can be roughly stated as follows: the stronger, the fewer. Of the fourteen kinds of particles listed in Table 27.1, eight (including all of the mesons and baryons) experience strong interactions, eleven (all but the neutrinos and the graviton) experience electromagnetic interactions, thirteen (all but the graviton) experience weak interactions, and all fourteen experience gravitational interactions.* Or, turning the rule around: *The weaker the interaction, the larger the number of particles it embraces.* Moreover, a particle that experiences any interaction in the hierarchy always experiences all weaker interactions as well; as one goes down the list toward weaker interactions, names are added to the list of particles but not subtracted. Thus the eight strongly interacting families of particles also experience electromagnetic, weak, and gravitational interactions. It is interesting that the heaviest eight families of particles (pions and upward) are the ones that interact strongly. At the next rung down the ladder, the lighter muon, electron, and photon join the list. At each of the last two rungs, massless particles are added. None of these facts is understood.

An empirical rule: Weaker interactions affect more particles

Finally, there is a most interesting connection between strengths of interaction and conservation laws. The seven absolute conservation laws discussed in Chapter 4 govern all the particle interactions. But in addition to these, there are some partial conservation laws obeyed by some interactions and not by others. The rule is that the stronger the interaction, the more it is hemmed in by additional conservation laws that limit the possible transformations among the particles. The strong interactions are subject to laws of conservation of

Another rule: Stronger interactions obey more conservation laws

---

* Recall that the influence of gravity on massless particles is a consequence of the Principle of Equivalence (Section 22.3).

TABLE 27.1   SOME OF THE MORE IMPORTANT ELEMENTARY PARTICLES*

Family Name	Particle Name	Symbol	Mass (MeV)	Spin (unit $\hbar$)	Electric Charge (unit e)	Antiparticle	Number of Distinct Particles	Average Lifetime (sec)	Typical Mode of Decay
	Photon	γ (gamma ray)	0	1	0	Same particle	1	Infinite	
	Graviton		0	2	0	Same particle	1	Infinite	
Electron family	Electron's neutrino	ν_e	0	$\frac{1}{2}$	0	$\overline{\nu}_e$	2	Infinite	
	Electron	e^-	0.51100	$\frac{1}{2}$	-1	e^+ (positron)	2	Infinite	
Muon family	Muon's neutrino	ν_μ	0(?)	$\frac{1}{2}$	0	$\overline{\nu}_\mu$	2	Infinite	
	Muon	μ^-	105.660	$\frac{1}{2}$	-1	μ^+	2	2.20×10^{-6}	$\mu^- \rightarrow e^- + \overline{\nu}_e + \nu_\mu$
Mesons	Pion	π^+	139.57	0	$+1$	π^- } same as the particles	3	2.60×10^{-8}	$\pi^+ \rightarrow \mu^+ + \nu_\mu$
		π^-	139.57	0	-1	π^+		2.60×10^{-8}	$\pi^- \rightarrow \mu^- + \overline{\nu}_\mu$
		π^0	134.96	0	0	π^0		0.8×10^{-16}	$\pi^0 \rightarrow \gamma + \gamma$
	Kaon	K^+	493.7	0	$+1$	$\overline{K^+}$ (negative)	4	1.24×10^{-8}	$K^+ \rightarrow \pi^+ + \pi^0$
		K^0	497.7	0	0	$\overline{K^0}$		0.88×10^{-10} and†	$K^0 \rightarrow \pi^+ + \pi^-$
								5.2×10^{-8}	$K^0 \rightarrow \pi^+ + e^- + \overline{\nu}_e$
	Eta	η	549	0	0	Same particle	1	2×10^{-19}	$\eta \rightarrow \gamma + \gamma$
Baryons	Nucleon	p (proton)	938.26	$\frac{1}{2}$	$+1$	$\overline{p}$ (negative)	4	Infinite	
		n (neutron)	939.55	$\frac{1}{2}$	0	$\overline{n}$		920	$n \rightarrow p + e^- + \overline{\nu}_e$
	Lambda	Λ^0	1,115.6	$\frac{1}{2}$	0	$\overline{\Lambda^0}$	2	2.5×10^{-10}	$\Lambda^0 \rightarrow p + \pi^-$
	Sigma	Σ^+	1,189.3	$\frac{1}{2}$	$+1$	$\overline{\Sigma^+}$ (negative)	6	0.80×10^{-10}	$\Sigma^+ \rightarrow n + \pi^+$
		Σ^-	1,197.3	$\frac{1}{2}$	-1	$\overline{\Sigma^-}$ (positive)		1.5×10^{-10}	$\Sigma^- \rightarrow n + \pi^-$
		Σ^0	1,192.5	$\frac{1}{2}$	0	$\overline{\Sigma^0}$		About 10^{-20}	$\Sigma^0 \rightarrow \Lambda^0 + \gamma$
	Xi	Ξ^-	1,321.3	$\frac{1}{2}$	-1	$\overline{\Xi^-}$ (positive)	4	1.7×10^{-10}	$\Xi^- \rightarrow \Lambda^0 + \pi^-$
		Ξ^0	1,315	$\frac{1}{2}$	0	$\overline{\Xi^0}$		3.0×10^{-10}	$\Xi^0 \rightarrow \Lambda^0 + \pi^0$
	Omega	Ω^-	1,673	$\frac{3}{2}$	-1	$\overline{\Omega^-}$ (positive)	2	1.3×10^{-10}	$\Omega^- \rightarrow \Xi^0 + \pi^-$
							36		

*This table is a duplicate of Table 3.1. It includes all known particles that do not decay by means of the strong interactions.
†The K^0 meson has two different lifetimes. All other particles have only one.

parity, charge conjugation, isospin, and strangeness. (The meaning of these laws will be discussed later in the chapter. We are here interested only in the number of laws.) The weaker interactions then become lawbreakers. The electromagnetic interactions "violate" the law of isospin conservation (in other words, electromagnetic interactions are not limited by this law). The weak interactions go further and violate all four of these special conservation laws. Since nothing is actually known of the gravitational interaction on the elementary submicroscopic level, it remains an open question whether or not the gravitational interaction goes even further in lawlessness and breaks one or more of the "absolute" conservation laws. If it does so, the consequences would probably be significant only in the cosmological domain. For example, violation of the law of baryon conservation by gravitational interaction could lead to the gradual creation of new protons and neutrons, as proposed in the continuous-creation theory of the universe, or to a gradual erosion of these units of matter, undermining the material structure of the world. Fortunately, we know from experiment that the latter process, if it occurs at all, is too slow to be of any consequence in the life history of the solar system.

27.2 Muons and electrons

In the muon and the electron, nature has presented us with a puzzling pair of "identical" twins, exact copies of each other except that one is a giant, the other a dwarf. The muon is about two hundred times as massive as the electron, yet in almost every other way it is indistinguishable from its small brother.

Actually, the *family* of electron together with its neutrino is a twin system to the two members of the muon family. Because of the near identity of the two neutrinos, one can speak of the muon and electron separately as almost twins. Each is a negatively charged particle with a positively charged antiparticle; each has one-half unit of spin; each participates in a simple family-number conservation law; and, most important, each of these two small families seems to have precisely the same interactions with all of the other elementary particles. This is the only such pairing known in the particle world, and it is like a sema-phore signal waving before the eyes of the particle physicist. But so far the message has not been read.

The puzzling similarity of
μ-ν_μ *and* e-ν_e

PUZZLE OF THE MUON MASS

There must be a "reason" for the chasm between the masses of these twin particles, a reason that ought to be reflected in some other differences in their properties. So far, however, no other difference has shown up, in spite of the fact that the muon is by far the most accurately studied of the short-lived particles. Nor has any convincing theoretical explanation for the mass difference been offered. The puzzle of the muon-electron mass difference belongs to that class of questions that we have learned enough to ask but not enough to answer.

Why, exactly, is the mass difference of the muon and the electron a "problem"? Why is the great difference in their lifetimes not considered significant? We shall consider these two questions in order.

We have no deep theoretical understanding of the nature of mass, of why the proton—or any other particle—has just so much energy locked up within it in the form of mass and not more or less. Yet, through the raw experimental data of particle masses, nature has yielded several clues about the origin and the magnitude of masses. It is on the basis of the superficial knowledge built on these clues that the muon-electron mass difference seems paradoxical.

Some pairs of particles have no mass difference whatever. These are particle-antiparticle pairs, such as electron-positron, proton-antiproton, or oppositely charged pions, π^+-π^-. Other sets of particles have small mass differences, less than 10 MeV in energy units. These are particles that differ only electromagnetically. Neutron and proton are such a pair, as are K^0 and K^+. A chart of particle rest energies (Figure 27.1) shows other such sets. Note the three sigma particles, Σ^+, Σ^0, and Σ^-, for example, whose rest energies are 1,189.4 MeV, 1,192.5 MeV, and 1,197.3 MeV. These three particles experience identical strong interactions but differ in charge and in magnetic moment. Apparently, electromagnetism has something to do with their relatively small mass differences. The electron and its neutrino may also be considered a particle pair in this category. They experience the same strong interaction—namely, none—but differ electrically. Their mass difference (again in energy units) is 0.5 MeV. On the basis of this much evidence, the muon begins to look out of place. Although, like the electron, it has no strong interaction, it differs in mass from its neutrino by more than 100 MeV.

According to quantum mechanics, a particle, even when alone, is interacting, for it is emitting and absorbing virtual particles. This self-interaction should contribute to the self-energy of a particle and could even be responsible for the entire mass of the particle. The magnitude of this effect has not proved calculable. Nevertheless, experimental masses are suggestive. The strongly interacting particles in Figure 27.1 range from the π^0 (135 MeV) to the Ω^- (1,673 MeV). Apparently, the strong interaction contributes masses and mass differences measured in hundreds of MeV, much greater than the few MeV associated with electromagnetic mass differences. This is consistent with what we know about the relative strength of the strong and electromagnetic interactions. Also consistent is the mass of the electron, 0.5 MeV, which can reasonably be attributed entirely to electromagnetic self-interaction. From this view of particle masses, the muon seems even more obviously out of place. In the energy-level diagram it is at 106 MeV, not far below the strongly interacting pions; yet, it has no strong interaction and "belongs" down near the electron. Why has the muon so much mass? No one knows.

The muon lives for 2 μsec, and the electron apparently lives forever. The second question to be disposed of was: Why is this great difference in lifetime of no real significance? The answer to this question, like many questions, depends on the point of view taken. The modern physicist's point of view is that it is only "by chance" that the electron lives forever. The law of charge conservation thwarts the natural inclination of the electron to end its life by transforming into lighter particles, whereas because the muon can decay without violating any conservation principle, it does so. It should be noted, incidentally, that in the particle world, 2 μsec is an extraordinarily long time.

Electromagnetic mass differences typically a few MeV

Masses attributable to strong interactions are hundreds of MeV

Muon mass is out of place

Electron is stable "by chance"

FIGURE 27.1 Energy-level diagram for the elementary particles of Table 27.1 (antiparticles are not included). Plotted vertically is the particle mass expressed in energy units. Plotted horizontally in each of three categories is particle charge. Note the change of energy scale for the baryons. Implicit in such a presentation is the idea that different particles are different energy states of some underlying substratum. Particles differing only in charge have small mass differences. Particles differing in their strong interaction properties have large mass differences.

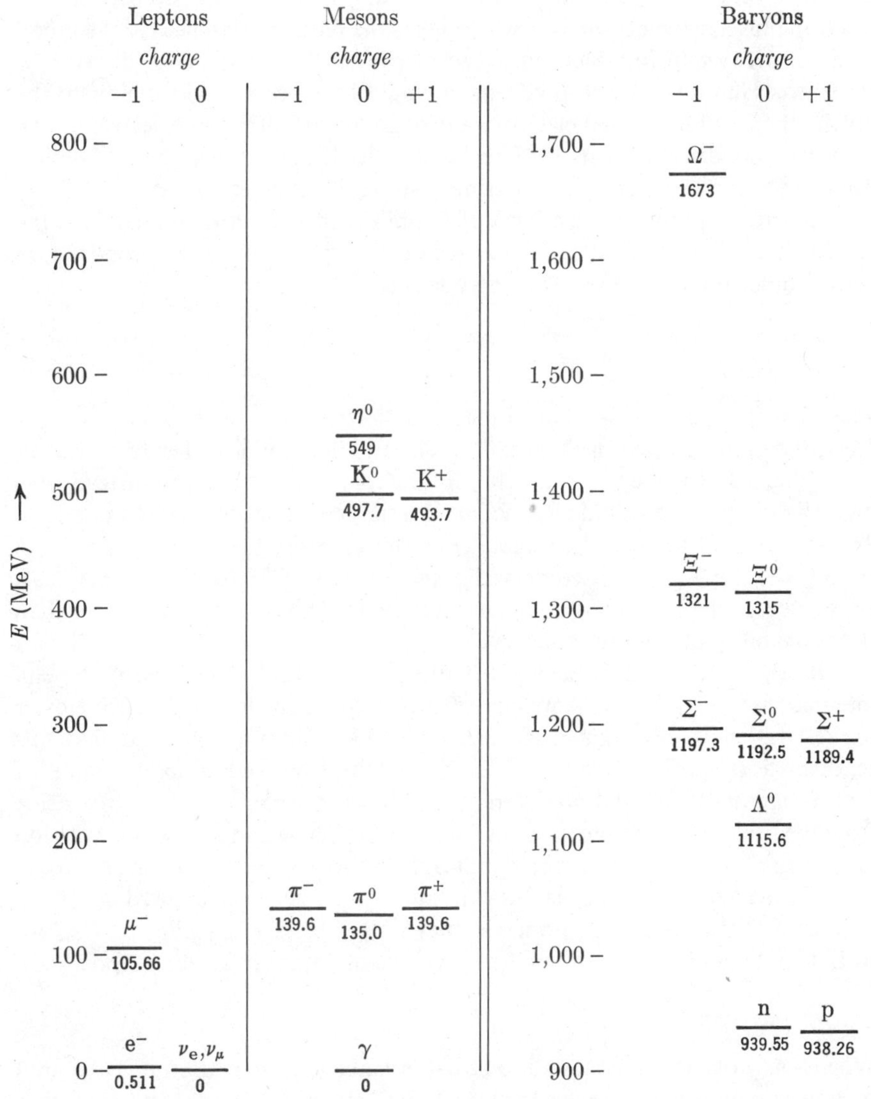

PION DECAY

Just what is the evidence that muon and electron are "identical"? Many experimental facts point to this conclusion; we shall discuss only two of them here. One has to do with the way in which a pion decays. A positive pion may end its life in either of two ways:

Pion decay modes

$$\pi^+ \rightarrow \mu^+ + \nu_\mu,$$
$$\pi^+ \rightarrow e^+ + \nu_e.$$

Out of a large number of positive pions, 99.986 percent will transform to a positive muon plus a neutrino, and only 0.014 percent will transform to a positron plus a neutrino. So overwhelming is the pion's preference for the muon mode of decay that for some time it was believed that pions never decayed to electrons. Had this proved to be true, it would have been a serious blow to the "twin" theory of muon and electron. Fortunately, the infrequent electron mode of decay was discovered in 1958 to bolster the idea that electron and muon (together with their respective neutrinos) are really alike except in mass.

According to the modern form of Fermi's theory of weak interactions, the chance that a pion decays into a muon or into an electron should be proportional among other things, to the following quantity:

$$1 - \frac{v}{c},$$

where v is the speed of the created muon or electron and c is the speed of light. Now, the muon created in the usual mode of pion decay is rather fast. For it, $v/c = 0.27$. But if the pion had chosen to decay into an electron instead, this much lighter particle would have acquired a far greater speed, in fact more than 99.99 percent of the speed of light. For the electron, the quantity $1 - (v/c)$ is only about 3.7×10^{-5}, compared with a value of 0.73 for the muon.* As a consequence, the probability of pion-to-electron decay is very much less than the probability of pion-to-muon decay.

It can be regarded as merely a mathematical quirk of the theory of weak interactions that the pion happens to prefer to decay into a heavier slower particle rather than a lighter speedier one. The important point is that this mathematical quirk accounts perfectly for the observed preponderance of pion-to-muon decays, and no difference at all between muon and electron aside from their mass is needed to account for the big difference in the two ways a pion may decay. Until the tiny but significant fraction of pion-to-electron decays was discovered, it looked as though muon and electron showed a "real" difference. Moreover, the principle that nature does everything that is not forbidden by a conservation law was saved from an unexplained exception.

Mass difference alone explains difference in rates

MUONIC ATOMS

When a negative muon is slowed to near-thermal energy in matter, it is captured by an atom and then cascades through bound states of motion until it reaches

---

* See Problem 21.7.

its ground state (a 1s state). The photons that it emits during this cascade provide further evidence that except for its mass, the muon is the same as an electron. Since the muon's Bohr radius is about 200 times less than the electron's Bohr radius, the low states of the muon lie well inside the innermost electron shell. During the last part of its cascade, the muon is experiencing the electric force of the nucleus, essentially unperturbed by the electrons. Its observed energy differences can be compared with accurately calculable theoretical energy differences. These comparisons indicate that the muon is a spin one-half particle, obeying Dirac's relativistic quantum equation.

Muonic atom is "hydrogenic"

For the innermost states of the muon, observed energies differ from the energies expected for a point nucleus. These differences, however, have all been successfully explained in terms of the electromagnetic interaction of the muon with a nucleus of finite size. No special or "anomalous" interaction need be invoked. The possibility of such an additional nonelectromagnetic interaction, which would distinguish the muon from the electron, is so intriguing that ever-more-refined experiments on muonic atoms continue to be carried out.

Nuclear effect is entirely electromagnetic

27.3   Strongly interacting particles

Neutrons and protons are strongly interacting particles, and the nuclear force that binds them together is one manifestation of the strong interactions. The pion, whose exchange contributes most to the nuclear force, is another strongly interacting particle. Although these are the particles most important for nuclear structure, they are but a small fraction of the numerous strongly interacting particles now known. Besides the eta, the kaon, the lambda, the sigma, the xi, and the omega, listed in Table 27.1 and charted in Figure 27.1, dozens of other particles have been discovered in recent years with lifetimes so short that they can leave no measurable track in a bubble chamber, nor can they otherwise be directly detected. All of these super-short-lived particles—or *resonances*, as they have come to be called—are also strongly interacting. Indeed, the very profusion of strongly interacting particles is itself a feature of special interest about these particles. It tells us clearly that not all these particles can be elementary but must be various manifestations of some deeper and simpler structure. A second feature of special interest about the strongly interacting particles is the special set of conservation laws that constrain the strong interactions alone, not the weak or electromagnetic interactions. (A strongly interacting particle can also interact weakly or electromagnetically. When it does, it is free to violate these partial conservation laws.)

A profusion of strongly interacting particles

STRANGE PARTICLES

The first of what have come to be called strange particles showed up in cloud chambers at the University of Manchester in 1947. Because the decay of these particles produced V-shaped tracks, they were at first known as V particles. A more recent picture of such a V track is shown in Figure 27.2. The track of an incoming kaon terminates in the chamber; separated from it by a few centimeters is a V, with its vertex pointing toward the end of the incoming kaon

The early V particles

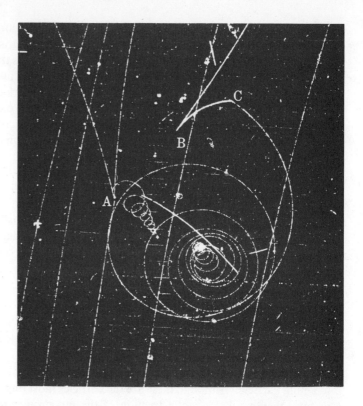

FIGURE 27.2   Example of *V*-shaped track characteristic of strange-particle decay. A lambda particle created at point A decays at point B into a proton, a negative muon, and an unseen antineutrino. The muon in turn decays at point C. The lambda was born at point A in the reaction $K^- + p \rightarrow \Lambda^0 + \pi^- + \pi^+$. The kaon track enters the chamber from below; the two pions fly upward from point A. (Photograph courtesy of Lawrence Radiation Laboratory, University of California, Berkeley.)

track (point A in the figure). Since the particles in the chamber moved through a known magnetic field, measurements of the radii of curvature of the visible tracks provide values of momentum of the charged particles (Equation 16.30: $p \sim r$). Together with application of the law of momentum conservation, such measurements make it possible to infer that a neutral particle was created at point A and that it decayed at point B into a pair of oppositely charged particles.

Analysis of this kind soon revealed the properties of the new particles. We now know that among the first V particles observed were neutral kaons and lambdas, which were decaying according to the schemes

$$K^0 \rightarrow \pi^+ + \pi^-,$$

$$\Lambda^0 \rightarrow p + \pi^-.$$

Within a few years, the K^+ and K^- particles had been identified, and the sigma and xi particles had been discovered. (For the characteristic open-*V* track produced by Ξ^- decay, look back to Figure 3.6, page 58.) By 1964 enough order had appeared in the catalog of particles to make possible the prediction of the omega baryon before its discovery in a Brookhaven bubble chamber.

The study of the new particles had not proceeded very far before something peculiar about them appeared. In spite of the fact that they had gone unnoticed during many years of cloud-chamber studies, they were, in fact, not especially rare. In very energetic nuclear collisions, the chance of creating one of the new particles was so great that there was no escape from the conclusion that the new particles must interact strongly, like the pions and nucleons. Particles that experience only electromagnetic and/or weak interactions could not be produced as frequently as the new particles. Expressed in terms of a time, one of the new particles could be produced after only 10^{-22} sec if enough energy were available. Yet, once produced, they lived a million million times longer than that, about 10^{-10} sec. Because of this "strange" behavior, the new particles were called the strange particles.

Strange particles: strong production and weak decay

The long life of a pion or a muon is understandable because it decays into particles that interact only weakly. But in the decay of a lambda, for example,

$$\Lambda^0 \to p + \pi^-,$$

the products of the decay—proton and pion—are both strongly interacting particles, and so is the lambda itself, as proved by the ease with which it can be created. It was very hard to see what kept the lambda alive so long, why it did not take advantage of the strong interactions to convert itself immediately into proton and pion.

An answer to the puzzle of the lambda's long life was provided independently in 1953 by two young physicists, Murray Gell-Mann in America (then aged 23) and Kazuhiko Nishijima in Japan (then 26). What makes the proton live forever is the law of baryon conservation. Suppose, said Gell-Mann and Nishijima, there is another conservation law, a new one that makes the lambda live "almost forever." Some new physical quantity, some new "thing," has to be held constant, or conserved. Gell-Mann's name for the new conserved quantity is "strangeness."

Law of strangeness conservation

Table 27.2 lists the strangeness quantum number assignments for the strongly interacting particles included in Figure 27.1. Those of nonzero strangeness are the so-called strange particles. Such assignments and classification may seem rather arbitrary, but they work. In the absence of any deeper knowledge, strangeness is as good a guide as we have to the rate of production and decay

TABLE 27.2 STRANGENESS QUANTUM NUMBERS OF STRONGLY INTERACTING PARTICLES

For antiparticles, reverse the sign of the strangeness.

Particle		Strangeness
Name	Symbol	S
Pion	π^-, π^0, π^+	0
Kaon	K^0, K^+	$+1$
Eta	η^0	0
Nucleon	n, p	0
Lambda	Λ^0	-1
Sigma	$\Sigma^-, \Sigma^0, \Sigma^+$	-1
Xi	Ξ^-, Ξ^0	-2
Omega	Ω^-	-3

of strongly interacting particles. The conservation law is this: In every strong interaction process, the total strangeness is conserved.*

In a pion-production process, such as

$$p + p \rightarrow p + n + \pi^+,$$

the new conservation law is satisfied, for the total strangeness number is zero before the collision and zero afterward. But what if a strange particle is produced? This can be managed only if at least two strange particles are produced together, with opposite signs for their strangeness numbers. A typical allowed process is

$$p + p \rightarrow p + \Lambda^0 + K^+.$$

The strangeness of the two colliding protons is zero. The strangeness numbers -1 and $+1$ for the lambda and kaon cancel to conserve the total of zero. This phenomenon, christened "associated production," was proposed first by Abraham Pais shortly before the appearance of the strangeness theory of Gell-Mann and Nishijima. There is now ample evidence that in the collisions of pions and nucleons, strange particles are always produced at least two at a time. This was not noticed at first because one member of the pair frequently escaped the cloud chamber undetected, leaving only one to be seen. Figure 3.5 provides a good example of associated production, and another example is shown in Figure 27.3.

If a strange particle strikes a nucleon, again the strangeness-conservation law dictates what may happen. A typical allowed process is

$$\Lambda^0 + p \rightarrow n + p + \overline{K^0}.$$

A lambda particle vanishes in collision with a proton, but to preserve the total strangeness number of -1, another strange particle must be formed, in this case an antikaon. In Figure 3.6, the reaction

$$\overline{K^+} + p \rightarrow K^+ + \Xi^-$$

was illustrated; test it for strangeness conservation.

As these examples show, the concept of strangeness constitutes more than a feeble attempt at humor. The power of this new conservation law, like that of every conservation law, lies in what it forbids. There are a vast number of strong-interaction processes that are forbidden only by the conservation of strangeness; none of them has ever been detected. There can be no doubt that strangeness, whatever its deeper meaning might be, is an important attribute of the particles that strongly limits their possible transformations.

What does strangeness conservation have to say about strange-particle decay? As the simplest example, consider the kaon. It is the lightest strange particle (just as the electron is the lightest charged particle, and the proton is the lightest baryon). If strangeness conservation were an absolute law, the kaon could not decay at all and would join the ranks of the stable particles. But since strangeness conservation governs only the strong interactions and not

---

* It is now common to characterize strongly interacting particles by hypercharge Y rather than strangeness S. The two concepts are simply related by $Y = S + B$, where B is baryon number. Since B is absolutely conserved, Y and S obey equivalent partial conservation laws.

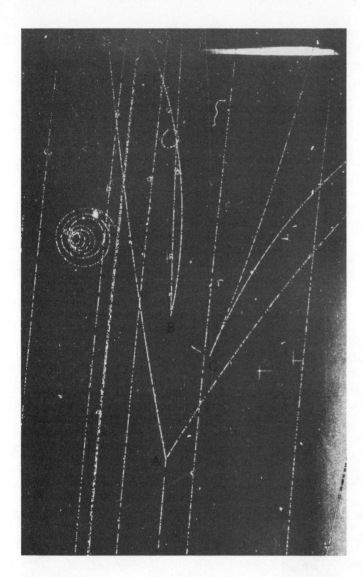

FIGURE 27.3 Associated production. A lambda particle and a kaon are created together at point A in the reaction, $p + p \rightarrow \Lambda^0 + K^0 + p + \pi^+$. These neutral particles decay with characteristic V tracks at points B and C. (Photograph courtesy of Brookhaven National Laboratory.)

the weak, the kaon is inhibited only from undergoing the very rapid decay (after about 10^{-22} sec) that would characterize the strong interactions. Since the weak interactions violate strangeness conservation, they act in their own leisurely fashion and bring about the kaon decay after about 10^{-10} sec. Even the weak interactions have some respect for strangeness. It is found experimentally that weak decays change strangeness as little as possible:

It is violated by the weak interactions

$$\Delta S = \pm 1.$$

No example of a particle transformation with $\Delta S = \pm 2$ has been seen.

RESONANCES

Resonances, although the most recently discovered class of particles, are the most numerous. Some are strange particles and some are not. Some are baryons and some are not. *All* are strongly interacting.

The main thing the resonances have taught us is that the 35 particles listed in Table 27.1 (not counting the graviton) are far from the end of the story. The particles in Table 27.1 are those that are stable and those whose decay is mediated by weak or electromagnetic interactions, not by strong interactions. The resonances round out the picture. They are the particles that interact strongly and that are not prevented by any conservation law from following their natural inclination for very rapid decay. Hence in the short time characteristic of strong interactions, they vanish and give way to lighter particles.

A typical resonance is born and dies all within a space considerably smaller than a single atom. That it ever existed can only be inferred from studies of the longer-lived products of its decay. Suppose, for example, that a proton and antiproton annihilate to create five pions:

$$\bar{p} + p \rightarrow \pi^{+} + \pi^{+} + \pi^{-} + \pi^{-} + \pi^{0}.$$

This process is illustrated in Figure 27.4. The bubble-chamber photograph shows the track of the incoming antiproton and the tracks of the four charged pions, apparently all emerging from exactly the same point. Energy and

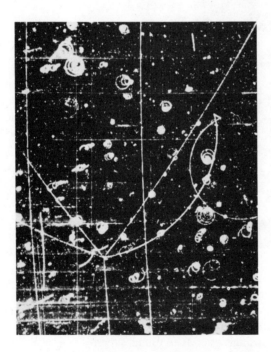
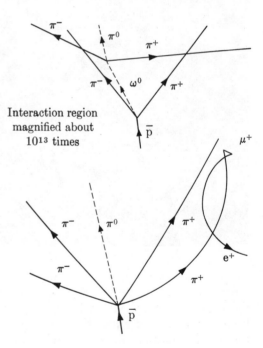

FIGURE 27.4 Production of an omega resonance. The antiproton entering from the bottom annihilates with a proton in the bubble chamber, forming two pions and an omega meson. After a time of about 10^{-22} sec, the omega decays into three more pions. The transitory existence of the omega is inferred only from studies of the pion tracks. (Notice that one of the positive pions is also observed to undergo decay into a muon through the reaction, $\pi^{+} \rightarrow \mu^{+} + \nu_{\mu}$, and the muon, in turn, decays into a positron according to $\mu^{+} \rightarrow e^{+} + \nu_{e} + \bar{\nu}_{\mu}$. The neutrinos are of course unseen.) (Photograph courtesy of Lawrence Radiation Laboratory, University of California, Berkeley.)

momentum conservation require that one unseen neutral pion also flew from this point. Study of many such events shows that groups of these pions tend to come off in a certain relation to each other, which implies that they must be the decay products of a single particle. This correlation of the final pions shows that what actually happens (some of the time) is a two-stage process in which, first, an omega meson* is created:

$$\bar{p} + p \rightarrow \omega^0 + \pi^+ + \pi^-;$$

then the omega decays:

$$\omega^0 \rightarrow \pi^+ + \pi^- + \pi^0.$$

There is no doubt that the omega existed as an independent entity even though it had no time to move a measurable distance away from the point of its creation.

Quantum mechanics plays an interesting direct role in the measurement of resonance lifetimes. Because of the uncertainty principle, the shorter the lifetime of a resonance, the easier it is to measure the lifetime. The energy-time form of the uncertainty principle is directly applicable:

$$\Delta E \, \Delta t \cong \hbar.$$

The more tightly is the particle squeezed in time (Δt), the greater must be the uncertainty of its energy (ΔE). This energy uncertainty in turn appears as a variability in the apparent mass of the particle. Consider, for example, a resonance whose lifetime is 10^{-23} sec. The energy uncertainty for this short a lifetime is

$$\Delta E = \frac{\hbar}{\Delta t} = \frac{6.58 \times 10^{-22} \text{ MeV sec}}{10^{-23} \text{ sec}} = 66 \text{ MeV}.$$

Short lifetime means uncertain mass

This is the energy equivalent of about 130 electron masses. No measurement can determine the mass of the resonance to an accuracy greater than this. In a series of many identical measurements, a distribution of values of mass spread over a range of about 130 electron masses would be obtained. In this way resonances are identified and their lifetimes measured. Counting different charges and antiparticles separately, more than 200 resonances have already been identified.

PARTICLE SPECTROSCOPY

The proliferation of particles, especially strongly interacting particles, has produced a situation reminiscent of spectroscopy in the nineteenth century.† More and more spectral lines were discovered and classified. Finally Balmer, Rydberg, and others brought some of these lines into mathematical order. Through the idea of the photon, Einstein tied spectral frequency to energy. Bohr related photon energy to the energy difference of stationary states of

---

* The omega meson, designated by ω, is distinct from the omega baryon, which is designated by Ω.

† See Victor F. Weisskopf, "The Three Spectroscopies," *Scientific American*, May, 1968.

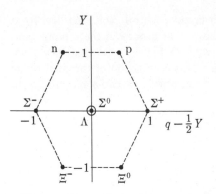

FIGURE 27.5 Diagram to display quantum numbers of a related set of strongly interacting particles. All have spin one-half. Hypercharge Y labels the vertical axis. (For these particles, $Y = S + 1$, where S is strangeness.) A combination of charge q and hypercharge Y labels the horizontal axis.

atomic motion. Finally, the thousands of known spectral lines were unified by atomic theory, which accounts for all of them in terms of the transitions of a single fundamental particle, the electron.

Particle physicists today see themselves following a similar path. Now that so many different particles have been identified, the most intensive effort is being devoted to the search for order—for simple regularities in the masses and other properties of the particles. The particles of course do not correspond exactly to spectral lines. A better analogy is that of a set of atoms whose properties are so markedly altered from one stationary state to another that every state of every atom can be regarded as a separate particle.

Particles are likely to be states of an underlying system

The modern methods of seeking order among the particles are more sophisticated than Balmer's numerology but neither so simple nor so deep as Bohr's theory of the atom. Nevertheless, there has been real and encouraging progress. Through a new classification scheme, Gell-Mann and others have delineated family groups of eight and ten particles, a unification that goes beyond two- and three-particle groupings such as the neutron-proton group or the group of three pions. According to this scheme, for instance, the nucleon, lambda, sigma, and xi particles (eight altogether) are various faces of a single entity, an entity with different states of charge and different states of strangeness (Figure 27.5).

The difficulties of particle spectroscopy spring primarily from a single source—the large magnitude of energy differences. When a hydrogen atom is excited from its ground state to its first excited state of motion, its mass increases by about one part in 10^8. When a nucleon is excited to a resonant state, its mass increases by about 10 percent. In the particle world, every change is a drastic change. Yet as particle data multiply, physicists hope that a combination of their own free imagination plus the hard evidence from several hundred particle states will lead to the unifying principle that is still missing.

27.4   Neutrinos

The neutrinos are unique and uniquely interesting. They are all weak. What makes them interesting is what they lack—charge, mass, electromagnetic interactions, and strong interactions. What makes them vital in the structure of modern physics is what they have—energy, momentum, angular momentum, and either electron-family number or muon-family number. Without neutrinos, four fundamental conservation laws would be in trouble.

A simple example that adequately illustrates the role of the neutrino is the beta decay of the free neutron, indicated by

$$n \to p + e^- + \bar{\nu}_e.$$

Beta decay of the neutron

A proton, an electron, and an antineutrino are created. Figure 27.6 shows a possible result of the decay of a neutron. As a reminder that the neutrino is not actually seen, the "after" diagram is repeated with the path and spin of the neutrino deleted. Evidently, the neutrino is needed for the conservation of energy, momentum, and angular momentum. It also contributes to the new conservation law of electron-family number.

The process in nature whereby a stable particle comes into existence is usually quite similar to the process whereby it is absorbed, or annihilated. Thus a photon is born by the oscillation of electric charge and, upon absorption, sets charge into motion. An electron may be born simultaneously with its antiparticle, the positron; it can die if it meets a positron with which to annihilate. The neutrino comes into existence in processes of beta decay or in other decay processes brought about by the weak interactions. It can be absorbed and observed only via further weak interactions. In this lies the key to understanding the difficulty of observing the neutrino. It is observable only when it interacts in some way with matter, but the chance that it interacts is very small indeed. The mean penetration distance of a 1-MeV neutrino through solid matter is roughly 1,000 light-years. Fortunately, the quantum-mechanical rules of probability cause a few neutrinos—a very few—to interact much sooner, after penetrating only a few miles, or even a few centimeters, of matter.

Neutrino detection must use the weak interaction

FIGURE 27.6   Beta decay of the neutron.

Before

After

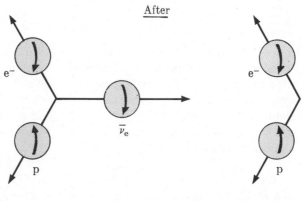

A possible result   What is seen

DETECTION OF THE ANTINEUTRINO

For years, the reality of the neutrino had to be accepted on the basis of rather indirect evidence. Finally, in 1956 it was directly detected (more exactly, the antineutrino was detected) in an experiment carried out at Savannah River, South Carolina, by Clyde Cowan and Frederick Reines, two physicists from the Los Alamos Scientific Laboratory in New Mexico. Savannah River, the site of a powerful reactor, offered a rich source of antineutrinos. The interior of a reactor is highly radioactive, second only to a nuclear explosion in the intensity of its beta radioactivity. This comes about because of the neutron excess in fission fragments. In one among many possible modes of fission, a nucleus of ^{236}U might split into nuclei of molybdenum and tin plus several extra neutrons:

Reactor is strong antineutrino source

$$^{236}_{92}U \rightarrow \ ^{104}_{42}Mo + \ ^{128}_{50}Sn + 4n.$$

Both these nuclei are overly neutron-rich, the heaviest stable isotope of molybdenum being ^{100}Mo, that of tin, ^{124}Sn. Accordingly, both are radioactive. In fact, each undergoes a chain of two beta decays (to $^{104}_{44}Ru$ and $^{128}_{52}Te$) so that in this example a single fission event results finally in four antineutrinos.

The rate of production of antineutrinos in the Savannah River reactor could be calculated, as could the chance that any one of them would be stopped within the experimental apparatus. The infinitesimally small chance of catching one antineutrino multiplied by the enormous number of antineutrinos available gave the number that should be caught in the apparatus. Reines and Cowan reckoned that they could stop one antineutrino every twenty minutes.

The Reines-Cowan detection apparatus

The heart of the experimental arrangement was a sandwich of tanks, ordinary water in a three-inch-thick "meat" layer and a liquid scintillator in the two-foot-thick "bread" layers. The actual apparatus was a "club sandwich" (Figure 27.7), taller than a man and nearly as broad and as deep as it was tall. The scintillator layers, which emit weak pulses of light when fast charged particles or gamma rays pass through them, were surrounded by photoelectric cells. Outside these, earth and lead blocks shielded the entire detector from unwanted particles. This shielding offered no impediment, of course, to antineutrinos.

Each molecule of water in the "meat" layers contains two protons (the hydrogen nuclei). These protons are the targets for the important antineutrino capture reaction,

$$\overline{v_e} + p \rightarrow n + e^+.$$

Figure 27.7 shows a typical sequence of events following such a capture event. The newly created neutron and positron fly apart in different directions, but then each gradually loses energy in the water and is slowed down. The positron, being charged, experiences an electric interaction with all the electrons in neighboring atoms and is very rapidly brought to rest (in about 10^{-9} sec, after covering less than 1 cm). Almost immediately, it annihilates with one of the atomic electrons in the reaction

$$e^+ + e^- \rightarrow \gamma + \gamma.$$

Each of the two photons acquires an energy equivalent to the mass of one electron. Since they fly apart in opposite directions, the photons will usually

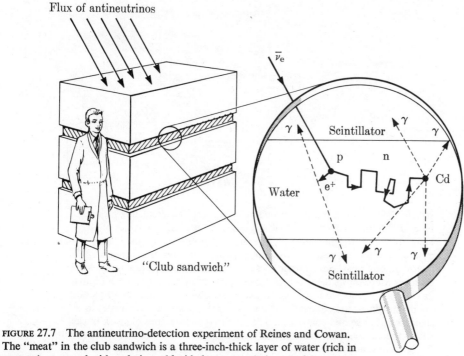

Flux of antineutrinos

$\bar{\nu}_e$

"Club sandwich"

FIGURE 27.7   The antineutrino-detection experiment of Reines and Cowan. The "meat" in the club sandwich is a three-inch-thick layer of water (rich in protons), seasoned with cadmium chloride because cadmium nuclei capture neutrons readily. The "bread" is a two-foot-thick tank of liquid scintillator viewed by photoelectric tubes. The chain of events set off by an antineutrino capture is described in the text.

enter two neighboring scintillation tanks, where they will produce characteristic pulses of light seen by the photocells.

The events initiated by the positron all occur in a time much less than a millionth of a second. Meanwhile, the uncharged neutron is making its way through the water in more leisurely fashion, caroming off nuclei for several millionths of a second before being slowed to thermal speed. Wanting to be sure that the neutron, once slowed down, is promptly captured, the experimenters added to the water some cadmium in the form of cadmium chloride. Following the neutron capture, the cadmium nucleus emits one or more gamma rays that fly into the scintillation tank to signal the capture event.

Altogether, then, three pulses of energy result from the capture of an antineutrino by a proton. The first two are simultaneous pulses in each of two neighboring scintillators as a pair of photons signal the annihilation of a positron. The third is a pulse of one or more photons occurring several millionths of a second later signaling the capture of a neutron. Moreover, each of these three pulses has a characteristic identifying energy that the photo cells can measure— 0.5 MeV for each of the annihilation photons and about 9 MeV total for the neutron-capture photons. In 1956, five years after the first efforts to trap the antineutrino began, Reines and Cowan announced the definite observation of the electron's antineutrino through the identification of this characteristic

The three-pulse signature of the antineutrino

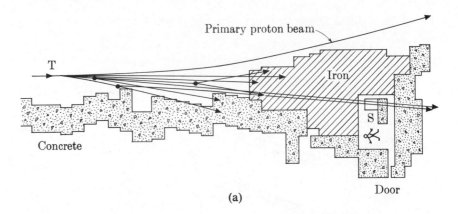

(a)

FIGURE 27.8   Discovery of the second neutrino. (a) The circulating proton
beam in the Brookhaven AGS strikes a target T; secondary particles of all
kinds spray to the right.   Lines penetrating 44 feet of iron and the spark
chamber S represent neutrinos from pion decay.   The iron or concrete stops
almost all other particles (shorter lines).   A reclining experimenter in the spark-
chamber room shows the scale.   (Magnets guiding the primary proton beam in
its circle are not shown.)   (b) The 10-ton spark chamber containing 90 parallel
aluminum plates, each about 4 feet square.   Sparks jump between plates to
signal the passage of a charged particle.   (c) Two photographs of spark tracks
left by muons created when neutrinos were captured in the chamber.   To record
29 significant muon events, about 3×10^{17} protons were accelerated in the
AGS and 10^{14} neutrinos passed through the chamber.   [Photograph (b)
courtesy of Brookhaven National Laboratory; photograph (c) courtesy of
Nevis Laboratories, Columbia University.]

sequence of scintillation pulses about three times per hour while the reactor
was in operation.

THE MUON'S NEUTRINO

The observation of the muon's neutrino in 1962 by Leon Lederman, Melvin
Schwartz, Jack Steinberger, and their colleagues* required the use of a wholly
different set of experimental tools.   The basic capture reactions,

$$\overline{v}_\mu + p \rightarrow n + \mu^+ \quad \text{and} \quad v_\mu + n \rightarrow p + \mu^-,$$

can take place only if the neutrinos (and antineutrinos) have sufficient energy—
over 100 MeV—to create the mass of a muon.   The chance that the capture will
occur increases as the energy of the neutrinos increases, so a prerequisite for
success in this experiment was high energy, which dictated the use of the largest
available accelerator.   The successful experiment was carried out at the Alternating Gradient Synchrotron at Brookhaven.   Actually, for a reason to be
mentioned below, the machine was operated at only 15 GeV for this experiment,
about half its maximum energy.

   Via a short chain of intermediate events, the Brookhaven AGS readily
provides a copious supply of high-energy neutrinos (see Figure 27.8).   Energetic

---

* G. Danby, J.-M. Gaillard, K. Goulianos, L. M. Lederman, N. Mistry, M. Schwartz, and
   J. Steinberger, "Observations of High-Energy Neutrino Reactions and the Existence of Two
   Kinds of Neutrinos," *Physical Review Letters* **9**, 36 (1962).

(b)

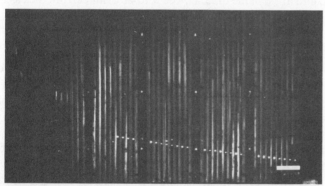

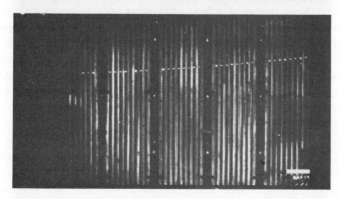

(c)

protons within the machine collide with nuclei in a target, producing a spray of secondary particles. Numerous among these are pions. As they fly from the accelerator, the charged pions undergo spontaneous decay to provide the needed neutrinos, according to the transformations

Decaying pions provide neutrinos

$$\pi^+ \rightarrow \mu^+ + \nu_\mu \quad \text{and} \quad \pi^- \rightarrow \mu^- + \overline{\nu_\mu}.$$

Because of momentum conservation, the neutrinos and antineutrinos—along with all the other debris from the collision—fly forward in a narrow cone.

In order to get rid of unwanted particles and study the neutrinos alone, the experimenters erected, in the way of this heterogeneous beam, a solid wall of iron 44 feet thick. Behind the wall stood a spark chamber (Figure 27.8). At the chosen machine energy of 15 GeV, the iron battlement was sufficient to stop all of the secondary particles except neutrinos; at the full machine energy of 33 GeV, it would not have been sufficient.

Passing through the spark chamber, each neutrino or antineutrino had about 1 chance in 10^{12} to be captured, via the reactions

Capture events produce observable muons

$$\nu_\mu + n \rightarrow p + \mu^-,$$
$$\overline{\nu_\mu} + p \rightarrow n + \mu^+.$$

If the muon's neutrino were the same as the electron's neutrino, the creation of electrons and positrons should also occur, with the same probability as the creation of negative and positive muons. In about 300 hours of operation the Columbia University-Brookhaven group observed 29 significant muon tracks in their chamber and no electron tracks. They thereby positively identified the muon's neutrino and at the same time showed it to be distinct from the electron's neutrino.

SOLAR NEUTRINOS

Every star is a copious source of neutrinos (see Section 26.7). Just as the earth receives most of its light, photons, from the sun, so it receives most of its neutrinos from our own sun. For every million neutrinos striking the atmosphere, one comes from outer space and the other 999,999 come from the sun. On each square centimeter of the earth in each second, the sun pours about 4×10^{10} neutrinos and about ten million times as many photons. In the time it takes to blink an eye, a man is struck by more than 10^{12} neutrinos. Despite this enormous flux, the solar neutrinos are even more difficult to detect than the neutrinos created on Earth. Nevertheless, it is worth the effort because neutrinos are the only direct messengers from the thermonuclear furnace at the center of the sun.* A large-scale effort to detect solar neutrinos, carried out by Raymond Davis, Jr. and coworkers from Brookhaven, may have succeeded by the time this text is in print. In an underground tank containing 10^5 gallons of cleaning fluid (C_2Cl_4), a few chlorine nuclei are expected to be transformed to argon nuclei via the neutrino capture reaction

Enormous flux of solar neutrinos

Expected reaction in cleaning fluid

$$\nu_e + {}^{37}_{17}Cl \rightarrow {}^{37}_{18}Ar + e^-.$$

---

* See John N. Bahcall, "Neutrinos from the Sun," *Scientific American*, July, 1969.

The argon atoms, after separation from the cleaning fluid, should reveal their presence by their characteristic radioactivity. With a half life of 34 days, ^{37}Ar decays back to ^{37}Cl via orbital capture, with secondary X-ray emission. Neutrinos from the sun's proton-proton reaction,

$$p + p \rightarrow d + e^+ + \nu_e,$$

although most numerous, are not the ones captured by chlorine 37. Instead, the rarer but more energetic neutrinos from a subsidiary decay process are the ones to be detected. Their source is boron 8, which emits neutrinos of energy up to 14 MeV when it undergoes positron decay:

$$_5^8 B \rightarrow \, _4^8 Be + e^+ + \nu_e.$$

27.5   The spacetime view of interactions: Feynman diagrams

The fact that the significant events in the particle world are events of annihilation and creation occurring at single spacetime points makes it convenient and useful to catalog particle interactions with the help of world-line diagrams. Such diagrams were introduced in Section 20.10. Some examples from the domain of particles are shown in Figure 27.9. The first one shows the process of photon

Convenience of world-line diagrams for particle events

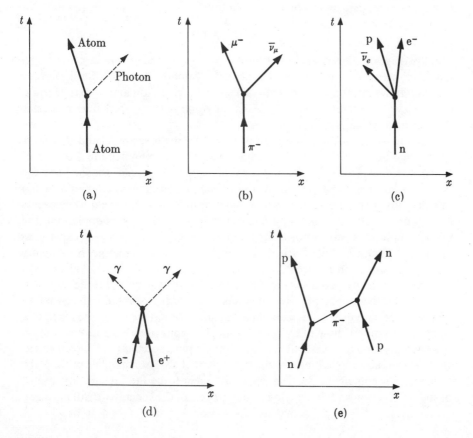

FIGURE 27.9 World lines of various occurrences in the particle world. (a) Emission of photon by an atom. (b) Pion decay. (c) Beta decay of a neutron. (d) Positron-electron annihilation. (e) Pion exchange process.

emission by an atom. Initially (starting at the bottom of the diagram), an atom is at rest. Accordingly, it traces out a straight vertical world line. It then emits a photon that flies off to the right, and the atom itself, having fired the photon, recoils and moves off more slowly to the left. Recall that the slower a particle moves, the more nearly vertical is its world line. A horizontal world line, corresponding to infinite velocity, can represent nothing physical. The photon line is tipped the maximum amount away from the vertical; the inverse of its slope is the speed of light.

The next diagram, Figure 27.9(b), illustrates pion decay:

$$\pi^- \rightarrow \mu^- + \overline{\nu}_\mu.$$

At some point, indicated by the heavy dot, the negative pion ceases to exist. Coincident with its annihilation is the creation of a negative muon and an antineutrino, whose tipped world lines indicate that they fly apart. Since the antineutrino is massless, its world line is tipped at the angle corresponding to the speed of light.

Diagram 27.9(c) shows the beta decay of the neutron,

$$n \rightarrow p + e^- + \overline{\nu}_e.$$

This time, the crucial event in spacetime involves the destruction of one particle and the creation of three others. The next diagram shows the annihilation of an electron and a positron to create two photons:

$$e^- + e^+ \rightarrow \gamma + \gamma.$$

Finally, diagram 27.9(e) illustrates a pion-exchange process that contributes to the force between a neutron and a proton. Initially (bottom of diagram), a neutron and a proton are present. They exchange a pion and exchange roles, emerging with different speeds. This is only one of many exchange processes that can take place.

Before we go on to the question of how these pictures are related to what is "really" going on at the submicroscopic level, one warning flag must be raised. It is possible, indeed probable, that some of the single "events" indicated by the black dots are really complex sequences of events that all happen within such a tiny domain of space and such a short span of time that they seem to be events at only one single spacetime point. It is already known, for example, that the phenomenon of electron-positron annihilation does not proceed exactly as pictured in Figure 27.9(d). Rather, the two photons actually emerge from slightly different points, as in Figure 27.10.

So far, particle events seem to occur at spacetime points

We must be prepared for the possibility that the future will reveal an inner structure to other apparently simple events, even for the possibility that what we now describe as acts of sudden annihilation and creation are really the result of a smooth, continuous flow of events over tinier regions of space and time than it has been possible to investigate so far. This is pure speculation. Down to the shortest distances (10^{-16} m) and shortest times (10^{-24} sec) man has probed, the elementary events of the particle world still seem to be the catastrophic events of sudden creation and destruction of the packets of field energy we call particles.

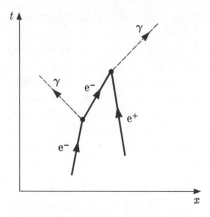

FIGURE 27.10   What "really" happens in a positron-electron annihilation process, a corrected version of Figure 27.9(d).

PHOTON EXCHANGE AND LOCAL ACTION

Contrast this new view of particle interactions with the classical view. According to the old view, a pair of electrons, approaching each other, feel a mutual repulsive force, and are deflected. The new view attributes the force to a specific mechanism of photon exchange and replaces the idea of smooth continuous change with the idea of abrupt discontinuous change. In Figure 27.11 we see two electrons approaching one another. At point A, the electron on the left emits a photon and changes its speed. At point B, the electron on the right absorbs the photon and changes *its* speed. The two electrons have interacted, or exerted a force on each other, because their motion has been altered. It was the photon that mediated the interaction. Strictly speaking, the basic interaction was not between the two electrons at all but between each electron and a photon. The second electron is only indirectly aware of the presence of the first. The old idea of action at a distance, of a force "reaching out" from one to the other, is completely abandoned. It is replaced by the idea of a "local interaction," of each electron interacting locally—that is, at its own location—with a photon.

Local action between charged particle and photon

Of course, the particular diagram illustrated here is only one of many; the others involve more complicated exchanges between the electrons. The net

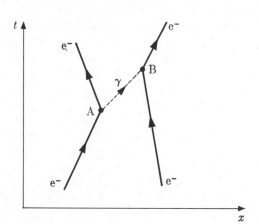

FIGURE 27.11   World-line diagram for the mutual interaction and deflection of two electrons.

effect of all the possible exchanges is to approximate the classical electron motion in regions where the classical description is valid.

According to the present theory of the interactions of electrons and photons, Figure 27.11 is a picture of what "really" happens on the submicroscopic scale. Such a diagram is called a Feynman diagram after Richard Feynman, who showed in 1949 that such pictures have an exact correspondence to mathematical expressions in the field theory of electrons and photons. These diagrams, therefore, portray what is "really" happening and provide a convenient way to catalog the various possible processes of creation, annihilation, and exchange.

FUNDAMENTAL INTERACTION VERTICES

The key points of a Feynman diagram are the "vertices," representing those points at which (in this example) photons are created or absorbed. All processes involving photons, and therefore *all* the interactions associated with electromagnetism, arise from elementary events of photon creation or photon annihilation. These fundamental interaction events are represented by a single kind of vertex that looks like either of the diagrams in Figure 27.12. The solid lines represent charged particles and the dashed line represents a photon. The points A and B in Figure 27.11 are vertices of this kind.

Interaction vertex: Every particle is annihilated or created

If the solid lines represent the world lines of electrons, for example, it appears that the fundamental interaction event may be regarded as an event in which a photon is created or absorbed and an electron simultaneously changes its state of motion. There is, however, a more general and more fruitful interpretation. The vertex may be taken to represent a point where the world line of one electron terminates and the world line of another begins. According to this view, the vertex represents a truly catastrophic event. Nothing survives it. Rather than thinking of a single electron being changed at the vertex, one can think of one electron being destroyed and another electron being created. Since all electrons are indistinguishable, it has no real meaning to say that the outgoing electron is the same as or different from the incoming electron. To think of the outgoing electron as a new and different electron, however, corresponds more closely to the mathematical theory of the fundamental interaction. The creation-destruction interpretation also leads to a simple, unified description of particle events and antiparticle events.

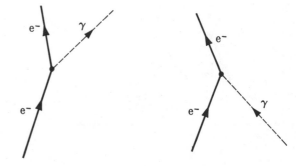

FIGURE 27.12   Basic electron-photon interaction vertices.

The vertex on the right in Figure 27.10 seems to differ from those in Figures 27.11 and 27.12. Rather than a point where one electron world line ends and another begins, this vertex is a point where both an electron world line and a positron world line end. There is a simple artistic trick by which we can change the picture significantly. Suppose we turn around the arrow on the positron line. The arrowhead was, after all, redundant since all particles move forward in time. We can use it instead as a label to distinguish particles from antiparticles. An arrowhead pointing in the "right" direction will indicate a particle (for example, an electron); an arrowhead pointing in the "wrong" direction will indicate an antiparticle (a positron). Using this revised notation, we show in Figure 27.13(a) an electron-positron annihilation vertex and in Figure 27.13(b) an electron-positron creation vertex. These vertex diagrams involving positrons look like twisted versions of the fundamental vertex diagrams in Figure 27.12. The generalized conclusion is that the fundamental electron-photon vertex with its limbs twisted in all possible directions in space-time represents all the possible basic interactions among electrons, positrons, and photons. This provides a magnificently simple and general view of the underlying basis of all electromagnetic phenomena.

The general vertex of electromagnetism

ARE POSITRONS TIME-REVERSED ELECTRONS?

What Feynman showed when he discussed the connection between such world-line diagrams and the structure of the mathematical theory of the electron-positron-photon interaction was that the device of the reversed arrowhead is much more than an artistic trick. According to the field theory of electrons, the creation of a positron is "equivalent" to the annihilation of an electron (they are not identical processes, but the theory says that whenever one can happen, the other must also be able to happen). Moreover, the mathematical description of a positron field propagating forward in time is identical with the description of an electron field propagating backward in time. It is perfectly possible and consistent to think of particles moving backward in time as well as forward.

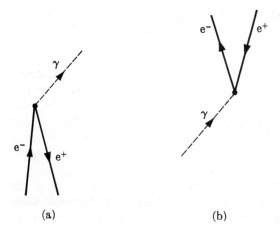

(a)   (b)

FIGURE 27.13   Additional fundamental electron-photon interaction vertices which include antiparticles (positrons).

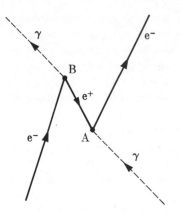

FIGURE 27.14   A Feynman diagram for photon-electron scattering (the Compton effect). Other diagrams also contribute to the same overall process.

This circumstance need not lead us to deep philosophical conclusions, although philosophical implications are hard to escape. The positron *may* be described as an electron moving backward in time, but it does not *have* to be so described. An alternative description is equally possible in which the positron is a normal particle moving forward in time. Nevertheless, this idea of backward motion in time is a tantalizing one that simplifies the view of elementary interactions and provides a "natural explanation" for the existence of antimatter. Consider, for example, the Feynman diagram of Figure 27.14, which depicts one mechanism of photon-electron scattering (the Compton effect). According to the normal view of time unrolling in one direction, we start at the bottom of the diagram and read up. First, an electron and a photon are approaching each other. At vertex A, the photon creates an electron-positron pair. The new electron flies away, while the positron collides with the first electron at vertex B. There they undergo mutual annihilation and a new photon is born. The alternative view, which Feynman showed to be also consistent, is to imagine the first electron proceeding to point B, where it emits a photon and reverses its path through time. It "then" travels to point A, where it absorbs the incoming photon and once again reverses its course through time, flying off in the "right" direction. Either view is permissible and logically consistent.

Simplest interpretation of theory: Electrons can move forward or backward in time

27.6   The TCP theorem

The connection between time-reversed trajectories and antiparticles, a connection that reflects a basic spacetime symmetry in the elementary-particle world, has found expression in the "TCP theorem," whose three letters stand for three hypothetical operations: T, time reversal; C, charge conjugation, the technical name for interchanging particles and antiparticles; P, space inversion, which is approximately equivalent to taking a mirror image of space (this is sometimes called the parity operation, hence the P). The TCP theorem is actually an invariance principle of a special kind. It may prove to be a law governing all the interactions in nature (it remains to be accurately tested for the weak interactions). It says that if the three operations of T, C, and P are all applied to any physical process, the result of this mangling of what actually happened is another physical process that could have happened. This is not as complicated as it

A new law of invariance

sounds; you may easily perform the TCP operations on any of the Feynman diagrams illustrated in these pages. The only equipment needed is one wall mirror and a little imagination.

First, turn to any page containing a "proper" Feynman diagram—one with its antiparticle arrowheads pointing downward. Figure 27.11 or any later one will do. Now, to perform the operation C, simply imagine all arrowheads turned around; this interchanges all particles and antiparticles. (A backward-pointing arrow on a photon is all right, for a photon is its own antiparticle, a property it shares with the neutral pion.) For example, the operation C converts the negative pion decay,

$$\pi^- \rightarrow \mu^- + \overline{\nu_\mu},$$

into the positive pion decay,

$$\pi^+ \rightarrow \mu^+ + \nu_\mu,$$

Recipes for T, C, *and* P *operations*

since the positive pion is the antiparticle of the negative pion.

To perform the operation P, space reversal, turn the page of the book away from you and look at the diagram reflected in the mirror. This interchanges left and right. (There are fuller implications of P than this, concerned with particle spin; they will be considered in Section 27.8.)

Finally, turn the book upside down and look at the inverted diagram. This has obviously turned time around—the operation T—but it has also turned all the arrowheads around (operation C) and has interchanged left and right (operation P). The upside-down diagram therefore represents the application of all three transformations, T, C, and P, to the original physical process. The upside-down picture is another Feynman diagram that illustrates an actual, physically allowed process (*if* the TCP theorem is valid). In general it will not be the process you started with; it may even be quite different. But, according to the TCP theorem, since the original diagram represented a real physical process, so does the triply inverted diagram.

To see the effect of time reversal alone, we must undo the arrowhead reversal and the left-right inversion. Turn the book upside down, then look at the upside-down diagram in the mirror *and* imagine the arrowheads reversed. The diagram resulting from this manipulation illustrates the purely time-reversed process. Other combinations may be tried. The mirror view with arrowheads reversed is the result of the double operation PC, and so on.

Note that the TCP theorem, like other invariance principles and conservation laws, is a law of prohibition. Only those events can occur, it says, whose TCP inversions are also possible real physical events. If the process represented by the triply inverted diagram were not allowed, the original process would also be forbidden.

In the next three sections we consider invariance principles associated with the operations T, P, and C separately.

27.7   Time-reversal invariance

In Section 14.10, the time-reversal invariance that seems to govern nature in the small was contrasted with the "arrow of time," the unique sense of time direction that is evident in everyday affairs.* For complex systems, one direction of the unfolding of events (the entropy-increasing direction) is so much more probable than the opposite direction (the entropy-decreasing direction) that we call one direction in time possible, the other direction impossible.

To see nature's basic symmetry of time, we must examine simple processes involving very few objects. Suppose a space traveler bound for another galaxy takes along a moving picture of our solar system to show his hosts. If the picture had been taken from a point a few hundred billion miles distant in the general direction of the North Star, it would show the planets as tiny dots tracing out their elliptical orbits in a counter-clockwise direction about a central sun. The creatures of the other galaxy, being well versed in the laws of mechanics, would watch the picture with interest and conclude that there were no tricks, that it did indeed depict an actual physical chain of events. But had the film been run off backward, they would have been equally convinced. The backward view of planetary motion, although "untrue," since, in fact, our planets do not move that way, is nevertheless "possible," for it is consistent with the same laws of mechanics.

Time-reversal invariance in classical mechanics

Now allow our space traveler to proceed to another galaxy whose residents are intelligent and mathematically adept but scientifically primitive. One audience of these creatures is shown the planetary film in the forward direction; another audience is shown the same film run backward. Both audiences are asked to deduce the law of gravitational attraction and the law of mechanical motion from what they have seen. If they are collectively as clever as Newton, both groups will arrive at the correct, and identical, laws.

Forward and backward views imply the same laws

This is the real significance of time-reversal invariance. Under a hypothetical reversal of the direction of time, the laws of nature are unchanged. This is the statement of the principle that emphasizes *invariance*. To emphasize the *constraint* imposed by the law, we must phrase it somewhat differently. Only those things can happen that can also happen in the opposite order. Or, still more negatively: if a time-reversed process is impossible, then the process itself must be impossible.

Time-reversal invariance finds its simplest application in the world of particles, where it appears to govern the strong and electromagnetic interactions and possibly also the weak.† The figure in the margin illustrates electron-positron annihilation. The time-reversed process is the creation of an electron-positron pair by the collision of two photons. Recall the directions given in the preceding section for time-inverting a Feynman diagram. Turn the page upside down, view it in a mirror, and mentally turn the arrows around. You then see

---

* See Martin Gardner, "Can Time Go Backward?," *Scientific American*, January, 1967.

† In 1964 a group at Princeton University learned by studying kaon decay that the product of space inversion and charge conjugation (PC) is not a completely valid invariance principle for the weak interactions. This discovery has a possible implication for time-reversal invariance. If the TCP theorem is valid, T-invariance must also be violated to a small degree in order that the product of all three operations may provide an absolute invariance. On the other hand, time-reversal invariance may survive further tests. If it does, the TCP theorem will fail as a completely general principle, although it will surely retain an approximate validity.

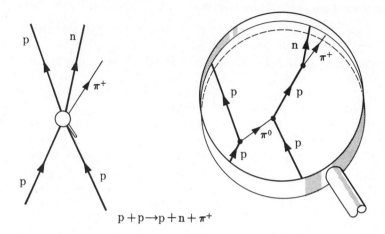

$$p + p \rightarrow p + n + \pi^+$$

FIGURE 27.15   Creation of a pion in a proton-proton collision. The time-reversed process is possible but far less likely than the direct process.

two photons coming together from the bottom and an electron and a positron flying apart at the top. According to time-reversal invariance, this reverse process is not only possible but can occur in every detail as the inverted sequence of fundamental interaction events. Since the "strength" of interaction at each vertex is unchanged, there is a precise numerical ratio between the probability of pair creation and the probability of pair annihilation which is implied by the law.

Time-reversed Feynman diagrams show possible processes

The role of probability in time-reversed events, so painfully obvious for a secretary untyping or a barber unclipping, makes itself felt in the particle world as well. A simple process of pion creation, for example, is impossible to reverse in practice. Two protons may collide to yield proton, neutron, and positive pion, as shown in Figure 27.15. The time-reversed process requires the nearly simultaneous collision of three particles, too unlikely to achieve in practice. But the requirement that *each* fundamental event is time reversible is a constraining condition that influences the possible form of the pion-nucleon interaction and therefore has an important effect on the forward-in-time process, whether or not the time-reversed process is likely, or experimentally possible. This is an exceedingly important aspect of invariance principles related to their increasingly central role in physics. The laws of mechanics to which the planets are subjected are partially determined by the condition of time-reversal invariance. Therefore, the actual way in which the planets arc through the sky is dictated in part by time-reversal invariance, even though it is entirely out of the question to stop the planets and turn them back in their tracks. Similarly, time-reversal invariance may be tested in particle interactions even if it is impractical to study the reversed process.*

The role of probability

* See Oliver E. Overseth, "Experiments in Time Reversal," *Scientific American,* October, 1969.

27.8   Space-inversion invariance: parity

The parity principle, or the principle of space-inversion invariance, says there is a symmetry between the world and its mirror image.* To state this in terms closer to those we used for time-reversal invariance: The mirror image of any physical process depicts a possible physical process, one that is governed by the same laws as the process itself. If the space traveler described in the last section inverted his film left-for-right, he would be showing a mirror view of the solar system—not a true picture of the solar system but a picture of a possible physical system.

Not every mirror view appears normal. The mirror view of a printed page, for example, looks "wrong." But there is nothing impossible about it. A printer could design inverted type and produce a page, which, viewed directly, would be identical to the mirror view of the normal page (Figure 27.16).

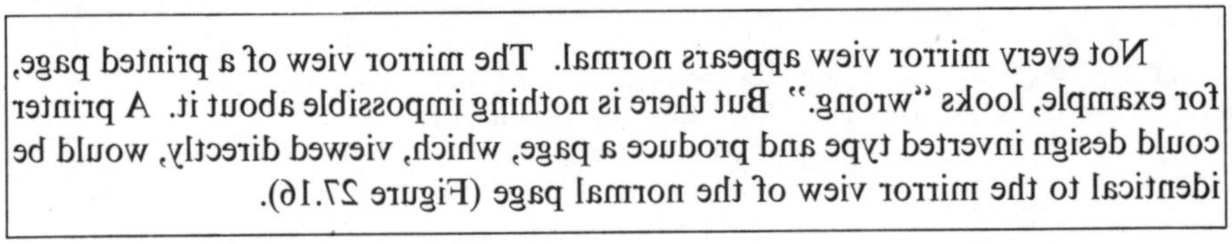

FIGURE 27.16   Parity transformation applied to a printed page.

> *Not every mirror view appears normal. The mirror view of a printed page, for example, looks "wrong." But there is nothing impossible about it. A printer could design inverted type and produce a page, which, viewed directly, would be identical to the mirror view of the normal page (Figure 27.16).*

Mirror invariance a partial conservation law

The situation with the space-inverted view of the world differs completely from that with the time-inverted view. The mirror view of the world looks quite normal, on the whole, and prepares us to believe in parity conservation, or space-inversion invariance. The time-reversed view of the world, on the other hand, looks ridiculous and impossible and prepares us to resist the idea of time-reversal invariance. The particles have fooled us on both counts. Time-reversal invariance proves to be an absolute conservation law, so far as we know now, and space-inversion invariance turns out to be only a partial conservation law, one that is completely violated by the weak interactions. This means that the mirror view of an actual weak interaction process, such as beta decay, shows something that *cannot* happen. Even scientists had discarded their normal caution and had come to regard parity conservation as an absolute law. When, following a suggestion by Tsung Dao Lee and Chen Ning Yang,† it was verified in 1956 that the weak interactions do *not* have mirror symmetry, it came as rather a shock to the scientific community, a useful reminder that an untested theory is a house built on sand.

---

* Space inversion may be defined as reflection of every point in space through the origin of a coordinate system, which is equivalent to changing the sign of all three Cartesian coordinates: $x \rightarrow -x$, $y \rightarrow -y$, and $z \rightarrow -z$. A mirror image is equivalent to space inversion plus an unimportant rotation. To see this equivalence, visualize the mirror image of a set of Cartesian axes. If the axes form a right-handed coordinate system, the mirror image is a left-handed system.

† *Physical Review* **104**, 254 (1956). For their work on parity nonconservation, Lee and Yang shared the Nobel Prize in physics in 1957. At the time they challenged the law of parity conservation, Lee was 29 years old and Yang 33. The author of this book, although also young at the time, took a more conservative position and lost fifty cents betting that parity conservation would prove to be a generally valid law.

THE PROOF OF PARITY NONCONSERVATION

The radioactive nucleus of cobalt 60 ($^{60}_{27}$Co), the same nucleus that could threaten human life if nations made and used "cobalt bombs,"* was responsible for bringing about the first enlightenment on the violation of parity conservation in weak interactions. Reduced to its essentials, the experiment of Chien-Shiung Wu was exceedingly simple. The cobalt nuclei were lined up so that their intrinsic rotational motion, as viewed from the top, was counterclockwise. See the "direct view" in the upper left of Figure 27.17, which shows a ^{60}Co nucleus with its spin angular momentum directed upward. In the experiment, a large number of ^{60}Co nuclei were oriented in exactly the same way. It was then observed that, as the nuclei one by one underwent their explosive process of beta decay, almost all the ejected electrons flew off in the downward direction. The solid arrows in the diagram represent the preferred flight direction of the electrons. The mirror view of this process shows a ^{60}Co nucleus apparently rotating in the opposite direction but with the electrons still coming out mostly downward. (It is to be borne in mind, of course, that a single ^{60}Co nucleus ejects only one electron.) On the other hand, if the whole experimental apparatus, including all the nuclei, were turned upside down, the direction of rotation of the nuclei would be changed, *and* the direction of emission of the electrons would also be changed. The inescapable conclusion is that the upside-down view and the mirror view of the original process are inconsistent with each other: One or the other (or both) must be impossible.

We have good reason to believe that the upside-down view depicts a

Asymmetric decay of aligned nuclei

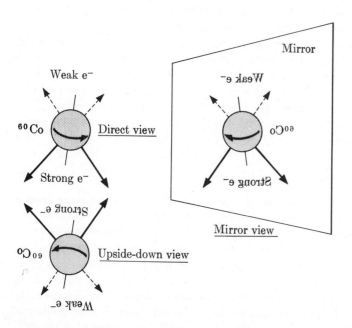

FIGURE 27.17 Decay of an oriented ^{60}Co nucleus and other views of the process. The turned-around labels are without significance. Only the physically measurable things have meaning in the various views.

---

* A "cobalt bomb" is a thermonuclear weapon encased in ^{59}Co. Neutron capture in the case would create in quantity the isotope ^{60}Co, whose half life is 5.26 years.

possible process. The experimenter can turn his apparatus upside down and not change his results (since gravity plays no role). In saying this, we are in fact invoking an invariance principle—the isotropy of space—which underlies the law of angular-momentum conservation. Indeed, there is ample evidence that the weak interactions are not influenced by rotation in space. This being so, the experimental results summarized in Figure 27.17 imply a failure of space-inversion invariance. The mirror view of ^{60}Co decay is a view of the impossible.

Parity nonconservation: The mirror view shows an impossible process

The value of every conservation law or invariance principle is that it imposes constraints, restricting nature's freedom. For the ^{60}Co experiment, mirror invariance would require that just as many electrons fly up as down, in fact that the pattern of emerging electrons be exactly symmetric between up and down, for only then would the upside-down view and the mirror view agree. If the law of parity conservation were suspended, this restriction would be removed, and the electrons would be permitted to fly out in any way at all (consistent with *other* conservation laws). As it happens, the weak interactions violate parity conservation to the maximum possible extent.

Why did more than fifty years elapse between the discovery of beta decay and the discovery that the beta-decay process lacks mirror invariance? There is a simple thermodynamic reason for this. The ^{60}Co experiment was actually a good deal more complicated than our discussion has indicated. Lining up nuclei so that they all rotate in the same direction is a difficult process because the energy of thermal agitation at normal temperatures far exceeds the energy of alignment that comes from the interaction of the nuclear magnetic moment with an externally applied magnetic field. Even if a strong magnetic field is applied at room temperature in order to get a "handle" on the nuclei, thermal agitation prevents alignment. It is clear that the ^{60}Co experiment would have been useless had half the nuclei been spinning one way and half the other way. In that case, as many electrons would have come out upward as downward, and nothing would have been learned about mirror invariance. To line up the nuclei and keep them that way, Mme. Wu enlisted the aid of a group at the National Bureau of Standards who were expert at achieving very low temperatures. At a temperature of less than 0.1 K, the thermal agitation was reduced sufficiently to allow the cobalt nuclei to be maintained with oriented spins so that the desired experiment could be carried out.

Alignment requires low temperature

LEFT-HANDED NEUTRINOS

Among the many further proofs of the failure of mirror invariance, none is simpler or more convincing than the discovery that the neutrino is "left-handed." It has been found experimentally that all neutrinos move with their spin vectors **S** aligned antiparallel to their momentum vectors **p**. This is so-called left-handed motion. (Antineutrinos, always having **S** parallel to **p**, are right-handed.) Since the mirror view of a left-handed neutrino (Figure 27.18) is a right-handed neutrino and since no right-handed neutrino has ever been found in nature, the mirror view is a view of the impossible. Any imbalance in the number of left-handed and right-handed neutrinos would imply a violation of parity conservation. The fact that *all* neutrinos are left-handed is a consequence of the maximal parity violation of the weak interactions.

Left-handed neutrino shows maximal parity violation

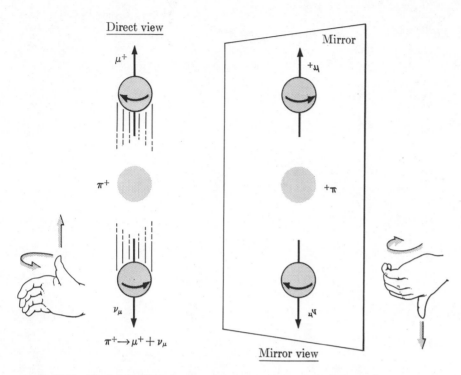

FIGURE 27.18   The left-handed neutrino created in the decay of a positive pion and its right-handed mirror image.

CONSERVATION OF PARITY

So far we have emphasized the *failure* of parity conservation. In all but the weak interactions it is actually a powerful and valid law that limits what can happen. For example, had the ^{60}Co nuclei undergone gamma decay instead of beta decay, as many photons would have emerged upward as downward. In that case, only the electromagnetic interaction would have been at work, not the weak interaction, and mirror invariance would have required the symmetric result.

All but the weak interactions conserve parity

Similarly, the decay of the neutral pion into two photons,

$$\pi^0 \rightarrow \gamma + \gamma,$$

which is the result of the combined action of strong and electromagnetic interactions, is quite different from the weak decay of the charged pion. Suppose that for a particular decay the photons come out left-handed (Figure 27.19). The mirror view of this process shows right-handed photons, so mirror invariance requires that decay into right-handed photons is also possible. In fact, it requires that decay into right-handed photons is exactly equally probable because all the laws of nature (governing *this* process) are the same in the mirror world as in the real world. If decay into left-handed photons were preferred by however small a margin in the real world, right-handed photons would be preferred by the same margin in the mirror world, and this would be a violation of space-inversion invariance.

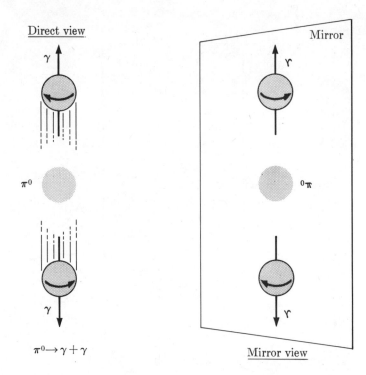

FIGURE 27.19   Decay of the neutral pion, and its mirror image. Because the interactions governing this decay possess mirror invariance, the mirror view pictures a possible mode of neutral pion decay. The photons may be either left-handed or right-handed.

In prequantum physics, parity conservation was recognized but considered unimportant. In quantum physics its power was recognized because of the restrictions it imposed on the flow of events governed by laws of probability. It has now become doubly important through the discovery that some interactions obey the law and some do not. A good reason why the weak interactions are parity violators has yet to be found.

27.9   Charge-conjugation invariance

Charge conjugation is defined as the interchange of particles and antiparticles. The fact that it has anything to do with time inversion and space inversion comes about because antiparticles may be described as particles moving backward in time. Hand in hand with the overthrow of parity went the less-heralded overthrow of charge-conjugation invariance. The present situation is this: P invariance and C invariance are grossly violated by the weak interactions but in such a way that combined PC invariance is nearly valid. And T invariance is at least approximately—and perhaps absolutely—valid for the weak interactions. For the strong and electromagnetic interactions, so far as we know now, all three inversion invariances, T, C, and P, are separately valid laws.

The left-handed neutrino, which violates space-inversion invariance, also

Status of P, C, *and* T

violates charge-conjugation invariance. Consider the decay of the positive pion, symbolically written

$$\pi^+ \rightarrow \mu_L^+ + \nu_{\mu L}.$$

The subscripts L indicate that neutrino and positive muon fly apart with left-handed spin. We know that the action of C on this process is to interchange particles and antiparticles, whereas the action of P is to convert left-handed motion to right-handed motion (subscripts R). Thus we get the following transformed processes:

$$C: \pi^- \rightarrow \mu_L^- + \overline{\nu_{\mu L}}, \qquad \text{No.}$$

$$P: \pi^+ \rightarrow \mu_R^+ + \nu_{\mu R}, \qquad \text{No.}$$

$$PC: \pi^- \rightarrow \mu_R^- + \overline{\nu_{\mu R}}, \qquad \text{Yes.}$$

*Combined **PC** invariance*

The C transformation leads to an "impossible" process (one that has never been seen) since it converts a left-handed neutrino to a left-handed antineutrino, and antineutrinos are right-handed. Therefore, this weak interaction decay violates C invariance. The P transformation applied to the original process of positive pion decay converts the left-handed neutrino into a right-handed neutrino, again giving a process that has never been seen. But P and C together change the left-handed neutrino to a right-handed antineutrino. The last line in this list of symbolic decays represents what is actually seen in the decay of the negative pion. The PC transformation applied to a physically allowed process yields a process that is also physically allowed. Through this and a number of other examples, it has been verified that even the undisciplined weak interactions do not grossly violate the combined PC invariance. Unfortunately for the view of simplicity in nature, which is what the physicist constantly struggles to attain, the weak decay of the kaon has shown combined PC invariance to be only approximately, not absolutely, valid.

To complete the TCP picture, we list the results of two more kinds of nversion on the process of positive pion decay:

$$T: \nu_{\mu L} + \mu_L^+ \rightarrow \pi^+, \qquad \text{Yes.}$$

$$TCP: \overline{\nu_{\mu R}} + \mu_R^- \rightarrow \pi^-, \qquad \text{Yes.}$$

Theoretically allowed processes

Time inversion alone changes the order of events in the original process. All three inversions together change left to right, particles to antiparticles, and before to after. Each of these transformed processes is almost certainly physically possible, but there is no hope of testing either of them experimentally.

27.10 Isospin

Every basic fact about the behavior of matter finds its origin in a conservation law. This appealing but still unproved assertion receives some support from the history of two other conservation laws—strangeness and isospin.

The strange facts of the rapid production and slow decay of certain new particles, the existence of some processes and the absence of others, found a simple explanation in terms of the conservation of some new property of matter,

Review of strangeness concept

which was christened *strangeness*. Its underlying invariance principle remains unknown. All we know is that if, to every particle, we assign a strangeness number—in addition to its charge and spin and baryon or electron or muon family number—the conservation of strangeness in strong interactions serves to account for a large array of experimental facts, most notably for the absence of a number of processes that should otherwise be observed.

Isospin, another property with an odd name, is of the same type. It is some extra "thing" carried by the strongly interacting particles. During processes of change governed by the strong interactions, it remains constant. Unlike charge, baryon number, and strangeness, which are numerical quantities, isospin is a vector quantity, and its conservation law encompasses both its magnitude and its direction. However, it points in no direction in ordinary space. It exists in a separate abstract space called isospin space, or simply *I* space, which lies outside the range of human perception.

Isospin a vector in I space

Concepts like this are not introduced in physics without good reason—in this case, the simplification of our description of nature even at the price of coping with a new abstraction. Isospin was the invention of Werner Heisenberg; he presented it in his first paper on the neutron and nuclear structure in 1932. Immediately impressed by the kinship of neutron and proton, Heisenberg seized on their similarities and showed that these two particles could be regarded as two states of a *single* particle, the nucleon. If the isospin vector of a nucleon points "up" (which has nothing to do with the "up" of ordinary space), we see it as a proton. If it points "down," we see it as a neutron. If two or more nucleons exist together, as in a nucleus, their separate *I* vectors may add up to a total *I* vector that may point up, down, or in other possible directions.

According to the Heisenberg theory, the nucleon is a doublet; that is, it can exist in just two possible states, as neutron or as proton. But this was not the first such doublet behavior noticed in nature. A particle with one-half unit of spin, such as the proton or the electron, can exist with its spin pointing either up or down (in *ordinary* space). The quantization of orientation restricts its allowed spin directions to two. Heisenberg's method of describing proton and neutron as two states of the same particle is mathematically identical to the description of spin. Hence the new property is called a kind of spin—not a very good name, in fact, because it is only mathematically, not physically, related to spin. Since the change of a neutron to a proton changes one nucleus to another and since individual nuclei are called isotopes, the new quantity was named isotopic spin, later shortened to isospin. For a group of nucleons, a rotation of the total isospin vector in *I* space corresponds to changing from one nucleus to another without changing the total number of nucleons. Thus beta decay is a process that rotates the isospin vector.

For the nucleon doublet,
$$I = \tfrac{1}{2}$$

Other particle multiplets

The significance of isospin in the modern description of particles rests on two facts. First, many particles come in closely linked groups, like proton and neutron. Each group may be regarded as a single particle showing itself in several manifestations of different charge, depending upon the orientation of an isospin vector. The three pions, for example, form a charge triplet. They are successfully described as three different faces of a single entity with one unit of isospin. The nucleon doublet and the kaon doublet are each characterized by one-half unit of isospin. The neutral lambda, with no charged partner, stands alone as a singlet; it has zero isospin. Isospin quantum numbers of strongly

TABLE 27.3 ISOSPIN QUANTUM NUMBERS OF STRONGLY INTERACTING PARTICLES

For antiparticles, I is unchanged, and the sign I_3 is reversed.

Particle	Isospin	Charge State of Particle	Component of Isospin in "z direction"
	I		I_3
Pion	1	π^-	-1
		π^0	0
		π^+	$+1$
Kaon	$\frac{1}{2}$	K^0	$-\frac{1}{2}$
		K^+	$+\frac{1}{2}$
Eta	0	η^0	0
Nucleon	$\frac{1}{2}$	n	$-\frac{1}{2}$
		p	$+\frac{1}{2}$
Lambda	0	Λ^0	0
Sigma	1	Σ^-	-1
		Σ^0	0
		Σ^+	$+1$
Xi	$\frac{1}{2}$	Ξ^-	$-\frac{1}{2}$
		Ξ^0	$+\frac{1}{2}$
Omega	0	Ω^-	0

interacting particles are listed in Table 27.3.

Second, and more important, an isospin conservation law is found to be obeyed by the strong interactions. Technically, this means that the probability of any process or the strength of any interaction is unchanged if the total isospin vector is rotated in I space. One consequence of this law is that the interaction between a proton and a positive pion must be exactly the same as that between a neutron and a negative pion because the change from $(p + \pi^+)$ to $(n + \pi^-)$ is equivalent to turning over both the nucleon and pion isospins, from "up" to "down."

Isospin conservation, a law for strong interactions

The significance of the law of isospin conservation is to be found in the idea of *charge independence*. Roughly speaking, we can say that the strong interactions do not care how much charge a particle carries. Proton and neutron are on an equal footing; positive, negative, and neutral pions all interact in the same way. It is as if different charges come in different colors and the strong interactions can see only black and white.

A photon, on the other hand, can see the colors very clearly. It interacts with charged particles but not readily with neutral particles. Therefore, the electromagnetic interactions violate the law of isospin conservation. As far as we know now, this is the *only* conservation law not common to the strong interactions and the electromagnetic interactions.

Violation of the law by other interactions

Not surprisingly, the weak interactions also violate the law of isospin conservation. In the decay of the lambda, for example,

$$\Lambda^0 \to p + \pi^- \quad \text{or} \quad \Lambda^0 \to n + \pi^0,$$

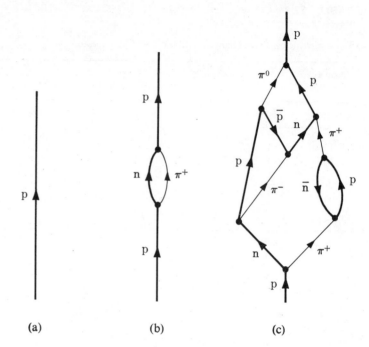

FIGURE 27.20   Feynman diagrams associated with a single isolated proton.

(a)   (b)   (c)

the initial isospin is zero. But the final nucleon has one-half unit of isospin and the final pion one unit. These two can combine to a total of either one half or three halves, in either case different from zero. According to present evidence, the lambda chooses the less flagrant violation, going to the final combination with one-half unit.

27.11   Submicroscopic chaos

Most of the Feynman diagrams presented earlier in this chapter represent more or less what is actually observed. But a few—those involving virtual particles—do not. The diagram of Figure 27.9(e), for example, shows a virtual pion exchanged between two nucleons to produce a force between them. The experimenter sees only the nucleons and must infer from their behavior that in a time of about 10^{-23} sec a pion went from one to the other. Virtual particles appear also in Figures 27.11 and 27.14.

As emphasized in Section 25.6, virtual particles play an especially important and interesting role in what is called self-interaction. We shall now pictorially reexamine this phenomenon using Feynman diagrams. A free particle's tendency to interact with itself displays most clearly the new view of the submicroscopic world—a view of continual chaotic activity from which no particle can be isolated.

A single proton sitting motionless and alone in free space has, as far as macroscopic observation can reveal, a straight vertical world line [Figure 27.20(a)]. At the submicroscopic level, however, the picture is very different.

The transitory violation of the law of energy conservation permitted by the Heisenberg uncertainty principle introduces a rich complexity into the world-line pattern of even a single isolated particle. A proton can, for example, emit and reabsorb a pion [Figure 27.20(b)]. Or, on an even shorter time scale, it can further strain the law of energy conservation with more numerous virtual particles. Figure 27.20(c) shows a possible sequence of events, unsymmetrical and complicated—"messy," a physicist would say—but real. Every proton occasionally goes through exactly this dance of creation and destruction, emerging unscathed at the other end, as well as through every other tortuous chain that is in consonance with the other conservation laws and with the uncertainty principle. As far as we know, violations of charge conservation and the three family-number conservation laws are not permitted, even for an instant of time. Therefore, at every vertex in the diagram of Figure 27.20(c), these laws are satisfied. Each vertex involves an "incoming" baryon line, an "outgoing" baryon line, and a pion line. Altogether, Figure 27.20(c) includes protons, antiprotons, neutrons, antineutrons, and positive, negative, and neutral pions.

The complex behavior of a "motionless" particle

Charge and other quantities conserved at every vertex

Since even a lone particle is in such a continual state of agitation, we might ask about the still simpler situation of plain empty space. Field theory provides the answer that empty space, far from being truly void, is a lively place. Transitory violations of energy conservation permit particles to be formed from nothing, then vanish. The "vacuum diagrams" illustrated in Figure 27.21 show some of the things that can (and indeed do) transpire in empty space. The name "physical vacuum" has been given to space filled continually with all of these momentary comings and goings in order to distinguish it from the unreal "bare vacuum." In a similar vein, the hypothetical and purely inert particle of Figure 27.20(a) is termed a "bare particle" in order to distinguish it from the real "physical particle," or "dressed particle," that exists part of the time in states of activity such as are pictured in Figures 27.20(b) and (c).

The lively physical vacuum

By its very complexity, Figure 27.20(c) carries a special message about the submicroscopic world, a message of chaos: the *chaos* provoked by the fundamental events of annihilation and creation underlying an *order* imposed by the conservation laws. This theme of order and chaos, already touched upon, illustrates as clearly as anything can the complete revolution in our view of the world that has been brought about by the achievements of physics in this century.

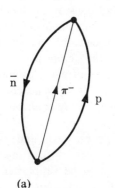

(a)

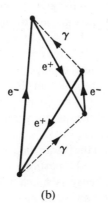

(b)

FIGURE 27.21 Vacuum diagrams illustrating the transitory existence of particles in empty space.

Briefly stated, the new view is a view of chaos *beneath* order. This is in startling contrast to the view developed and solidified in the three centuries from Kepler to Einstein, a view of order beneath chaos. In spite of the haphazard and unpredictable nature of the world around us, as the old argument ran, nature's basic laws are fundamentally simple and orderly; therefore, the behavior of nature at the submicroscopic level is fundamentally simple and orderly too. The building blocks of the universe are elementary objects, each one by itself simple and predictable. Complexity and unpredictability, according to the classical view, arise from the manifold interactions in a collection of many elementary objects. Probability, for instance, shows itself only in the large, not in the small.

This older view of chaos (or at least complexity) in the large and order (or simplicity) in the small contains, of course, much truth. Bulk properties of matter are reduced to a molecular explanation; the enormous variety of molecules are accounted for with fewer than 100 elements. Yet, as we probe deeper, a more fundamental chaos shows itself. Quantum rules of probability become more, not less, important as scales of time and distance shrink. Most particles are found to have a transitory existence. Even those that endure, engaged as they are in constant frenzied dances with swarms of virtual particles, are anything but simple. Empty space itself is a site of disordered activity.

Since the complexity engendered by size and organization is still quite real, the revolution of thought has not been a complete reversal of classical ideas about order and chaos. The revolution has rather been to shift the source of order from the elementary interactions and *activity* of particles to the overriding *constraints* of conservation laws. The emerging conception of the world is that of a nearly limitless chaos governed only by a set of constraining laws, a world in which apparently everything that *can* happen, subject only to the straitening effect of these conservation laws, *does* happen.

Is this fundamental chaos of nature a temporary phenomenon in science that will be replaced by a deeper order in the future? Perhaps. There is no evidence at all upon which to base an answer to this question, but two main possibilities need to be cited. On the one hand, the elementary event of creation and annihilation that now appears to occur catastrophically at a single point in spacetime may, upon closer inspection, prove to be a swift but smooth and more orderly unrolling of a chain of events. The probability of quantum mechanics may prove to rest only upon the great complexity of the things we now regard as simple. On the other hand, our view of the world of the very small could easily become more chaotic, not less so. Lying dormant thus far in our view of the world is spacetime itself. Whereas fields and particles come and go, space and time lie inert and provide the stage upon which the actors play their roles. There is some reason to believe that the future theory of particles may involve space and time as actors and not merely as the stage. If so, weird convolutions of space and time and/or the quantization of spacetime may contribute more to the chaos in our view of the world.

In whatever direction the future theory of particles proceeds (and speculation on this score is rather an idle pastime, unlikely to bear fruit), it must be emphasized that present theory is much more likely to be supplemented than rejected. Just as Newtonian mechanics is still entirely adequate for describing the motion of planets, present theories of particles are likely to remain adequate for describing all those features of the particle world that have been so far understood quantitatively. Nevertheless, it is the deepest theory that most strongly affects our *image* of the world, and this image may be drastically altered in the future.

In the seventeenth century, man looked upward and outward into the universe and was humbled as his earth took its diminutive place as a speck of matter in a corner of the cosmos. In the present century, we look downward and inward and find new reasons for humility. Where we might have expected to find some firm lumps of matter as the building blocks of man and his world, we find a chaos of annihilation and creation, a swarm of transitory bits of matter, and the tenuous substance of wave fields. Where we might have expected to find laws of certainty, we find laws of probability, and we seem to see the hand of chance working at every turn—chance that any particles are stable, chance that the neutron can live forever within a nucleus, chance that we are free of the threat of annihilation by antiparticles. Above the chaos and the probability stand the conservation laws, imposing their order upon the undisciplined energy of the universe to make possible the marvelously intricate, incredibly organized structures of the world around us.

Summary of ideas and definitions

All known interactions among elementary particles belong to one of four classes, widely different in strength: (1) strong, (2) electromagnetic, (3) weak, and (4) gravitational.

Strong interactions influence the pion and all heavier particles, but not lighter particles.

Strong interactions obey the largest number of conservation laws.

The muon mass is puzzling because it is great enough to be attributed to strong interactions, but the muon does not interact strongly.

Except for their distinguishability in weak interactions and their different mass, the muon and the electron seem to be identical.

Strongly interacting particles possess a strangeness quantum number and obey a law of strangeness conservation. This accounts for the strong production and weak decay of particles such as Λ, Σ, and K.

Particles that decay by the strong interactions, with lifetimes of 10^{-20} sec or less, are called resonances.

Strongly interacting particles are exceedingly numerous.

Almost surely, they must be states of some underlying system.

Neutrinos are produced in weak interactions and can be detected only via weak interactions.

The electron's antineutrino was detected in 1956 through the inverse beta decay reaction, $\overline{\nu}_e + p \rightarrow n + e^+$.

The muon's neutrino and antineutrino were detected in 1962 in a high-energy experiment, using the reactions

$$\nu_\mu + n \rightarrow p + \mu^- \quad \text{and} \quad \overline{\nu}_\mu + p \rightarrow n + \mu^+.$$

An effort to detect solar neutrinos uses the reaction

$$\nu_e + {}^{37}\text{Cl} \rightarrow {}^{37}\text{Ar} + e^-.$$

World-line diagrams are convenient for cataloging particle interactions because all interactions involve events of annihilation and creation at spacetime points.

At the fundamental interaction vertex underlying all electromagnetic interactions, one charged particle is annihilated, another is created, and a photon is either annihilated or created.

The quantum theory of photons and electrons (quantum electrodynamics) shows that a positron may be regarded as an electron moving backward in time.

Time-reversal invariance (T): If a sequence of events is possible in one order, it is possible in the opposite order. This law is obeyed by the strong and electromagnetic interactions; its validity for weak interactions is uncertain.

Time-reversal invariance appears to be violated in the macroscopic world because one order of events (the entropy-increasing order) is far more probable than the opposite order.

Charge-conjugation invariance (C): If a process is possible, the same process, with all particles and antiparticles interchanged, is also possible. This law is obeyed by the strong and electromagnetic interactions and is maximally violated by the weak interactions.

Space-inversion invariance (P): If a process is possible, its mirror image depicts another possible process. This law is obeyed by the strong and electromagnetic inter-actions and is maximally violated by the weak interactions.

Combined PC invariance is violated only slightly by the weak interactions. Combined TCP invariance is believed to be an absolutely valid law but has not been accurately tested for the weak interactions.

Strongly interacting particles carry an isospin quantum number and obey a law of isospin conservation. The isospin concept accounts for charge multiplets (such as the nucleon doublet and the pion triplet) and for the charge independence of nuclear forces.

Current theory describes the subnuclear domain in terms of continual chaotic activity. Simplicity and order are attributed to the constraining conservation laws and invariance principles rather than the basic units of matter and energy.

QUESTIONS

Section 27.1   **Q27.1**   Which among the four classes of interactions come into play when you grasp this book and lift it from a desk?

Q27.2   Which of the four classes of interaction influence each of the following particles: (a) neutron, (b) pion, (c) neutrino, (d) electron? Call attention to the correlation between number of interactions and mass of particle.

Q27.3   A "superweak" interaction has been postulated, weaker than the weak interactions although stronger than gravity. (1) If it exists, would you expect it to influence more or fewer particles than are influenced by the strong interactions? (2) Would you expect it to obey more or fewer conservation laws than are obeyed by the weak interactions?

Section 27.2   **Q27.4**   (1) Are there any charged particles of zero mass? (2) Are there any uncharged particles of nonzero mass? (3) What is the heaviest particle that experiences no strong interaction? (4) What is the lightest strongly interacting particle?

Q27.5   The electron can be described as a "charged neutrino" (or the neutrino as a "neutral electron"). Name some features of the particles e and ν_e that make them appear to be a closely linked pair.

Q27.6   (1) Name one way in which a negative muon can be created. (2) Name one way in which a negative muon can be annihilated.

Q27.7   A *negative* muon, after being slowed to relatively low speed in matter, is captured by an atom and forms a muonic atom. It cascades through bound states and finally decays or reacts with the atomic nucleus (see Exercise 27.2). Describe the probable fate of a *positive* muon that enters a piece of solid matter.

Section 27.3   **Q27.8**   What is the direction of the magnetic field applied to the bubble chamber pictured in Figure 27.2?

Q27.9   (1) The omega particle has strangeness -3. A typical mode of its decay is $\Omega^- \rightarrow \Xi^0 + \pi^-$. Explain why this is a "slow" decay process (mean life about 10^{-10} sec). (2) A particle called $\Xi(1530)$ (see Exercise 27.9) can decay into the same pair of product particles as the Ω^-, but it does so with a very much shorter lifetime than the lifetime of the Ω^-. What is the strangeness of the $\Xi(1530)$?

Q27.10 (1) The Σ^- and Λ^0 particles have the same strangeness. Why does the Σ^- not decay very rapidly (through strong interactions) into a Λ^0 and other particle(s)? (2) A rare mode of decay of the Σ^- is the following:

$$\Sigma^- \rightarrow \Lambda^0 + e^- + \bar{\nu}_e.$$

Is this decay mediated by the electromagnetic, weak, or gravitational interaction?

Q27.11 (1) The particles must surely be different manifestations of some deeper substratum. A simple unifying principle will be discovered. (2) The subnuclear domain is intrinsically more complex than the atomic and molecular domain. There is no reason to expect simple regularity among the particles. Defend one position or the other.

Q27.12 Some people are troubled by the concept of a particle that has neither mass nor charge. (1) List several measurable properties that such a particle *does* have. (2) Can you conceive of an entity that has no mass, no charge, *and no energy* (so that it could neither add nor subtract energy from a system and would be uninfluenced by gravity)? Could such a hypothetical particle have *any* measurable property?

Section 27.4

Q27.13 Explain why any stellar fusion process whose net effect is the transformation of hydrogen to helium produces neutrinos, not antineutrinos. (HINT: One or more conservation laws is at work.)

Q27.14 Fission reactors are strong sources of antineutrinos. Will future fusion reactors powered by DD and DT reactions be strong sources of either neutrinos or antineutrinos?

Q27.15 (1) Imagine creatures on another planet who see neutrinos of a few MeV instead of photons of a few eV. Describe their view of the world. Would the sun be brighter than the stars? Would there be a difference between day and night? Between up and down? (2) Why is the existence of such creatures "impossible," that is, inconsistent with what we know about nature?

Q27.16 Describe in words the process depicted by the accompanying Feynman diagram. What particle labels should be attached to the segments A and B?

Section 27.5

Q27.17 In each of the family-number conservation laws, particles are assigned positive family number and antiparticles are assigned negative family number. Discuss this fact in terms of the vertices of Feynman diagrams, explaining how this sign convention is simply and logically connected to the behavior of lines coming into and going out of the fundamental interaction vertices.

Q27.18 Feynman diagrams illustrate many of the conservation laws in a clear pictorial way. (1) Explain how the form of the basic electron-photon vertices in Figures 27.12 and 27.13 shows the conservation of charge and of electron-family number. (2) Find Feynman diagrams in this chapter that illustrate two other conservation laws.

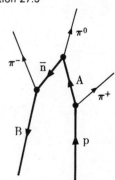

Q27.19   In his Nobel address, Richard Feynman said that when he was a graduate student at Princeton University, his professor John Wheeler called him up one day and said, "Feynman, I know why all electrons have the same charge and the same mass. Because they are all the same electron!" Using the idea of world lines that go forward and backward in time, explain Wheeler's idea. (Keep in mind that at any given instant, we are aware of only one slice of spacetime.) (Feynman's very readable Nobel lecture appears in *Physics Today*, August, 1966.)

Section 27.6   Q27.20   What is the result of two successive applications of (a) the time-reversal operation? (b) the charge-conjugation operation? (c) the space-inversion operation?

Q27.21   The Feynman diagrams accompanying Exercises 27.16–27.18 represent physically allowed processes. What is the implication of the TCP theorem applied to each of these processes?

Section 27.7   Q27.22   Planetary motion is an example of a process in the macroscopic world that possesses time-reversal invariance. (1) Name one other macroscopic process that exhibits, at least approximately, time-reversal invariance. (2) Name two macroscopic processes that violate time-reversal invariance.

Q27.23   Name one classical law that conforms to time-reversal invariance and one that is incompatible with time-reversal invariance.

Q27.24   The principle of time-reversal invariance is sometimes stated as follows: If the direction of time could be reversed, the laws of nature would be unchanged. This can be a confusing formulation because it refers to a seemingly impossible contingency—reversing the direction of time. Express the principle in a way that makes reference to processes or sequences of events in the real world, not in a hypothetical time-reversed world.

Q27.25   A high-energy particle slams into a nucleus, breaking it into several pieces and also creating several new particles. Discuss carefully the question of whether this process is or is not time-reversal invariant.

Q27.26   Write a paragraph reconciling the obvious asymmetry of time in the macroscopic world with the symmetry of time that appears to characterize the laws of the submicroscopic world. (NOTE: If a violation of time-reversal invariance is discovered for particles, it will not affect the argument. The macroscopic asymmetry is *not* attributable to a slight imperfection of the submicroscopic symmetry.)

Section 27.8   Q27.27   Name (a) a specific object in the macroscopic world whose mirror image depicts something that *does* exist in the world, and (b) a specific object in the macroscopic world whose mirror image depicts something that does *not* exist in the world. Explain why the existence of the latter object does not violate the law of space-inversion invariance.

Q27.28   (1) Explain how satellite orbits possess mirror invariance. (2) Invent a rule for satellite orbits that violates mirror invariance. (HINT: To violate mirror invariance, the satellite must move in three dimensions, not two.)

Q27.29   So far as we know, a conservation law is not subject to laws of probability. It either governs a particular process at all times, or it never does so. Nevertheless we speak of "partial conservation laws." Explain exactly what is meant by a partial conservation law, and contrast it with an absolute conservation law.

Q27.30   A negative kaon decays sometimes into a negative muon and one other particle. (1) What is the other particle? (2) Is the spin of the muon constrained to point in a certain direction? If so, what direction? (3) This decay must involve the weak interaction. Why?

Q27.31   A radar antenna can be designed that emits only right-handed photons. (Classically, the wave is said to be right-circularly polarized.) Explain why the existence of this antenna does not violate the law of parity conservation.

Q27.32   If an antineutron could avoid annihilation long enough to undergo spontaneous decay, (1) what would be the products of its decay? (2) What would be its lifetime?

Section 27.9

Q27.33   One can imagine charge-conjugate *entities* as well as charge-conjugate *processes*. (1) What is the charge-conjugate of a hydrogen atom ($_1^1H$)? Describe some of its properties. (2) If the Balmer series were observed in the light of a distant galaxy, would astronomers have any way to know for sure whether the light came from hydrogen atoms or from their charge-conjugates?

Q27.34   Discuss the reason why the strong interaction between a Σ^+ and a K^+ is identical to the strong interaction between a Σ^- and a K^0, whereas the electromagnetic interactions between these two pairs are not the same.

Section 27.10

Q27.35   Are the neutron-neutron and proton-proton forces identical in all respects? Are they identical in some respects?

Q27.36   Science is the *discovery* of the reality of nature. It is also the *creation* of a simple description of nature. Based on specific things you have learned about physics, write briefly in support of the thesis that these two views of science are consistent and both correct.

The nature of science

Q27.37   Past scientific advance has resulted from a constant interplay between theory and experiment. Do you think that either theory or experiment will play a more dominant role in the future progress of physics? Which one, and why?

EXERCISES

E27.1   In round numbers, the radius of the universe is 10^{10} light-years and the radius of an elementary particle is 1 fm. (1) Show that the ratio of these two distances is roughly 10^{41}, the same as the ratio of the strengths of the strong and gravitational interactions. (2) Some physicists speculate that the equality of these two ratios is a significant feature of nature, not a coincidence. If they are right, how did the strengths of the strong and gravitational interactions compare in the past? How will they compare in the future? *Optional:* Can you think of any way in which this speculation might be subjected to experimental test?

Section 27.1

E27.2   A weak-interaction process closely related to beta decay is orbital capture; it can occur for muons as well as electrons. (1) Write transformation formulas for the capture of a negative muon by (a) a proton and (b) a nucleus of $_7^{14}N$. (Note that this form of "radioactivity" can disrupt normally stable nuclei.) (2) About how much energy is released in the μ^- capture process?

Section 27.2

E27.3   Complete the following table.

Element	Nuclear radius (fm)	Bohr radius of muonic 1s state (fm)	Muonic Bohr radius / Nuclear radius
$_1$H	1	256	256
$_6$C	3		
$_{34}$Se	5		
$_{82}$Pb	7		

E27.4   (1) Verify that according to a Bohr-theory calculation, the binding energy of a muon in its 1s state in a lead atom ($Z = 82$) is about 19 MeV. (SUGGESTION: Scale from the known binding energy of 13.6 eV for an electron in the hydrogen atom.) (2) Experimentally, the binding energy of a muon in its 1s state in lead is only about half of this calculated value. Why do the experimental and calculated binding energies differ so greatly? (It may be helpful to complete the table in the preceding exercise before answering this question.)

Section 27.3   E27.5   Any negatively charged particle can substitute for an electron to form a short-lived atom. (1) Arrange the following in order of increasing size (assuming the same nucleus in each case and assuming the nucleus to be heavy enough so that reduced-mass corrections are unnecessary): (a) a muonic atom with principal quantum number $n = 1$, (b) a pionic atom with $n = 2$, (c) a kaonic atom with $n = 3$, (d) an antiprotonic atom with $n = 4$. (2) A muon normally reaches its 1s state before it decays or is captured. A pion, kaon, or antiproton is likely to interact with the nucleus before reaching the 1s state. Why the difference?

E27.6   Write two reaction processes among strongly interacting particles that would violate strangeness conservation if they occurred, but are consistent with all of the absolute conservation laws.

E27.7   (1) Which of the following reactions illustrate associated production of strange particles?

$$\text{(a) } p + n \to p + \Sigma^- + K^+$$
$$\text{(b) } \gamma + p \to p + \mu^+ + \mu^-$$
$$\text{(c) } p + p \to n + \Sigma^+ + K^0 + \pi^+$$

(2) Complete the following reaction formula, taking account of the conservation of charge, baryon number, and strangeness. (More than one answer is possible, and more than one particle is necessary.)

$$p + p \to \Xi^0 +$$

E27.8   (1) Which of the following reactions and decay processes conserve strangeness? (2) Which interaction—strong, weak, or electromagnetic—is responsible for each process?

$$\text{(a) } \pi^0 \to \gamma + \gamma$$
$$\text{(b) } p + n \to p + p + \pi^-$$
$$\text{(c) } \mu^- + p \to n + \nu_\mu$$
$$\text{(d) } \Lambda^0 \to p + \pi^-$$
$$\text{(e) } \Lambda^0 + p \to \Sigma^+ + n$$

E27.9 The mass of a resonance is not well defined. Measurements of the mass of the resonance called $\Xi(1530)$, for instance, yield an average value $m_{av} = 3{,}000 m_e$ with a range of uncertainty $\Delta m = 14 m_e$ (m_e is the mass of an electron). (1) What is the approximate mean life of the $\Xi(1530)$? (2) At $v = 0.1c$, how far does this particle move on the average before it decays? (NOTE: The nomenclature 1530 refers to the approximate rest energy of the resonance in MeV.)

E27.10 The π, η, K, and $\overline{\text{K}}$ mesons form an "octet" (a group of 8 particles analogous to the baryons n, p, Λ, Σ, and Ξ). Prepare a diagram like the diagram in Figure 27.5 that displays the pattern of charge and hypercharge for this meson octet. (Hypercharge is defined in the footnote on page 1374. For antiparticles, both charge and hypercharge are reversed in sign.)

E27.11 The mean penetration distance of a 1-MeV neutrino through solid matter (density 10^3 kg/m^3) is about 1,000 light-years. Carry out a simple numerical calculation that provides some information on the probability that a 1-MeV neutrino can cross the universe unimpeded (distance $= 10^{10}$ light-years, mean density $= 10^{-27}$ kg/m^3).

Section 27.4

E27.12 Neutrinos of a certain energy have a mean free path of 10^{15} m (about 0.1 light-year) in solid iron. If a flux of 10^{12} such neutrinos per sec strike an iron plate 0.1 m thick, what is the average waiting time of an experimenter between neutrino absorption events?

E27.13 Sketch world-line diagrams for processes a and c in Exercise 27.8.

Section 27.5

E27.14 Sketch world-line diagrams for the following sequences of events in the macroscopic world. (1) A vertically fired shell explodes into three fragments that fly off to the left and right. Include only horizontal components of motion in the diagram. (2) A baseball player intending to bunt holds his bat stationary. Ball and bat remain briefly in contact. The ball then reverses the direction of its velocity and the bat recoils. (3) A cargo spacecraft drifts toward an orbiting laboratory. A mail bag is tossed from one to the other and they drift apart. For each of these three situations, name an elementary particle phenomenon characterized by a very similar world-line diagram.

E27.15 Classically, electromagnetic waves do not interact with each other (the principle of superposition applies). Quantum-mechanically, photons can interact. Using only the basic interaction vertices of the kind shown in Figures 27.12 and 27.13, construct a Feynman diagram representing the scattering of light by light: Two photons approach each other, interact, and then two photons recede from the region of interaction.

E27.16 (1) To what physical process does the sequence of events shown in the accompanying Feynman diagram 1 contribute? Write a reaction formula for it. (2) What physical process is represented if the charge-conjugation operation C is applied to the diagram? Is it possible? Is it likely to be observed in practice? (3) What physical process is represented if the time-reversal operation T is applied to the diagram? Is it possible? Is it likely to be observed in practice?

Section 27.6

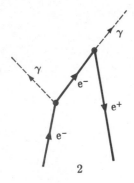

2

E27.17   Answer the questions in Exercise 27.16 for the accompanying Feynman diagram 2.

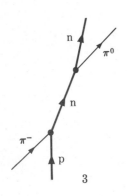

3

E27.18   Answer the questions in Exercise 27.16 for the accompanying Feynman diagram 3.

Section 27.7   E27.19   Sketch a hypothetical satellite trajectory that does not obey time-reversal invariance.

E27.20   Specify elementary-particle processes that have the following properties. (1) The time-reversed process is the same as the original process. (2) The time-reversed process, although not the same as the original process, is common and easy to achieve. (3) The time-reversed process, although possible in principle, is impossible to achieve in practice.

Section 27.9   E27.21   An antineutrino strikes a proton and stimulates the following inverse beta decay reaction:

$$\overline{\nu}_{eR} + p \rightarrow n + e_R^+.$$

The subscript R indicates right-handed motion. (1) What is the charge-conjugate process? (2) Is it possible in principle? Why or why not? (3) Is it possible in practice? Why or why not?

E27.22   Apply the operations P, PC, and T to the reaction displayed in the preceding exercise. Which of the transformed processes are possible in principle? Are any of them practical for laboratory study?

E27.23   (1) Name one process that is its own charge-conjugate. (2) Name one process other than pion decay whose charge-conjugate is impossible.

Section 27.10   E27.24   A quartet of resonances known as $\Delta(1236)$ are known to have nearly the same mass and to have charges $+2$, $+1$, 0, and -1. (1) What is the isospin of $\Delta(1236)$? (2) Each of these resonances decays via strong interactions to a nucleon and a pion. Is this consistent with isospin conservation? (3) What is the strangeness of $\Delta(1236)$?

E27.25 An electron-positron pair materializes out of nothing in vacuum. (1) About how long a time may elapse before this pair annihilates itself? (2) Over how great a distance in space can this transitory phenomenon spread itself? Compare this distance with the size of an atom and with the size of a nucleus.

Section 27.11

PROBLEMS

P27.1 A beam of negative muons with an intensity $I = 10^{10}$ muons/sec strikes a target. The portion of the target where the particles are slowed and captured to form muonic atoms contains $N = 10^{21}$ atoms. Answer the following questions both algebraically and numerically. (1) If the average lifetime of a muonic atom is $\tau = 2$ μsec, what is the approximate number n of muonic atoms in the target at any one time? (2) What is the approximate probability that during a time $T = 1$ hr, a double-muonic atom (an atom containing two muons) will be formed?

Double-muonic atoms are rare

P27.2 An experimenter studies antiproton annihilation events of the form

$$\bar{p} + p \rightarrow \pi^+ + \pi^- + \pi^0,$$

in which the initial kinetic energies of the proton and antiproton are negligible. (1) If the three pions are created simultaneously (at point A in diagram a), the π^0 total energies should cover a range between minimum and maximum values. What are these limiting values E_{min} and E_{max}? (For the rest energies of the particles, see Table 27.1.) (2) If the process includes a resonance ρ and proceeds in two stages (see diagram b: $\bar{p} + p \rightarrow \rho + \pi^0$ at point B, followed by $\rho \rightarrow \pi^+ + \pi^-$ at point C), a group of neutral pions with a narrow range of energy should be observed. Explain the reason for this. (3) The experimenter finds an unusual number of π^0 particles with total energies near 787 MeV. What mass M (in MeV units) does he calculate for the unseen resonance?

Kinematic evidence for a resonance

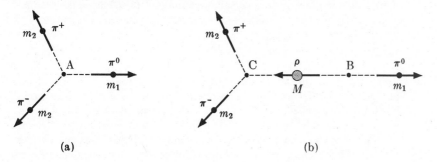

(a)   (b)

P27.3 (1) The resonance discovered by the experimenter in the preceding problem has a mean life of 5.3×10^{-24} sec. What is the approximate energy spread that he observes for the group of π^0 particles created with the ρ resonances? (2) Discuss carefully the experimental implications of the short lifetime of the resonance. Suppose that its lifetime were even shorter. How short would it have to be to cause the effect of the resonance to be "washed out" (so that the two-stage process of diagram b could not be distinguished from the one-stage process of diagram a)? Compare the distance moved by the resonance with the range of the nuclear force.

Strong-interaction vertices   **P27.4**   The basic electromagnetic interaction is represented by three-pronged vertices such as those shown in Figures 27.12 and 27.13; two charged-particle lines and one photon line meet at a spacetime point. The basic strong-interaction vertices are also three-pronged; two baryon lines and one meson line meet at a point. (1) Sketch several basic strong-interaction vertices that conserve charge, baryon number, and strangeness. (2) Using such basic vertices, sketch world-line diagrams for (a) the associated production of strange particles in a proton-proton collision and (b) a kaon-proton collision from which neither the kaon nor the proton emerges.

Classical time reversal   **P27.5**   In classical physics, the time-reversal operation consists of reversing the sign of the time variable t wherever it appears. The second law of thermodynamics, for instance, is transformed by the T operation from $dS/dt \geq 0$ to $dS/dt \leq 0$. Since the latter inequality does not correctly describe nature, the second law of thermodynamics is not time-reversal invariant. (1) The time-reversal operation changes the sign of velocity but not of acceleration. Why? (2) The time-reversal operation changes the sign of magnetic field but not of electric field. Why? (HINT: Think of the behavior of the charges and currents that are the *sources* of the fields). (3) Discuss the time-reversal invariance (or lack of it) for Newton's second law applied to each of the following examples of motion: (a) a particle moving in a central field; (b) a droplet acted upon by gravity and by a drag force given by Stokes's law; (c) a charged particle moving near a current-carrying wire; (d) a charged particle moving between capacitor plates.

Lambda decay   **P27.6**   Experiment has established that in the lambda decay process $\Lambda^0 \to p + \pi^-$, the proton emerges preferentially in the direction of the lambda spin **S** and the pion emerges preferentially in the direction opposite to **S** (see the figure). (1) Explain why this directional property of the decay violates parity conservation. (2) Sketch a figure showing the charge-conjugate decay process. Given that this decay is brought about by the weak interactions, do you think that your drawing shows an allowed process? (3) What are the products of the antilambda decay? Specify the expected directional properties of this decay process.

Vacuum polarization   **P27.7**   Empty space is full of virtual electrons and positrons. Near an atomic nucleus, the virtual electrons are attracted to the nucleus and the virtual positrons are repelled. This leads to a slight separation of charge in the space near the nucleus, an effect known as vacuum polarization. Discuss the effect of vacuum polarization on the potential within and near the nucleus. Discuss its effect on the energies of atomic electrons. Does vacuum polarization increase or decrease electron binding energies? Is its effect greater on s states or p states? Is its effect greater in a muonic atom or an ordinary atom? (NOTE: Vacuum polarization is one contributor to the Lamb shift in the hydrogen atom.)

Appendices

APPENDIX 1. Units in the international system (SI)

(This appendix is adapted from E. A. Mechtly, "The International System of Units," NASA Report SP-7012, 1969, available for 30 cents from the Superintendent of Documents, U.S. Government Printing Office, Washington, D.C. 20402.)

Basic units

Length	The METER (m) is the length equal to 1,650,763.73 wavelengths in vacuum of the radiation corresponding to the transition between the levels $2p_{10}$ and $5d_5$ of the krypton 86 atom.
Mass	The KILOGRAM (kg) is the mass of the international prototype of the kilogram (a particular cylinder of platinum-iridium alloy preserved in a vault in Sèvres, France).
Time	The SECOND (sec*) is the duration of 9,192,631,770 periods of the radiation corresponding to the transition between the two hyperfine levels of the ground state of the cesium 133 atom.
Current	The AMPERE (A) is that constant current which, if maintained in two straight parallel conductors of infinite length, of negligible circular cross section, and placed 1 m apart in vacuum, would produce between those conductors a force per unit length equal to 2×10^{-7} N/m.
Temperature	The KELVIN (K) is the fraction 1/273.16 of the thermodynamic temperature of the triple point of water.
Luminous intensity	The CANDELA (cd) is the luminous intensity, in the perpendicular direction, of a surface of $1/600,000$ m^2 of a blackbody at the temperature of freezing platinum under a pressure of 101,325 N/m^2.

Some other important units

Force	The NEWTON (N) is that force which gives to a mass of 1 kg an acceleration of 1 m/sec^2.
Energy	The JOULE (J) is the work done when the point of application of 1 N is displaced a distance of 1 m in the direction of the force.
Power	The WATT (W) is the power which gives rise to the production of energy at the rate of 1 J/sec.
Charge	The COULOMB (C) is the charge transported in 1 sec by a current of 1 A.
Potential	The VOLT (V) is the difference of potential between two points of a conducting wire carrying a constant current of 1 A when the power dissipated between these points is equal to 1 W.
Resistance	The OHM (Ω) is the resistance between two points of a conductor

---

* The symbol s is also commonly used for the second.

A3

when a constant difference of potential of 1 V, applied between these two points, produces in this conductor a current of 1 A, this conductor not being the source of any electromotive force.

Capacitance

The FARAD (F) is the capacitance of a capacitor between the plates of which there appears a difference of potential of 1 V when it is charged by 1 C.

Inductance

The HENRY (H) is the inductance of a closed circuit in which an electromotive force of 1 V is produced when the current in the circuit varies uniformly at a rate of 1 A/sec.

Magnetic flux

The WEBER (Wb) is the magnetic flux which, linking a circuit of one turn, produces in it an electromotive force of 1 V as it is reduced to zero at a uniform rate in 1 sec.

APPENDIX 2. Physical quantities: symbols and SI units

Quantity	Common Symbol	Unit	Unit Expressed in Terms of Basic SI Units
Acceleration	**a**	m/sec^2	m/sec^2
Angle	θ, φ	radian	
Angular acceleration	α	radian /sec^2	sec^{-2}
Angular frequency	ω	radian/sec	sec^{-1}
Angular momentum	**L, J**	kg m^2/sec	kg m^2/sec
Spin	**S**		
Angular velocity	ω	radian/sec	sec^{-1}
Angular speed	ω		
Area	**S**, A	m^2	m^2
Atomic number	Z		
Capacitance	C	farad (F) (= C/V)	A^2 sec^4/kg m^2
Charge	q, e	coulomb (C)	A sec
Charge density			
Volume	ρ	C/m^3	A sec/m^3
Surface	σ	C/m^2	A sec/m^2
Line	τ	C/m	A sec/m
Conductivity	σ	1/Ω m	A^2 sec^3/kg m^3
Current	I	AMPERE	A
Current density	**J**	A/m^2	A/m^2
Density	ρ	kg/m^3	kg/m^3
Dielectric constant	κ_e		
Displacement	**s**	METER	m
Distance	d		
Length	l, L		
Electric dipole moment	**p**	C m	A sec m
Electric field	**E**	V/m	kg m/A sec^3
Electric flux	Φ_E	V m	kg m^3/A sec^3
Electromotive force	$\mathscr{V}$	volt (V)	kg m^2/A sec^3

Quantity	Common Symbol	Unit	Unit Expressed in Terms of Basic SI Units
Energy	E	joule (J)	kg m^2/sec^2
Internal energy	U		
Kinetic energy	K		
Potential energy	U		
Entropy	S	J/K (often kcal/K)	kg m^2/sec^2 K
Force	**F**	newton (N)	kg m/sec^2
Frequency	ν	hertz (Hz)	sec^{-1}
Heat	Q	joule (J) (often cal or kcal)	kg m^2/sec^2
Inductance	L	henry (H)	kg m^2/A^2 sec^2
Magnetic dipole moment	$\boldsymbol{\mu}$	N m/T	A m^2
Magnetic field	**B**	tesla (T) (= Wb/m^2)	kg/A sec^2
Magnetic flux	Φ_B	weber (Wb)	kg m^2/A sec^2
Mass	m, M	KILOGRAM	kg
Mass number	A		
Molar specific heat	C'	J/kmole K (often kcal/kmole K)	kg m^2/sec^2 kmole K
Molecular weight	$M.W.$	kg/kmole (= gm/mole) (= amu/molecule)	kg/kmole
Moment of inertia	I	kg m^2	kg m^2
Momentum	**p**	kg m/sec	kg m/sec
Period	T	sec	sec
Permeability	κ_m		
Permeability constant	μ_0	N/A^2 (= H/m)	kg m/A^2 sec^2
Permittivity of space	ϵ_0	C^2/N m^2 (= F/m)	A^2 sec^4/kg m^3
Pole strength	P	N/T	A m
Potential Voltage	V	volt (V) (= J/C)	kg m^2/A sec^3
Power	P	watt (W) (= J/sec)	kg m^2/sec^3
Pressure	P, p	N/m^2	kg/m sec^2
Resistance	R	ohm (Ω) (= V/A)	kg m^2/A^2 sec^3

Quantity	Common Symbol	Unit	Unit Expressed in Terms of Basic SI Units
Specific heat (see also molar specific heat)	C	J/kg K (often kcal/kg K)	m^2/sec^2 K
Temperature	T	KELVIN	K
Time	t	SECOND	sec
Torque	**T**	N m	kg m^2/sec^2
Velocity Speed	**v** v	m/sec	m/sec
Volume	V	m^3	m^3
Wave function	ψ	Usually $m^{-3/2}$ ($m^{-1/2}$ in one dimension)	$m^{-3/2}$
Wave number	$k, 1/\lambda$	m^{-1}	m^{-1}
Wavelength	λ	m	m
Work	W	joule (J) (= N m)	kg m^2/sec^2

ALPHABETICAL LIST OF STANDARD ABBREVIATIONS OF UNITS

Abbreviation	Unit	Abbreviation	Unit
A	ampere	Hz	hertz
Å	angstrom	in	inch
A.U.	astronomical unit	J	joule
amu	atomic mass unit	K	kelvin
atm	atmosphere	kcal	kilocalorie
C	coulomb	kg	kilogram
°C	degree Celsius	kmole	kilomole
cal	calorie	lb	pound
cm	centimeter	m	meter
deg	degree (angle)	min	minute
esu	electrostatic unit	N	newton
eV	electron volt	°R	degree Rankine
F	faraday	rpm	revolutions per minute
°F	degree Fahrenheit	sec	second
fm	fermi, femtometer	T	tesla
ft	foot	V	volt
G	gauss	W	watt
gm	gram	Wb	weber
H	henry	μm	micrometer, micron
hr	hour	Ω	ohm

APPENDIX 3.   Numerical data

For physical data, see, in addition to this appendix, appropriate tables in the text.

A. Physical constants

[This table is adapted from B. N. Taylor, W. H. Parker, and D. N. Langenberg, *The Fundamental Constants and Quantum Electrodynamics* (New York: Academic Press, 1969). A good popular article on the fundamental constants, by the same authors, is to be found in the October, 1970, issue of *Scientific American*. The numbers recorded here have been truncated so that the uncertainty in each is at most ± 1 in the last digit.]

Quantity	Symbol	Value
Gravitational constant	G	6.67×10^{-11} N m^2/kg^2 (or m^3/kg sec^2)
Avogadro's number	N_0	6.0222×10^{23} particles/mole (or amu/gm)
Boltzmann's constant (microscopic gas constant)	k	1.3806×10^{-23} J/K 8.617×10^{-5} eV/K
	$\dfrac{1}{k}$	11,605 K/eV
Macroscopic gas constant	$R \,(= N_0 k)$	8.314 J/mole K 1.9872 kcal/kmole K
Quantum unit of charge	e	1.60219×10^{-19} C 4.8033×10^{-10} esu
Faraday constant (1 mole of electricity)	$F \,(= N_0 e)$	9.6487×10^4 C/mole 2.8926×10^{14} esu/mole

Quantity	Symbol	Value
Permittivity of space	$\epsilon_0 \left(= \dfrac{1}{\mu_0 c^2} \right)$	8.85419×10^{-12} C^2/N m^2
	$4\pi\epsilon_0 \left(= \dfrac{4\pi}{\mu_0 c^2} \right)$	1.112650×10^{-10} C^2/N m^2
	$\dfrac{1}{4\pi\epsilon_0} \left(= \dfrac{\mu_0 c^2}{4\pi} \right)$	8.98755×10^9 N m^2/C^2
Permeability constant	μ_0	$4\pi \times 10^{-7}$ N/A^2 *exact, by definition* or 1.256637×10^{-6} N/A^2
	$\dfrac{\mu_0}{4\pi}$	*exactly* 10^{-7} N/A^2
Speed of light	c	2.997925×10^8 m/sec
Planck's constant	h	6.6262×10^{-34} J sec 4.1357×10^{-15} eV sec 4.1357×10^{-21} MeV sec
	$\hbar \left(= \dfrac{h}{2\pi} \right)$	1.05459×10^{-34} J sec 6.5822×10^{-16} eV sec 6.5822×10^{-22} MeV sec
Charge-to-mass ratio or electron	$\dfrac{e}{m_e}$	1.75880×10^{11} C/kg 5.2728×10^{17} esu/gm
Mass of electron	m_e	9.1096×10^{-31} kg 5.4859×10^{-4} amu
Mass of proton	m_p	1.67261×10^{-27} kg 1.0072766 amu $1836.11 m_e$
Mass of neutron	m_n	1.67492×10^{-27} kg 1.0086652 amu $1838.64 m_e$
Intrinsic energy of electron	$m_e c^2$	0.51100 MeV
Intrinsic energy of proton	$m_p c^2$	938.26 MeV
Intrinsic energy of neutron	$m_n c^2$	939.55 MeV
Rydberg constant for infinitely massive nucleus	$\mathscr{R}_\infty \left[= \left(\dfrac{1}{4\pi\epsilon_0} \right)^2 \dfrac{m_e e^4}{4\pi\hbar^3 c} \right]$	1.0973731×10^7 m^{-1}
Rydberg constant for hydrogen 1	$\mathscr{R}_H$	1.0967758×10^7 m^{-1}
Fine structure constant	$\alpha \left(= \dfrac{1}{4\pi\epsilon_0} \dfrac{e^2}{\hbar c} \right)$	7.29735×10^{-3} or $1/137.036$

Quantity	Symbol	Value
Bohr radius	$a_0 \left(= \dfrac{4\pi\epsilon_0 \hbar^2}{m_e e^2} \right)$	5.29177×10^{-11} m 0.529177 Å
Compton wavelength of the electron	$\lambda_C \left(= \dfrac{h}{m_e c} \right)$	2.42631×10^{-12} m
Reduced Compton wavelength of the electron	$\lambdabar_C \left(= \dfrac{\hbar}{m_e c} \right)$	3.86159×10^{-13} m 386.159 fm
Bohr magneton	$\mu_B \left(= \dfrac{e\hbar}{2m_e} \right)$	9.2741×10^{-24} J/T

Useful Combinations of Constants

$\dfrac{e^2}{4\pi\epsilon_0}$		2.3071×10^{-28} J m 14.400 eV Å 1.4400 MeV fm
$\hbar c$		3.1616×10^{-26} J m 1.97329×10^3 eV Å 197.329 MeV fm
$\dfrac{\hbar^2}{2m_e}$		6.1044×10^{-39} J m^2 3.8100 eV Å^2 3.8100×10^4 MeV fm^2
$\dfrac{\hbar^2}{2m_p}$		3.3246×10^{-42} J m^2 2.0751×10^{-3} eV Å^2 20.751 MeV fm^2
c^2		8.98755×10^{16} J/kg 9.3148×10^8 eV/amu 931.48 MeV/amu

B. Terrestrial data*   (Footnote on page A12)

Quantity	Value
Acceleration of gravity at sea level (g)	9.80665 m/sec^2, standard reference value 9.7804 m/sec^2 at equator 9.8322 m/sec^2 at poles
Mass of earth (M_E)	5.98×10^{24} kg
Mass of earth times gravitational constant ($M_E G$)	3.9860×10^{14} N m^2/kg (or m^3/sec^2)
Radius of earth (R_E)	6.37×10^6 m $\left. \right\}$ 6370 km $\Big\}$ approximate average value 3960 miles $\left. \right\}$ 6378.2 km at equator 6356.8 km at poles
Equatorial circumference of earth	4.008×10^7 m 24,902 miles

Quantity	Value
The Atmosphere	
Standard air pressure at sea level (760 mm of Hg)	1.013×10^5 N/m^2
Standard dry air density at sea level and 0 °C	1.293 kg/m^3
Typical moist air density at sea level and 20 °C	1.20 kg/m^3
Speed of sound in standard air at 0 °C	331 m/sec 740 mile/hr
Typical speed of sound in moist air at 20 °C	344 m/sec 770 mile/hr
Approximate composition of atmosphere, by number of molecules	N$_2$, 78 percent O$_2$, 21 percent Ar, 1 percent
Mean molecular weight of dry air	28.97
Specific heats of standard air	$C_p = 0.2403$ kcal/kg K $C_v = 0.1715$ kcal/kg K $C_p' = 3.503R$ $C_v' = 2.500R$
Ratio of specific heats of standard air (γ)	1.401

C. Densities of common materials at standard conditions of temperature and pressure

Substance	Density (gm/cm^3)	(kg/m^3)
Hydrogen (H$_2$)	8.99×10^{-5}	0.0899
Helium (He)	1.785×10^{-4}	0.1785
Nitrogen (N$_2$)	1.250×10^{-3}	1.250
Oxygen (O$_2$)	1.429×10^{-3}	1.429
Air	1.293×10^{-3}	1.293
Gasoline	$\sim 0.7 \sim 700$	660–690
Alcohol (ethanol)	0.806	806
Water	1.000	1.000×10^3
Mercury	13.60	1.360×10^4
Aluminum	2.70	2.70×10^3
Iron	7.86	7.86×10^3
Copper	8.96	8.96×10^3
Lead	11.4	1.14×10^4

D. Astronomical data*

Quantity	Value
Distance from center of earth to center of moon	3.844×10^8 m 2.389×10^5 miles
Period of moon	27.32 days 2.360×10^6 sec
Mass of moon	7.35×10^{22} kg $0.0123 M_E$
Radius of moon	1.738×10^6 m $0.2728 R_E$
Acceleration of gravity at the surface of the moon	1.62 m/sec^2 $0.165g$
Distance from center of earth to center of sun (1 A.U.)	1.496×10^{11} m $\Big\}$ average 9.30×10^7 miles 1.471×10^{11} m at perihelion 1.521×10^{11} m at aphelion
Mass of sun (M_S)	1.99×10^{30} kg $3.329 \times 10^5 M_E$
Mass of sun times gravitational constant ($M_S G$)	1.3272×10^{20} N m^2/kg (or m^3/sec^2)
Radius of sun (R_S)	6.960×10^8 m $109.2 R_E$
Period of earth	365.26 days 3.156×10^7 sec
Average orbital speed of earth	2.98×10^4 m/sec
Average orbital acceleration of earth	5.93×10^{-3} m/sec^2 $6.05 \times 10^{-4} g$

* Reference: C. W. Allen, *Astrophysical Quantities*, second edition (London: The Athlone Press, University of London, 1963). Other useful references for physical data are the *Handbook of Chemistry and Physics* (Cleveland, Ohio: The Chemical Rubber Co.), frequently revised; and the *American Institute of Physics Handbook*, third edition (New York: McGraw-Hill Book Co., 1972).

APPENDIX 4. Conversion factors

For convenience in units arithmetic, this appendix lists conversion factors directly (such as 2.54 cm/in.) rather than equations (such as 1 in. = 2.54 cm). Any quantity can be multiplied or divided by appropriate conversion factors since each conversion factor is equivalent to unity.

Conversion factors preceded by a dot (●) are exact and serve to define one unit in terms of another. For example, the factor 0.3048 m/ft defines the foot as exactly 0.3048 m.

1. Length
- 10^2 cm/m
- 10^3 m/km

- 2.54 cm/in.
- 12 in./ft
- 5,280 ft/mile

- 0.3048 m/ft
- 1.609344×10^3 m/mile
- 1.609344 km/mile

  1.49598×10^{11} m/A.U.
  9.461×10^{15} m/light-year
  3.084×10^{16} m/parsec

- 10^{-6} m/μm (or m/micron)
- 10^{-10} m/Å
- 10^{-15} m/fm

2. Volume
- 10^{-3} m³/liter
- 10^3 cm³/liter
  0.94635 liter/quart
  3.7854×10^{-3} m³/gallon

3. Time
  (The day is a mean solar day; the year is a sidereal year.)
- 3,600 sec/hr
- 8.64×10^4 sec/day
  365.26 day/year
  3.1558×10^7 sec/year

4. Speed
- 0.3048 (m/sec)/(ft/sec)
  1.609×10^3 (m/sec)/(mile/sec)
  0.4470 (m/sec)/(mile/hr)
  1.609 (km/hr)/(mile/hr)

5. Acceleration
- 0.3048 (m/sec²)/(ft/sec²)

6. Angle
- 60 second of arc($''$)/minute of arc($'$)
- 60 minute of arc($'$)/deg
- $180/\pi$ ($\cong$ 57.30) deg/radian
- 2π ($\cong$ 6.283) radian/revolution

7. Mass
- 10^3 gm/kg

  453.59 gm/lb
  0.45359 kg/lb
  2.2046 lb/kg

  1.66053×10^{-27} kg/amu
  6.0222×10^{26} amu/kg
  6.0222×10^{23} amu/gm

8. Density
- 10^3 (kg/m³)/(gm/cm³)
  16.018 (kg/m³)/(lb/ft³)
  1.6018×10^{-2} (gm/cm³)/(lb/ft³)

9. Force
- 10^5 dyne/N
- 10^{-5} N/dyne
  4.4482 N/lbf
  (1 lbf = weight of 1 pound at standard gravity [g = 9.80665 m/sec²])

10. Pressure
- 0.1 $(N/m^2)/(dyne/cm^2)$
- 10^5 $(N/m^2)/bar$

- 1.01325×10^5 $(N/m^2)/atm$
- 1.01325×10^6 $(dyne/cm^2)/atm$
- 1.01325 bar/atm

  133.32 $(N/m^2)/mm$ of Hg (0 °C)
  3.386×10^3 $(N/m^2)/in.$ of Hg (0 °C)

  6.895×10^3 $(N/m^2)/(lbf/in.^2,$ or psi)

11. Energy

  (For mass-to-energy conversion, see the values of c^2 at the end of Appendix 3A.)

- 10^7 erg/J
- 10^{-7} J/erg

- 4.184 J/cal
- 4,184 J/kcal
- 10^3 cal/kcal

  (The kilocalorie [kcal] is also known as the food calorie, the large calorie, or the Calorie.)

  1.60219×10^{-19} J/eV
  1.60219×10^{-13} J/MeV

- 10^6 eV/MeV

- 3.60×10^6 J/kW hr

  4.20×10^{12} J/kiloton
  4.20×10^{15} J/megaton

  0.04336 (eV/molecule)/(kcal/mole)
  23.06 (kcal/mole)/(eV/molecule)

12. Power
- 746 W/horsepower

13. Temperature
- 1.00 F°/R°
- 1.00 C°/K
- 1.80 F°/C°
- 1.80 R°/K
- $T(K) = T(°C) + 273.15$
- $T(°C) = [T(°F) - 32]/1.80$
- $T(K) = T(°R)/1.80$

14. Electrical quantities

  (Note that 2.9979 is well approximated by 3.00.)

  Charge: 2.9979×10^9 esu/C
  Current: 2.9979×10^9 (esu/sec)/A
  Potential: 299.79 V/statvolt
  Electric field: 2.9979×10^4
    (V/m)/(statvolt/cm)

- Magnetic field: 10^4 G/T
- Magnetic flux: 10^8 G cm^2/Wb
- Pole strength: 10 cgs unit/michell

  (cgs unit = $\sqrt{\text{erg cm}}$;
  michell   = A m)

APPENDIX 5. Equations of electromagnetism for SI (mks) and Gaussian (cgs) units

Magnetic poles are excluded from the equations that follow. Equation numbers match those of the text.

A. Equations that are the same for both sets of units

Description of Equation's Content	Equation	
Relation of current and charge	$I = \dfrac{dq}{dt}$	(15.5)
Relation of electric field and electric force	$\mathbf{F_E} = q'\mathbf{E}$	(15.18)
Definition of electric flux	$\Phi_E = \displaystyle\int \mathbf{E} \cdot d\mathbf{S}$	(15.30)
Definition of magnetic flux	$\Phi_B = \displaystyle\int \mathbf{B} \cdot d\mathbf{S}$	(16.19)
Solenoidal character of magnetic field	$\displaystyle\oint \mathbf{B} \cdot d\mathbf{S} = 0$	(16.23)
Definition of potential	$V = \dfrac{U}{q}$	(15.55)
Relations of potential and static electric field	$V_2 - V_1 = -\displaystyle\int_{\mathbf{r_1}}^{\mathbf{r_2}} \mathbf{E} \cdot d\mathbf{s}$	(15.48)
	$\mathbf{E} = -\nabla V$	(15.67)
Ohm's law	$\mathbf{J} = \sigma \mathbf{E}$	(15.84)
	$V = IR$	(15.88)
Power associated with current and potential difference	$P = IV$	(15.57)
Power in linear circuit	$P = I^2 R$	(15.107)
	$P = \dfrac{V^2}{R}$	(15.108)
Definition of electric dipole moment	$\mathbf{p} = q\mathbf{l}$	(15.71)
Energy of electric dipole	$U = -\mathbf{p} \cdot \mathbf{E}$	(15.73)
Energy of magnetic dipole	$U = -\boldsymbol{\mu} \cdot \mathbf{B}$	(16.16)
Definition of capacitance	$C = \dfrac{q}{V}$	(15.109)
Energy stored in capacitor	$U = \tfrac{1}{2}CV^2$	(15.119)
Definition of inductance	$L = -\dfrac{\mathcal{V}}{\left(\dfrac{dI}{dt}\right)}$	(17.44)
Energy stored in inductor	$U = \tfrac{1}{2}LI^2$	(17.71)

B. Equations that are different for the two sets of units

Description of Equation's Content	Equation for SI Units	Equation for Gaussian Units
Coulomb's law	$\mathbf{F}_{12} = \dfrac{1}{4\pi\epsilon_0}\dfrac{q_1 q_2 \mathbf{i}_{12}}{r^2}$ (15.15)	$\mathbf{F}_{12} = \dfrac{q_1 q_2 \mathbf{i}_{12}}{r^2}$
Electric field of point charge	$\mathbf{E} = \dfrac{1}{4\pi\epsilon_0}\dfrac{q\mathbf{i}_r}{r^2}$ (15.20)	$\mathbf{E} = \dfrac{q\mathbf{i}_r}{r^2}$
Potential of point charge	$V = \dfrac{1}{4\pi\epsilon_0}\dfrac{q}{r}$ (15.60)	$V = \dfrac{q}{r}$
Gauss's law	$\oint \mathbf{E}\cdot d\mathbf{S} = \dfrac{q}{\epsilon_0}$ (15.36)	$\oint \mathbf{E}\cdot d\mathbf{S} = 4\pi q$
Electric field near a conductor	$E = \dfrac{\sigma}{\epsilon_0}$ (15.44)	$E = 4\pi\sigma$
Capacitance of a parallel plate capacitor	$C = \dfrac{\epsilon_0 A}{d}$ (15.112)	$C = \dfrac{A}{4\pi d}$
Energy density of electromagnetic field	$u = \tfrac{1}{2}\epsilon_0 E^2 + \dfrac{1}{2\mu_0}B^2$ (16.25)	$u = \dfrac{1}{8\pi}(E^2 + B^2)$
Magnetic force on a moving charge	$\mathbf{F_M} = q'\mathbf{v}\times\mathbf{B}$ (16.27)	$\mathbf{F_M} = \dfrac{q'}{c}\mathbf{v}\times\mathbf{B}$
Magnetic force on a current element	$d\mathbf{F} = I'\,d\mathbf{s}\times\mathbf{B}$ (16.43)	$d\mathbf{F} = \dfrac{I'}{c}\,d\mathbf{s}\times\mathbf{B}$
Magnetic field created by a moving charge	$\mathbf{B} = \dfrac{\mu_0}{4\pi}\dfrac{q\mathbf{v}\times\mathbf{i}_r}{r^2}$ (16.36)	$\mathbf{B} = \dfrac{q}{c}\dfrac{\mathbf{v}\times\mathbf{i}_r}{r^2}$
Magnetic field created by a current element	$d\mathbf{B} = \dfrac{\mu_0}{4\pi}\dfrac{I\,d\mathbf{s}\times\mathbf{i}_r}{r^2}$ (16.56)	$d\mathbf{B} = \dfrac{I}{c}\dfrac{d\mathbf{s}\times\mathbf{i}_r}{r^2}$
Radius of curvature of charge orbiting in magnetic field	$r = \dfrac{p_\perp}{q'B}$ (16.30)	$r = \dfrac{p_\perp c}{q'B}$
Magnetic moment of circling particle	$\boldsymbol{\mu} = \dfrac{q}{2m}\mathbf{L}$ (16.54)	$\boldsymbol{\mu} = \dfrac{q}{2mc}\mathbf{L}$
Magnetic moment of current loop	$\mu = IA$ (16.49)	$\mu = \dfrac{IA}{c}$
Force per unit length on parallel currents	$\dfrac{dF}{ds} = \dfrac{\mu_0}{2\pi}\dfrac{I_1 I_2}{d}$ (16.74)	$\dfrac{dF}{ds} = \dfrac{2I_1 I_2}{c^2 d}$
Magnetic field of long straight wire	$B = \dfrac{\mu_0 I}{2\pi x}$ (16.61)	$B = \dfrac{2I}{cx}$
Magnetic field within a long solenoid	$B = \mu_0 nI$ (16.69)	$B = \dfrac{4\pi nI}{c}$
Law of electromagnetic induction	$\oint \mathbf{E}\cdot d\mathbf{s} = -\dfrac{d\Phi_B}{dt}$ (17.1)	$\oint \mathbf{E}\cdot d\mathbf{s} = -\dfrac{1}{c}\dfrac{d\Phi_B}{dt}$

Description of Equation's Content	Equation for SI Units	Equation for Gaussian Units
Ampère's law and law of magnetoelectric induction	$\oint \mathbf{B} \cdot d\mathbf{s} = \mu_0 I + \mu_0 \epsilon_0 \dfrac{d\Phi_E}{dt}$ (17.29)	$\oint \mathbf{B} \cdot d\mathbf{s} = \dfrac{4\pi I}{c} + \dfrac{1}{c}\dfrac{d\Phi_E}{dt}$
The speed of light	$c = \dfrac{1}{\sqrt{\mu_0 \epsilon_0}}$ (17.77)	No counterpart; c appears explicitly in the Gaussian equations

C. The differential form of Maxwell's equations

SI	Gaussian
$\nabla \cdot \mathbf{E} = \dfrac{\rho}{\epsilon_0}$	$\nabla \cdot \mathbf{E} = 4\pi\rho$
$\nabla \cdot \mathbf{B} = 0$	$\nabla \cdot \mathbf{B} = 0$
$\nabla \times \mathbf{E} = -\dfrac{\partial \mathbf{B}}{\partial t}$	$\nabla \times \mathbf{E} = -\dfrac{1}{c}\dfrac{\partial \mathbf{B}}{\partial t}$
$\nabla \times \mathbf{B} = \mu_0 \mathbf{J} + \mu_0 \epsilon_0 \dfrac{\partial \mathbf{E}}{\partial t}$	$\nabla \times \mathbf{B} = \dfrac{4\pi \mathbf{J}}{c} + \dfrac{1}{c}\dfrac{\partial \mathbf{E}}{\partial t}$

APPENDIX 6. Mathematical formulas

Some of the formulas below go beyond the immediate needs of this text in order to provide a reference source for other courses or for optional additional work an instructor may wish to assign. For a much more extensive compendium of formulas, see Herbert Dwight's *Tables of Integrals and Other Mathematical Data*, 4th edition (New York: The Macmillan Company, 1961). This excellent reference volume, modest in size and price, is a good investment. It will prove useful throughout one's student and professional careers.

A. Mathematical signs

$=$ is equal to
$\neq$ is not equal to
$\cong$ is approximately equal to
$\equiv$ is identical to, is defined as
$>$ is greater than
$\geq$ is greater than or equal to
$\gg$ is much greater than
$<$ is less than
$\leq$ is less than or equal to
$\ll$ is much less than
$\sim$ is proportional to

B. Arithmetic: powers of 10

$$10^a 10^b = 10^{a+b}$$

$$10^a / 10^b = 10^{a-b}$$

$$(10^a)^b = 10^{ab}$$

C. Algebra

FRACTIONS

$$a\left(\frac{b}{c}\right) = \frac{ab}{c}$$

$$\frac{\left(\frac{b}{c}\right)}{d} = \frac{b}{cd}$$

$$\left(\frac{a}{b}\right)\left(\frac{c}{d}\right) = \frac{ac}{bd}$$

$$\frac{\left(\frac{a}{b}\right)}{\left(\frac{c}{d}\right)} = \frac{ad}{bc}$$

$$\frac{a}{b} + \frac{c}{d} = \frac{ad + bc}{bd}$$

A18

ROOTS OF A QUADRATIC EQUATION

If $ax^2 + bx + c = 0$ then $x = \dfrac{-b \pm \sqrt{b^2 - 4ac}}{2a}$.

If $x^2 + 2\beta x + \gamma = 0$ then $x = -\beta \pm \sqrt{\beta^2 - \gamma}$.

BINOMIAL EXPANSIONS

Factorial of an integer n: $n! = n(n - 1)(n - 2)\cdots 2 \cdot 1$

Binomial coefficient for integers q and n: $\dbinom{q}{n} = \dfrac{q!}{n!\,(q - n)!}$

$(a \pm b)^2 = a^2 \pm 2ab + b^2$

$(a \pm b)^3 = a^3 \pm 3a^2 b + 3ab^2 \pm b^3$

To evaluate $(a + b)^p$, write it as

   $a^p(1 + x)^p$,   where $x = b/a$, or as

   $b^p(1 + x)^p$,   where $x = a/b$.

$(1 \pm x)^p = 1 \pm px + \dfrac{p(p - 1)}{2!}\, x^2 \pm \dfrac{p(p - 1)(p - 2)}{3!}\, x^3 + \cdots .$

   This is a finite series if p is a positive integer. For other values of p, it is an infinite series that converges for $|x| < 1$.

Special cases:

$p = -1$: $\dfrac{1}{1 \pm x} = 1 \mp x + x^2 \mp x^3 + x^4 \mp \cdots$

$p = -2$: $\dfrac{1}{(1 \pm x)^2} = 1 \mp 2x + 3x^2 \mp 4x^3 + 5x^4 \mp \cdots$

$p = \tfrac{1}{2}$: $\sqrt{1 \pm x} = 1 \pm \tfrac{1}{2}x - \tfrac{1}{8}x^2 \pm \tfrac{1}{16}x^3 - \cdots$

$p = -\tfrac{1}{2}$: $\dfrac{1}{\sqrt{1 \pm x}} = 1 \mp \tfrac{1}{2}x + \tfrac{3}{8}x^2 \mp \tfrac{5}{16}x^3 + \cdots$

COMPLEX NUMBERS

$(a + ib) + (c + id) = (a + c) + i(b + d)$

$(a + ib)(c + id) = (ac - bd) + i(bc + ad)$

$\dfrac{a + ib}{c + id} = \dfrac{(a + ib)(c - id)}{c^2 + d^2}$

$|a + ib|^2 = (a + ib)^*(a + ib) = (a - ib)(a + ib) = a^2 + b^2$

$a + ib = re^{i\theta}$,   where $r = \sqrt{a^2 + b^2}$, $\theta = \arctan(b/a)$

$e^{i\theta} = \cos \theta + i \sin \theta$

D. Trigonometry

DEFINITIONS OF TRIGONOMETRIC FUNCTIONS

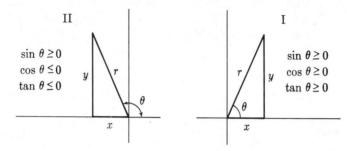

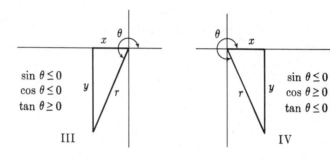

$$\sin \theta = \frac{y}{r} \qquad\qquad \csc \theta = \frac{1}{\sin \theta} = \frac{r}{y}$$

$$\cos \theta = \frac{x}{r} \qquad\qquad \sec \theta = \frac{1}{\cos \theta} = \frac{r}{x}$$

$$\tan \theta = \frac{\sin \theta}{\cos \theta} = \frac{y}{x} \qquad\qquad \text{ctn } \theta = \frac{1}{\tan \theta} = \frac{x}{y}$$

Inverse functions: If $u = \sin \theta$, then $\theta = $ arc sin u, sometimes written $\theta = \sin^{-1} u$. The other inverse functions are similarly designated: arc cos u, arc tan u, etc.

SIMPLE PROPERTIES

$$\sin (-\theta) = -\sin \theta \qquad\qquad\qquad \cos (-\theta) = \cos \theta$$

$$\sin \left(\theta \pm \frac{\pi}{2}\right) = \pm\cos \theta \qquad\qquad \cos \left(\theta \pm \frac{\pi}{2}\right) = \mp\sin \theta$$

$$\sin (\theta \pm \pi) = -\sin \theta \qquad\qquad\qquad \cos (\theta \pm \pi) = -\cos \theta$$

$$\tan (-\theta) = -\tan \theta$$

$$\tan \left(\theta \pm \frac{\pi}{2}\right) = -\frac{1}{\tan \theta} = -\text{ctn } \theta$$

$$\tan (\theta \pm \pi) = \tan \theta$$

VALUES FOR SPECIAL ANGLES

Function	0 deg	30 deg	Angle 45 deg	60 deg	90 deg
$\sin \theta$	0	$\dfrac{1}{2}$	$\dfrac{1}{\sqrt{2}} = 0.7071$	$\dfrac{\sqrt{3}}{2} = 0.8660$	1
$\cos \theta$	1	$\dfrac{\sqrt{3}}{2} = 0.8660$	$\dfrac{1}{\sqrt{2}} = 0.7071$	$\dfrac{1}{2}$	0
$\tan \theta$	0	$\dfrac{1}{\sqrt{3}} = 0.5774$	1	$\sqrt{3} = 1.7321$	∞

For other values and for graphs, see Appendix 7.

TRIGONOMETRIC FORMULAS

$$\sin^2 \theta + \cos^2 \theta = 1 \qquad \sec^2 \theta - \tan^2 \theta = 1 \qquad \csc^2 \theta - \mathrm{ctn}^2 \theta = 1$$

$$\sin 2\theta = 2 \sin \theta \cos \theta \qquad\qquad \sin \tfrac{1}{2}\theta = \sqrt{\frac{1 - \cos \theta}{2}}$$

$$\cos 2\theta = \cos^2 \theta - \sin^2 \theta \qquad\qquad \cos \tfrac{1}{2}\theta = \sqrt{\frac{1 + \cos \theta}{2}}$$
$$= 2 \cos^2 \theta - 1$$
$$= 1 - 2 \sin^2 \theta$$

$$\tan 2\theta = \frac{2 \tan \theta}{1 - \tan^2 \theta} \qquad\qquad \tan \tfrac{1}{2}\theta = \sqrt{\frac{1 - \cos \theta}{1 + \cos \theta}}$$

$$\sin (A \pm B) = \sin A \cos B \pm \cos A \sin B$$

$$\cos (A \pm B) = \cos A \cos B \mp \sin A \sin B$$

$$\tan (A \pm B) = \frac{\tan A \pm \tan B}{1 \mp \tan A \tan B}$$

$$\sin A \pm \sin B = 2 \sin \left[\tfrac{1}{2}(A \pm B)\right] \cos \left[\tfrac{1}{2}(A \mp B)\right]$$

$$\cos A + \cos B = 2 \cos \left[\tfrac{1}{2}(A + B)\right] \cos \left[\tfrac{1}{2}(A - B)\right]$$

$$\cos A - \cos B = 2 \sin \left[\tfrac{1}{2}(A + B)\right] \sin \left[\tfrac{1}{2}(B - A)\right]$$

$$\tan A \pm \tan B = \frac{\sin (A \pm B)}{\cos A \cos B}$$

$$\sin A \sin B = \tfrac{1}{2}[\cos (A - B) - \cos (A + B)]$$

$$\cos A \cos B = \tfrac{1}{2}[\cos (A - B) + \cos (A + B)]$$

$$\sin A \cos B = \tfrac{1}{2}[\sin (A - B) + \sin (A + B)]$$

$$\sin \theta + \sin 2\theta + \sin 3\theta + \cdots + \sin n\theta = \frac{\sin \left[\tfrac{1}{2}(n + 1)\theta\right] \sin (\tfrac{1}{2}n\theta)}{\sin (\tfrac{1}{2}\theta)}$$

$$\cos \theta + \cos 2\theta + \cos 3\theta + \cdots + \cos n\theta = \frac{\cos \left[\tfrac{1}{2}(n + 1)\theta\right] \sin (\tfrac{1}{2}n\theta)}{\sin (\tfrac{1}{2}\theta)}$$

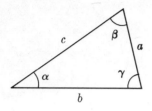

PROPERTIES OF A TRIANGLE

$\alpha + \beta + \gamma = \pi$

$a^2 = b^2 + c^2 - 2bc \cos \alpha$

$b^2 = c^2 + a^2 - 2ca \cos \beta$

$c^2 = a^2 + b^2 - 2ab \cos \gamma$

$$\frac{a}{\sin \alpha} = \frac{b}{\sin \beta} = \frac{c}{\sin \gamma}$$

For a right triangle $\left(\gamma = \dfrac{\pi}{2}\right)$, $a^2 + b^2 = c^2$

SERIES EXPANSIONS

$$\sin x = x - \frac{x^3}{3!} + \frac{x^5}{5!} - \frac{x^7}{7!} + \cdots$$

$$\cos x = 1 - \frac{x^2}{2!} + \frac{x^4}{4!} - \frac{x^6}{6!} + \cdots$$

These series converge for all x.

E. Exponential and logarithmic functions

For graphs and numerical values, see Appendices 8 and 9.

$e = 2.71828$ $e^0 = 1$

$e^x e^y = e^{x+y}$ $e^x / e^y = e^{x-y}$

$(e^x)^n = e^{nx}$ $a^x = e^{x \ln a}$

$e^{\ln x} = x$ $e^{-\ln x} = 1/x$

$e^{-t/\tau} = 0.5$ for $t = \tau \ln 2 = 0.6931\tau$

$e^{t/\tau} = 2$ for $t = \tau \ln 2 = 0.6931\tau$

$$e^{\pm x} = 1 \pm x + \frac{x^2}{2!} \pm \frac{x^3}{3!} + \frac{x^4}{4!} \pm \cdots.$$

Series converges for all x.

$\ln e = 1$ $\ln 1 = 0$

$\ln (xy) = \ln x + \ln y$ $\ln (x/y) = \ln x - \ln y$

$\ln (1/x) = -\ln x$ $\ln (x^n) = n \ln x$

$\ln (e^x) = x$ $\ln (a^x) = x \ln a$

$\ln a = 2.3026 \log_{10} a$ $\log_{10} a = 0.43429 \ln a$

$$\ln (1 \pm x) = \pm x - \frac{x^2}{2} \pm \frac{x^3}{3} - \frac{x^4}{4} \pm \cdots$$

$$\ln \left(\frac{1 + x}{1 - x}\right) = 2 \left(x + \frac{x^3}{3} + \frac{x^5}{5} + \frac{x^7}{7} + \cdots\right)$$

Series converge for $|x| < 1$.

F. Calculus

In what follows, f, g, and u are functions; a, b, and n are constants.

SOME RULES OF DIFFERENTIATION

$$\frac{d}{dx}(fg) = \frac{df}{dx}g + f\frac{dg}{dx}$$

$$\frac{d}{dx}\left(\frac{f}{g}\right) = \frac{\frac{df}{dx}g - f\frac{dg}{dx}}{g^2}$$

$$\frac{d}{dx}[f(u)] = \frac{df}{du}\frac{du}{dx}$$

LINEARITY PROPERTIES

$$\frac{d}{dx}(af + bg) = a\frac{df}{dx} + b\frac{dg}{dx}$$

$$\int (af + bg)\,dx = a\int f\,dx + b\int g\,dx$$

THE DEFINITE INTEGRAL

$$D = \int_a^b f(x)\,dx = I(x)\bigg|_a^b = I(b) - I(a),$$

where I is the indefinite integral, $I(x) = \int f(x)\,dx$, or the antiderivative: $f(x) = dI(x)/dx$.

INTEGRATION BY PARTS

$$\int_a^b f(x)\frac{dg}{dx}\,dx = f(x)g(x)\bigg|_a^b - \int_a^b \frac{df}{dx}g(x)\,dx$$

TAYLOR SERIES

If all derivatives of a function exist at a certain point, the function may be written as a power series about that point. Empirical functions may be similarly approximated.

$$f(x) = f(x_0) + (x - x_0)\left(\frac{df}{dx}\right)_{x_0} + \frac{(x - x_0)^2}{2!}\left(\frac{d^2f}{dx^2}\right)_{x_0}$$
$$+ \frac{(x - x_0)^3}{3!}\left(\frac{d^3f}{dx^3}\right)_{x_0} + \cdots.$$

All the derivatives are evaluated at $x = x_0$.

SOME DERIVATIVES   (See also Table 5.2.)

$$\frac{d}{dx}(x^n) = nx^{n-1}$$

$$\frac{d}{dx}(\sin ax) = a\cos ax$$

$$\frac{d}{dx}(\cos ax) = -a\sin ax$$

$$\frac{d}{dx}(\tan ax) = a\sec^2 ax = \frac{a}{\cos^2 ax}$$

Appendices

$$\frac{d}{dx}\left(\text{arc sin } \frac{x}{a}\right) = \frac{\pm 1}{\sqrt{a^2 - x^2}}$$

+ sign in 1st and 4th quadrants
− sign in 2nd and 3rd quadrants

$$\frac{d}{dx}\left(\text{arc cos } \frac{x}{a}\right) = \frac{\mp 1}{\sqrt{a^2 - x^2}}$$

− sign in 1st and 2nd quadrants
+ sign in 3rd and 4th quadrants

$$\frac{d}{dx}\left(\text{arc tan } \frac{x}{a}\right) = \frac{a}{a^2 + x^2}$$

$$\frac{d}{dx}(e^{ax}) = ae^{ax}$$

$$\frac{d}{dx}(\ln ax) = \frac{1}{x}$$

SOME INDEFINITE INTEGRALS (See also Table 5.7)

To each of the following integrals an arbitrary constant should be added.

$$\int x^n \, dx = \frac{x^{n+1}}{n + 1}, \qquad n \neq -1$$

$$\int \frac{1}{x} \, dx = \ln |x|$$

$$\int (a + bx)^n \, dx = \frac{(a + bx)^{n+1}}{b(n + 1)}, \qquad n \neq -1$$

$$\int \frac{dx}{a + bx} = \frac{1}{b} \ln |a + bx|$$

$$\int \frac{dx}{a^2 + x^2} = \frac{1}{a} \text{ arc tan } \frac{x}{a}$$

$$\int \frac{dx}{a^2 - x^2} = \frac{1}{2a} \ln \left|\frac{a + x}{a - x}\right|$$

$$\int \sqrt{a + bx} \, dx = \frac{2}{3b}(a + bx)^{3/2}$$

$$\int \frac{dx}{\sqrt{a + bx}} = \frac{2}{b} \sqrt{a + bx}$$

$$\int \sqrt{x^2 + a^2} \, dx = \tfrac{1}{2}x\sqrt{x^2 + a^2} + \tfrac{1}{2}a^2 \ln (x + \sqrt{x^2 + a^2})$$

$$\int \frac{dx}{\sqrt{x^2 + a^2}} = \ln (x + \sqrt{x^2 + a^2})$$

$$\int \sqrt{x^2 - a^2} \, dx = \tfrac{1}{2}x\sqrt{x^2 - a^2} - \tfrac{1}{2}a^2 \ln |x + \sqrt{x^2 - a^2}|$$

$$\int \frac{dx}{\sqrt{x^2 - a^2}} = \ln |x + \sqrt{x^2 - a^2}|$$

$$\int \sqrt{a^2 - x^2}\, dx = \tfrac{1}{2}x\sqrt{a^2 - x^2} + \tfrac{1}{2}a^2 \arcsin \frac{x}{a}$$

$$\int \frac{dx}{\sqrt{a^2 - x^2}} = \arcsin \frac{x}{a}$$

$$\int \sin ax\, dx = -\frac{1}{a} \cos ax$$

$$\int \cos ax\, dx = \frac{1}{a} \sin ax$$

$$\int \tan ax\, dx = -\frac{1}{a} \ln |\cos ax|$$

$$\int \csc ax\, dx = \frac{1}{a} \ln |\tan \tfrac{1}{2}ax|$$

$$\int \sec ax\, dx = \frac{1}{2a} \ln \left(\frac{1 + \sin ax}{1 - \sin ax}\right)$$

$$\int \operatorname{ctn} ax\, dx = \frac{1}{a} \ln |\sin ax|$$

$$\int \arcsin \frac{x}{a}\, dx = x \arcsin \frac{x}{a} + \sqrt{a^2 - x^2}$$

$$\int \arccos \frac{x}{a}\, dx = x \arccos \frac{x}{a} - \sqrt{a^2 - x^2}$$

$$\int \arctan \frac{x}{a}\, dx = x \arctan \frac{x}{a} - \tfrac{1}{2}a \ln (a^2 + x^2)$$

$$\int e^{ax}\, dx = \frac{1}{a} e^{ax}$$

$$\int xe^{ax}\, dx = \frac{1}{a}\left(x - \frac{1}{a}\right) e^{ax}$$

$$\int \ln ax\, dx = x \ln ax - x$$

$$\int x \ln ax\, dx = \tfrac{1}{2}x^2 \ln ax - \tfrac{1}{4}x^2$$

G. Vectors

Unit vectors **i**, **j**, and **k** are parallel to the x, y, and z axes respectively.

Vector in terms of Cartesian components: $\mathbf{a} = a_x\mathbf{i} + a_y\mathbf{j} + a_z\mathbf{k}$

The position vector: $\mathbf{r} = x\mathbf{i} + y\mathbf{j} + z\mathbf{k}$

Magnitude of a vector: $|\mathbf{a}| = a = \sqrt{a_x^2 + a_y^2 + a_z^2}$

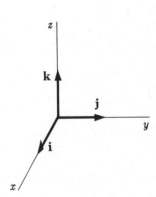

SCALAR PRODUCT

$\mathbf{a} \cdot \mathbf{b} = ab \cos \theta$; θ is the smaller angle between **a** and **b**.

$\mathbf{a} \cdot \mathbf{b} = a_x b_x + a_y b_y + a_z b_z$

$\mathbf{a} \cdot \mathbf{b} = \mathbf{b} \cdot \mathbf{a}$

VECTOR PRODUCT

$\mathbf{a} \times \mathbf{b} = (a_y b_z - a_z b_y)\mathbf{i} + (a_z b_x - a_x b_z)\mathbf{j} + (a_x b_y - a_y b_x)\mathbf{k}$

$|\mathbf{a} \times \mathbf{b}| = ab \sin \theta; \quad \theta$ is the smaller angle between $\mathbf{a}$ and $\mathbf{b}$.

$\mathbf{a} \times \mathbf{b} = -\mathbf{b} \times \mathbf{a}$

PROPERTIES OF UNIT VECTORS

$\mathbf{i} \cdot \mathbf{i} = \mathbf{j} \cdot \mathbf{j} = \mathbf{k} \cdot \mathbf{k} = 1$

$\mathbf{i} \cdot \mathbf{j} = \mathbf{j} \cdot \mathbf{k} = \mathbf{k} \cdot \mathbf{i} = 0$

$\mathbf{i} \times \mathbf{j} = \mathbf{k}, \qquad \mathbf{j} \times \mathbf{k} = \mathbf{i}, \qquad \mathbf{k} \times \mathbf{i} = \mathbf{j}$

$\mathbf{j} \times \mathbf{i} = -\mathbf{k}, \qquad \mathbf{k} \times \mathbf{j} = -\mathbf{i}, \qquad \mathbf{i} \times \mathbf{k} = -\mathbf{j}$

H. Vector calculus

$\mathbf{F}$ and $\mathbf{G}$ are vector functions; f is a scalar function; a and b are numerical constants.

DERIVATIVES

$$\frac{d\mathbf{F}}{dt} = \frac{dF_x}{dt}\mathbf{i} + \frac{dF_y}{dt}\mathbf{j} + \frac{dF_z}{dt}\mathbf{k}$$

$$\frac{d}{dt}(f\mathbf{F}) = \frac{df}{dt}\mathbf{F} + f\frac{d\mathbf{F}}{dt}$$

$$\frac{d}{dt}(a\mathbf{F} + b\mathbf{G}) = a\frac{d\mathbf{F}}{dt} + b\frac{d\mathbf{G}}{dt}$$

$$\frac{d}{dt}(\mathbf{F} \cdot \mathbf{G}) = \frac{d\mathbf{F}}{dt} \cdot \mathbf{G} + \mathbf{F} \cdot \frac{d\mathbf{G}}{dt}$$

$$\frac{d}{dt}(\mathbf{F} \times \mathbf{G}) = \frac{d\mathbf{F}}{dt} \times \mathbf{G} + \mathbf{F} \times \frac{d\mathbf{G}}{dt}$$

INTEGRALS

$$\int \mathbf{F}(t)\, dt = \left[\int F_x(t)\, dt \right]\mathbf{i} + \left[\int F_y(t)\, dt \right]\mathbf{j} + \left[\int F_z(t)\, dt \right]\mathbf{k}$$

Line integral: $\int \mathbf{F} \cdot d\mathbf{s} = \int F_\| \, ds$, where $F_\|$ is the component of $\mathbf{F}$ parallel to the designated path of integration at each point.

Surface integral: $\int \mathbf{F} \cdot d\mathbf{S} = \int F_\perp \, dS$, where $F_\perp$ is the component of $\mathbf{F}$ perpendicular to the designated surface of integration (or parallel to the vector $d\mathbf{S}$) at each point.

VECTOR OPERATIONS NEEDED IN MORE ADVANCED WORK

The *gradient* of a scalar function is a vector function:

$$\nabla f = \frac{\partial f}{\partial x}\mathbf{i} + \frac{\partial f}{\partial y}\mathbf{j} + \frac{\partial f}{\partial z}\mathbf{k}$$

The *divergence* of a vector function is a scalar function:

$$\nabla \cdot \mathbf{F} = \frac{\partial F_x}{\partial x} + \frac{\partial F_y}{\partial y} + \frac{\partial F_z}{\partial z}$$

The *curl* of a vector function as an axial vector function:

$$\nabla \times \mathbf{F} = \left(\frac{\partial F_z}{\partial y} - \frac{\partial F_y}{\partial z} \right)\mathbf{i} + \left(\frac{\partial F_x}{\partial z} - \frac{\partial F_z}{\partial x} \right)\mathbf{j} + \left(\frac{\partial F_y}{\partial x} - \frac{\partial F_x}{\partial y} \right)\mathbf{k}$$

APPENDIX 7. Trigonometric functions

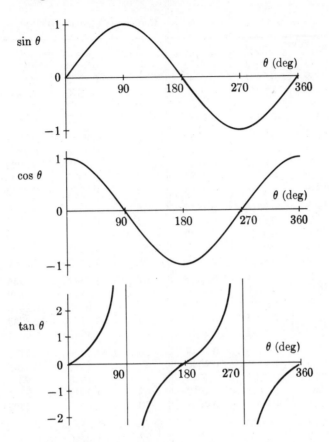

The table on the next page gives sin θ, cos θ, and tan θ in the first quadrant
(0 ≤ θ ≤ 90 deg).

For the second quadrant, measure backward from 180 deg, and use
$$\sin (\pi - \theta) = \sin \theta$$
$$\cos (\pi - \theta) = -\cos \theta$$
$$\tan (\pi - \theta) = -\tan \theta$$

For the third quadrant, measure forward from 180 deg, and use
$$\sin (\pi + \theta) = -\sin \theta$$
$$\cos (\pi + \theta) = -\cos \theta$$
$$\tan (\pi + \theta) = \tan \theta$$

For the fourth quadrant, measure backward from 0 deg (or 360 deg), and use
$$\sin (-\theta) = -\sin \theta$$
$$\cos (-\theta) = \cos \theta$$
$$\tan (-\theta) = -\tan \theta$$

Other trigonometric functions are defined by

$$\csc \theta = \frac{1}{\sin \theta} \qquad \sec \theta = \frac{1}{\cos \theta} \qquad \operatorname{ctn} \theta = \frac{1}{\tan \theta}$$

A27

Angle θ		sin θ	cos θ	tan θ	Angle θ		sin θ	cos θ	tan θ
Degree	Radian				Degree	Radian			
0	0.0000	0.0000	1.0000	0.0000					
1	0.0175	0.0175	0.9998	0.0175	46	0.8029	0.7193	0.6947	1.0355
2	0.0349	0.0349	0.9994	0.0349	47	0.8203	0.7314	0.6820	1.0724
3	0.0524	0.0523	0.9986	0.0524	48	0.8378	0.7431	0.6691	1.1106
4	0.0698	0.0698	0.9976	0.0699	49	0.8552	0.7547	0.6561	1.1504
5	0.0873	0.0872	0.9962	0.0875	50	0.8727	0.7660	0.6428	1.1918
6	0.1047	0.1045	0.9945	0.1051	51	0.8901	0.7771	0.6293	1.2349
7	0.1222	0.1219	0.9925	0.1228	52	0.9076	0.7880	0.6157	1.2799
8	0.1396	0.1392	0.9903	0.1405	53	0.9250	0.7986	0.6018	1.3270
9	0.1571	0.1564	0.9877	0.1584	54	0.9425	0.8090	0.5878	1.3764
10	0.1745	0.1736	0.9848	0.1763	55	0.9599	0.8192	0.5736	1.4281
11	0.1920	0.1908	0.9816	0.1944	56	0.9774	0.8290	0.5592	1.4826
12	0.2094	0.2079	0.9781	0.2126	57	0.9948	0.8387	0.5446	1.5399
13	0.2269	0.2250	0.9744	0.2309	58	1.0123	0.8480	0.5299	1.6003
14	0.2443	0.2419	0.9703	0.2493	59	1.0297	0.8572	0.5150	1.6643
15	0.2618	0.2588	0.9659	0.2679	60	1.0472	0.8660	0.5000	1.7321
16	0.2793	0.2756	0.9613	0.2867	61	1.0647	0.8746	0.4848	1.8040
17	0.2967	0.2924	0.9563	0.3057	62	1.0821	0.8829	0.4695	1.8807
18	0.3142	0.3090	0.9511	0.3249	63	1.0996	0.8910	0.4540	1.9626
19	0.3316	0.3256	0.9455	0.3443	64	1.1170	0.8988	0.4384	2.0503
20	0.3491	0.3420	0.9397	0.3640	65	1.1345	0.9063	0.4226	2.1445
21	0.3665	0.3584	0.9336	0.3839	66	1.1519	0.9135	0.4067	2.2460
22	0.3840	0.3746	0.9272	0.4040	67	1.1694	0.9205	0.3907	2.3559
23	0.4014	0.3907	0.9205	0.4245	68	1.1868	0.9272	0.3746	2.4751
24	0.4189	0.4067	0.9135	0.4452	69	1.2043	0.9336	0.3584	2.6051
25	0.4363	0.4226	0.9063	0.4663	70	1.2217	0.9397	0.3420	2.7475
26	0.4538	0.4384	0.8988	0.4877	71	1.2392	0.9455	0.3256	2.9042
27	0.4712	0.4540	0.8910	0.5095	72	1.2566	0.9511	0.3090	3.0777
28	0.4887	0.4695	0.8829	0.5317	73	1.2741	0.9563	0.2924	3.2709
29	0.5061	0.4848	0.8746	0.5543	74	1.2915	0.9613	0.2756	3.4874
30	0.5236	0.5000	0.8660	0.5774	75	1.3090	0.9659	0.2588	3.7321
31	0.5411	0.5150	0.8572	0.6009	76	1.3265	0.9703	0.2419	4.0108
32	0.5585	0.5299	0.8480	0.6249	77	1.3439	0.9744	0.2250	4.3315
33	0.5760	0.5446	0.8387	0.6494	78	1.3614	0.9781	0.2079	4.7046
34	0.5934	0.5592	0.8290	0.6745	79	1.3788	0.9816	0.1908	5.1446
35	0.6109	0.5736	0.8192	0.7002	80	1.3963	0.9848	0.1736	5.6713
36	0.6283	0.5878	0.8090	0.7265	81	1.4137	0.9877	0.1564	6.314
37	0.6458	0.6018	0.7986	0.7536	82	1.4312	0.9903	0.1392	7.115
38	0.6632	0.6157	0.7880	0.7813	83	1.4486	0.9925	0.1219	8.144
39	0.6807	0.6293	0.7771	0.8098	84	1.4661	0.9945	0.1045	9.514
40	0.6981	0.6428	0.7660	0.8391	85	1.4835	0.9962	0.0872	11.430
41	0.7156	0.6561	0.7547	0.8693	86	1.5010	0.9976	0.0698	14.301
42	0.7330	0.6691	0.7431	0.9004	87	1.5184	0.9986	0.0523	19.081
43	0.7505	0.6820	0.7314	0.9325	88	1.5359	0.9994	0.0349	28.636
44	0.7679	0.6947	0.7193	0.9657	89	1.5533	0.9998	0.0175	57.290
45	0.7854	0.7071	0.7071	1.0000	90	1.5708	1.0000	0.0000	∞

APPENDIX 8.   The exponential function

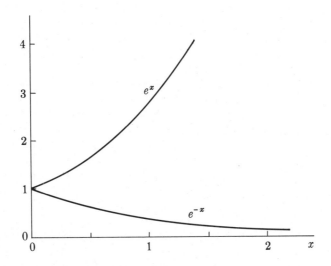

x	e^x	e^{-x}	x	e^x	e^{-x}
0	1.0000	1.0000	2.6	13.464	0.07427
0.1	1.1052	0.9048	2.8	16.445	0.06081
0.2	1.2214	0.8187	3.0	20.086	0.04979
0.3	1.3499	0.7408	3.2	24.533	0.04076
0.4	1.4918	0.6703	3.4	29.964	0.03337
0.5	1.6487	0.6065	3.6	36.598	0.02732
0.6	1.8221	0.5488	3.8	44.701	0.02237
0.7	2.0138	0.4966	4.0	54.598	0.01832
0.8	2.2255	0.4493	4.2	66.686	0.01500
0.9	2.4596	0.4066	4.4	81.451	0.01228
1.0	2.7183	0.3679	4.6	99.484	0.01005
1.1	3.0042	0.3329	4.8	121.51	0.00823
1.2	3.3201	0.3012	5.0	148.41	0.00674
1.3	3.6693	0.2725	5.5	244.69	0.00409
1.4	4.0552	0.2466	6.0	403.43	0.00248
1.5	4.4817	0.2231	6.5	665.14	0.00150
1.6	4.9530	0.2019	7.0	1096.6	0.00091
1.7	5.4739	0.1827	7.5	1808.0	0.00055
1.8	6.0496	0.1653	8.0	2981.0	0.00034
1.9	6.6859	0.1496	8.5	4914.8	0.00020
2.0	7.3891	0.1353	9.0	8103.1	0.00012
2.2	9.025	0.11080	9.5	13,360.	0.00007
2.4	11.023	0.09072	10.0	22,026.	0.00005

APPENDIX 9. The logarithmic function

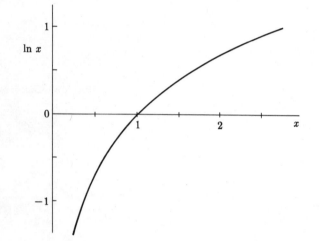

x	ln x	x	ln x
10^{-9}	−20.723	1.05	0.0488
10^{-6}	−13.816	1.10	0.0953
10^{-5}	−11.513	1.15	0.1398
10^{-4}	−9.210	1.20	0.1823
10^{-3}	−6.908	1.25	0.2231
0.01	−4.6052	1.30	0.2624
0.02	−3.9120	1.35	0.3001
0.03	−3.5066	1.40	0.3365
0.04	−3.2189	1.45	0.3716
0.05	−2.9957	1.50	0.4055
0.06	−2.8134	1.55	0.4383
0.07	−2.6593	1.60	0.4700
0.08	−2.5257	1.65	0.5008
0.09	−2.4079	1.70	0.5306
0.10	−2.30259	1.75	0.5596
0.12	−2.1203	1.80	0.5878
0.14	−1.9661	1.85	0.6152
0.16	−1.8326	1.90	0.6419
0.18	−1.7148	1.95	0.6678
0.20	−1.6094	2.00	0.69315
0.22	−1.5141	2.1	0.7419
0.24	−1.4271	2.2	0.7885
0.26	−1.3471	2.3	0.8329
0.28	−1.2730	2.4	0.8755
0.30	−1.2040	2.5	0.9163
0.35	−1.0498	2.6	0.9555
0.40	−0.9163	2.7	0.9933
0.45	−0.7985	2.8	1.0296
0.50	−0.6931	2.9	1.0647
		3.0	1.0986
0.55	−0.5978	3.1	1.1314
0.60	−0.5108	3.2	1.1632
0.65	−0.4308	3.3	1.1939
0.70	−0.3567	3.4	1.2238
0.75	−0.2877	3.5	1.2528
0.80	−0.2231	3.6	1.2809
0.85	−0.1625	3.7	1.3083
0.90	−0.1054	3.8	1.3350
0.95	−0.0513	3.9	1.3610
1.00	0.0000	4.0	1.3863

x	ln x	x	ln x
4.2	1.4351	16	2.773
4.4	1.4816	17	2.833
4.6	1.5261	18	2.890
4.8	1.5686	19	2.944
5.0	1.6094	20	2.996
5.2	1.6487	22	3.091
5.4	1.6864	24	3.178
5.6	1.7228	26	3.258
5.8	1.7579	28	3.332
6.0	1.7918	30	3.401
6.2	1.8245	32	3.466
6.4	1.8563	34	3.526
6.6	1.8871	36	3.584
6.8	1.9169	38	3.638
7.0	1.9459	40	3.689
7.2	1.9741	42	3.738
7.4	2.0015	44	3.784
7.6	2.0281	46	3.829
7.8	2.0541	48	3.871
8.0	2.0794	50	3.912
8.2	2.1041	55	4.007
8.4	2.1282	60	4.094
8.6	2.1518	65	4.174
8.8	2.1748	70	4.248
9.0	2.1972	75	4.317
9.2	2.2192	80	4.382
9.4	2.2407	85	4.443
9.6	2.2618	90	4.500
9.8	2.2824	95	4.554
10.0	2.30259	100	4.605
10.5	2.3514	200	5.298
11.0	2.3979	300	5.704
11.5	2.4423	400	5.991
12.0	2.4849	500	6.215
12.5	2.5257	600	6.397
13.0	2.5649	10^3	6.908
13.5	2.6027	10^4	9.210
14.0	2.6391	10^5	11.513
14.5	2.6741	10^6	13.816
15.0	2.7081	10^9	20.723

Index

INDEX

For names and topics that appear often in the book, only the more important page references are given. Italic letters following page numbers are used with the following meanings: *f*, figure; *n*, footnote; and *t*, table. Parentheses following a page number enclose the number of a question, exercise, or problem; such an end-of-chapter item is referenced only if it contains factual information that does not occur elsewhere in the book. Authors cited only in footnotes are not indexed.